INTERNATIONAL ENERGY AGENCY

WORLD ENERGY OUTLOOK

2008

INTERNATIONAL ENERGY AGENCY

The International Energy Agency (IEA) is an autonomous body which was established in November 1974 within the framework of the Organisation for Economic Co-operation and Development (OECD) to implement an international energy programme.

It carries out a comprehensive programme of energy co-operation among twenty-eight of the OECD thirty member countries. The basic aims of the IEA are:

■ To maintain and improve systems for coping with oil supply disruptions.

■ To promote rational energy policies in a global context through co-operative relations with non-member countries, industry and international organisations.

■ To operate a permanent information system on the international oil market.

■ To improve the world's energy supply and demand structure by developing alternative energy sources and increasing the efficiency of energy use.

■ To promote international collaboration on energy technology.

■ To assist in the integration of environmental and energy policies.

The IEA member countries are: Australia, Austria, Belgium, Canada, Czech Republic, Denmark, Finland, France, Germany, Greece, Hungary, Ireland, Italy, Japan, Republic of Korea, Luxembourg, Netherlands, New Zealand, Norway, Poland, Portugal, Slovak Republic, Spain, Sweden, Switzerland, Turkey, United Kingdom and United States. The European Commission also participates in the work of the IEA.

ORGANISATION FOR ECONOMIC CO-OPERATION AND DEVELOPMENT

The OECD is a unique forum where the governments of thirty democracies work together to address the economic, social and environmental challenges of globalisation. The OECD is also at the forefront of efforts to understand and to help governments respond to new developments and concerns, such as corporate governance, the information economy and the challenges of an ageing population. The Organisation provides a setting where governments can compare policy experiences, seek answers to common problems, identify good practice and work to co-ordinate domestic and international policies.

The OECD member countries are: Australia, Austria, Belgium, Canada, Czech Republic, Denmark, Finland, France, Germany, Greece, Hungary, Iceland, Ireland, Italy, Japan, Republic of Korea, Luxembourg, Mexico, Netherlands, New Zealand, Norway, Poland, Portugal, Slovak Republic, Spain, Sweden, Switzerland, Turkey, United Kingdom and United States.
The European Commission takes part in the work of the OECD.

Out of the turmoil of the energy markets of the last 12 months and our evaluation of future influences on the sector has emerged a new underlying price assumption for the *World Energy Outlook* — an oil price through to 2030 which nudges twice the level in *WEO-2007*. The era of cheap oil is over.

This alone should be enough to make policy makers sit up. But so should the results set out in this volume. On present trends, just to replace the oil reserves that will be exhausted and to meet the growth in demand, between now and 2030 we will need 64 mb/d of new oil-production capacity, six times the size of Saudi Arabia's capacity today. The big resources lie, increasingly, in a few countries, whose share of the world market climbs inexorably. The international oil companies have diminishing access to these reserves. Investment per barrel of oil produced has shot up. But big producers are becoming so wealthy that they are losing the incentive to invest. Though the resources are there, the world will struggle to satisfy its thirst for oil, even at today's prices.

Consumers and producers are not at loggerheads. Producers have a sovereign right to determine what pace of development of their resources is in their national interest. Consumers respect this, though they also expect commitments to be met. But in any case, demand is booming in Middle East countries, too: they account for 20% of oil demand growth over the period to 2030. If prices rise still higher, they will drive even faster the search for non-oil solutions in OECD countries and oil-importing countries elsewhere.

High oil prices do, over time, serve one purpose now almost unanimously accepted worldwide: to cut greenhouse-gas emissions to levels which will not cause irreparable damage to the world's climate. Relative to *WEO-2007*, this year's figures show lower global fossil-fuel energy use and greenhouse-gas emissions. But, despite the price changes, the reduction is nowhere near enough. Global energy-related greenhouse-gas emissions still *increase* by 45% by 2030.

This situation can be changed. Negotiators at Copenhagen in 2009 will seek to do that. Energy is a big part of the total climate change picture — over 60% of greenhouse-gas emissions come from energy production and use — but still only part. We show here how energy relates to the total picture and, in detail, how to go about making the energy future sustainable as part of a global climate solution. All nations would need to be involved, in a fair and proportionate manner.

We have two options. We can accept as broadly inevitable the outcome portrayed here in the first part of our analysis, which shows the destination of the course on which we are now set; and prepare ourselves to adapt to that uncertain even alarming, future. This path would lead to possible energy-related conflict and social disruption. Or we can plan and implement a new course, drawing on a united determination on the part of governments and action by committed citizens across the globe. The International Energy Agency sets out here what needs to be done to arrive at a supportable and sustainable future. The IEA will work with all nations, member countries and non-member countries alike, to help effect the necessary changes. For those who wish to see, this *WEO* points the way.

As last year, I pay tribute to Fatih Birol, who has conceived and directed this analysis, his team and the many others who have contributed. The calibre of their work matches, in depth, the profundity of the problems.

Nobuo Tanaka
Executive Director

This study was prepared by the Office of the Chief Economist (OCE) of the International Energy Agency (IEA) in co-operation with other offices of the Agency. The study was designed and directed by **Fatih Birol**, Chief Economist of the IEA. **Trevor Morgan** was in charge of co-ordinating the analysis on oil and gas supply; **Laura Cozzi** was responsible for the co-ordination of the analysis of climate-policy scenarios; **Hideshi Emoto** was in charge of modelling of energy demand, **Maria Argiri** of power generation analysis and **Olivier Rech** of oil-supply modelling. **Teresa Malyshev** co-ordinated the work on sub-Saharan Africa. **Kamel Bennaceur, Raffaella Centurelli, Michael-Xiaobao Chen, Paul Dowling, Lorcan Lyons, Bertrand Magne, Chris Mullin, Uğur Öcal, Pawel Olejarnik, Fabien Roques, Olivier Sassi** and **Ralph Sims** also authored different chapters of the book and were instrumental in delivering the study. **Sandra Mooney** provided essential support. For more information on the members of the OCE and their contribution to the *World Energy Outlook*, please visit www.worldenergyoutlook.org.

Robert Priddle carried editorial responsibility.

Our analysis of oil supply is based on a vast amount of field-by-field data that we compiled from a range of different sources. The primary source of this was IHS Energy, without whose assistance we would not have been able to carry out this work. We gratefully acknowledge their contribution. We are also indebted to the United Nations Framework Convention on Climate Change (UNFCCC) Secretariat for very helpful discussions when building our climate-change scenarios.

Our strategic approach and analysis benefited greatly from the expertise of the *World Energy Outlook's* two Advisory Panels, comprising prominent experts in the fields of oil and climate change. We are very grateful to our distinguished panel members for their guidance:

Advisory Panel on Oil Supply Prospects

Guy Caruso (former Administrator of Energy Information Administration, US)
Robert Fryklund (Vice President of Industry Relations, IHS)
Leo Roodhart (President, Society of Petroleum Engineers, 2009)
Ramzi Salman (former Deputy Secretary General, OPEC and former Advisor to the Minister of Energy, Qatar)
Adnan Shihab-Eldin (former Secretary General, OPEC)

Advisory Panel on Climate Change

Yvo de Boer (Secretary General, UNFCCC)
Rajendra K. Pachauri (Chairman, Intergovernmental Panel on Climate Change)
Nicholas Stern (London School of Economics)
David Victor (Stanford University)
Dadi Zhou (former Director General, Energy Research Institute, National Development and Reform Commission, China)

A number of other international experts provided invaluable contributions throughout the preparation of this book: Paul Bailey (Department for Business, Enterprise and Regulatory Reform, UK), Paul Baruya (IEA Clean Coal Centre), Adam Chambers (IIASA), Donald Gautier (US Geological Survey), Jan-Hein Jesse (Shell), Bertrand Michel (Université Paris XI), Nebojsa Nakicenovic (Technical University of Vienna), Shaun Ragnauth (Environmental Protection Agency, US), Ivan Sandrea (StatoilHydro), and Detlef van Vuuren (Netherlands Environment Assessment Agency).

The study benefited from input provided by IEA experts in different offices. Richard Bradley, Head of Energy Efficiency and Environment Division, made invaluable contributions to our climate-change analysis. The work also greatly benefited from the expertise of Nigel Jollands on cities, Ian Cronshaw on gas and Brian Ricketts on coal. Other IEA colleagues who provided input to different parts of the book include: Richard Baron, Aad van Bohemen, Amos Bromhead, Pierpaolo Cazzola, Ian Cronshaw, Muriel Custodio, Paolo Frankl, Lew Fulton, David Fyfe, Rebecca Gaghen, Jean-Yves Garnier, Dolf Gielen, Tim Gould, Hiroshi Hashimoto, Neil Hirst, Didier Houssin, Kierean Mcnamara, Andrea Nour, Cédric Philibert, Bertrand Sadin, Jonathan Sinton, Ulrik Stridbaek and Michael Taylor. Thanks also go to Marilyn Smith for proofreading the text.

The work could not have been achieved without the substantial support and co-operation provided by many government bodies, international organisations and energy companies worldwide, notably:

Deloitte and Touche, United Kingdom; the European Commission; Dutch Ministry of Economic Affairs; Foreign and Commonwealth Office, United Kingdom; Direction Générale de l'Energie et du Climat, France; IEA Clean Coal Centre; Korean Ministry of Commerce, Industry and Energy; Michelin, France; Norwegian Ministry of Foreign Affairs; Schlumberger Ltd; Shell; StatoilHydro; Sustainable Energy Ireland; Swiss Federal Department of the Environment, Transport, Energy and Communications; the Government of Denmark; Ministry of Economy, Trade and Industry, Japan; HM Treasury, United Kingdom; International Energy Forum, Saudi Arabia; the Renewable Energy and Energy Efficiency Partnership (REEEP), Austria; CIRED, Toyota Motor Corporation, Japan; US Department of Energy; US Environment; Protection Agency; US Geological Survey and US National Petroleum Council.

Many international experts provided input, commented on the underlying analytical work, and reviewed early drafts of each chapter. Their comments and suggestions were of great value. They include:

Oil supply prospects

Paul Alba	Consultant, France
Paul Bailey	Department for Business, Enterprise and Regulatory Reform, UK
Ashok Belani	Schlumberger, France
Johannes Benigni	JBC Energy, Austria
Jan Bygdevoll	Norwegian Petroleum Directorate
Alessandro Campo	Unicredit, Italy

Joel Couse	Total, France
Bernhard Cramer	Federal Institute for Geosciences and Natural Resources, Germany
William Davie	Schlumberger, France
John Fitzgerald	The Economic and Social Research Institute, Ireland
Dario Garofalo	Ministry of Foreign Affairs, Italy
John Guy	National Petroleum Council, US
Gilbert Hamaide	GDF Suez, France
Sigurd Heiberg	StatoilHydro, Norway
Anouk Honoré	Oxford Institute for Energy Studies, UK
Peter Jackson	IHS Energy
Tor Kartevold	StatoilHydro, Norway
Jostein Dahl Karlsen	Ministry of Petroleum and Energy, Norway
Ryan Kauppila	Lehman Brothers, UK
Tim Klett	US Geological Survey
David Knapp	Energy Intelligence, US
Sally Kornfeld	Department of Energy, US
Ken Koyama	The Institute of Energy Economics, Japan
Alessandro Lanza	Eni, Italy
Colin Lyle	International Gas Union, UK
William Martin	Washington Policy and Analysis, US
Yves Mathieu	IFP, France
Kenneth McKellar	Deloitte and Touche, UK
Pedro Antonio Merino	Repsol, Spain
Nasarudin Md Idris	Petronas, Malaysia
Rodolphe Olard	ING, UK
Stephen Plumb	Chevron, US
Xavier Preel	Total, France
Dinko Raytchev	Directorate-General Energy and Transport, European Commission
Kenneth Rogoff	Harvard University, US
Rafael Sandrea	IPC Petroleum Consultants, US
Richard Schimpf	E.ON, Germany
Adam Sieminski	Deutsche Bank, US
Pierre Sigonney	Total, France
Bob Skinner	StatoilHydro, Norway
Jonathan Stern	Oxford Institute for Energy Studies, UK

Lynsey Tinios	Department for Business, Enterprise and Regulatory Reform, UK
Coby van der Linde	Clingendael International Energy Programme, Netherlands
Noé van Hulst	International Energy Forum, Saudi Arabia
Laszlo Varro	MOL Group, Hungary
Frank Verrastro	Center for Strategic and International Studies, US

Climate change

Jun Arima	Ministry of Economy, Trade and Industry, Japan
Terry Barker	Cambridge Centre for Climate Policy Research, UK
Morgan Bazilian	Department of Communications, Energy and Natural Resources, Ireland
Christine Berg	Directorate-General Energy and Transport, European Commission
Geoffrey Blanford	Electric Power Research Institute, US
Jean-Paul Bouttes	EDF Energy, France
Peter Brun	Vestas, Denmark
Per Callesen	Danish Ministry of Finance
Christa Clapp	Environmental Protection Agency, US
Carmen Difiglio	Department of Energy, US
Bhava Dhungana	UNFCCC
Richard Folland	JP Morgan, UK
Peter Fraser	Ontario Energy Board, Canada
Christoph Frei	World Economic Forum, Switzerland
Dario Garofalo	Ministry of Foreign Affairs, Italy
Rainer Görgen	Federal Ministry of Economics and Technology, Germany
Michael Grubb	The Carbon Trust, UK
Reinhard Haas	Technical University of Vienna, Austria
Donald Hanson	Argonne National Laboratory, US
Colin Henderson	IEA Clean Coal Centre, UK
James Hewlett	Department of Energy, US
Takashi Hongo	Japan Bank for International Cooperation
John Houghton	Intergovernmental Panel on Climate Change
Jeff Huntington	European Environment Agency
Craig Jones	Department for Business, Enterprise and Regulatory Reform, UK
Julia King	Aston University, UK

Ger Klaassen	Directorate-General Environment, European Commission
Doug Koplow	Earthtrack, US
Takayuki Kusajima	Toyota, Japan
Kate Larsen	Department of State, US
Audrey Lee	Department of Energy, US
Joan MacNaughton	Alstom Power
Ritu Mathur	The Energy and Resources Institute, India
Neil McMurdo	HM Treasury, UK
Bert Metz	Netherlands Environmental Assessment Agency
Jan Mizgajski	Ministry of Economy, Poland
Arne Mogren	Vattenfall, Sweden
Helen Mountford	OECD Environment Directorate
Patrick Oliva	Michelin, France
Paul Oliver	World Energy Forum
Ayse Yasemin Orucu	Ministry of Energy and Natural Resources, Turkey
John Paffenbarger	Constellation Energy, US
Binu Parthan	Renewable Energy and Energy Efficiency Partnership, Austria
Gustav Resch	Vienna University of Technology, Austria
Hans-Holger Rogner	International Atomic Energy Agency
Leo Schrattenholzer	IRM, Austria
PR Shukla	Indian Institute of Management
Bjorn Stigson	World Business Council for Sustainable Development
Sven Teske	Greenpeace
Fridtjof Unander	Enova, Norway
Tom Van Ierland	Directorate-General Environment, European Commission
Henning Wüster	UNFCCC
Arthouros Zervos	Global Wind Energy Council

Sub-Saharan Africa

Edward Caldwell	ERC Consultants, Canada
Heleen de Coninck	Energy Research Centre of the Netherlands
Karim Dahou	OECD Directorate for Financial and Enterprise Affairs
Stanislas Drochon	PFC Energy, France
Jean-Pierre Favennec	IFP, France
Stephen Gitonga	UN Development Programme
Beejaye Kokil	African Development Bank
Michael Levitsky	World Bank

Vijay Modi	Columbia University, US
Petter Nore	Norwegian Agency for Development Cooperation
Yinke Omorogbe	University of Ibadan, Nigeria
Francisco Paris	Extractive Industries Transparency Initiative, Norway
George Person	Department of Energy, US
Jürgen Reitmaier	Extractive Industries Transparency Initiative, Norway
Kenneth Ruffing	OECD Development Centre
Connie Smyser	Smyser Associates, US
Luigi Tessiore	UN Development Programme, Senegal
Noé van Hulst	International Energy Forum, Saudi Arabia
Hans Terje Ylvisåker	Norwegian Embassy, Mozambique

Energy use in cities

Shobhakar Dhakal	Global Carbon Project, Japan
Leticia Guimaraes	University of Maryland, US
Stephen Hammer	Columbia University, US
Stephen Kenihan	ICLEI – Oceania, Australia
Lily Parshall	Columbia University, US
Matthias Ruth	University of Maryland, US
Niels Schulz	Imperial College London, UK
Wayne Wescott	ICLEI – Oceania, Australia

The individuals and organisations that contributed to this study are not responsible for any opinions or judgements contained in this study. All errors and omissions are solely the responsibility of the IEA.

Comments and questions are welcome and should be addressed to:

Dr. Fatih Birol
Chief Economist
Director, Office of the Chief Economist
International Energy Agency
9, rue de la Fédération
75739 Paris Cedex 15
France

Telephone: (33-1) 4057 6670
Fax: (33-1) 4057 6659
Email: weo@iea.org

TABLE OF CONTENTS

List of figures

Part A: Global energy trends to 2030

List of tables

Part C: The role of energy in climate policy

List of boxes

List of spotlights

World Energy Outlook Series

World Energy Outlook 1993
World Energy Outlook 1994
World Energy Outlook 1995
World Energy Outlook 1996
World Energy Outlook 1998
World Energy Outlook: 1999 Insights
      Looking at Energy Subsidies: Getting the Prices Right
World Energy Outlook 2000
World Energy Outlook 2001 Insights
      Assessing Today's Supplies to Fuel Tomorrow's Growth
World Energy Outlook 2002
World Energy Investment Outlook: 2003 Insights
World Energy Outlook 2004
World Energy Outlook 2005
      Middle East and North Africa Insights
World Energy Outlook 2006
World Energy Outlook 2007
      China and India Insights
World Energy Outlook 2008
World Energy Outlook 2009 (forthcoming)

More information available at www.worldenergyoutlook.org

The world's energy system is at a crossroads. Current global trends in energy supply and consumption are patently unsustainable — environmentally, economically, socially. But that can — and must — be altered; *there's still time to change the road we're on*. It is not an exaggeration to claim that the future of human prosperity depends on how successfully we tackle the two central energy challenges facing us today: securing the supply of reliable and affordable energy; and effecting a rapid transformation to a low-carbon, efficient and environmentally benign system of energy supply. What is needed is nothing short of an energy revolution. This *World Energy Outlook* demonstrates how that might be achieved through decisive policy action and at what cost. It also describes the consequences of failure.

Oil is the world's vital source of energy and will remain so for many years to come, even under the most optimistic of assumptions about the pace of development and deployment of alternative technology. But the sources of oil to meet rising demand, the cost of producing it and the prices that consumers will need to pay for it are extremely uncertain, perhaps more than ever. The surge in prices in recent years culminating in the price spike of 2008, coupled with much greater short-term price volatility, have highlighted just how sensitive prices are to short-term market imbalances. They have also alerted people to the ultimately finite nature of oil (and natural gas) resources. In fact, the immediate risk to supply is not one of a lack of global resources, but rather a lack of investment where it is needed. Upstream investment has been rising rapidly in nominal terms, but much of the increase is due to surging costs and the need to combat rising decline rates — especially in higher-cost provinces outside of OPEC. Today, most capital goes to exploring for and developing high-cost reserves, partly because of limitations on international oil company access to the cheapest resources. Expanding production in the lowest-cost countries will be central to meeting the world's needs at reasonable cost in the face of dwindling resources in most parts of the world and accelerating decline rates everywhere.

Preventing catastrophic and irreversible damage to the global climate ultimately requires a major decarbonisation of the world energy sources. On current trends, energy-related emissions of carbon-dioxide (CO_2) and other greenhouse gases will rise inexorably, pushing up average global temperature by as much as $6\,°C$ in the long term. Strong, urgent action is needed to curb these trends. The 15th Conference of the Parties, to be held in Copenhagen in November 2009, provides a vital opportunity to negotiate a new global climate-change policy regime for beyond 2012 (the final year of coverage of the first commitment period of the Kyoto Protocol). The conference will need to put in place a framework for long-term co-operative action to bring the world onto a well-defined policy path towards a clear, quantified global goal for the stabilisation of greenhouse gases in the atmosphere. It will also need to ensure broad participation and put in place robust policy mechanisms to achieve the agreed objective.

The energy sector will have to play the central role in curbing emissions — through major improvements in efficiency and rapid switching to renewables and other low-carbon technologies, such as carbon capture and storage (CCS).

Securing energy supplies and speeding up the transition to a low-carbon energy system both call for radical action by governments — at national and local levels, and through participation in co-ordinated international mechanisms. Households, businesses and motorists will have to change the way they use energy, while energy suppliers will need to invest in developing and commercialising low-carbon technologies. To make this happen, governments have to put in place appropriate financial incentives and regulatory frameworks that support both energy-security and climate-policy goals in an integrated way. Removing subsidies on energy consumption, which amounted to a staggering $310 billion in the 20 largest non-OECD countries in 2007, could make a major contribution to curbing demand and emissions growth. High international oil prices, by deterring consumption and encouraging more efficient demand-side technologies, push in the same direction, but only at the expense of economic growth and of living standards in consuming countries, both rich and poor. And some of the alternatives to conventional oil that high prices encourage are even more carbon-intensive. Many countries have made progress in crafting national responses, but much more needs to be done. A new international climate agreement is but a first essential step on the road towards a sustainable energy system; effective implementation is just as crucial. Delay in doing either would increase the eventual cost of meeting any given global climate target.

More of the same: a vision of a *laisser-faire* fossil-energy future

In our Reference Scenario, world primary energy demand grows by 1.6% per year on average in 2006-2030, from 11 730 Mtoe to just over 17 010 Mtoe — an increase of 45%. To illustrate the course on which we are set, this scenario embodies the effects of those government policies and measures that were enacted or adopted up to mid-2008, but not new ones. This provides a baseline against which we can quantify the extent to which we need to change course. Demand grows at a slower rate than projected in *WEO-2007*, mainly due to higher energy prices and slower economic growth, especially in OECD countries. Fossil fuels account for 80% of the world's primary energy mix in 2030 — down slightly on today. Oil remains the dominant fuel, though demand for coal rises more than demand for any other fuel in absolute terms. The share of the world's energy consumed in cities — an estimated 7 900 Mtoe in 2006 — grows from two-thirds to almost three-quarters in 2030.

Due to continuing strong economic growth, China and India account for just over half of the increase in world primary energy demand between 2006 and 2030. Middle East countries strengthen their position as an important demand centre, contributing a further 11% to incremental world demand. Collectively, non-OECD countries account for 87% of the increase. As a result, their share of world primary energy demand rises from 51% to 62%. Their energy consumption overtook that of the OECD in 2005.

Global primary demand for oil (excluding biofuels) rises by 1% per year on average, from 85 million barrels per day in 2007 to 106 mb/d in 2030. However, its share of world energy use drops, from 34% to 30%. Oil demand in 2030 has been revised downwards by 10 mb/d since last year's *Outlook*, reflecting mainly the impact of much higher prices and slightly slower GDP growth, as well as new government policies introduced in the past year. All of the projected increase in world oil demand comes from non-OECD countries (over four-fifths from China, India and the Middle East); OECD oil demand falls slightly, due largely to declining non-transport oil demand. Global demand for natural gas grows more quickly, by 1.8% per year, its share in total energy demand rising marginally, to 22%. Most of the growth in gas use comes from the power-generation sector. World demand for coal advances by 2% a year on average, its share in global energy demand climbing from 26% in 2006 to 29% in 2030. Some 85% of the increase in global coal consumption comes from the power sector in China and India. The share of nuclear power in primary energy demand edges down over the *Outlook* period, from 6% today to 5% in 2030 (its share of electricity output drops from 15% to 10%), reflecting the consistency of our rule not to anticipate changes in national policies — notwithstanding a recent revival of interest in nuclear power. Nuclear output nonetheless increases in absolute terms in all major regions except OECD Europe.

Modern renewable technologies grow most rapidly, overtaking gas to become the second-largest source of electricity, behind coal, soon after 2010. Falling costs as renewable technologies mature, assumed higher fossil-fuel prices and strong policy support provide an opportunity for the renewable industry to eliminate its reliance on subsidies and to bring emerging technologies into the mainstream. Excluding biomass, non-hydro renewable energy sources — wind, solar, geothermal, tide and wave energy — together grow faster than any other source worldwide, at an average rate of 7.2% per year over the projection period. Most of the increase occurs in the power sector. The share of non-hydro renewables in total power generation grows from 1% in 2006 to 4% in 2030. Hydropower output increases, though its share of electricity drops two percentage points to 14%. In the OECD, the increase in renewables-based power generation exceeds that in fossil-based and nuclear power generation combined.

Massive investments in energy infrastructure will be needed

The Reference Scenario projections call for cumulative investment of over $26 trillion (in year-2007 dollars) in 2007-2030, over $4 trillion more than posited in *WEO-2007*. The power sector accounts for $13.6 trillion, or 52% of the total. Most of the rest goes to oil and gas, mainly for exploration and development and mostly in non-OECD regions. Unit capital costs, especially in the oil and gas industry, have continued to surge in the last year, leading to an upward revision in our assumed costs for the projection period. That increase outweighs the slower projected expansion of the world energy system. The current financial crisis is not expected to affect long-term investment, but could lead to delays in bringing current projects to completion, particularly in the power sector. Just over half of projected global energy investment in 2007-2030 goes simply to maintain the current level of supply capacity: much of the world's current infrastructure for supplying oil, gas, coal and electricity will need to be replaced by 2030. To provide adequate assurances about the circumstances that will govern future investment in energy-supply infrastructure, negotiations need to be concluded urgently on an international agreement on combating climate change and the implications for national policies quickly assessed.

These projections are based on the assumption that the IEA crude oil import price averages $100 per barrel (in real year-2007 dollars) over the period 2008-2015, rising to over $120 in 2030. This represents a major upward adjustment from last year's *Outlook*, reflecting the higher prices for near-term physical delivery and for futures contracts, as well as a reassessment of the prospects for the cost of oil supply and the outlook for demand. In nominal terms, prices double to just over $200 per barrel in 2030. However, pronounced short-term swings in prices are likely to remain the norm and temporary price spikes or sharp falls cannot be ruled out. Prices are likely to remain highly volatile, especially in the next year or two. A worsening of the current financial crisis would most likely depress economic activity and, therefore, oil demand, exerting downward pressure on prices. Beyond 2015, we assume that rising marginal costs of supply exert upward pressure on prices through to the end of the projection period.

Combined with our oil-demand projections, these assumptions point to persistently high levels of consumer spending on oil in both OECD and non-OECD countries. As a share of world GDP at market exchange rates, spending soared from 1% in 1998 to around 4% in 2007, with serious adverse implications for the economies of consuming countries. That share is projected to stabilise at more than 5% over much of the *Outlook* period. For non-OECD countries, the share averages 6% to 7%. The only time the world has ever spent so much of its income on oil was in the early 1980s, when it exceeded 6%. On the other hand, OPEC oil and gas export revenues jump from under $700 billion in 2006 to over $2 trillion in 2030, with their share of world GDP rising from 1.2% to 2%.

Most incremental oil and gas will come from OPEC – *if they invest enough*

World oil supply is projected to rise from 84 mb/d in 2007 to 106 mb/d in 2030 in the Reference Scenario. Netting out processing gains in refining, global production reaches 104 mb/d. Although global oil production in total is not expected to peak before 2030, production of conventional oil – crude oil, natural gas liquids (NGLs) and enhanced oil recovery (EOR) – is projected to level off towards the end of the projection period. Conventional crude oil production alone increases only modestly over 2007-2030 – by 5 mb/d – as almost all the additional capacity from new oilfields is offset by declines in output at existing fields. The bulk of the net increase in total oil production comes from NGLs (driven by the relatively rapid expansion in gas supply) and from non-conventional resources and technologies, including Canadian oil sands.

The bulk of the increase in world oil output is expected to come from OPEC countries, their collective share rising from 44% in 2007 to 51% in 2030. Their reserves are, in principle, large enough (and development costs low enough) for output to grow faster than this. But investment by these countries is assumed to be constrained by several factors, including conservative depletion policies and geopolitics. Saudi Arabia remains the world's largest producer throughout the projection period, its output climbing from 10.2 mb/d in 2007 to 15.6 mb/d in 2030. Non-OPEC conventional oil production is already at plateau and is projected to start to decline by around the middle of the next decade, accelerating through to the end of the projection period. Production has already peaked in most non-OPEC countries and will peak in most others before 2030. Falling crude oil and NGLs production is largely offset by rising non-conventional output, which keeps total non-OPEC output broadly flat over the second half of the projection period. Conventional capacity, net of natural production declines at existing fields, is set to grow in the near term, but dwindling new discoveries and a fall in the size of new fields are expected to drive up marginal development costs, leading to a drop in output.

The projected increase in global oil output hinges on adequate and timely investment. Some 64 mb/d of additional gross capacity — the equivalent of almost six times that of Saudi Arabia today — needs to be brought on stream between 2007 and 2030. Some 30 mb/d of new capacity is needed by 2015. There remains a real risk that under-investment will cause an oil-supply crunch in that timeframe. The current wave of upstream investment looks set to boost net oil-production capacity in the next two to three years, pushing up spare capacity modestly. However, capacity additions from current projects tail off after 2010. This largely reflects the upstream development cycle: many new projects will undoubtedly be sanctioned in the near term as oil companies complete existing projects and move on to new ones. But the gap now evident between what is currently being built and what will be needed to keep pace with demand is set to widen sharply after 2010. Around 7 mb/d of additional capacity (over and above that from all current projects) needs to be brought on stream by 2015, most of which will need to be sanctioned within the next two years, to avoid a fall in spare capacity towards the middle of the next decade.

Production of natural gas is also set to become more concentrated in the most resource-rich regions. Some 46% of the projected growth in world gas production in 2006-2030 comes from the Middle East, its output tripling to around 1 trillion cubic metres (tcm) by 2030. About 60% of the region's incremental output is consumed locally, mainly in power stations. Most of the remaining increase in world output is provided by Africa and Russia. If investments in these countries falter, lower gas supply could lead to greater reliance on coal and higher CO_2 emissions.

The world is not running short of oil or gas just yet

The world's total endowment of oil is large enough to support the projected rise in production beyond 2030 in the Reference Scenario. Estimates of remaining proven reserves of oil and NGLs range from about 1.2 to 1.3 trillion barrels (including about 0.2 trillion barrels of non-conventional oil). They have almost doubled since 1980. This is enough to supply the world with oil for over 40 years at current rates of consumption. Though most of the increase in reserves has come from revisions made in the 1980s in OPEC countries rather than from new discoveries, modest increases have continued since 1990, despite rising consumption. The volume of oil discovered each year on average has been higher since 2000 than in the 1990s, thanks to increased exploration activity and improvements in technology, though production continues to outstrip discoveries (despite some big recent finds, such as in deepwater offshore Brazil).

Ultimately recoverable conventional oil resources, which include initial proven and probable reserves from discovered fields, reserves growth and oil that has yet to be found, are estimated at 3.5 trillion barrels. Only a third of this total, or 1.1 trillion barrels, has been produced up to now. Undiscovered resources account for about a third of the *remaining* recoverable oil, the largest volumes of which are thought to lie in the Middle East, Russia and the Caspian region. Non-conventional oil resources, which have been barely developed to date, are also very large. Between 1 and 2 trillion barrels of oil sands and extra-heavy oil may be ultimately recoverable economically. These resources are largely concentrated in Canada (mainly in Alberta province) and Venezuela (in the Orinoco Belt). The total long-term potentially recoverable oil-resource base, including extra-heavy oil, oil sands and oil shales (another largely undeveloped, though costly resource), is estimated at around 6.5 trillion barrels. Adding coal-to-liquids and gas-to-liquids increases this potential to about 9 trillion barrels.

Globally, natural gas resources are large, but, like oil, are highly concentrated in a small number of countries and fields. Remaining proven reserves amount to 180 tcm — equal to around 60 years of current production. Three countries — Russia, Iran and Qatar — hold 56% of the world's reserves, while just 25 fields worldwide hold almost half. OPEC countries also hold about half. Remaining reserves have more than doubled since 1980, with the biggest increases coming from the Middle East. Although the size of gas discoveries has been steadily declining in recent decades in the same way as for oil, discoveries continue to exceed production. Ultimately recoverable remaining resources of conventional natural gas, including remaining proven reserves, reserves growth and undiscovered resources, could amount to well over 400 tcm. Cumulative production to 2007 amounts to less than one-sixth of total initial resources. Non-conventional gas resources — including coalbed methane, tight gas sands and gas shales — are much larger, amounting perhaps to over 900 tcm, with 25% in the United States and Canada combined.

But field-by-field declines in oil production are accelerating...

Globally, oil resources might be plentiful, but there can be no guarantee that they will be exploited quickly enough to meet the level of demand projected in our Reference Scenario. One major uncertainty concerns the rate at which output from producing oilfields declines as they mature. This is a critical determinant of the amount of new capacity and investment that will be needed globally to meet projected demand. The findings of a detailed field-by-field analysis of the historical production trends of 800 fields, set out in Part B of this *Outlook*, indicate that *observed* decline rates (the observable fall in production) are likely to accelerate in the long term in each major world region. This results from a fall in the average size of field and, in some regions, an increase in the share of production that is expected to come from offshore fields. Our analysis demonstrates that, in general, the larger a field's reserves, the lower the peak relative to reserves and the slower the decline once the field has passed its peak. Rates are also lower for onshore than offshore (especially deepwater) fields. Investment and production policies also affect decline rates.

We estimate that the average production-weighted observed decline rate worldwide is currently 6.7% for fields that have passed their production peak. In our Reference Scenario, this rate increases to 8.6% in 2030. The current figure is derived from our analysis of production at 800 fields, including all 54 super-giants (holding more than 5 billion barrels) in production today. For this sample, the observed post-peak decline rate averaged across all fields, weighted by their production over their whole lives, was found to be 5.1%. Decline rates are lowest for the biggest fields: they average 3.4% for super-giant fields, 6.5% for giant fields and 10.4% for large fields. Observed decline rates vary markedly by region; they are lowest in the Middle East and highest in the North Sea. This reflects, to a large extent, differences in the average size of fields, which in turn is related to the extent to which overall reserves are depleted and whether they are located onshore or offshore. Adjusting for the higher decline rates of smaller fields explains the higher estimated decline rate for the world, compared with that based on our dataset.

Natural, or underlying, decline rates are about a third higher on average than observed decline rates, though the difference varies across regions reflecting differences in investment. (The natural decline rate strips out the effects of ongoing and periodic investment.) For the world as a whole, it is estimated at 9% for post-peak fields. In other words, the decline in production from existing fields would have been around one-third faster had there been no capital spending on those fields once they had passed their peak. Our Reference Scenario projections imply an increase in the global average natural decline rate to around 10.5% per year by 2030 (almost two percentage points higher than the observed rate), as all regions experience a drop in average field size and most see a shift in production to offshore fields over the projection period. This means that total upstream investment in some countries will need to rise, in some cases significantly, just to offset this faster decline. The implications are far-reaching: investment in 1 mb/d of *additional* capacity – equal to the entire capacity of Algeria today – is needed each year by the end of the projection period just to offset the projected acceleration in the natural decline rate.

...and barriers to upstream investment could constrain global oil supply

Faster natural decline rates will mean a need for more upstream investment, both in existing fields (to combat natural decline) and in new fields (to offset falling production from existing fields and to meet rising demand). In fact, total upstream investment (in oil and gas fields) has been rising rapidly in recent years, more than tripling between 2000 and 2007 to $390 billion in nominal terms. Most of this increase was to meet higher unit costs: in cost-inflation adjusted terms, investment in 2007 was 70% higher than in 2000. Worldwide, upstream costs rose on average by an estimated 90% between 2000 and 2007 and by a further 5% in the first half of 2008, according to the IEA Index of Upstream Capital Costs. Most of the increase occurred in 2004-2007. Based on the plans of 50 of the world's largest companies surveyed for this *Outlook* (accounting for more than three-quarters of world oil and gas production), global upstream oil and gas investment is expected to continue to rise, to just over $600 billion in nominal terms by 2012 – an increase of more than half over 2007. If costs level off, as assumed, real spending in the five years to 2012 would grow by 9% per year – about the same rate as in the previous seven years.

The Reference Scenario projections imply a need for cumulative investment in the upstream oil and gas sector of around $8.4 trillion (in year-2007 dollars) over 2007-2030, or $350 billion per year on average. That is significantly less than is currently being spent. This is due to a major shift in where that investment is needed. Much more capital needs to go to the resource-rich regions, notably the Middle East, where unit costs are lowest. In short, the opportunities for international companies to invest in non-OPEC regions will diminish as the resource base contracts, eventually leaving the countries holding the bulk of the world's remaining oil and gas reserves to take on a larger burden of investment, either directly through their national companies or indirectly, in partnership with foreign investors. It cannot be taken for granted that these countries will be willing to make this investment themselves or to attract sufficient foreign capital to keep up the necessary pace of investment.

Stronger oil company partnerships could bring mutual benefits

Major structural changes are underway in the upstream oil and gas industry, with the national companies playing an increasingly dominant role. In the Reference Scenario, they account for about 80% of total incremental production of both oil and gas between 2007 and 2030. In most of the countries with the largest oil and gas reserves, national companies dominate the upstream industry and foreign companies are either not allowed to own and develop reserves or are subject to tight restrictions. Higher oil prices and a growing conviction among political leaders that national companies serve the nation's interests better than private and foreign oil companies have boosted the confidence and aspirations of national companies, some of them rivalling the international companies for technical capability and efficiency. The international oil companies, which have traditionally dominated the global oil and gas industry, are increasingly being squeezed by the growing power of the national companies and by dwindling reserves and production in accessible mature basins outside OPEC countries. The super-majors have been struggling to replace their proven reserves and expand production, while the share of their cash earnings that is returned to shareholders has been growing.

How the structure of the global oil and gas industry evolves in the coming decades will have important implications for investment, production capacity and prices. The increasing dominance of national companies may make it less certain that the investment projected in this *Outlook* will actually be made. The long-term policies of some major resource-rich countries in support of national goals may lead to slower depletion of their resources. Although some national companies, like Saudi Aramco, perform strongly in most areas, others may be less well placed to address the financing, technical and managerial challenges of bringing new upstream capacity on stream. Partnerships between the national and international companies could help address these challenges. The mutual benefits that could accrue are compelling: the national companies control most of the world's remaining reserves, but some lack the technology and skilled personnel to do much more than simply maintain existing producing assets; the international companies are opportunity-constrained, but have the management skills and technology to help national companies develop their reserves.

Oil-rich African countries have no excuse for their citizens' energy poverty

A number of sub-Saharan African countries hold large oil and gas resources, which are expected to underpin strong growth in their production and exports in the coming two decades or so. Conventional oil production in the ten largest hydrocarbon-producing countries in sub-Saharan Africa reached 5.6 mb/d in 2007, of which 5.1 mb/d was exported. In the Reference Scenario, output rises to 7.4 mb/d and oil exports to 6.4 mb/d in 2030. Gas production in these countries increases more than four-fold, from 36 billion cubic metres in 2006 to 163 bcm in 2030, with most of the increase going to export. These projections hinge on a reduction in gas flaring, adequate investment and avoiding disruptions to supplies through civil unrest. Cumulative government revenues from oil and gas output (from royalties and taxes) in these ten countries are projected, in aggregate, to total $4 trillion over 2007-2030. Nigeria and Angola remain the largest exporters, with combined cumulative government revenues of about $3.5 trillion. Taxes on oil and gas production account for more than 50% of total government revenues in most of the oil- and gas-rich sub-Saharan African countries.

Despite the vast hydrocarbon wealth of these ten countries, most of their citizens remain poor. As a result, household use of modern energy services is very limited. Two-thirds of households do not have access to electricity and three-quarters do not have access to clean fuels for cooking, relying instead on fuelwood and charcoal. Unless there are major government initiatives to address this problem, the number of electricity-deprived people is projected to increase over the projection period, as the population grows. And more than half of the total population of these countries still relies on fuelwood and charcoal for cooking in 2030.

Tackling energy poverty is well within these countries' means, but major institutional reforms are needed. We estimate the capital cost of providing minimal energy services (electricity and liquefied petroleum gas stoves and cylinders) to these households over the *Outlook* period to be about $18 billion. This is equivalent to only 0.4% of cumulative government revenues from oil and gas. An improvement in the efficiency and transparency of revenue allocation and the accountability of governments in the use of public funds would improve the likelihood that oil and gas revenues are actually used to alleviate poverty generally and energy poverty specifically.

The consequences for the global climate of policy inaction are shocking

The projected rise in emissions of greenhouse gases in the Reference Scenario puts us on a course of doubling the concentration of those gases in the atmosphere by the end of this century, entailing an eventual global average temperature increase of up to 6°C. The Reference Scenario trends point to continuing growth in emissions of CO_2 and other greenhouse gases. Global energy-related CO_2 emissions rise from 28 Gt in 2006 to 41 Gt in 2030 — an increase of 45%. The 2030 projection is only 1 Gt lower than that projected in last year's *Outlook*, even though we assume much higher prices and slightly lower world GDP growth. World greenhouse-gas emissions, including non-energy CO_2 and all other gases, are projected to grow from 44 Gt CO_2-equivalent in 2005 to 60 Gt CO_2-eq in 2030, an increase of 35% over 2005.

Three-quarters of the projected increase in energy-related CO_2 emissions in the Reference Scenario arises in China, India and the Middle East, and 97% in non-OECD countries as a whole. On average, however, non-OECD per-capita emissions remain far lower than those in the OECD. Emissions in the OECD reach a peak after 2020 and then decline. Only in Europe and Japan are emissions in 2030 lower than today. The bulk of the increase in global energy-related CO_2 emissions is expected to come from cities, their share rising from 71% in 2006 to 76% in 2030 as a result of urbanisation. City residents tend to consume more energy than rural residents, so they therefore emit more CO_2 per capita.

The road from Copenhagen must be paved with more than good intentions

Strong, co-ordinated action is needed urgently to curb the growth in greenhouse-gas emissions and the resulting rise in global temperatures. The post-2012 global climate-change policy regime that is expected to be established at the Copenhagen conference in 2009 will provide the international framework for that action. With energy-related CO_2 accounting for 61% of global greenhouse-gas emissions, the energy sector will have to be at the heart of discussions on what level of concentration to aim for and how to achieve it. The target that is set for the long-term stabilisation of greenhouse-gas concentration will determine the pace of the required transformation of the global energy system, as well as how stringent the policy responses will need to be. Successfully meeting that target will hinge on effective implementation.

The choice of global emissions trajectory will need to take into account technological requirements and costs in the energy sector. The normal cycle of capital replacement is a key constraint on the speed with which low-carbon technologies can enter into use without incurring disproportionate cost. The energy sector has a relatively slow rate of capital replacement in general, due to the long lifetime of much of its capital — for producing, supply and using energy. As a result, more efficient technologies normally take many years to spread through the energy sector. It will be necessary to face up to the reality of the cost of early capital retirement if radical measures are to be taken to speed up this process so as to deliver deep cuts in emissions. The rate of capital-stock turnover is particularly slow in the power sector, where large up-front costs and long operating lifetimes mean that plants that have already been built — and their associated emissions — are effectively "locked-in". In the Reference Scenario, three-quarters of the projected output of electricity worldwide in 2020 (and more than half in 2030) comes from power stations that are already operating today. As a result, even if all power plants built from now onwards were carbon-free, CO_2 emissions from the power sector would still be only 25%, or 4 Gt, lower in 2020 relative to the Reference Scenario.

Any agreement will need to take into account the importance of a handful of major emitters. The five largest emitters of energy-related CO_2 — China, the United States, the European Union, India and Russia — together account for almost two thirds of global CO_2 emissions; in the Reference Scenario, this proportion is expected to remain similar in 2020. The contributions to emissions reduction made by China and the United States will be critical to reaching a stabilisation goal. The scale of the reduction in energy-related emissions by country or region varies markedly with different levels of international participation.

The stabilisation goal will determine the scale of the energy challenge

This *Outlook* considers two climate-policy scenarios corresponding to long-term stabilisation of greenhouse-gas concentration at 550 and 450 parts per million of CO_2 equivalent. The 550 Policy Scenario equates to an increase in global temperature of approximately 3°C, the 450 Policy Scenario to a rise of around 2°C. The 550 Policy Scenario involves a plateauing of greenhouse-gas emissions by 2020 and reductions soon after. The 450 Policy Scenarios involves much more substantial reductions after 2020. Even then, emissions overshoot the trajectory needed to meet the 450 ppm CO_2-eq target, requiring greater emissions reductions after 2030. In both scenarios, total emissions are significantly lower in 2030 in all major emitting countries. To reach either of these outcomes, hundreds of millions of households and businesses around the world would need to be encouraged to change the way they use energy. This will require innovative policies, an appropriate regulatory framework, the rapid development of a global carbon market and increased investment in energy research, development and demonstration.

There is a wide range of international policy mechanisms that could be adopted to meet an agreed climate objective. However, as current political debate shows, and given practical issues in the energy sector, the reality is that nations adopt the approach or approaches that best reflect their varied interests and capabilities. This *Outlook* analyses the implications for the energy sector of a hybrid policy framework involving one particular combination of cap-and-trade systems, sectoral agreements (in the transport and industry sectors) and national policies and measures. Cap-and-trade systems are assumed to play an important role in the OECD regions. The carbon price there reaches $90/tonne of CO_2 in 2030 in the 550 Policy Scenario and $180/tonne in the 450 Policy Scenario.

In the 550 Policy Scenario, world primary energy demand expands by about 32% between 2006 and 2030 with the share of fossil fuels falling markedly. Demand grows on average by 1.2% per year, compared with 1.6% in the Reference Scenario. By 2030, demand is 9% lower than in the Reference Scenario, mainly as a result of efficiency gains. Global energy-related CO_2 emissions peak in 2025 and then decline slightly to 33 Gt in 2030, while greenhouse-gas emissions plateau by 2020 and are broadly flat through to 2030. Both total greenhouse-gas and energy-related CO_2 emissions are 19% lower in 2030 than in the Reference Scenario. The energy mix in this scenario is markedly different to that of the Reference Scenario, with fossil fuels losing market share to renewables and nuclear power. Oil demand rises to 98 mb/d in 2030 — almost 9 mb/d less than in the Reference Scenario. More than half of the oil savings occur in the transport sector in OECD countries and other major economies, as a result of sectoral agreements to reduce emissions from light-duty vehicles and aviation. Oil prices are around $100 per barrel (in year-2007 dollars) in 2030, 18% lower than in the Reference Scenario, due to lower demand. OPEC production still increases, to 49 mb/d in 2030, almost 13 mb/d higher than today (but 4 mb/d less than in the Reference Scenario). CCS is also deployed more quickly. In 2030, the installed capacity of CCS plants amounts to over 160 GW worldwide, of which about 70% is in OECD countries. CCS capacity is negligible in the Reference Scenario.

The 450 Policy Scenario assumes much stronger and broader policy action from 2020 onwards, inducing quicker development and deployment of low-carbon technologies. Global energy-related CO_2 emissions are assumed to follow broadly the same trajectory as in the 550 Policy Scenario until 2020, and then to fall more quickly. They peak in 2020 at 32.5 Gt and then decline to 25.7 Gt in 2030. This scenario requires emissions in OECD countries to be reduced by almost 40% in 2030, compared with 2006 levels. Other major economies are required to limit their emissions growth to 20%. Participation in an international cap-and-trade system is assumed to be broader than in the 550 Policy Scenario, covering all major emitting countries from 2020 onwards. Hydropower, biomass, wind and other renewables see faster deployment in power generation, accounting for 40% of total generation worldwide in 2030. An additional 190 GW of CCS is deployed in the last decade of the projection period compared with the 550 Policy Scenario.

The scale of the challenge in the 450 Policy Scenario is immense: the 2030 emissions level for the world as a whole in this scenario is less than the level of projected emissions for non-OECD countries alone in the Reference Scenario. In other words, the OECD countries alone cannot put the world onto the path to 450-ppm trajectory, even if they were to reduce their emissions to zero. Even leaving aside any debate about the political feasibility of the 450 Policy Scenario, it is uncertain whether the scale of the transformation envisaged is even technically achievable, as the scenario assumes broad deployment of technologies that have not yet been proven. The technology shift, if achievable, would certainly be unprecedented in scale and speed of deployment. Increased public and private spending on research and development in the near term would be essential to develop the advanced technologies needed to make the 450 Policy Scenario a reality.

Tackling climate change will require big shifts in spending

The profound shifts in energy demand and supply in the two climate-policy scenarios call for huge increases in spending on new capital stock, especially in power plants and in more energy-efficient equipment and appliances. The 550 Policy Scenario requires $4.1 trillion more investment in total between 2010 and 2030 than in the Reference Scenario — equal on average to 0.24% of annual world GDP. Most of this goes to deploying and improving existing technologies. Investment in power plants is $1.2 trillion higher, with close to three-quarters of this additional capital going to OECD countries. Additional expenditures on the demand side are even bigger. Most of the extra spending is by individuals, who have to pay more for more efficient cars, appliances and buildings. This extra cost amounts to $17 per person per year on average throughout the world. But these investments are accompanied by large savings on energy bills. Improved energy efficiency lowers fossil-fuel consumption by a cumulative amount of 22 billion tonnes of oil equivalent over 2010-2030, yielding cumulative savings of over $7 trillion.

The additional up front expenditures on energy-related capital are, unsurprisingly, considerably larger in the 450 Policy Scenario. An additional $2.4 trillion needs to be invested in low- or zero-carbon power-generation capacity and an additional $2.7 trillion invested in more energy-efficient equipment, appliances and buildings than in the 550 Policy Scenario. Together, these costs equal on average 0.55% of annual world GDP. These expenditures are particularly great during the last decade of the projection period, when CO_2 emissions fall most rapidly and the marginal cost of abatement options rises sharply. Galvanising these investments would require clear price signals (including through a broad-based, efficient carbon market), appropriate fiscal incentives and well-targeted regulation. At $5.8 trillion, the cumulative savings on fuel bills are smaller than in the 550 Policy Scenario, because higher electricity prices offset the bigger energy savings.

The energy future will be very different

For all the uncertainties highlighted in this report, we can be certain that the energy world will look a lot different in 2030 than it does today. The world energy system will be transformed, but not necessarily in the way we would like to see. We can be confident of some of the trends highlighted in this report: the growing weight of China, India, the Middle East and other non-OECD regions in energy markets and in CO_2 emissions; the rapidly increasing dominance of national oil companies; and the emergence of low-carbon energy technologies. And while market imbalances could temporarily cause prices to fall back, it is becoming increasingly apparent that the era of cheap oil is over. But many of the key policy drivers (not to mention other, external factors) remain in doubt. It is within the power of all governments, of producing and consuming countries alike, acting alone or together, to steer the world towards a cleaner, cleverer and more competitive energy system. Time is running out and the time to act is now.

Global energy at a crossroads

Purpose and scope of the study

It is not an exaggeration to say that the future of human prosperity hinges on finding a way of supplying the world's growing energy needs in a way that does not irreparably harm the environment. Until recently, it looked as if we had plenty of time to meet that challenge. No longer. Surging oil and gas prices have drawn attention to the physical and political constraints on raising production — and the vital importance of affordable supplies to the world economy. And the latest scientific evidence suggests that the pace of climate change resulting from man-made emissions of greenhouse gases — the bulk of which come from burning fossil fuels — is faster than predicted. The urgent need for a veritable energy revolution, involving a wholesale global shift to low-carbon technologies, is now widely recognised.

This year's *World Energy Outlook*, as in all even-numbered years, provides a comprehensive update of long-term energy demand and supply projections to 2030, fuel by fuel and region by region. As a special feature this year, it examines how energy is used in cities and the implications for the future. The *Outlook* also takes a detailed look at the two headline issues that emerge from these projections: the prospects for oil and gas production, and the policy options for tackling climate change after 2012, when a new global agreement is due to take effect. The results of these analyses are intended to provide policy makers, investors and end users with a rigorous quantitative framework for assessing likely future trends in energy markets and the cost-effectiveness of new policies to tackle energy-security and environmental concerns.

Last year's *Outlook* drew attention to the risk of an oil-supply crunch by the middle of the next decade, were upstream investment to fall short of requirements, triggering a jump in prices. The surge in oil prices over the past year reflects, in large part, market expectations that such a scenario is set to become reality. A growing number of oil companies and analysts have suggested that oil production may peak within the next two decades, as a result of limits on the amount of investment that can be mobilised, rising costs and political and geological factors. Limited exploration activity is increasing the uncertainties about finding new oilfields; and the rate of decline in production at existing fields — especially the large, mature fields that have been the mainstay of global output for several decades — is faster than many believe. How decline rates at these fields evolve — with or without the deployment of enhanced recovery techniques — will have major implications for the need to invest in new fields, which are typically smaller, more complex and more costly to develop.

To shed light on these issues, this *Outlook* takes an in-depth look at the drivers of oil production, based on a detailed field-by-field analysis of production trends, investment and costs, and considers the opportunities for expanding capacity and the possible constraints and risks — both above and below ground. The aim is to support the cause of more transparency in data on oil and gas reserves and production; and provide valuable insights into the adequacy of current investment plans and the prospects for expanding output in the longer term.

Worries about oil-supply shortages are matched by long-term concerns about the threat of rising fossil-energy use on the global climate. In most countries, climate-change has risen to the top of the political agenda — the result of a growing body of evidence of actual global warming and ever-more startling predictions of the ecological consequences. Action in the energy sector, the major source of man-made greenhouse-gas emissions, will be fundamental to meeting the climate-change challenge. Much depends on government responses. Past editions of the *Outlook* showed that even if all the government policies and measures under discussion at that time had been implemented, the world would still not be on a sustainable path. Since the last *Outlook*, governments have adopted significant new measures. But limiting global warming to a maximum of 2°C will require a much bigger and co-ordinated global effort. Negotiations on an international agreement to succeed the Kyoto Protocol are scheduled to end in 2009 with a meeting of the Conference of the Parties of the UN Framework Convention on Climate Change in Copenhagen. This year's report aims to inform and support the climate negotiations by presenting information and analysis of a combination of policy options and approaches available to policy makers and their implications for the energy sector.

Methodology

As in previous *Outlooks*, a scenario approach is used to examine future energy trends. The projection period runs to 2030. The projections are derived from a large-scale mathematical model, the World Energy Model (WEM), which has been completely overhauled and updated, drawing on the most recent historical data and revised assumptions. The core projections, the Reference Scenario, indicate what would happen if, among other things, there were to be no new energy-policy interventions by governments beyond those already adopted by mid-2008. This will not happen and the Reference Scenario is not a forecast: it is a baseline picture of how global energy markets would evolve if the underlying trends in energy demand and supply are not changed. This allows us to test alternative assumptions about future government policies. Additional scenarios and cases are included in the analyses of oil-production prospects and climate-policy options, as described below.

Oil and gas supply prospects

A central pillar of our analysis of the prospects for oil production to 2030 is a detailed field-by-field assessment of the production outlook for the world's largest oilfields currently in production, the biggest of which, in most cases, have been in operation for many years. The analysis covers around 800 oilfields. To our knowledge, this is the most detailed and comprehensive study of its kind that has ever been made public. The work also involved a bottom-up assessment of near-term investment plans and capacity additions at existing and new oil and gas fields, based on the compilation of detailed project-by-project and company-by-company data. In recognition of the uncertainties surrounding the outlook for sustaining oil production at existing fields and fields that will be developed in the future, we have modelled the sensitivity of production to different production-decline rates and drawn out the implications for upstream investment and international oil markets.

This analysis also considers the prospects for further advances in upstream technologies, the potential for improved and enhanced recovery techniques to bolster conventional oil and gas output and recovery rates, and the prospects for producing oil and gas from non-conventional sources. It also looks at the factors that may hinder capital flows to the upstream industry and capacity additions – including limitations on the opportunities for the international oil companies to invest in developing reserves in many key resource-rich countries and the willingness and ability of the resource-rich countries and their national companies to expand capacity. Higher prices have driven up the revenues earned by oil and gas exporters, which may paradoxically reduce the incentive for some countries to expand capacity in the medium term – partly because of limits on the rate at which they can absorb the additional earnings. The implications for the relationships between international oil companies, national companies and oil services providers are also assessed.

As a special focus, we also look at the outlook for oil and gas production in ten oil- and gas-exporting sub-Saharan African countries, the revenues it will generate and the prospects for energy poverty. It is well established that the reasons for the persistence of poverty in resource-exporting countries are mismanagement of hydrocarbon revenues, poor governance and a lack of transparency. This study shows what could be achieved to end reliance on traditional biomass and provide general access to electricity by calculating the investment costs associated with increasing energy access and comparing them with total government revenues from hydrocarbon exploitation.

Climate change scenarios

We examine in detail, through scenario analysis, how different international agreements and national/regional commitments on climate change could affect the evolution of energy markets after 2012. The analysis focuses on three of the most commonly discussed elements of a post-2012 climate framework, namely cap-and-trade, international sectoral agreements and national policies and measures. A plausible combination of these mechanisms, or hybrid approach, is modelled, using the WEM, in two scenarios: one in which it is agreed to limit the greenhouse-gas concentration in the atmosphere to 550 ppm (in CO_2-equivalent terms) and another in which the concentration is held to 450 ppm.

The mix of approaches differs between three groups of countries: "OECD+" countries (a group that includes the OECD and non-OECD EU countries), "Other Major Economies" (including China, Russia, India, Indonesia, Brazil and Middle East) and "Other Countries". A cap-and-trade system, similar in concept to the Emissions Trading Scheme that is currently operating in the European Union, is assumed to be implemented by the OECD+ countries in the 550 Policy Scenario and in the Other Major Economies too in the 450 Policy Scenario. The system is assumed to cover power generation and the industrial sector. The Other Major Economies are assumed to introduce national policies and measures covering power generation and industry, aimed generally at improving energy security and mitigating local pollution, as well as helping to reduce CO_2 emissions. In addition, to limit the risk of carbon leakage from countries covered by the cap-and-trade system, sector-specific energy-efficiency standards are assumed to be introduced in a number of industrial sectors. Achieving abatement of emissions in these countries is essential to meet ambitious climate targets, so these countries must have strong incentives to act, even for the 550 ppm objective to be met.

We have assumed that international sectoral agreements are adopted and implemented in the transport and industry sectors in OECD+ and Other Major Economies. Such an approach is already being taken by the European Union, which currently excludes road transport from its emissions-trading scheme and is instead negotiating vehicle fuel-efficiency standards and renewable fuel mandates. In the buildings sector, it is assumed that all countries undertake national policies and measures tailored to the national potential for energy savings. These could require formal international approval. It is assumed that the least-developed countries with low per-capita emissions are not required to play any part in a cap-and-trade system or adopt sectoral agreements. Nonetheless, they do act to limit emissions through national policies and measures, and have opportunities to earn emission credits under the Clean Development Mechanism and gain access to global technology or financing programmes.

PART A
**GLOBAL ENERGY
TRENDS TO 2030**

PREFACE

Higher energy prices and slower economic growth have left their mark on the assumptions for this year's *World Energy Outlook*. As a result, energy growth to 2030 is slower than in *WEO-2007*, though other trends are broadly unchanged – persistent dominance of fossil fuels in the energy mix (despite additional action taken in the last twelve months to mitigate climate change), an inexorable rise in CO_2 emissions and a strongly rising share for developing countries in global energy consumption: almost all the increase in fossil fuel consumption over the period occurs in non-OECD countries.

Following the pattern which will be familiar to regular *WEO* readers, this first part of the book, Part A, sets out in detail this year's world energy projections in the Reference Scenario. The main assumptions underpinning these projections are set out in Chapter 1. Chapter 2 summarises the global trends in energy demand and supply, as well as the implications for investment. The detailed projections for oil, gas, coal, electricity and renewables are then set out in Chapters 3-7.

In an innovation this year, Chapter 8 examines the special place of urban energy consumption in global usage. By 2030, urban use accounts for nearly three-quarters of total energy use worldwide.

CHAPTER 1

CONTEXT AND PRINCIPAL ASSUMPTIONS

H I G H L I G H T S

- The Reference Scenario embodies the effects of those government policies and measures that were enacted or adopted by mid-2008, even though many of them have not yet been fully implemented. Possible, potential or even likely future policy actions are not taken into account. Many countries subsidise energy, in some cases heavily. Most have policies to phase out subsidies, and are accordingly assumed to reduce them progressively.

- World population is assumed to grow at an annual average rate of 1%, from an estimated 6.5 billion in 2006 to 8.2 billion in 2030. Population growth slows progressively over the projection period, in line with past trends: population expanded by 1.4% per year from 1990 to 2006. The population of non-OECD countries as a group continues to grow most rapidly.

- The rate of growth in world GDP — the main driver of energy demand in all regions — is assumed to average 3.3% per year over the period 2006-2030. It averaged 3.2% from 1990 to 2006. The increase reflects the rising weight in the world economy of the non-OECD countries, where growth will remain fastest. The average growth rate nonetheless falls progressively over the projection period, from 4.2% in 2006-2015 to 2.8% in 2015-2030. Growth remains highest in China, India and the Middle East.

- The IEA crude oil import price, a proxy for international prices, is assumed to average $100 per barrel in real year-2007 dollars over the period 2008-2015 and then to rise in a broadly linear manner to over $120 in 2030. This represents a major upward adjustment from last year's *Outlook*, reflecting higher prices for near-term physical delivery and for futures contracts, as well as a reassessment of the prospects for the cost of oil supply and the outlook for demand. In nominal terms, prices double to just over $200 per barrel in 2030.

- Natural gas prices are assumed to rise in 2008 and then to fall back slightly through to 2010 in lagged adjustment to oil prices. Gas prices begin to rise after 2015 in line with oil prices. Coal prices, which have also risen sharply in recent years, are assumed to settle at around $120 per tonne in 2010, remaining flat through to 2015 and then falling back slightly to $110 in 2030.

- The average energy efficiency of equipment currently in use is generally assumed to improve progressively over the projection period, though at varying rates according to the type of equipment and the rate of retirement and replacement of the stock of capital. Some major new supply-side technologies, including carbon capture and storage, second-generation biofuels and coal-to-liquids, are assumed to be deployed on a small scale before the end of the projection period.

Government policies and measures

As in previous editions of the *World Energy Outlook*, the Reference Scenario, the results of which are set out in Part A, takes into consideration all government policies and measures that were enacted or adopted by the middle of the current year, including those that have not yet been fully implemented. The policies considered cover a wide array of sectors and a variety of instruments. Some measures not directly addressed at the energy sector nonetheless have important consequences for energy markets and have been taken into account. Most recent policy initiatives directed at the energy sector, in both OECD and non-OECD countries, are designed to improve energy security, combat climate change and address other environmental problems through improved energy efficiency, switching to lower carbon fuels and enhanced indigenous energy production. They include the Energy Independence and Security Act in the United States and the European Commission's climate action plan (the provisions of which are taken into account in the Reference Scenario), which includes a binding target to raise the share of renewable energy in the European Union's primary consumption to 20% by 2030 (Table 1.1). The impact on energy demand and supply of recently adopted measures does not show up in historical market data, which are available only up to 2006 for all countries (preliminary data for 2007 is to hand for OECD countries). Some policies adopted earlier are not yet fully implemented but have been taken into account in the Reference Scenario.

Table 1.1 ● **Major new energy-related policy initiatives adopted between mid-2007 and mid-2008**

Country/region	Policy/measure	Implementation in the Reference Scenario
European Union	European Commission integrated energy and climate action plan	$30/t CO_2 price (in year-2007 prices) in the EU trading scheme sectors is assumed Increased use of renewable energy Improved energy efficiency Increased use of biofuels in transport
United States	Energy Independence and Security Act	Tightened corporate average fuel-economy standards, resulting in lower transport-fuel intensity Increase in biofuels consumption Tougher appliance standards and incentives result in lower energy intensity in buildings and industry
Japan	Revision of Act on the Rational Use of Energy Revision of Law on Global Warming Countermeasures	Improved energy efficiency and reduced CO_2 emissions in the residential/services and other sectors (both measures)
China	Renewable Energy Development Plan	Increased use of renewable energy
	Revision of Law on Energy Conservation	Improved energy efficiency

Note: More details about the policies in the Reference Scenario can be found at the WEO website www.worldenergyoutlook.org.

Importantly, the Reference Scenario does not include possible, potential or even likely future policy initiatives. For that reason, the projections in this scenario *cannot be considered forecasts of what is likely to happen*. Rather, they should be seen as a baseline vision of how energy markets are likely to develop should government policy making develop no further. Major new energy-policy initiatives will inevitably be implemented during the projection period, but it is impossible to predict exactly which measures will eventually be adopted in each country and how they will be implemented, especially towards the end of the projection period. The climate-policy scenarios set out in Part C analyse the impact of a range of possible future policy interventions.

Box 1.1 ● **Improvements to the modelling framework in *WEO-2008***

The IEA's World Energy Model (WEM) — a large-scale mathematical construct designed to replicate how energy markets function — is the main tool used to generate the sector-by-sector and fuel-by-fuel projections by region or country for all the scenarios in this *Outlook*.[1] The model, which has been developed over several years, comprises five main modules: final energy demand, power generation, refining and other transformation, investment and carbon-dioxide (CO_2) emissions, all of which are modelled on a country or regional basis; and fossil-fuel and biofuels supply, which is modelled by major producer. This year, all the WEM modules were overhauled and major new elements were introduced, including the following:

● The demand module for all regions was completely rebuilt, involving re-estimating parameters using more recent time-series data and introducing more detailed coverage of demand by sector and fuel.

● The oil and gas production and trade models were expanded to take better account of economic variables and to reflect the recent surge in cost inflation and the fall in the value of the US dollar against most other currencies.

● Oilfield decline rates were analysed in detail on a field-by-field basis in order to assess the prospects for future decline rates (see Chapter 10).

● Biofuels demand was modelled in more detail, taking account of technical and economic factors.

● Power-generation capital and operating costs were assessed in detail and the cost assumptions in the WEM were revised to take account of recent cost inflation (see Chapter 6).

In addition, the integration of the WEM into a general equilibrium model, started in 2007, was taken a step further, in order to model more precisely the feedback links between energy markets and the macro-economy.

---

1. A detailed description of the WEM can be found at www.worldenergyoutlook.org.

Although the Reference Scenario assumes the implementation of currently adopted energy and environmental policies during the projection period, how those policies are implemented in practice is nonetheless assumed to vary by fuel and by country. For example, while nuclear energy is assumed to remain an option for power generation in those countries that have not officially banned it or decided to phase it out (though not for others), the pace of construction of new plants differs among countries, reflecting differences in the degree of commitment to that energy source.

Pricing and other market reforms are also assumed to be implemented at different rates. In most non-OECD countries, at least one fuel or form of energy continues to be subsidised, most often through price controls that hold the retail or wholesale price below the true market level. Other forms of direct financial intervention by government, such as grants, tax rebates or deductions and soft loans, are commonplace. Indirect interventions also occur, such as the free provision of energy infrastructure and services. Some of these interventions are more justified than others; for example, support to overcome market obstacles to the development and deployment of new technology. According to our calculations,[2] energy-related consumption subsidies, which encourage consumption by pricing energy below market levels, amounted in 20 non-OECD countries (accounting for over 80% of total non-OECD primary energy demand) to about $310 billion in 2007 (Figure 1.1). Oil products account for one-half, or $150 billion. Most of these countries do have policies eventually to phase out consumption subsidies and we accordingly assume that these subsidies are gradually reduced, though at varying rates across regions. Consumption subsidies are minimal in OECD countries. In all cases, the rates of *ad valorem* taxes and excise duties on fuels are assumed to remain unchanged.

Figure 1.1 • **Energy subsidies by fuel in non-OECD countries, 2007**

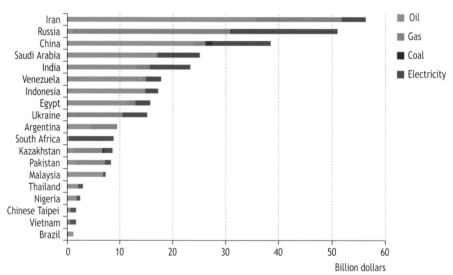

Source: IEA analysis.

2. See *World Energy Outlook 2006* (Box 11.2) for a discussion of the price-gap methodology used to estimate subsidies (IEA, 2006). The IEA plans to publish a special report on subsidies in 2009.

Population

Population growth affects the size and composition of energy demand, directly and through its impact on economic growth and development. Our population assumptions are drawn from the most recent United Nations projections (UNPD, 2007a). World population is projected to grow from an estimated 6.5 billion in 2006 to around 8.2 billion in 2030 — an average rate of increase of 1% per year (Figure 1.2). By 2030, 52% of the world's population will be in non-OECD Asia, down slightly from 53% today. China will remain the world's most heavily populated country, with more than 1.46 billion people, though India's population all but reaches China's by 2030. The OECD's share of global population is set to slide further, from 18% today to less than 16% in 2030.

Figure 1.2 ● **Population by major region**

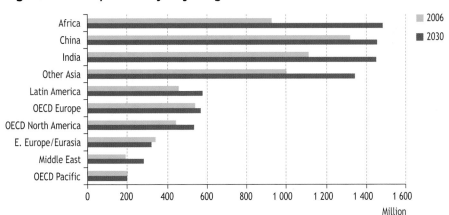

The emerging economies will continue to experience the fastest rate of population growth. The population of non-OECD countries in total is projected to grow by 1.1% per year, against 0.4% per year in the OECD (Table 1.2). The population of all regions expands, with the exception of OECD Pacific, largely due to Japan, where population is projected to fall by 0.3% per year, and Eastern Europe/Eurasia, largely due to Russia, where population slides by 0.6% per year. By 2030, Russia's population is expected to be 13% smaller than today. Most of the growth in the OECD population comes from North America. Several European countries, including Germany and Italy, are expected to experience significant population declines. All regions will experience continued ageing in the coming decades as fertility and mortality rates decline. Worldwide, the proportion of people over 60 years old is projected to rise from 11% now to about 15% by 2030 (UNPD, 2007b). This will have far-reaching economic and social consequences, which will inevitably affect both the level and pattern of energy use. Older people, for example, tend to travel less for work and leisure.

All of the increase in world population in aggregate will occur in urban areas: the rural population is expected to start to decline in about a decade. In 2008, for the first time in history, the urban population will equal the rural population of the world; from then on, the greater part of the world population will be urban (UNPD, 2007c). Major parts of the world, particularly in Africa, will remain largely rural. Continuing rapid urbanisation in non-OECD countries will have a major impact on demand for modern energy, the bulk of which is consumed in or close to towns and cities (see Chapter 8).

Table 1.2 ● Population growth by region (average annual growth rates)

	1980-1990	1990-2006	2006-2015	2006-2030
OECD	0.8%	0.8%	0.5%	0.4%
North America	1.2%	1.2%	0.9%	0.8%
United States	*0.9%*	*1.1%*	*0.9%*	*0.8%*
Europe	0.5%	0.5%	0.3%	0.2%
Pacific	0.8%	0.5%	0.1%	-0.1%
Japan	*0.6%*	*0.2%*	*-0.1%*	*-0.3%*
Non-OECD	2.0%	1.5%	1.3%	1.1%
E. Europe/Eurasia	0.8%	-0.2%	-0.2%	-0.2%
Russia	*n.a.*	*-0.3%*	*-0.5%*	*-0.6%*
Asia	1.8%	1.4%	1.1%	0.9%
China	*1.5%*	*0.9%*	*0.6%*	*0.4%*
India	*2.1%*	*1.7%*	*1.4%*	*1.1%*
Middle East	3.6%	2.3%	1.9%	1.7%
Africa	2.9%	2.4%	2.2%	2.0%
Latin America	2.0%	1.5%	1.2%	1.0%
Brazil	*2.1%*	*1.5%*	*1.2%*	*0.9%*
World	1.7%	1.4%	1.1%	1.0%
European Union	*n.a.*	*0.3%*	*0.1%*	*0.0%*

Note: These assumptions also apply to the climate-change scenarios described in Part C.

Economic growth

Economic growth is by far the most important determinant of the overall demand for energy services. The pattern of economic development also affects the fuel mix. As a result, the energy projections in the *Outlook* are highly sensitive to underlying assumptions about rates and patterns of economic growth. Extremely rapid economic expansion in many countries outside the OECD — especially in Asia - is the main reason why energy demand has accelerated in recent years. Nonetheless, over the long term, the income elasticity of energy demand — the change in demand relative to the change in GDP - has fallen in most parts of the world, though it has picked up since the start of the current decade. Between 1971 and 1990, each 1% increase in global GDP (in purchasing power parity, or PPP, terms) was accompanied by a 0.66% increase in primary energy consumption.[3] Between 1990 and 2000, the corresponding increase in demand dropped to only 0.44%, but it rebounded to 0.68% in 2000-2006, largely due to an increase in the energy intensity of China's economic growth.

---

3. All GDP data cited in this report are expressed in year-2007 dollars using purchasing power parities (PPP) (Box 1.2).

There are strong signs that the global economy, which has expanded briskly in recent years, is slowing, partly as a consequence of higher energy and other commodity prices and the financial crisis that began in 2007. GDP growth has already fallen in most OECD economies, particularly in the United States, where a slump in the housing market has contributed to the credit squeeze, the consequences of which are being felt throughout the global financial system. Many OECD countries are now on the verge of recession. Most non-OECD countries have so far been less affected by financial market turbulence and have continued to grow rapidly, led by China, India and the Middle East (where growth has been boosted by surging oil-export revenues). This momentum is provided by strong productivity gains as these countries progressively integrate into the global economy, by improved terms of trade for commodity producers on the back of soaring prices for oil and other raw materials and by policy improvements. But there are signs that activity in developing Asian countries, too, is now beginning to slow. Headline inflation has increased around the world, especially in the emerging economies, with surging food and energy prices.

The International Monetary Fund (IMF) projects world GDP in PPP terms to drop sharply from an above-trend 5% in 2006 and 2007 to 4.1% in 2008 and 3.9% in 2009.[4] It projects inflation to rise from 2.2% in 2007 to 3.4% in 2008 in the advanced economies (essentially those of the OECD) and from 6.4% to 9.1% in the emerging economies. Trade in goods and services is expected to slow. GDP growth in all regions is expected to fall, though non-OECD countries will continue to outpace the remainder of the world. In the United States, growth is projected to fall from 2.2% in 2007 to only 1.3% in 2008 and 0.8% in 2009, while China's growth falls from 11.9% to 9.7% in 2008 and 9.8% in 2009.

The continued housing-market correction in the United States, similar indications in Europe and other parts of the world, and the fall-out from the financial crisis are among the most obvious uncertainties surrounding the near-term economic outlook (IMF, 2008b). Further steep declines in asset prices and an abrupt reduction in the lending capacity of the banking system could lead to a global credit crunch, with potentially severe consequences for growth. Although the IMF judges the risks to its projections to be greater on the downside, there is some potential for an unexpectedly rapid recovery among the rich industrialised economies in 2009 if conditions in financial markets improve, lowering the current high price of credit (OECD, 2008).

This *Outlook* assumes that economic growth will recover to around 4.5% per year by the turn of the decade, but will slow progressively through to 2030. World GDP is assumed to grow by an average of 3.3% per year over the period 2006-2030 compared with 3.2% from 1990 to 2006 (Table 1.3). The increase reflects the rising weight in the world economy of the non-OECD countries, where growth will remain fastest. GDP growth is assumed to average 4.2% per year in 2006-2015 and 2.8% per year in 2015-2030. Growth is nonetheless somewhat lower than assumed in last year's *Outlook*, especially in OECD countries, in part because of the impact of higher energy prices and weaker prospects for global economic growth in the near term.

---

4. Taken from the July update of the projections in IMF (2008a), available at: www.imf.org/external/pubs/ft/weo/2008/update/02/index.htm.

Table 1.3 • **Real GDP growth by region** (average annual growth rates)

	1980-1990	1990-2006	2006-2015	2006-2030
OECD	3.0%	2.5%	2.3%	2.0%
North America	3.1%	2.9%	2.3%	2.2%
United States	*3.3%*	*2.9%*	*2.1%*	*2.1%*
Europe	2.4%	2.3%	2.3%	1.9%
Pacific	4.2%	2.2%	2.1%	1.6%
Japan	*3.9%*	*1.3%*	*1.3%*	*1.2%*
Non-OECD	2.5%	4.4%	6.7%	4.8%
E. Europe/Eurasia	0.0%	0.0%	5.6%	3.7%
Russia	*n.a.*	*-0.2%*	*5.7%*	*3.6%*
Asia	6.7%	7.2%	7.9%	5.7%
China	*8.8%*	*9.8%*	*9.2%*	*6.1%*
India	*5.8%*	*6.1%*	*7.8%*	*6.4%*
Middle East	1.3%	4.3%	5.4%	4.3%
Africa	2.4%	3.6%	5.8%	4.1%
Latin America	1.2%	3.2%	4.3%	3.1%
Brazil	*1.5%*	*2.7%*	*4.0%*	*3.0%*
World	2.8%	3.2%	4.2%	3.3%
European Union	*n.a.*	*2.1%*	*2.2%*	*1.8%*

Note: The regional aggregate growth rates are calculated based on GDP expressed in purchasing-power parity terms. These assumptions also apply to the climate-policy scenarios described in Part C.

These GDP assumptions take account of recent major revisions to PPPs, which lower the weight of China and other developing countries in global GDP, and explain in part the reduction in average GDP growth for the world over the projection period (Box 1.2). The economies of many regions are expected to shift away from energy-intensive heavy manufacturing towards lighter industries and services, though the pace of this process, which is well advanced in the OECD and some emerging economies, varies. Industrial production continues to grow in volume terms.

China and India are expected to continue to grow faster than other regions, followed by the Middle East. China is assumed to grow at 6.1% per year between 2006 and 2030, the second-highest rate in the world. India, which grows fastest at 6.4% per year on average, overtakes China as the fastest-growing major country in the 2020s, reflecting its more rapid population growth and its earlier stage in the development process. The growth rates of the economies of China, India and other emerging economies are expected to slow as they mature. Middle East countries also grow relatively quickly, supported by buoyant oil revenues. GDP growth is assumed to temper gradually in all three OECD regions in response to acute competition from the emerging economies and to the ageing and stabilisation or fall of the population (which will reduce the active labour force in most countries). North America is expected to remain the fastest growing OECD economy, partly due to its more rapidly expanding and relatively young population, though the rate of GDP growth is assumed to drop from an annual average of 2.9% in 1990-2006 to 2.2% per year over the *Outlook* period. Europe and the Pacific are expected to see the lowest GDP growth of any major region. Based on our population and GDP-growth assumptions, per-capita incomes grow most rapidly in China and India (Figure 1.3).

Box 1.2 • Implications of new estimates of purchasing power parity

Purchasing power parities (PPPs) measure the amount of a given currency needed to buy the same basket of goods and services, traded and non-traded, as one unit of the reference currency — in this report, the US dollar. By adjusting for differences in price levels, PPPs can, in principle, provide a more reliable indicator than market exchange rates of the true level of economic activity globally or regionally. Conversions based on market exchange rates typically underestimate the value of domestic economic activity and the output of developing countries relative to the industrialised economies. PPP rates can deviate by a large amount from the market exchange rate between two currencies. It is important to take account of the true level of economic activity in analysing the main drivers of energy demand or comparing energy intensities among countries.

In 2007, the World Bank released the results of a major update of PPP exchange rates, carried out under its International Comparison Program (World Bank, 2008). As a result, the PPP differences with market exchange rates were reduced for a number of countries, most importantly China and India, thus reducing their weights in global GDP. The PPP rates were increased for some other emerging countries, including oil exporters. Overall, the average annual rate of global GDP growth between 2000 and 2007 was revised downwards by around one-half of a percentage point. China still ranks as the world's second-largest economy, accounting for about 11% of world GDP in 2007, compared with about 16% using the old PPP rate. The share of the United States in global GDP has been revised up from 19% to 21%. In spite of these changes, it remains true that the emerging economies have recently been the main driver of global growth in PPP terms, led by China, which contributed nearly 27% to global growth in 2007 (IMF, 2008a).

Figure 1.3 • Rate of growth of per-capita income by region

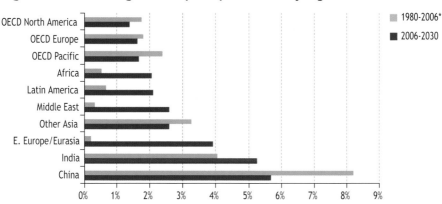

* 1990-2006 for E. Europe/Eurasia.

Energy prices

Energy prices are an exogenous determinant of the demand for and supply of each fuel and energy carrier in the WEM. The assumed trajectories for international energy prices in the Reference Scenario, summarised in Table 1.4, are based on a top-down assessment of the prices that would be needed to encourage sufficient investment in supply to meet projected demand over the *Outlook* period. In other words, they are derived iteratively to ensure their consistency with the overall global balance of supply and demand. They should not be interpreted as forecasts. Although the price paths follow smooth trends, this should not be taken as a prediction of stable energy markets: prices will, in reality, certainly deviate widely at times from these assumed trends. International prices are used to derive average end-user pre-tax prices for oil, gas and coal in each *WEO* region. Tax rates and subsidies are taken into account in calculating final post-tax prices, which help to determine final energy demand. Final electricity prices are derived from changes in marginal power-generation costs. All prices are expressed in US dollars and assume no change in exchange rates.

Table 1.4 ● **Fossil-fuel price assumptions** (dollars per unit)

	Unit	2000	2007	2010	2015	2020	2025	2030
Real terms (2007 prices)								
IEA crude oil imports	barrel	33.33	69.33	100.00	100.00	110.00	116.00	122.00
Natural gas								
US imports	MBtu	4.61	6.75	12.78	13.20	14.57	15.35	16.13
European imports	MBtu	3.35	7.03	11.15	11.50	12.71	13.45	14.19
Japan LNG	MBtu	5.63	7.80	12.70	13.16	14.52	15.28	16.05
OECD steam coal imports	tonne	40.06	72.84	120.00	120.00	116.67	113.33	110.00
Nominal terms								
IEA crude oil imports	barrel	28.00	69.33	107.34	120.27	148.23	175.13	206.37
Natural gas								
US imports	MBtu	3.87	6.75	13.72	15.88	19.64	23.18	27.28
European imports	MBtu	2.82	7.03	11.97	13.83	17.13	20.31	24.00
Japan LNG	MBtu	4.73	7.80	13.63	15.83	19.56	23.08	27.16
OECD steam coal imports	tonne	33.65	72.84	128.81	144.32	157.21	171.11	186.07

Note: Prices in the first two columns represent historical data. Gas prices are expressed on a gross calorific-value basis. All prices are for bulk supplies exclusive of tax. Nominal prices assume inflation of 2.3% per year from 2008.

Oil prices

The average IEA crude oil import price, a proxy for international prices, is assumed in the Reference Scenario to average $100 per barrel in real year-2007 dollars over the period 2008-2015 and then to rise in a broadly linear manner to $122 in 2030 (Figure 1.4).[5] This

---

5. In 2007, the average IEA crude oil import price was $2.87 per barrel lower than first-month forward West Texas Intermediate (WTI) and $3.06 lower than dated Brent.

represents a major upward adjustment from *WEO-2007*, reflecting to a large degree higher prices for near-term physical delivery and for futures contracts out to the middle of the next decade.[6] It also reflects a reassessment of the prospective marginal cost of oil supply, discussed in detail in Part B, and the outlook for demand, described in Chapter 3. In nominal terms, prices double to just over $200 per barrel in 2030.[7]

Figure 1.4 ● **Average IEA crude oil import price** (annual data)

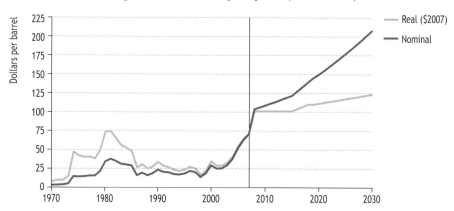

The surge in oil prices since the end of 2003, and especially since the beginning of 2007, can legitimately be described as an oil shock, albeit a slow-motion one. The price of West Texas Intermediate (WTI) – a leading benchmark crude – rose steadily from a low of $28 per barrel on average in September 2003 to $74 in July 2006, before falling back to $54 in January 2007. The price then resumed its upward path, hitting an intra-day peak of over $145 in July 2008 – an all-time record in both nominal and real terms. Prices rose on average in 41 of the 59 months between September 2003 and August 2008, and in all but four of the 17 months since February 2007. Prices have, however, since fallen back substantially, to around $100 in mid-September 2008.

A crucial difference with the price shocks of the 1970s is that the latter were caused by supply disruptions, whereas the recent shock has resulted largely from a tightening of market conditions, as demand (particularly for middle distillates) outstripped the growth in installed crude-production and oil-refining capacity, and from growing expectations of continuing supply-side constraints in the future – a risk highlighted in the Deferred Investment Scenario of past *WEOs*. Geopolitical factors, including civil strife in Nigeria and worries over Iran's nuclear programme, have magnified these upward pressures on prices. The role of speculation and the emergence of oil as an "asset class" for investors, especially in index commodity funds, remains unclear – partly because of a lack of information on real financial flows into the oil market

---

6. Other organisations, including the US Department of Energy and the Organization of the Petroleum Exporting Countries, have also recently revised their oil-price assumptions.

7. The dollar exchange rates used were those prevailing in mid-2008 (€0.64 and ¥106), which were assumed to remain unchanged over the projection period.

(see the *Spotlight* below).[8] In contrast, there is widespread agreement among analysts that oil prices have been bid up partly to hedge against the fall in the value of the US dollar – especially since 2007. Stripping out the currency impact since 2007 shows a close fit between oil prices and global balances.[9] The sudden drop in oil prices in August and early September 2008 - in the absence of any obvious major shift in demand or supply – lends support to the argument that financial investors have been playing a significant role in amplifying the impact of tighter market fundamentals on prices.

Rarely has the outlook for oil prices been more uncertain than now, in mid-September 2008. We assume in our Reference Scenario that the prices reached in mid-2008 are, to some extent, the result of transient factors and that a downward correction in prices that began in August continues through to the end of the year - in part thanks to some easing of market fundamentals. Our near-term analysis of investment and new capacity additions (set out in Chapter 13) points to little change in the balance in oil supply and demand through to the middle of the next decade; that is, projected increases in installed capacity are likely to be broadly matched by rising demand in the Reference Scenario, assuming investment is sustained beyond the end of the current decade. However, pronounced short-term swings in prices are likely to remain the norm and temporary price spikes or collapses cannot be ruled out. Prices are likely to remain highly volatile, especially in the next year or two. A worsening of the current financial crisis would most likely depress economic activity and, therefore, oil demand, exerting downward pressure on prices. On the other hand, any weakening of the dollar would help support prices. Beyond 2015, we assume that rising marginal costs of supply exert upward pressure on prices through to the end of the projection period.

There are acute risks to these assumptions on both sides: a continuing surge in demand, under-investment in oil-production or refining capacity, or a large and sustained supply disruption could result in higher prices. A further slide in the dollar could also push prices up in dollar terms (assuming no change in exchange rates). Yet a slump in demand – possibly caused by recession and more rapid oil-price subsidy reform than we assume – together with faster than expected growth in investment could drive prices down below our assumed level.

The assumption that governments implement policies to reduce subsidies (see above) has important implications for final oil prices to end users.[10] In 2007, most of the growth in world oil demand came from countries where oil-product prices are subsidised. In many countries, subsidies have risen sharply when governments have failed to increase regulated retail and wholesale prices as quickly as international prices. Iran, where retail oil prices are far below international levels, is an extreme example: the cost of those subsidies is estimated at $36 billion in 2007. Some countries, especially in Asia,

---

8. An IEA Expert Roundtable in March 2008 discussed the many influences on the current oil price. A wide range of views on the effects of money flows on the oil market was expressed, but no agreement was reached on the extent to which those flows affect prices. In the IEA's opinion, the limited information available makes it impossible to account meaningfully for the cross-market interactions that routinely take place between different futures exchanges and over-the-counter (OTC) markets. Gaps in market as well as financial data obscure the real drivers of prices.

9. IEA, *Oil Market Report*, May 2008.

10. The impact of a phase-out of oil subsidies is discussed in Chapter 3.

are now starting to rein in subsidies in the face of the mounting burden on government budgets, worries about their impact on incentives for refiners and importers to supply local markets and the prospect of persistently high prices in the medium term. Several countries, including China, India, Malaysia and Indonesia, increased prices in the first half of 2008, but some are now considering cutting them again, with the drop in international prices.

·····················S P O T L I G H T·····················

Are speculators to blame for soaring oil prices?

As is often the case when the price of any commodity jumps, the finger of blame for the recent surge in oil prices has been pointed squarely at speculators. The amount of money invested in commodity funds has certainly risen strongly in recent years –20-fold since 2003 to more than $250 billion on some estimates. A growing number of analysts believe that this represents a speculative bubble rather than the outcome of market fundamentals. Several governments, including that of India, have called for restrictions on speculation to be imposed.

But it is far from certain that the flow of money into oil trading has, in itself, driven up prices. Speculators, or financial investors, play both sides of the market, and what they buy, they eventually must sell (unless they take delivery and store physical oil, which is rare) and *vice versa*. Each barrel of oil that is bought for future delivery on the futures market must be sold on before the contract expires. Whatever the volume of futures trading (and there is no limit to the number of "paper" barrels that can be bought and sold), no oil is actually kept off the market. The amount of money currently invested in index funds is large in absolute terms, but pales beside the estimated $50 trillion-worth of contracts of all types traded on futures exchanges and over-the-counter spot markets in 2007.

Indeed, more speculative money left the regulated oil market than entered it over the first half of 2008. By mid-year, the scale of net long positions (that is, a commitment to buy at some point in the future) held by non-commercial participants in futures exchanges was roughly the same as it was in July 2007, when prices were little more than half as high. Moreover, the recent tightening of credit conditions has reduced liquidity in the world's financial system, which arguably helped fuel the speculative inflows into oil futures in previous years.

In the end, virtually the only buyers of physical crude oil are refiners, and their needs have continued to rise with robust end-use demand, especially for middle distillates. The fact that in recent months stocks have barely risen above average levels of the past five years suggests that supply has only just managed to keep pace with demand. Thus, physical market fundamentals appear to have played the leading role in driving up prices, though financial investors may have amplified the impact.

Natural gas prices

Natural gas prices have remained strongly linked to oil prices, either directly through indexation clauses in long-term supply contracts or indirectly through competition between gas and oil products in power generation and end-use markets. Thus, the prices of gas traded internationally and locally on open markets around the world have risen sharply in recent years with oil prices, though price differentials can fluctuate sharply.[11] Although only a small share of world gas is traded between regions, the links between oil and gas markets mean that regional gas prices tend to move in parallel. Lags in long-term contracts, which still account for a large share of the gas traded outside North America, mean that gas prices have not yet fully reflected the increase in oil prices. That is the main reason why gas prices have generally risen less rapidly than oil prices since the beginning of the current decade (Figure 1.5). Gas prices on average in early 2008 were highest in North America, where most gas is traded on short-term markets and few lags exist, but prices had fallen back sharply by mid-year, reflecting a surge in production, weak demand and rising stocks.

In our Reference Scenario, gas prices jump in all three regions in 2008 and then fall back slightly through to 2010 in lagged response to the fall in oil prices from their mid-2008 peaks. Prices begin to rise after 2015 in line with oil prices. Although the gradual development of gas-to-gas competition is expected to weaken the contractual links between oil and gas prices over the projection period, gas prices are not expected to fall relative to oil prices. Competition would be expected to exert some downward pressure on the prices of gas relative to those of oil. This is assumed to be offset by rising marginal supply costs for gas as the distances over which gas has to be transported, by pipeline or as liquefied natural gas (LNG) increase. The growing share of LNG in global gas supply and increasing opportunities for short-term trading of LNG are expected to contribute to a modest degree of convergence in regional prices over the projection period.

Figure 1.5 ● *Assumed natural gas and coal prices relative to crude oil**

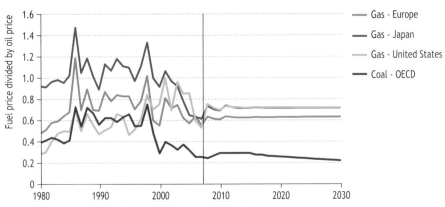

* Calculated on an energy-equivalent basis using real-2007 dollars.

---

11. The lags have nonetheless shortened, as more recent long-term contracts have generally been based on oil prices in the previous 3 to 6 months, rather than 6 to 12 months as in older contracts.

World Energy Outlook 2008 - **GLOBAL ENERGY TRENDS TO 2030**

Steam coal prices

International steam coal prices have surged in recent years. The average price of coal imported by OECD countries jumped from $42 per tonne in 2003 to $73 in 2007 (in year-2007 dollars) and soared to well over $100 in the first half of 2008.[12] Rising industrial production and electricity demand, especially in China, have boosted coal use. Higher gas prices have also encouraged some power stations and industrial end users to switch to coal and to invest in new coal-fired equipment. These factors have added to the upward pressure on coal demand and prices.

Coal prices are assumed to settle at around $120 per tonne in real terms in 2010. Thereafter, prices are assumed to remain flat through to 2015 and then to fall back slightly to $110 in 2030 as new mining and transportation capacity becomes available. As oil and gas prices are assumed to rise steadily after 2015, coal becomes increasingly competitive – at least in countries not actively seeking to limit CO_2 emissions. In reality, the possibility of a carbon value being introduced or increasing where it already exists, together with a tightening of other environmental regulations, is likely to affect the use of coal in all regions, or to increase the cost of using it, counterbalancing the impact on coal demand of relatively lower prices.

Technology

Technological innovation and the rate of deployment of new technologies for supplying or using energy have a major impact on energy balances, both in terms of the overall amount of energy used and the fuel mix. Our projections are, therefore, very sensitive to assumptions about technological developments. In general, it is assumed in the Reference Scenario that the performance of currently available technologies improves on various operational criteria, including energy efficiency. High energy prices are expected to contribute to this. However, our assumptions about the pace of technological advance vary for each fuel and each sector, depending on our assessment of the potential for efficiency improvements and the stage of technology development and commercialisation. Crucially, no altogether new technologies on the demand or supply side, beyond those known about today, are assumed to be deployed before the end of the projection period, since it cannot be known whether or when such breakthroughs might occur and how quickly they may be commercialised.

The average energy efficiency of equipment currently in use and the overall intensity of energy consumption are typically assumed to improve progressively over the projection period. However, the rate of improvement varies considerably among different types of equipment, primarily according to the rate of retirement and replacement of the capital stock. Since much of the energy-using capital stock in use today will be replaced only gradually, most of the impact of recent and future technological developments that improve energy efficiency will not be felt until near the end of the projection

---

12. In mid-2008, prices approached $200 per tonne for certain qualities of coal in some European markets and $150 in the United States.

period. Rates of capital-stock turnover differ greatly (Figure 1.6). Most of today's cars and trucks, heating and cooling systems, and industrial boilers will be replaced by 2030. But most existing buildings, roads, railways and airports, as well as many power stations and refineries, will still be in use then, barring strong government action to encourage or force early retirement (which is not assumed in the Reference Scenario). Despite slow capital stock turnover, refurbishment could, in some cases, significantly improve energy efficiency at acceptable economic cost.

On the supply side, technological advances are assumed to improve the technical and economic efficiency of producing and supplying energy. In some cases, they are expected to reduce unit costs and to lead to new and cleaner ways of producing and delivering energy services. For example, power-generation thermal efficiencies – as measured by the amount of useful electricity and heat energy produced, divided by the amount of energy contained in the fuel input – are assumed to improve over the projection period, but at different rates for different technologies. Exploration and production techniques for oil and gas are also expected to improve, boosting exploration success rates, raising recovery rates and opening up new opportunities for developing hard-to-exploit resources. Upstream technology research and development spending by the oil and gas industry has been rising rapidly in recent years (see Part B).

Some major new supply-side technologies that are approaching the commercialisation phase are assumed to become available and to be deployed to some degree before the end of the projection period. These include:

- **Carbon capture and storage (CCS):** This is a promising option for mitigating emissions of CO_2 from power plants and other industrial facilities, though it has not yet been deployed on a significant scale (IEA, 2008). The basic technology already exists to capture the gas and to transport and store it permanently in geological formations. There are at present four large-scale CCS projects in operation around the world, each involving the separation of around 1 Mt of CO_2 per year from produced natural gas: Sleipner and Snohvit in Norway, Weyburn in Canada (with the CO_2 sourced in the United States) and In Salah in Algeria. The captured CO_2 is used for enhanced oil recovery in the latter two projects. Yet there are a number of technical, economic and legal barriers to the more widespread and rapid deployment of CCS. In particular, it is very energy-intensive and expensive. Considerable research and development effort is currently going into CCS in power generation. Around 20 demonstration projects are already under construction or are planned, which are expected to lead to lower unit costs and improved operational performance. We assume that CCS will become commercially available after 2020 in countries where adequate financial incentives and/or regulatory measures to reduce CO_2 emissions are already in place.

- **Second-generation biofuels:** New biofuels technologies being developed today, notably hydrolysis and gasification of woody ligno-cellulosic feedstock to produce ethanol, are assumed to reach commercialisation by around 2020. Although the technology already exists, more research is needed to improve process efficiencies, especially enzymatic hydrolysis to extract fermentable sugar from the ligno-cellulosic material contained in plant material and to produce a fermented broth with a higher concentration of ethanol. There is virtually no commercial production

Figure 1.6 ● **Typical lifetimes of energy-related capital stock**

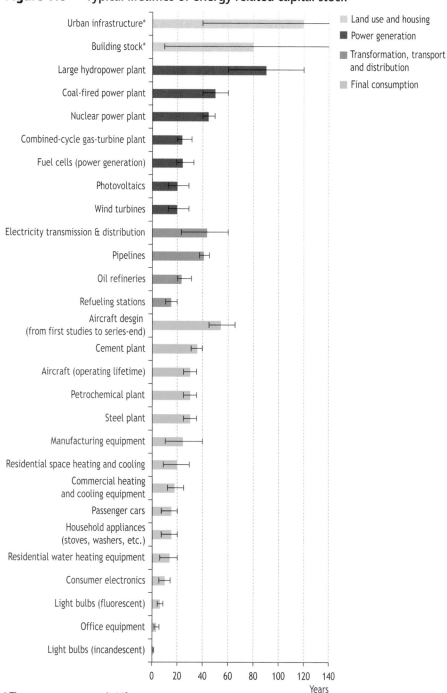

* The upper range exceeds 140 years.
Note: Bars indicate average lifetimes, lines indicate the typical range.
Source: IEA analysis.

of ethanol yet from cellulosic biomass, but there is substantial research going on in this area in several OECD countries. The US Energy Independence and Security Act mandated investment in advanced biofuels. Commercial-scale demonstration plants are under construction in the United States and several others are planned in Europe and other parts of the world.

- **Coal-to-liquids (CTL):** The indirect conversion of coal to oil products through gasification and Fischer-Tropsch synthesis processes – much like gas-to-liquids production – has been carried out commercially for many decades. Yet global production remains limited as CTL production has in most cases been uneconomic up to now, mainly because of the large amounts of energy and water used in the process, the high cost of building CTL plants and volatile oil and coal prices. Recently, research has been focused on direct liquefaction, which is much less energy-intensive than the indirect CTL method, though the liquids produced require further refining to meet applicable fuel standards, increasing unit costs. The Chinese coal company Shenhua is commissioning in 2008 a 20 000-b/d demonstration plant at Erdos in Inner Mongolia and more plants are planned in China and the United States. The full commercialisation of direct liquefaction technologies is expected to develop over the *Outlook* period, boosting their deployment in countries with abundant low-cost coal and freshwater resources (see Chapter 11 for detailed projections of CTL production).

CHAPTER 2

GLOBAL ENERGY TRENDS

H I G H L I G H T S

- World energy use continues to increase steadily in the Reference Scenario, but at a slower rate than projected in *WEO-2007*, mainly due to higher energy prices and slower economic growth. Global primary energy demand grows by 1.6% per year on average in 2006-2030. Oil demand increases progressively, though more slowly than in *WEO-2007*, particularly in the second half of the *Outlook* period.

- Fossil fuels account for 80% of the world's primary energy mix in 2030 – down slightly on today. Oil remains the dominant fuel, though demand for coal rises more than demand for any other fuel in absolute terms. The share of natural gas in total energy demand rises marginally, with most of the growth coming from the power-generation sector. Coal continues to account for about half of fuel needs for power generation. The contribution of non-hydro renewables to meeting primary energy needs inches up from 11% now to 12% in 2030.

- Due to strong economic growth, China and India account for 51% of incremental world primary energy demand in 2006-2030. Middle East countries emerge as an important demand centre. Of the global increase in oil demand, 43% comes from China, 20% from the Middle East and 19% from India. Over a quarter of the growth in world gas demand comes from the Middle East. Non-OECD countries account for 87% of the increase in global demand between 2006 and 2030. As a result, their share of world primary energy demand rises from 51% to 62%.

- Industry overtakes transport before 2010 to become the second-largest final energy-consuming sector, after the combined residential, services and agricultural sector. Among all final energy forms, electricity consumption grows fastest, nearly doubling in 2006-2030, boosting its share in total final energy consumption from 17% to 21%. Oil remains the single largest end-use fuel, though its share drops from 43% in 2006 to 40% in 2030.

- Almost all of the increase in fossil-fuel production over the *Outlook* period occurs in non-OECD countries. The Middle East and Africa are the biggest contributors to increased exports. As a result, the reliance on imported oil and gas of the main consuming regions, including the OECD and Asian economies, increases substantially, particularly in the second half of the projection period.

- Cumulative investment needs amount to $26.3 trillion (in year-2007 dollars) in 2007-2030, over $4 trillion more than posited in *WEO-2007*. The power sector accounts for $13.6 trillion, or 52% of the total. To provide adequate assurance for future investment in energy-supply infrastructure, negotiations need to be concluded on an international agreement on combating climate change and the implications for national policies quickly assessed.

Demand

Primary energy mix

Projected world primary energy demand in the Reference Scenario increases by 45% between 2006 and 2030 – an average annual rate of growth of 1.6% (Table 2.1).[1] This is 0.2 percentage points slower than the rate projected in last year's *Outlook*, largely due to changes in our assumptions for energy prices and economic growth, as well as new government policies introduced since last year (Box 2.1). It is also slower than the average growth of 1.9% per year from 1980 to 2006. World energy intensity — primary energy demand per unit of real GDP (in purchasing power parity, or PPP, terms) — is expected to decline over the projection period by 1.7% a year, 0.6 percentage points faster than over the past three decades. Lower energy intensity is primarily the result of acceleration in the transition to a service economy in many major non-OECD countries and more rapid efficiency improvements in the power and end-use sectors in the OECD.

Table 2.1 • World primary energy demand by fuel in the Reference Scenario (Mtoe)

	1980	2000	2006	2015	2030	2006-2030*
Coal	1 788	2 295	3 053	4 023	4 908	2.0%
Oil	3 107	3 649	4 029	4 525	5 109	1.0%
Gas	1 235	2 088	2 407	2 903	3 670	1.8%
Nuclear	186	675	728	817	901	0.9%
Hydro	148	225	261	321	414	1.9%
Biomass and waste**	748	1 045	1 186	1 375	1 662	1.4%
Other renewables	12	55	66	158	350	7.2%
Total	7 223	10 034	11 730	14 121	17 014	1.6%

* Average annual rate of growth.
** Includes traditional and modern uses.

World demand for coal advances by 2% a year on average, its share in global energy demand climbing from 26% in 2006 to 29% in 2030. Most of the increase in demand for coal comes from the power-generation sector. China and India together contribute 85% to the increase in world coal demand over the projection period. Oil remains the dominant fuel in the primary energy mix, but its share drops to 30% in 2030, from 34% in 2006. Oil demand grows far more slowly than demand for other fossil fuels, mainly because of high final prices. Gas demand increases at 1.8% per annum over the projection period and its share in world primary energy moves up slightly, to 22% in 2030. New power plants, using high-efficiency gas turbine technology for the most part, meet the bulk of incremental gas demand. The Middle East, developing Asian countries and the OECD see the biggest increases in gas demand.

The share of nuclear power in primary energy demand edges down over the *Outlook* period, from 6% today to 5% in 2030, reflecting the assumption of unchanging national

---

1. Projections of energy-related CO_2 emissions and local pollutants are covered in Chapter 16.

policies towards nuclear power. Nuclear output nonetheless increases in absolute terms in all major regions except OECD Europe. The largest increases will take place in developing Asia. There is considerable uncertainty about the prospects for nuclear power, given a recent revival of interest in re-evaluating the role of nuclear power in order to combat climate change. A change in policy could lead to a significantly higher share of nuclear power in the energy mix than assumed here (see Chapter 6).

Box 2.1 ● How do the new *WEO* assumptions affect global energy trends compared with last year?

Higher energy prices and slower economic growth than assumed last year are the main reasons why demand grows more slowly in this year's *Outlook*. World GDP is assumed to grow on average by 3.3% per year in 2006-2030, compared with 3.6% in *WEO-2007*. The IEA crude oil import price reaches $122 per barrel in real terms in 2030 in this year's *WEO*, very nearly twice the level in *WEO-2007*. Lower economic growth reduces the overall demand for energy services. Higher prices encourage consumers and businesses to conserve energy and to buy more efficient appliances and equipment. They also encourage manufacturers to develop more energy-efficient equipment.

Assumptions about policy and technology have also changed. A number of countries, mostly in the OECD, have adopted during the past year new policies that substantially affect energy-demand prospects. These are taken into account in the Reference Scenario. One example is the US Energy Independence and Security Act, which mandates vehicle fuel-economy improvements and higher production of biofuels (see Chapter 1). This year's *WEO* also assumes that carbon capture and storage (CCS) will be introduced in the power-generation and industry sectors towards the end of the projection period, although only a few plants are assumed to be in operation in 2030 (nearly all of them in OECD countries and China). By 2030, coal plants with CCS consume about 0.2% of all the coal used worldwide. This year's supply-side projections also reflect higher marginal costs and faster decline rate assumptions in the oil and gas sector in key producing countries.

As a result of these changes, demand for each fossil fuel grows less rapidly than projected last year. Global demand for coal is 86 Mtoe lower in 2030 than in *WEO-2007*, while gas demand is 278 Mtoe lower. The biggest change, however, is in global oil demand. In 2030, world primary oil consumption is 5 109 Mtoe in this year's *Outlook*, compared with 5 585 Mtoe last year. Higher oil prices and vehicle fuel-efficiency improvements are the main drivers of this change. Faster growth in the use of biofuels for transport, aided by the penetration of second-generation biofuel technologies towards the end of the *Outlook* period, also contributes. Excluding hydropower and biomass and waste, other renewables grow more quickly in this *WEO*, by 284 Mtoe in 2006-2030, compared with 247 Mtoe in 2005-2030 in last year's *WEO*.

Hydropower has long been a major source of electricity production and its relative importance does not change in the Reference Scenario. While most of the OECD's low-cost, hydro-electric resources have already been exploited, several large-scale projects in non-OECD countries are expected to be launched over the *Outlook* period (see Chapter 7). World hydropower production grows by an average 1.9% a year, its share of primary demand remaining constant at 2%. Hydropower's share in global electricity generation, however, drops two percentage points to 14% in 2030.

Figure 2.1 ● **World primary energy demand by fuel in the Reference Scenario**

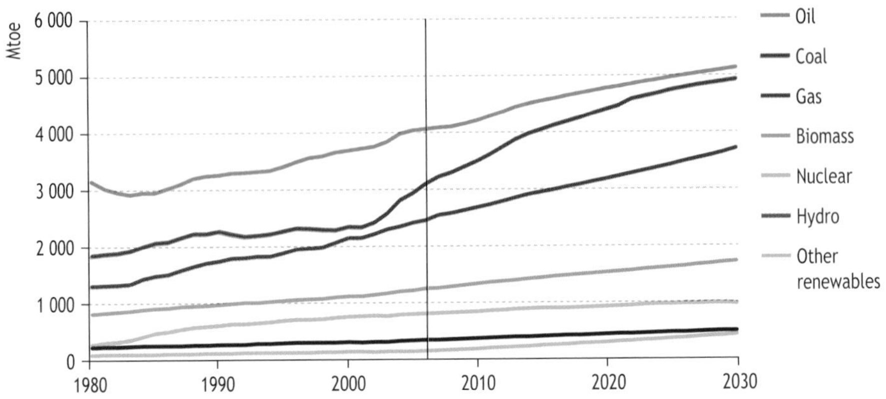

The use of biomass and waste for energy increases by 1.4% per year.[2] This figure masks considerable differences among countries in how this energy source is used: the use of biomass in modern applications such as biofuels and power generation rises quickly, while the use of traditional biomass in inefficient cooking stoves in poor households in less developed parts of the world grows at a much slower pace. The use of biomass and waste for power generation, mainly in OECD countries, grows at 5.4% per year, albeit from a low base. Other renewables, a category that includes wind, solar, geothermal, tidal and wave energy, grow faster than any other energy source, at an average rate of 7.2% per year over the projection period. Most of the increase is in the power sector. The share of other renewables in total power generation grows from 1% in 2006 to 4% in 2030.

Regional trends

Energy demand in non-OECD countries exceeded that in OECD countries in 2005 for the first time ever (Figure 2.2). The faster pace of demand growth outside the OECD is set to continue. Driven mainly by brisk growth in China and India, non-OECD countries account for 87% of the increase in global demand between 2006 and 2030. As a result, the non-OECD share of world primary energy demand rises from 51% in 2006 to 62% by

---

2. See Chapter 7 for a discussion of traditional biomass.

2030. Steady economic growth and industrial expansion, population increase and higher urbanisation rates drive demand growth in non-OECD countries. The replacement of fuelwood and charcoal with oil and gas also plays a major role. Growth in energy demand is fastest in the Middle East and Asia (Table 2.2).

Figure 2.2 ● **World primary energy demand by region in the Reference Scenario**

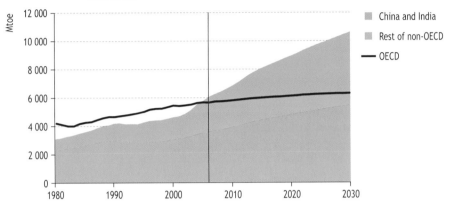

Table 2.2 ● **World primary energy demand by region in the Reference Scenario** (Mtoe)

	1980	2000	2006	2015	2030	2006-2030*
OECD	4 072	5 325	5 536	5 854	6 180	0.5%
North America	2 100	2 705	2 768	2 914	3 180	0.6%
United States	*1 809*	*2 300*	*2 319*	*2 396*	*2 566*	*0.4%*
Europe	1 504	1 775	1 884	1 980	2 005	0.3%
Pacific	467	845	884	960	995	0.5%
Non-OECD	3 043	4 563	6 011	8 067	10 604	2.4%
E. Europe/Eurasia	1 267	1 015	1 118	1 317	1 454	1.1%
Russia	*n.a.*	*615*	*668*	*798*	*859*	*1.1%*
Asia	1 072	2 191	3 227	4 598	6 325	2.8%
China	*604*	*1 122*	*1 898*	*2 906*	*3 885*	*3.0%*
India	*209*	*460*	*566*	*771*	*1 280*	*3.5%*
Middle East	133	389	522	760	1 106	3.2%
Africa	278	507	614	721	857	1.4%
Latin America	294	460	530	671	862	2.0%
World**	7 223	10 034	11 730	14 121	17 014	1.6%
European Union	*n.a.*	*1 722*	*1 821*	*1 897*	*1 903*	*0.2%*

* Average annual rate of growth.
** World includes international marine bunkers.

The volumetric increase in China's energy demand in 2006-2030 dwarfs that of all other countries and regions, the result of its rapid economic and population growth. The almost 2 000-Mtoe increase in demand in 2006-2030 is nearly four times bigger than the combined increase in all of the countries in Latin America and Africa, and more than three times as large as the increase in the OECD (Figure 2.3). China's contribution to incremental global oil demand is 43%. India accounts for 19%. The countries of the Middle East, most of them key oil and/or gas producers, emerge as a major oil- and gas-consuming region. It sees the second-largest increase in global oil demand, after China. This increase in the Middle East is underpinned by rapid economic growth and by persistent subsidies on oil products.[3] In the case of coal, China accounts for 66% of the global increase in demand. By 2030, OECD countries account for less than a quarter of global coal use. In contrast, OECD countries account for 46% of the global increase in the use of renewables.

Figure 2.3 ● **Incremental primary energy demand by fuel in the Reference Scenario, 2006-2030**

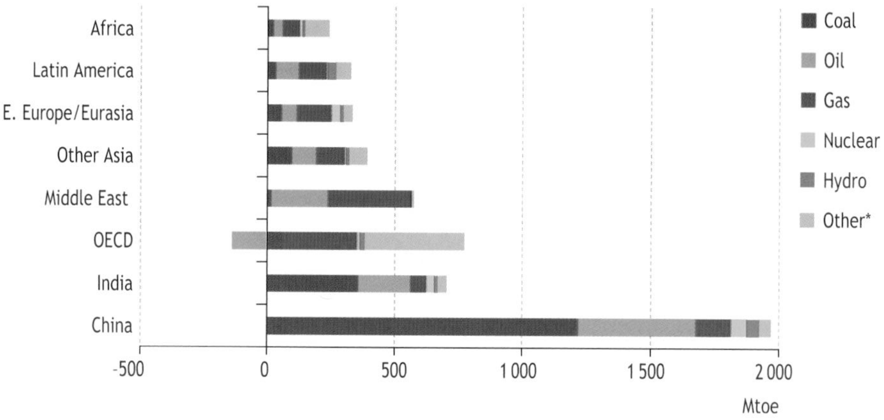

* Other includes biomass and waste, and other renewables.

Changes in the fuel mix vary considerably across regions. In the OECD, where overall demand grows very slowly over the projection period, oil demand falls slightly, while gas and non-hydro renewables make up most of the increase in energy demand. Demand in Eastern Europe and Eurasian countries (including Russia) grows by only 336 Mtoe between 2006 and 2030, with nearly 60% of this increase taking the form of natural gas and oil. While China and India continue to rely predominately on coal, incremental energy demand in other Asian countries and in Latin America is remarkably diverse. Despite having the highest regional rate of increase in coal consumption, the Middle East countries rely almost entirely on oil and gas to meet additional energy needs over the projection period. Incremental gas demand in this region is equal to 26% of the world total. The Middle East becomes the third-largest gas consumer, after OECD North America and OECD Europe, surpassing projected demand in the entire European

---

3. See Chapter 1 for a detailed discussion of subsidies.

Union in 2030. Under the assumptions of the Reference Scenario, the only region where nuclear power expands significantly is Asia, with most of the increase occurring in China. Biomass and waste and other renewables account for nearly 40% of incremental energy demand in Africa, consumed mostly as fuelwood, crop residues and charcoal for cooking and heating. By contrast, the 61% contribution of biomass and other non-hydro renewables to incremental energy demand in OECD countries is in the form of modern technologies, mostly wind.

In 2030, disparities in per-capita energy consumption among regions remain stark (Figure 2.4). Middle East countries see a rapid increase in per-capita consumption, over-taking OECD Europe by 2030. Despite the relatively small increase in energy demand over the *Outlook* period, Russia still has the highest per-capita energy consumption, at 7.0 toe, in 2030. Per-capita consumption increases rapidly from 1.4 toe in 2006 to 2.7 toe in 2030 in China, thanks to a booming economy and slower population growth compared with African and other Asian countries. India's per-capita energy use is only 0.9 toe in 2030, but up from 0.5 toe in 2006. On average across countries, per-capita consumption in sub-Saharan Africa is only 0.5 toe in 2030 — about a third of the level in Latin America and one-ninth of that in OECD countries.

Figure 2.4 ● Per-capita primary energy demand by region, 2030

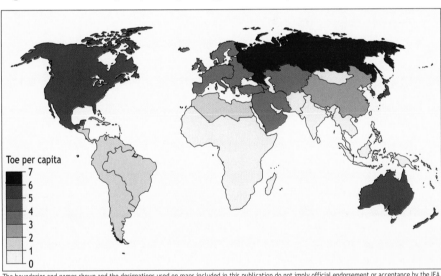

Toe per capita
- 7
- 6
- 5
- 4
- 3
- 2
- 1
- 0

The boundaries and names shown and the designations used on maps included in this publication do not imply official endorsement or acceptance by the IEA.

Sectoral trends

The combined power-generation and heat sector absorbs a growing share of global primary energy demand over the projection period. Its share reaches over 42% in 2030, compared with 38% in 2006. Coal remains the leading input for power-generation and heat, its share of total inputs holding steady at about 47% over the *Outlook* period. Oil's share falls from 6% in 2006 to 3% in 2030, while the share of gas rises from 21% to 23%. Nuclear power's contribution falls from 16% in 2006 to 13% in 2030. Hydropower's share remains steady at 6%. Inputs from non-hydro renewables, mostly wind and biomass and waste, grow worldwide at an average rate of 6.2% per year between 2006 and 2030, the fastest rate of all energy sources, with their share rising to 8% in 2030.

Aggregate demand in final-use sectors (industry, transport, residential, services, agriculture and non-energy use) is projected to grow by 1.4% per year from 2006 to 2030 — slightly more slowly than primary energy demand (Table 2.3). Industry demand grows most rapidly, at 1.8% per annum, overtaking transport before 2010 as the second-largest final-use sector, after the combined residential, services and agriculture sector. Industry demand increases everywhere, but fastest in the Middle East and non-OECD Asia. The rate of growth in global transport energy demand slows considerably over the *Outlook* period. It averages 1.5% per year on average in 2006-2030 compared with 2.3% in 1980-2006, largely as a result of improved fuel efficiency of the vehicle fleet (see Chapter 3). Residential, services and agriculture consumption grows at an average annual rate of 1.2%, slower than the rate of growth of 1.5% per year in 1980-2006, due to efficiency improvements and fuel switching.

Table 2.3 ● World final energy consumption by sector in the Reference Scenario (Mtoe)

	1980	2000	2006	2015	2030	2006-2030*
Industry	1 779	1 879	2 181	2 735	3 322	1.8%
Coal	421	405	550	713	838	1.8%
Oil	474	325	329	366	385	0.7%
Gas	422	422	434	508	604	1.4%
Electricity	297	455	560	789	1 060	2.7%
Other	165	272	307	359	436	1.5%
Transport	1 245	1 936	2 227	2 637	3 171	1.5%
Oil	1 187	1 844	2 105	2 450	2 915	1.4%
Biofuels	2	10	24	74	118	6.8%
Other	57	82	98	113	137	1.4%
Residential, services and agriculture	2 006	2 635	2 937	3 310	3 918	1.2%
Coal	244	108	114	118	100	-0.5%
Oil	481	462	472	493	560	0.7%
Gas	346	542	592	660	791	1.2%
Electricity	273	613	764	967	1 322	2.3%
Other	661	910	995	1 073	1 144	0.6%
Non-energy use	348	598	740	876	994	1.2%
Total	5 378	7 048	8 086	9 560	11 405	1.4%

* Average annual rate of growth.

Among all end-use sources of energy except other renewables, electricity is projected to grow most rapidly worldwide, by 2.5% per year from 2006 to 2030.[4] Electricity consumption nearly doubles over that period, pushing up its share in total final energy consumption from 17% to 21%. Electricity use expands most rapidly in non-OECD countries, by 3.8% per year; it increases by 1.1% per year in the OECD.

The share of coal in world final consumption remains broadly constant at about 9%. Coal use expands in industry, but only in non-OECD countries. The share of gas in world final consumption does not change. Final gas demand rises by 1.3% per year on average, with most of the increase in non-OECD countries. Oil demand grows by 1.2% per year, with almost three-quarters of the increase coming from transport. Biofuels for transport, nearly all of which are produced from first-generation technologies, account for 4% of total transport energy demand in 2030, a significant increase over the 1% share in 2006.

The use of biomass and waste rises in absolute terms in the residential, services and agriculture sector, but its share of total final energy use in these sectors combined drops from 28% in 2006 to 22% in 2030. The share of electricity in this sector rises to 34% in 2030 from 26% in 2006. Despite rapid growth in some countries, per-capita electricity consumption, particularly in Africa, remains far below that of OECD countries in 2030 (see Chapter 6). Per-capita annual electricity demand in the residential sector in OECD countries averages 2 835 kWh in 2030, compared with 565 kWh in non-OECD countries. In sub-Saharan Africa, it is only 132 kWh per capita in 2030.[5] Other renewables, mostly photovoltaic, achieve some penetration in the combined residential, services and agriculture sectors, but still meet only about 2% of this sector's global energy needs in 2030.

Energy production and trade

Resources and production prospects

We judge that the world's overall energy resources are adequate to meet the projected growth in energy demand to 2030. The key to tapping the available resources is mobilising investment in a timely manner. Restrictions on oil and gas investment in many of the most prospective areas mean that investment does not always go to developing the cheapest reserves. Increasingly, fossil-energy supplies will have to come from deposits that are more difficult and costly to exploit, including deepwater and non-conventional oil and gas resources. Yet technologies for extracting such resources are constantly improving. We expect non-conventional and frontier resources to carve out a growing share of global oil and gas supplies by 2030 (see Part B). The related costs

---

4. Other renewables, mostly solar heating and cooling, grow from a very low base and account for only 1% of global final energy demand in 2030.

5. See Chapter 15 for a discussion of electricity access in oil- and gas-rich countries of sub-Saharan Africa.

will undoubtedly be higher than in the past, with the technical challenge enhanced by higher raw material and equipment costs across the board. This is one reason why we are assuming higher prices in this year's *Outlook*.

Proven and probable reserves of natural gas are much larger than for oil. However, as for oil, some factors — such as geopolitical and technical risks, investment restrictions and national policy constraints in resource-rich countries — cast doubt over the extent to which the long-term potential can be converted to actual supply capacity. Concerns about the potential to expand coal supplies are less pronounced, though the associated costs are uncertain. There is a large quantity of uranium resources that could be mined for nuclear power production. Although location-specific, renewable energy sources are also abundant.

Most of the increase in oil production over the projection period is expected to come from a small number of countries where remaining resources are concentrated. These include several OPEC countries, mainly in the Middle East, and a handful of non-OPEC countries, notably Canada (with vast oil-sands reserves), the Caspian countries and Brazil. The majority of oil-producing countries will see their output drop. The OPEC share in total production in the Reference Scenario rises from 44% today to 51% in 2030, on the assumption that the requisite investment is forthcoming, which over the past decade has not always been the case. Natural gas liquids and non-conventional sources — mainly Canadian oil sands — make a growing contribution to world oil supplies over the *Outlook* period.

Production of natural gas resources, which are more widely dispersed than oil, increases in all regions except OECD Europe (see Chapter 4). The biggest increases are projected to occur in the Middle East and Africa, where large, low-cost reserves are found. Gas production triples in the Middle East and more than doubles in Africa. Supply costs have been rising quickly as a result of both the cost inflation that has afflicted all parts of the energy sector and the increased length of supply chains as consuming regions become more reliant on more distant sources.

Although there are abundant coal reserves in most regions, increases in coal production are likely to be concentrated where extraction, processing and transportation costs are lowest. China is set to reinforce its position as the world's leading coal producer, accounting for close to two-thirds of the increase in global output over the projection period in the Reference Scenario (though this is not sufficient to meet domestic demand growth). The United States, India and Australia remain the next biggest producers. Most of the increase in world coal production takes the form of steam coal.

The shift in the geographical sources of incremental energy supplies over the *Outlook* period is pronounced. Gas production in the OECD as a whole declines by 31 bcm, due to a 88-bcm decline in production in OECD Europe. Oil production increases in the OECD, but only by 1.4 mb/d (Figure 2.5). The increase in oil production in non-OECD countries in 2007-2030 is 20 mb/d. Most of the incremental coal production comes from non-OECD countries; OECD countries contribute about 10% to the global increase.

Figure 2.5 ● Incremental world fossil-fuel production in the Reference
Scenario

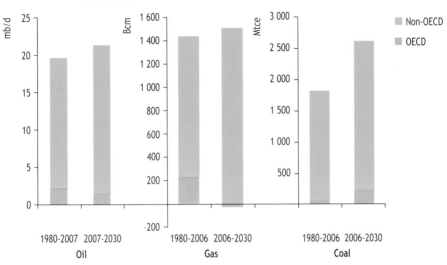

Inter-regional trade

International trade in energy is expected to expand, in both absolute terms and as a share of production, to accommodate the mismatch between the location of demand and that of production. The share of oil traded between *WEO* regions is projected to grow by 35% between 2007 and 2030, as production becomes increasingly concentrated in a small number of resource-rich countries. The decline in gas production in OECD countries leads to more imports in the form of liquefied natural gas (LNG) and, to a lesser extent, by pipeline. Coal trade also increases. Even China, the world's largest coal producer, sees its coal imports rise to meet its galloping demand (see Chapter 5). Inter-regional trade in other fuels and carriers remains small.

Growing fossil-energy trade has major implications for energy security, a point highlighted in last year's *Outlook* (IEA, 2007). Of the net oil-importing regions today – the three OECD regions and non-OECD Asia – OECD Europe and Asia become even more dependent on imports over the projection period (see Chapter 3). While still remaining significant oil importers, the OECD North America and Pacific regions see their net imports decline. The Middle East, already the biggest exporting region, sees its share of inter-regional oil trade rise from 49% in 2007 to 52% in 2030. Such a development intensifies concerns about the world's vulnerability to a price shock induced by a supply disruption. Maintaining the security of international sea lanes and pipelines will become more important as oil and gas supply chains lengthen (see Figure 3.11 in Chapter 3 and Figure 4.6 in Chapter 4).

Energy investment

Trends by region and energy source

The Reference Scenario projections call for cumulative investment in energy-supply infrastructure of $26.3 trillion (in year-2007 dollars) over 2007-2030 (Table 2.4). This amount is around $4.4 trillion higher than in *WEO-2007*, because of an upward revision in assumed unit costs. More than half of global investment, or $13.6 trillion, goes towards the power sector. Oil- and gas-sector investments total $11.7 trillion, $2.2 trillion higher than last year's *Outlook*, with over 65% required in non-OECD countries. Coal-industry investments (not including transportation) are much smaller, totalling less than $730 billion, or 3% of total energy investment. The production of coal is inherently much less capital intensive than that of oil, gas or electricity.

Unit capital costs, especially in the oil and gas industry, have surged in the last year, leading to an upward revision in our assumed costs for the projection period (see Chapter 13). Huge inflows of capital are needed to expand supply capacity to meet rising demand, as well as to replace existing and future supply facilities that will be retired during the projection period. Just over half of projected global energy investment goes simply to maintain the current level of supply capacity: much of the world's current production capacity for oil, gas, coal and electricity will need to be replaced by 2030. In addition, some of the new production capacity brought on stream in the early years of the projection period will need to be replaced before 2030. Many power plants, electricity and gas transmission and distribution facilities, and oil refineries will also need to be replaced or refurbished.

Table 2.4 ● Cumulative investment in energy-supply infrastructure in the Reference Scenario, 2007-2030 ($ billion in year-2007 dollars)

	Coal	Oil	Gas	Power	Total
OECD	165	1 437	2 286	5 708	9 739
North America	87	1 023	1 675	2 645	5 490
Europe	39	304	417	2 259	3 099
Pacific	39	110	195	804	1 149
Non-OECD	521	4 635	3 044	7 897	16 187
E. Europe/Eurasia	53	1 079	859	916	2 913
Russia	*36*	*544*	*653*	*440*	*1 674*
Asia	431	916	682	5 327	7 386
China	*323*	*515*	*234*	*3 099*	*4 186*
India	*70*	*179*	*82*	*1 455*	*1 791*
Middle East	1	997	597	509	2 107
Africa	23	868	608	447	1 949
Latin America	13	775	298	697	1 832
Inter-regional transport	42	225	122	n.a.	389
World	728	6 296	5 452	13 604	26 315

Note: Regional totals include a total of $234 billion investment in biofuels.

The Reference Scenario projections of electricity supply call for cumulative investment of $13.6 trillion, 58% of which is needed in non-OECD countries. Power generation accounts for half of this amount (Figure 2.6). Global needs in this sector are over $2 trillion more than projected in *WEO-2007*. Much of the increase is due to rising raw material and equipment costs (see Chapter 6). Financing the building of new energy infrastructure will be a major challenge, especially for poorer countries that rely on public sources of finance.

Due to the world's rising reliance on oil and gas from the Middle East, Africa and other non-OECD countries, the rapid development of power infrastructure in many of these countries and fast-rising energy needs in China and India, most of the required investment is needed in non-OECD countries. Mobilising this investment will require the lowering of regulatory and market barriers. Many major oil and gas producers in Africa, the Middle East and Latin America recognise the need for — and value of — foreign involvement. Algeria, Egypt, Libya, Nigeria and several countries in the Middle East have attracted joint-venture investment by international oil companies, although the dominance of national oil companies is growing in many other countries (see Chapter 14). Key coal producers also need to attract capital to meet their medium-term production targets. Foreign investment could bring better management and a greater willingness to use the best available technologies, as well as access to capital, to many emerging economies. Many countries are liberalising and restructuring their electricity industries in order to attract private domestic and foreign investment, and to improve the way energy companies are run.

Figure 2.6 ● **Cumulative investment in energy-supply infrastructure in the Reference Scenario, 2007-2030**

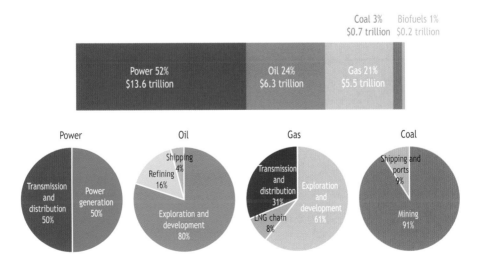

Total investment = $26.3 trillion (in year-2007 dollars)

CHAPTER 3

OIL MARKET OUTLOOK

H I G H L I G H T S

- Global primary demand for oil (excluding biofuels) in the Reference Scenario rises by 1% per year on average, from 85 million barrels per day in 2007 to 106 mb/d in 2030. This is a significant downward revision from last year's *Outlook*, reflecting mainly the impact of much higher prices and slightly slower GDP growth. New government policies introduced in the past year also contribute to lower demand.

- All the increase in world oil demand comes from non-OECD countries. India sees the fastest growth, averaging 3.9% per year over the *Outlook* period, followed by China, at 3.5%. High as they are, these growth rates are still significantly lower than historic trends. Other emerging Asian economies and the Middle East also see rapid growth. By contrast, demand in all three OECD regions falls, due largely to declining non-transport demand. As a result of these trends, the share of OECD countries in global oil demand drops from 57% in 2007 to 43% in 2030.

- These oil-demand projections, combined with our oil-price assumptions, point to persistently high levels of spending on oil in both OECD and non-OECD countries. As a share of world GDP at market exchange rates, oil spending soared from a little over 1% in 1999 to around 4% in 2007, with serious implications for the economies of consuming countries. That share is projected to stabilise at around 5% over much of the *Outlook* period. For non-OECD countries, the share averages 6% to 7%.

- Most of the projected increase in world oil supply comes from OPEC countries, which hold the majority of the world's remaining reserves of conventional oil. Their share of global output rises from 44% in 2007 to 51% in 2030. Their reserves are big enough for output to grow faster, but investment is assumed to be constrained, notably by conservative depletion policies and geopolitical factors.

- Although global oil production is not expected to peak before 2030, output of conventional crude oil and natural gas liquids levels off towards the end of the projection period. Non-conventional oil production, mainly from oil sands in Canada, continues to grow steadily, keeping total non-OPEC output broadly flat over the second half of the projection period.

- The projected increase in global oil output hinges on adequate and timely investment. There remains a real risk of a supply crunch in the medium term as the gap between the capacity that is due to come on stream from current projects and that needed to keep pace with demand widens sharply after 2010, squeezing spare capacity and driving up oil prices – possibly to new record highs.

● The volume of inter-regional oil trade increases by a third between 2007 and 2030. The Middle East, already the biggest exporting region, sees its net exports rise most. OECD Europe and Asia become even more dependent on imports over the projection period, but net imports drop in North America and in OECD Pacific. Though increased trade consolidates mutual dependence, it also enhances the risk of short-term supply interruptions, particularly as much of the additional oil imports will have to come from the Middle East and transit vulnerable maritime routes.

Demand

Trends in primary oil demand

Global primary oil demand[1] is projected to grow by 1.0% per year on average in the Reference Scenario, from 85 million barrels per day in 2007 to 94 mb/d in 2015 and to 106 mb/d in 2030 (Table 3.1). The share of oil in global primary energy demand drops from 34% in 2006 to 30% in 2030. This is a significant, 10-mb/d downward revision from last year's *Outlook*, reflecting the impact of much higher prices and slightly slower GDP growth. A number of new government policies introduced in the past year — notably moves in the United States and Europe to promote more fuel-efficient vehicles and encourage biofuels supply — also contribute to the reduction. The pace of demand growth slackens progressively over the projection period, from an average of 1.3% per year in 2007-2015 to 0.8% per year in 2015-2030.

Economic activity remains the principal driver of oil demand in all regions. Since 1980, each 1% per year increase in gross domestic product has been accompanied by a 0.3% rise in primary oil demand (Figure 3.1). This ratio — the oil intensity of GDP, or the amount of oil needed to produce one dollar of GDP — has fallen steadily over the last three decades. However, the decline has accelerated since 2004, mainly as a result of higher oil prices, which have encouraged conservation, more efficient oil use and switching to other fuels. In 2007, global oil intensity (expressed in purchasing power parities, or PPP) was barely half the level of the early 1970s.

---

1. Preliminary data on total oil demand by region only are available for 2007. The breakdown of oil demand by sector is available to 2006. Oil does not include biofuels derived from biomass, though transport demand for oil is modelled in a way that takes account of the use of biofuels. Regional totals do not include international marine bunkers. For these reasons, the oil projections in this report are not directly comparable with those published in the IEA's *Oil Market Report*. See Annex B for a detailed definition of oil.

Table 3.1 ● **World primary oil demand* in the Reference Scenario**
(million barrels per day)

	1980	2000	2007	2015	2030	2007-2030**
OECD	41.7	46.0	46.5	45.7	43.9	-0.2%
North America	20.9	23.3	24.6	23.9	23.9	-0.1%
United States	*17.4*	*19.3*	*20.2*	*19.3*	*19.0*	*-0.3%*
Europe	14.6	14.3	14.0	13.9	13.1	-0.3%
Pacific	6.1	8.4	7.9	7.8	7.0	-0.5%
Japan	*4.9*	*5.4*	*4.8*	*4.4*	*3.5*	*-1.4%*
Non-OECD	20.9	27.3	34.9	44.6	57.7	2.2%
E. Europe/Eurasia	9.5	4.4	4.8	5.7	5.9	0.9%
Russia	*n.a.*	*2.7*	*2.8*	*3.3*	*3.4*	*0.7%*
Asia	4.5	11.5	15.8	21.4	30.8	3.0%
China	*2.0*	*4.7*	*7.5*	*11.3*	*16.6*	*3.5%*
India	*0.7*	*2.3*	*2.9*	*4.1*	*7.1*	*3.9%*
Middle East	2.0	4.6	6.2	8.4	10.5	2.3%
Africa	1.3	2.3	2.9	3.2	3.7	1.0%
Latin America	3.5	4.5	5.2	5.9	6.8	1.2%
Brazil	*1.3*	*1.9*	*2.0*	*2.4*	*2.8*	*1.5%*
International marine bunkers	2.3	3.0	3.8	4.1	4.7	1.0%
World	64.8	76.3	85.2	94.4	106.4	1.0%
European Union	*n.a.*	*13.6*	*13.4*	*13.2*	*12.4*	*-0.3%*

* Excludes biofuels demand, which, after adjusting for energy content, is projected to rise from just over 0.8 mb/d in 2007 to 2 mb/d in 2015 and 3.2 mb/d in 2030 in the Reference Scenario (see Chapter 7).
** Average annual rate of growth.

Figure 3.1 ● **Change in world primary oil demand and real GDP growth**

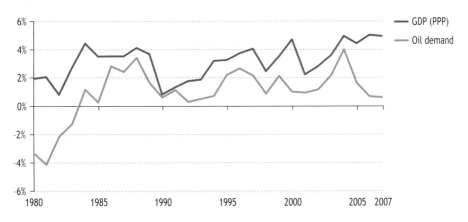

The downward trend in global oil intensity is projected to continue through the projection period: by 2.2% per year on average between 2007 and 2030 compared with 2.1% in 1980-2007. At present, non-OECD countries are more oil-intensive than the OECD as a whole (using GDP on a PPP basis). By around 2015, their intensities more or less converge and then continue to decline at similar rates through to 2030 (Figure 3.2). The faster rate of decline in oil intensity in non-OECD countries in the first half of the projection period results from a relatively higher percentage increase in prices to end users there as subsidies are reduced on prices which carry a smaller burden of taxation (which, in OECD countries, cushions the impact on demand of changes in international prices). Each percentage-point increase in world GDP yields an increase in oil demand of 0.31% in 2015 and 0.24% in 2030.

Figure 3.2 ● Oil intensity by region in the Reference Scenario

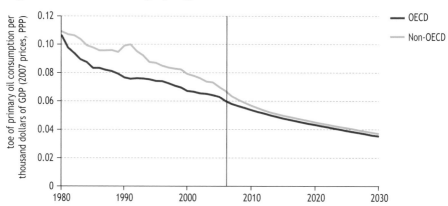

The apparent lack of responsiveness of global oil demand so far to the very substantial rise in international oil prices since the end of the 1990s and especially since 2004 contrasts sharply with the fall in demand that followed the two oil shocks of the 1970s (Figure 3.3). Five main factors explain this difference:

■ The recent price surge has been driven in part by very strong economic growth worldwide, which has pushed up demand. In contrast, the oil shocks of the 1970s were largely supply-driven and, given the higher oil intensity of the world economy at the time, quickly depressed economic activity.

■ Opportunities for end users to switch from oil to other fuels are more limited than in the past, largely because of the bigger share of oil use that now goes to transport. Viable alternatives to gasoline and diesel remain limited for now.

■ Price subsidies in many non-OECD countries, which prevent higher international crude oil and product prices from feeding through fully into final prices, thereby cushioning the impact on demand, have risen sharply (Box 3.1). The majority of oil consumers worldwide do not pay prices that fully reflect international market levels. By contrast, high excise-tax rates in most OECD countries mean that increases in international prices lead to much smaller proportionate increases in final prices.

- The depreciation of the dollar against most major currencies has offset part of the increase in spot prices in recent years. Expressed in euros, for example, prices since the beginning of 2000 to the middle of 2008 rose only 57% as much as in dollars (Figure 3.4).

- The increase in prices was very sudden in the first two oil shocks, whereas prices have risen in a much steadier manner since 2004.

Figure 3.3 ● **Global oil demand and the oil price in the three oil shocks**

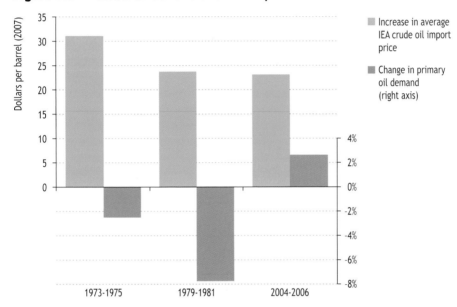

Figure 3.4 ● **Average IEA crude oil import price in different currencies**

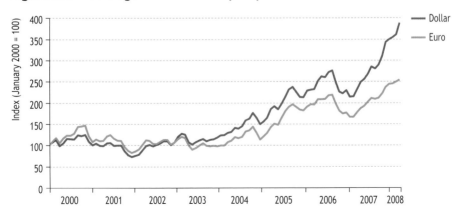

Box 3.1 ● The impact on demand of removing oil subsidies

With oil-product prices subject to government price controls in the majority of non-OECD countries, the run-up in international prices in recent years has led to much higher subsidies in most of them because retail prices have been adjusted only with a lag and not to the full extent of the international price change. In many countries, these subsidies — which are typically either covered directly out of government budgets or are absorbed by national companies — are reaching unsustainable levels. For example, if prices had remained at mid-year levels Venezuela's subsidy to oil products would have risen to around $14 billion in 2008, and the subsidy in Mexico, the only OECD country that still controls oil prices, to $20 billion — equal to several percentage points of GDP.

Several countries are starting to address this problem. In early 2008, Chinese Taipei and Sri Lanka raised gasoline and diesel prices. In May, Indonesia raised the prices of kerosene, diesel and gasoline by between a quarter and a third, though these fuels remain heavily subsidised. In June, China announced a rise of around 18% in the pump prices of gasoline and diesel, while India raised pump prices and the retail prices of bottled liquefied petroleum gas (LPG) by between 8% and 17%. Malaysia raised gasoline prices by around 40% and diesel prices by two-thirds. Some other Asian countries, including Bangladesh and Vietnam, are expected to follow suit. Public resistance generally remains a major constraint on effective political action to reduce and remove subsidies in non-OECD countries. Indeed, some countries with subsidies were considering lowering controlled prices in response to the drop in international oil prices in August and early September 2008.

Recent evidence and our estimates of the price elasticities of demand for oil products imply that moves to cut subsidies would have a significant effect on overall oil demand, especially in the long term. The demand response would vary markedly by country, according to the extent of the subsidy and the oil products concerned. A 90% jump in the pump prices of gasoline and diesel in Indonesia in October 2005, for example, caused consumption to drop by 13% in 2006. The recent cut in Malaysian subsidies is expected to lead to a drop in road-fuel use of around 5% in the next year or so. These moves will help to alleviate the upward pressure on international oil prices and domestic spending on transport in the coming years, as higher prices influence decisions to purchase cars and oil-consuming equipment.

There are, nonetheless, signs that high oil prices are beginning to affect oil demand, directly and indirectly, through their depressive impact on economic activity. The slowdown in demand has been most apparent in OECD countries, where prices have generally risen the most. Preliminary data point to a more than 1% drop in OECD inland deliveries (oil products supplied by refineries, pipelines and terminals) in June 2008 compared with June 2007. Consumption of transport fuels has fallen sharply in some countries, including the United States, as people drive less and begin to switch to smaller cars. For example, new car sales in the United Kingdom in August 2008 fell to their lowest level in 42 years. Sales of large sports utility vehicles have fallen in most countries, especially in the United States. Non-OECD oil demand, in contrast, continues to grow steadily, largely because incomes have continued to grow and prices in most countries have not risen so fast thanks to subsidies.

As a result of these factors, oil demand, in the short term at least, is relatively insensitive to movements in international crude oil prices. The weighted average crude oil price elasticity of total oil demand across all regions is estimated at -0.03 in the short term (in the first year following the price change) and -0.15 in the long term, based on econometric analysis of historical demand trends (IEA, 2006).[2] Using these estimates, we calculate that, had international prices not risen since 2003, global primary oil demand would have grown on average by 1.9% per year in the four years to 2007 — a mere 0.1 percentage points more than it actually did — on the assumption that nothing else was different. On this basis, world demand would, therefore, have been about 300 kb/d higher in 2007.

Regional trends

All the increase in world oil demand between 2007 and 2030 comes from non-OECD countries in the Reference Scenario. Their demand rises by 22.8 mb/d, offsetting a 2.5 mb/d fall in the OECD (international bunker demand rises by almost 1 mb/d). India sees the fastest rate of growth, averaging 3.9% per year over the *Outlook* period, followed by China, at 3.5%. High as they are, these growth rates are still significantly lower than historic trends. India's oil use grew by 5.6% per year between 1980 and 2007 (quadrupling), while Chinese oil use increased almost as fast (from a larger base). In volumetric terms, China remains the single biggest contributor to the growth in world oil demand, accounting for 43% of the total projected increase in 2007-2030 (Figure 3.5). Other emerging Asian

Figure 3.5 ● Change in primary oil demand by region in the Reference Scenario, 2007-2030

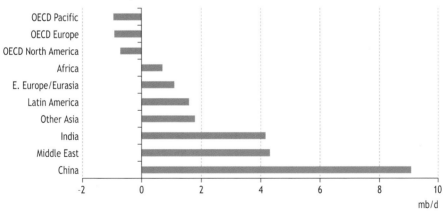

2. The price elasticity of demand for oil products based on *final prices* is significantly higher and more ho-mogeneous, as the impact of differences in tax and subsidy policies is stripped out. The final price elasticity of road-transport fuels, for example, is estimated at -0.15 in the short run (after one year) and -0.44 in the long run (IEA, 2006).

economies and the Middle East also see rapid rates of growth. The latter region has emerged as a major oil consuming as well as producing region, on the back of a booming economy (helped by high oil prices) and heavily subsidised prices. Middle East countries account for 20% of the growth in oil demand over the projection period. Demand in all three OECD regions, by contrast, falls, most heavily in volume terms in the Pacific region and Europe. As a result of these trends, the non-OECD countries' share of global oil demand (excluding international marine bunkers) rises from 43% in 2007 to 57% in 2030.

The differences in per-capita oil consumption across regions remain striking. The population of the Middle East reaches only 281 million in 2030, compared with nearly 1.5 billion in China. Yet China's oil use is only half as high as the Middle East's. Per-capita oil consumption reaches 13.6 barrels in the Middle East in 2030, compared with only 4.2 barrels in China and 12.3 barrels in the OECD.

Sectoral trends

Around three-quarters of the projected increase in oil demand worldwide comes from the transport sector, the sector least responsive, in the short term, to price changes (Figure 3.6). In the OECD, oil use falls in all sectors except transport (where it is essentially flat).

Figure 3.6 ● Incremental oil demand by sector in the Reference Scenario, 2006-2030

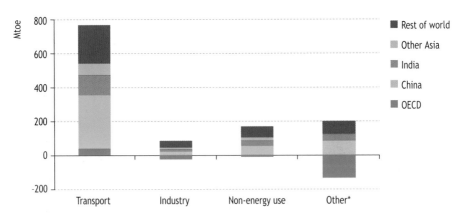

* Includes residential, services, agriculture, power generation and other energy sectors.

Residential and industrial demand falls most heavily. In non-OECD countries, transport is the biggest contributor to oil-demand growth, but the industrial, non-energy use, and residential, services and agriculture sectors also account for significant shares. The transport sector accounts for 57% of global primary oil consumption in 2030, compared with 52% now and 38% in 1980 (Table 3.2). Oil-based fuels continue to dominate transport energy demand, though their overall share falls slightly, from 94% in 2006 to 92% in 2030, due to growing use of biofuels (see Chapter 7).

Table 3.2 ● **Share of transport in primary oil demand by region in the Reference Scenario** (%)

	1980	2000	2006	2015	2030
OECD	40	54	57	60	62
North America	51	63	64	68	70
United States	*52*	*66*	*66*	*71*	*72*
Europe	31	50	53	57	58
Pacific	27	38	41	44	44
Japan	*23*	*36*	*37*	*39*	*38*
Non-OECD	29	39	41	44	50
E. Europe/Eurasia	24	37	42	45	45
Russia	*n.a.*	*36*	*40*	*44*	*44*
Asia	25	36	37	42	51
China	*17*	*32*	*36*	*43*	*54*
India	*37*	*29*	*27*	*32*	*45*
Middle East	32	36	40	39	43
Africa	46	51	50	51	54
Latin America	39	47	48	52	54
Brazil	*44*	*47*	*52*	*55*	*56*
World	38	51	52	54	57
European Union	*n.a.*	*51*	*54*	*58*	*59*

Despite continuing improvements in average vehicle fuel efficiency, spurred in part by high oil prices,[3] the sheer growth of the vehicle fleet – especially in non-OECD countries – is expected to continue to push up total oil use for transport purposes. There is not expected to be any major shift away from conventionally fuelled vehicles before 2030, though the penetration of hybrid-electric cars, including plug-ins (see the *Spotlight* below), is expected to rise, contributing to an overall improvement in fuel economy. Globally, passenger-car ownership is assumed to grow at 3.6% through the projection period, outpacing GDP slightly. The total light-duty vehicle stock rises from an estimated 650 million in 2005 to about 1.4 billion by 2030. The biggest increase in absolute terms is expected to occur in China, which accounts for almost one-third of

---

3. There are signs that consumers are beginning to switch to smaller, more fuel-efficient cars in response to higher oil prices, especially in countries with lower tax rates and where prices have risen most in percentage terms. In the United States, for example, which has the lowest rates of tax on gasoline in the OECD, sales of sports utility vehicles have fallen heavily in the last two to three years.

the global increase in cars (Figure 3.7). Most of the rest of the increase comes from other non-OECD countries. The average size and power of new cars in these countries is expected to be significantly lower than in the OECD at present, which accounts for part of the global improvement in fuel economy.

Figure 3.7 ● Light-duty vehicle stock by region in the Reference Scenario

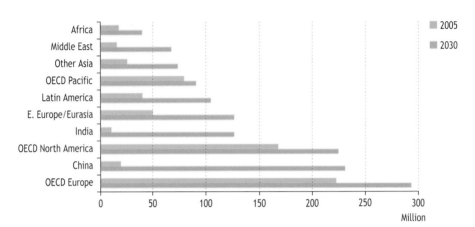

Power generation currently accounts for around 7% of global primary oil consumption, down from 14% in 1980. Its share is projected to decline further, to around 4% in 2030. The volume burned in power stations also drops, from 277 Mtoe to about 204 Mtoe. By the end of the projection period, close to 85% of oil use for power is in non-OECD regions — about 40% of which is in the Middle East. Investment in refinery upgrading units is expected to continue to reduce the proportion of residual heavy fuel oil — which makes up the bulk of the oil used by power stations and by ships — in the output of refined products. The fuel oil that is produced is increasingly concentrated in the power sector. While the share of oil in overall fuel inputs to power generation is projected to fall sharply over the projection period, there may be pronounced short-term swings in response to fluctuations in relative oil, gas and coal prices, delays in bringing generating capacity on line, and unplanned outages of other base-load plants. A shortfall in coal-fired capacity in China in 2004 led to a surge in oil burning, which contributed significantly to a jump in world oil demand and to upward pressures on international prices.

Implications for spending on oil

These oil-demand projections, combined with our oil-price assumptions (described in Chapter 1), point to persistently high levels of spending on oil in both OECD and non-OECD countries. As a share of world GDP at market exchange rates, oil spending

What is the scope for switching from oil-fuelled to electric vehicles?

3

Electric vehicles continue to struggle to compete with conventional oil-fuelled cars and trucks. Although fuel costs for owners of electric vehicles are lower, the savings are not big enough to offset the much higher prices of the vehicles themselves. Fuel subsidies in many non-OECD countries also undermine the attractiveness of electric vehicles.

Yet electric-vehicle technology is advancing rapidly. Vehicle hybridisation, involving the addition of an electric motor and an energy-storage system (typically a battery) to a conventional engine/fuel system, has attracted most investment and has already proved commercially successful – in spite of relatively high costs. Further improvements to storage systems are necessary to boost efficiency and lower costs: despite significant progress in recent years, even the best lithium-ion batteries available today suffer from inadequate performance and high costs. Ultra-capacitors, which store energy in charged electrodes rather than in an electrolyte, are increasingly being seen as a complement to batteries; they store less energy per unit weight than batteries but are able to deliver energy more quickly. Research into these technologies is expected to yield further major improvements in the coming years.

In the longer term, plug-in hybrids, fully electric vehicles and hydrogen fuel cells appear to offer the greatest potential for reducing or eliminating the need for oil-based fuels. Plug-in hybrids, in which the electric battery is recharged off the grid as well as through the vehicle's internal recharging system, combine the efficiency advantages of using an electric motor for short distances with the convenience and longer range of an internal combustion engine. How quickly plug-ins become commercially viable will hinge on substantial improvements in the performance of electric batteries. The prospects for fully electric vehicles are less certain, as battery capacity needs to be even greater than for hybrids. The need for quick recharging and related infrastructure is an additional barrier. A lot of research effort continues to be focused on fuel cells powered with hydrogen (stored on-board or supplied from a reformer using a hydrogen-rich feedstock). But, as with electric vehicles, a number of technical hurdles remain to be overcome in order to lower costs and make fuel-cell vehicles commercially viable.

Neither fully electric nor hydrogen-powered fuel-cell vehicles are expected to become widely available before 2030 unless research efforts are stepped up and technological breakthroughs are achieved (limited penetration of the former is assumed only in the 450 Policy Scenario). They could, however, be commercialised widely before 2050. In the IEA's most recent *Energy Technology Perspectives*, fuel-cell vehicles account for 33% to 50% of total car sales in the OECD and half those in the rest of the world by 2050 in scenarios that assume a significant increase in research spending over the next decade and rapid reductions in unit costs.

Source: IEA (2008).

soared from a little over 1% in 1998 to around 4% in 2007. On current trends, that share is set to approach 6% in 2008, stabilising at around 5% over much of the *Outlook* period (Figure 3.8). For non-OECD countries, the share is even higher, reaching 8% in 2008 and falling back to above 6% by 2030. Only in the early 1980s has this share been so high in both OECD and non-OECD regions.

Figure 3.8 ● **Share of oil spending in real GDP at market exchange rates in the Reference Scenario**

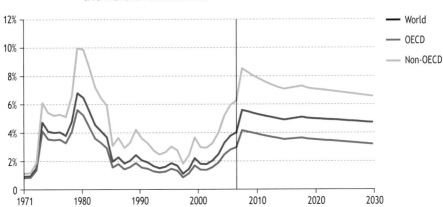

Production[4]

World oil supply is projected to rise from 84 mb/d in 2007 to 106 mb/d in 2030. Netting out processing gains in refining, production reaches 104 mb/d (Table 3.3). The bulk of the projected increase in world oil supply is projected to come from OPEC countries, where most of the world's remaining proven reserves of conventional crude oil are to be found. Their share of global output rises from 44% in 2007 to 51% in 2030 — though this is still below the historical peak of 53% in 1973. Their reserves are, in principle, big enough and development costs low enough for output to grow faster than this. However, investment is assumed to be constrained by several factors, including conservative depletion policies and geopolitics (see Chapter 13).

Non-OPEC conventional oil production is projected to peak by around the middle of the next decade and then to decline slowly through to the end of the projection period. This is largely offset by rising non-conventional output, which keeps total non-OPEC output broadly flat over the second half of the projection period. Higher prices have stimulated new upstream investment in the last few years, though much of the rise in this upstream expenditure is due to higher costs (see Chapter 13). This investment will boost capacity

4. This section summarises the Reference Scenario projections of global oil production, which are described in detail in Chapter 11 in Part B.

in the near term, more than offsetting natural production declines at existing fields (see Chapter 10). But dwindling new discoveries and a fall in the size of new fields are expected to drive up marginal development costs. As a result, oil prices are assumed to rise to stimulate the necessary investment. Production has already peaked in most non-OPEC countries and will peak in most others before 2030. Russian output is projected to edge up by 2015 but then to drift lower towards the end of the *Outlook* period.

Table 3.3 ● World oil supply in the Reference Scenario
(million barrels per day)

	1980	2000	2007	2015	2030	2007-2030*
Non-OPEC	35.5	42.9	46.3	47.6	50.9	0.4%
OECD	17.3	21.8	19.3	18.6	20.8	0.3%
North America	14.2	14.1	13.8	14.6	17.9	1.1%
Europe	2.6	6.8	4.9	3.4	2.2	-3.5%
Pacific	0.5	0.9	0.6	0.6	0.7	0.6%
E. Europe/Eurasia	12.1	8.1	12.9	14.3	16.6	1.1%
Russia	10.8	6.5	10.1	10.4	9.7	-0.2%
Asia	2.9	5.6	6.4	6.1	5.8	-0.4%
China	2.1	3.2	3.7	3.6	4.1	0.5%
India	0.2	0.7	0.8	0.8	0.5	-1.8%
Middle East	0.6	2.1	1.7	1.4	1.1	-1.8%
Africa	1.1	2.1	2.5	2.1	1.9	-1.1%
Latin America	1.6	3.2	3.5	5.1	4.6	1.2%
OPEC**	28.1	32.1	35.9	44.4	52.9	1.7%
Middle East	19.2	21.3	23.7	30.7	37.9	2.1%
Processing gains	1.7	1.7	2.1	2.3	2.6	1.0%
World	65.2	76.8	84.3	94.4	106.4	1.0%
Conventional***	63.1	73.8	80.7	87.4	95.0	0.7%
Non-conventional****	0.4	1.2	1.6	4.6	8.8	7.7%

* Average annual rate of growth.

** Includes Angola, which joined OPEC at the beginning of 2007.

*** Includes conventional crude oil, condensates, natural gas liquids (NGLs) and extra-heavy oil from Venezuela.

****Extra-heavy oil (excluding Venezuela), oil sands, chemical additives, gas-to-liquids and coal-to-liquids. Biofuels are *not* included.

Although global oil production is not expected to peak before 2030, conventional crude oil production (including natural gas liquids and enhanced oil recovery) is projected to level off towards the end of the projection period. A growing share of the increase in world output comes from non-conventional sources, mainly Canadian oil sands, extra-heavy oil, gas-to-liquids and coal-to-liquids (Figure 3.9). These increases in global oil output hinge on adequate and timely investment, which remains a critical uncertainty (see Chapter 13). There remains a real risk of an oil-supply crunch in the medium term resulting from under-investment (Box 3.2).

Figure 3.9 ● World oil production by source in the Reference Scenario

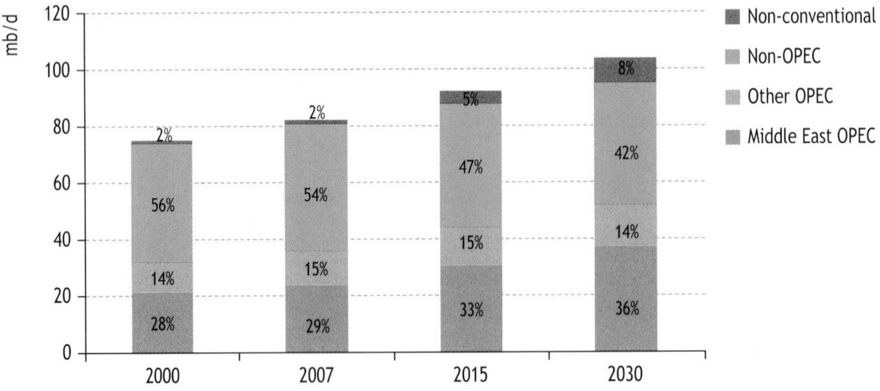

Note: Excludes processing gains. Conventional oil includes crude oil, condensates, natural gas liquids (NGLs) and extra-heavy oil from Venezuela.

Box 3.2 ● Averting a post-2010 oil-supply crunch

Despite shortages of equipment and labour, and lengthening delays in bringing new projects to completion, the current wave of upstream investment looks set to provide significant boost to oil-production capacity in the next two to three years. Based on our analysis of upstream investment, we expect gross capacity additions worldwide to cover demand growth and output declines from existing fields to 2010, pushing up spare capacity modestly (see Chapter 13 for details). However, capacity additions from current projects tail off after 2010. This largely reflects the upstream development cycle: many new projects will undoubtedly be sanctioned in the next two or three years as oil companies complete existing projects and move on to new ones. But the gap between what is currently being built and what will be needed to keep pace with demand is nonetheless set to widen sharply after 2010 (see Chapter 11). Around 7 mb/d of additional capacity needs to be brought on stream by 2015 (over and above the capacity that is already in the pipeline from current projects), most of which will need to be sanctioned within the next two years or so.

The sheer scale of the investment needed raises questions about whether all of the additional capacity we project will be needed will actually occur. If actual capacity additions fall short of this amount, spare production capacity would be squeezed and oil prices would undoubtedly rise — possibly to new record highs (Jesse and van der Linde, 2008; Stevens, 2008). These concerns are behind the initiative of the UK prime minister to invite major oil producing and consuming countries to a meeting in London in December 2008 to discuss ways of lowering barriers to investment, following up a meeting in Jeddah (in which the IEA participated) called by Saudi Arabia in June. Boosting investment in the resource-rich countries, which, in many cases, is restricted, will be of critical importance to averting a supply crunch.

Inter-regional trade

The mismatch between demand growth and the sources of incremental production means that inter-regional trade in oil (crude oil, NGLs and refined products) increases sharply during the projection period in the Reference Scenario. The volume of trade reaches 55 mb/d in 2030 – over half of global oil production and over 35% more than at present (Table 3.4). Net exports from the Middle East, already the biggest exporting region, rise from 19.9 mb/d in 2007 to 28.5 mb/d in 2030, representing 52% of global trade in 2030, up from 49% today. Net exports from Africa and Eastern Europe/Eurasia (thanks to the Caspian region) also continue to expand steadily. Brazil contributes most to the increase in net exports from Latin America in the early part of the *Outlook* period, and Venezuela thereafter.

Of the net oil-importing regions today – the three OECD regions and non-OECD Asia – Europe and Asia become even more dependent on imports over the projection period (Figure 3.10). By contrast, net imports into North America drop from 10.7 mb/d to 5.9 mb/d, largely thanks to rising Canadian oil sands production and a sharp slowdown in demand. Net imports into the United States alone drop much less, from 13.2 mb/d in 2007 to 11.9 mb/d in 2030 – equal to 63% of total consumption. Import dependency in the OECD Pacific region also falls slightly, to 90% in 2030 compared with 92% currently. OECD Europe, by contrast, sees a sharp rise in net import dependence, from 65% to 84%, as a result of the projected rapid decline in North Sea production. Net imports into the OECD as a whole decline as a share of total oil demand from 58% in 2007 to 52% in 2030. In Asia, the increase in dependence is dramatic in India, where imports meet almost all the country's needs in 2030, and in China, which became a net oil importer only in 1993. China's imports rise from 3.8 mb/d in 2007 to 12.5 mb/d in 2030, equal to 75% of China's total oil demand, compared with 50% in 2007.

Figure 3.10 ● Oil-import dependence by major importing region in the Reference Scenario

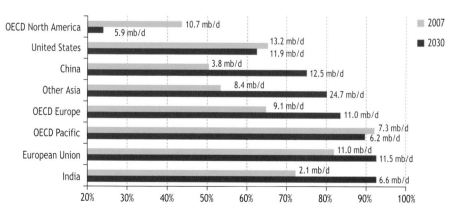

Increased trade consolidates global interdependence, but the risk to consuming countries of short-term supply interruptions grows as geographic supply diversity is actually reduced, increasing reliance on a few supply routes. Much of the additional oil imports will come from the Middle East, the scene of most of the biggest supply disruptions in the past, and will transit vulnerable maritime routes to both eastern and western markets. Almost all Middle East oil and gas exports, for example, transit the Straits of Hormuz at the mouth of the Arabian Gulf (Figure 3.11). Any supply disruption would drive up prices to all consuming countries, regardless of where they obtain their oil. The growing participation of China, India and other emerging countries in international oil trade amplifies the importance of their contribution to collective efforts to enhance global energy security (IEA, 2007).

Table 3.4 ● **Net inter-regional oil trade in the Reference Scenario**
(million barrels per day)

	1980	2000	2007	2015	2030
Net importers					
OECD	-24.4	-24.2	-27.1	-27.1	-23.1
North America	*-6.7*	*-9.2*	*-10.7*	*-9.3*	*-5.9*
United States	*-7.2*	*-11.3*	*-13.2*	*-12.3*	*-11.9*
Europe	*-12.0*	*-7.5*	*-9.1*	*-10.6*	*-11.0*
Pacific	*-5.6*	*-7.5*	*-7.3*	*-7.2*	*-6.2*
Japan	*-4.9*	*-5.4*	*-4.8*	*-4.4*	*-3.5*
Non-OECD Asia	0.0	-4.6	-8.4	-14.5	-24.7
China	*0.2*	*-1.4*	*-3.8*	*-7.7*	*-12.5*
India	*-0.5*	*-1.6*	*-2.1*	*-3.3*	*-6.6*
Net exporters					
Middle East	17.7	18.9	19.9	23.9	28.5
Africa	4.9	5.6	7.5	8.7	9.1
Latin America	0.3	2.3	1.5	2.3	1.7
Brazil	*-1.1*	*-0.7*	*-0.2*	*1.2*	*0.6*
E. Europe/Eurasia	2.6	4.0	8.1	8.6	10.7
Russia	*n.a.*	*3.8*	*7.2*	*7.0*	*6.3*
Total trade	27.6	34.7	40.7	46.6	55.1
European Union (imports)	*n.a.*	*-10.1*	*-11.0*	*-11.8*	*-11.5*

Note: Trade between *WEO* regions only. Positive figures denote exports; negative figures imports.

Figure 3.11 • Oil export flows from the Middle East

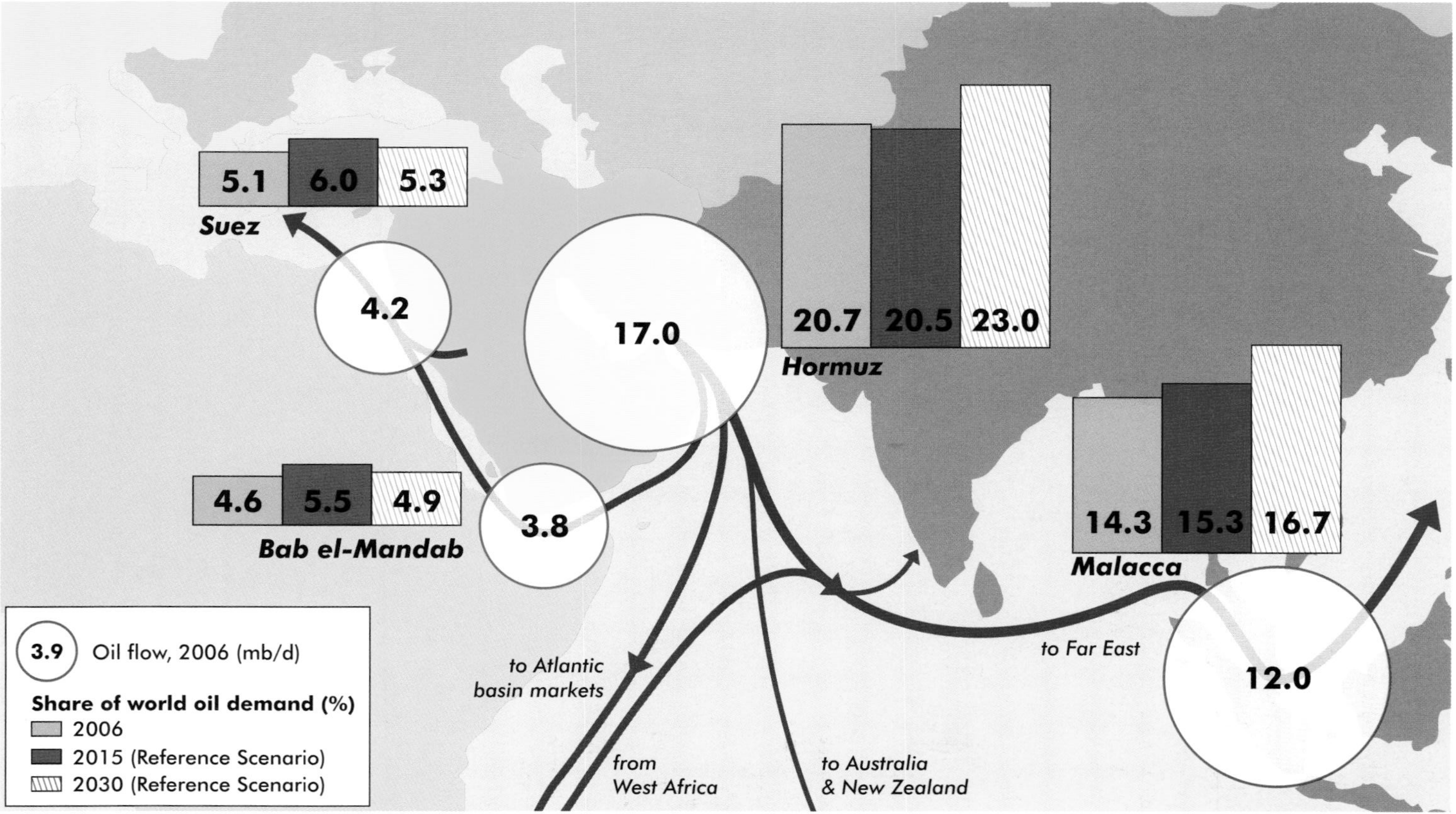

Hormuz

20.7 20.5 23.0

Malacca

14.3 15.3 16.7

17.0

12.0

3.8

4.2

Suez

5.1 6.0 5.3

Bab el-Mandab

4.6 5.5 4.9

to Far East

to Australia
& New Zealand

from
West Africa

to Atlantic
basin markets

3.9 Oil flow, 2006 (mb/d)

Share of world oil demand (%)
- 2006
- 2015 (Reference Scenario)
- 2030 (Reference Scenario)

The boundaries and names shown and the designations used on maps included in this publication do not imply official endorsement or acceptance by the IEA.

3

CHAPTER 4

NATURAL GAS MARKET OUTLOOK

H   I   G   H   L   I   G   H   T   S

- World primary demand for natural gas expands by just over half between 2006 and 2030 in the Reference Scenario to 4.4 trillion cubic metres, a rate of increase of 1.8% per year. The share of gas in total world primary energy demand increases marginally, from 21% in 2006 to 22% in 2030. The projected growth in gas use is nonetheless slower than in last year's *Outlook* — the result of higher assumed prices and less-rapid growth in gas-fired power generation.

- The bulk of the increase in global gas use over the projection period — more than three-quarters in total — comes from non-OECD regions, especially those that are well endowed with gas resources. Gas demand is projected to grow most in absolute terms in the Middle East. The *pace* of demand growth is fastest in China. Despite their much less rapid economic growth, North America and Europe still contribute a fifth of the global increase in gas demand.

- The power sector accounts for 57% of the projected increase in world gas demand to 2030, pushing up its share of global gas use from 39% now to 45%. The power sector is the main driver of gas demand in almost all regions, especially in non-OECD countries where electricity demand is projected to rise most rapidly. Despite the recent surge in price, gas remains competitive with other fuels in many cases, especially for mid-load generation and where coal has to be imported.

- Gas resources are sufficient to meet the projected increase in global demand, but production is set to become much more concentrated in the most resource-rich regions. Some 46% of the projected growth in world gas production in 2006-2030 comes from the Middle East, its output tripling to around 1 tcm by 2030. About 60% of the region's incremental output is consumed locally, mainly in power stations. Most of the remaining increase in world output is provided by Africa and Eastern Europe and Eurasia (mainly Russia). These capacity expansions hinge on timely investment.

- Inter-regional natural gas trade is projected to more than double over the projection period, from 441 billion cubic metres in 2006 to just over 1 tcm in 2030. Imports rise in all the regions except non-Russia Eurasia that are currently net importers of gas, both in volume and as a share of their total gas consumption. The European Union sees the biggest increase in import volumes.

- Most of the growth in gas exports over 2006-2030 comes from the Middle East and Africa. Together, they account for about 60% of total exports in 2030. Russia and the Caspian/Central Asian countries combined remain the other main exporting region. Most of the increase in inter-regional trade is in the form of liquefied natural gas, its share of trade rising from 52% in 2006 to 69% in 2030. Liquefaction capacity is set to expand markedly through to early in the 2010s, but a shortage could emerge thereafter if a wave of new investment is not sanctioned soon.

Demand

Global demand for natural gas is projected to increase by 52% between 2006 and 2030, from 2 916 bcm to 4 434 bcm (Table 4.1). Demand grows at an average annual rate of 1.8%, 0.3 percentage points lower than was projected in last year's *Outlook*. The share of gas in total world primary energy demand increases marginally, from 21% in 2006 to 22% in 2030. In 1980, the share of gas was only 17%.

Table 4.1 ● **World primary demand for natural gas in the Reference Scenario** (billion cubic metres)

	1980	2000	2006	2015	2030	2006-2030*
OECD	958	1 407	1 465	1 645	1 827	0.9%
North America	659	799	766	848	908	0.7%
United States	*581*	*669*	*611*	*652*	*631*	*0.1%*
Europe	264	478	541	614	694	1.0%
Pacific	35	130	158	183	225	1.5%
Japan	*25*	*82*	*94*	*104*	*128*	*1.3%*
Non-OECD	559	1 135	1 451	1 867	2 607	2.5%
E. Europe/Eurasia	438	606	676	779	846	0.9%
Russia	*n.a.*	*395*	*444*	*507*	*524*	*0.7%*
Asia	36	185	285	414	666	3.6%
China	*14*	*28*	*58*	*121*	*221*	*5.8%*
India	*1*	*25*	*38*	*57*	*117*	*4.8%*
Middle East	36	182	276	378	676	3.8%
Africa	14	62	90	124	168	2.6%
Latin America	36	100	124	174	252	3.0%
Brazil	*1*	*9*	*21*	*32*	*46*	*3.3%*
World	1 517	2 541	2 916	3 512	4 434	1.8%
European Union	*n.a.*	*482*	*532*	*606*	*681*	*1.0%*

* Average annual rate of growth.

The projected rate of growth in global gas demand is lower than over the past quarter of a century: demand rose by 2.6% per year between 1980 and 2006. Demand began to slow at the turn of the century, rising by only 2.3% per year over 2000-2006. Warmer winter weather across the northern hemisphere, coupled with higher prices, largely offset the impact of relatively rapid economic growth worldwide over that period. The increase in prices in recent years has affected gas demand more than has been the case for oil, mainly because there is more scope for consumers to switch at short notice to other fuels, especially in power generation and industry (see *Spotlight* below). The much higher level of gas prices, in absolute terms and relative to coal prices (see Chapter 1), is the main reason for the downward revision in projected gas-demand growth. Slower GDP growth, especially in the big gas-consuming OECD regions, also contributes.

Are high prices choking off demand for gas?

The scope for gas consumers to reduce their consumption of gas in the face of high prices varies by region and by sector. Most residential consumers have little option but to pay the higher cost, as they rarely have any back up for space and water heating, and for cooking. Moreover, switching to an alternative fuel when installing new equipment may not be attractive since heating oil and electricity prices have also risen in most cases. But some gas-fired power plants and industrial boilers can be switched to other fuels at short notice (environmental regulations permitting), usually heavy fuel oil in the case of conventional steam boilers and distillate in the case of gas turbines. In addition, some utilities and manufacturers maintain back-up capacity that allows them to switch quickly to a cheaper fuel.

Good statistics on the amount of such flexible capacity and the extent of switching in practice are rare outside the United States. The most recent survey of switching capacity in US manufacturing industry found that almost one-fifth of actual gas consumption could be avoided by switching to other fuels – a slightly lower share than in previous surveys (DOE/EIA, 2002). Roughly one-third of US power plants that use gas as the primary fuel were also able to run on oil products in 2007, even though most of the new gas-fired capacity added at the beginning of the current decade cannot use oil as a back up or alternative fuel.

There is evidence that the surge in gas prices in the United States and other OECD countries has prompted some switching from gas to oil and other fuels in recent years. Usually, this switching has been temporary. The share of gas in power generation in the United Kingdom, for example, dropped by three percentage points to 36% in 2006 in response to a spike in gas prices relative to coal prices, but rebounded to 42% in 2007 with higher coal prices. In some cases, where no fuel-switching capacity exists, industrial production has stopped altogether – sometimes permanently. Since 2000, 26 of the 56 nitrogen fertilizer plants in the United States have shut down as a result of the higher cost of gas. Natural gas accounts for up to 90% of the production cost of ammonia – the raw material for all nitrogen fertilizers. The use of gas as a petrochemical feedstock is growing much faster in non-OECD countries, especially the Middle East, with low-cost local supplies.

The decline in the gas intensity of economic activity worldwide has gathered pace since the beginning of the current decade, suggesting that higher prices are indeed tempering the growth in demand for gas (Figure 4.1). The decline in gas intensity has accelerated fastest on average in non-OECD countries – even though, in many cases, price controls have prevented much of the increase in market prices from feeding through into retail prices. Gas is subsidised in most non-OECD countries – in some cases, heavily. In Russia, for example, gas subsidies to households and industry totalled close to $30 billion in 2007 (see Chapter 1). The reduction of these subsidies contributes to the acceleration of the decline in gas intensity in non-OECD countries over the period 2006-2030.

Sources: IEA databases; Department of Energy/Energy Information Administration (www.eia.doe. gov/cneaf/electricity/epa/epa_sum.html); US Fertilizer Institute (www.tfi.org).

Figure 4.1 ● Change in gas intensity by region in the Reference Scenario

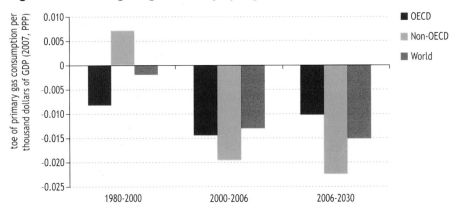

Regional trends

As with most other primary energy sources, the bulk of the increase in global gas use over the projection period — 76% in total — comes from non-OECD regions, especially those that are well endowed with gas resources (Figure 4.2). Gas demand is projected to grow most in absolute terms in the Middle East, where it jumps from 276 bcm in 2006 to 676 bcm in 2030 — an increase of 145%. Rising local availability of gas supplies is expected to fuel this expansion in demand, most of which comes from power generation and petrochemicals (for use as feedstock and heat generation). By 2030, the Middle East accounts for 15% of world gas consumption, compared with only 9% today and a mere 2% in 1980. Demand also grows strongly in non-OECD Asia, where gas captures market share from coal in industry. The pace of demand growth is fastest in

Figure 4.2 ● Increase in primary demand for natural gas by region in the Reference Scenario

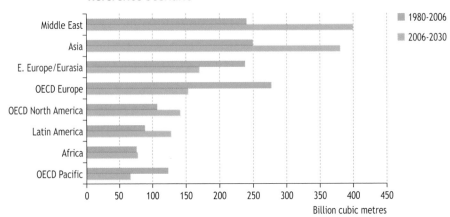

World Energy Outlook 2008 - **GLOBAL ENERGY TRENDS TO 2030**

China, at close to 6% per year, and India, at nearly 5% per year. Yet the two countries' combined share of world demand reaches only 8% in 2030, up from 3% in 2006, as they start from a low base. Demand rises much less quickly in Russia and in other Eastern European/Eurasian countries, mainly due to assumed progress in raising final prices to market levels, improvements in end-use energy efficiency, reduced waste and saturation effects.

Despite their much less rapid economic growth, North America and Europe both still account for a fifth of the overall growth in world gas use. With the exception of Eastern Europe/Eurasia and the Middle East, per-capita consumption in North America and Europe remains well above that of all other regions, for climate, economic and policy reasons. In many cases, gas continues to be favoured over coal and oil for environmental reasons, especially in power generation, where gas can be used in highly efficient combined-cycle gas turbines (see below). In Europe, carbon penalties under the EU Emissions Trading Scheme help gas to compete against more carbon-intensive coal in the power sector and heavy industry.

Sectoral trends

Gas use is projected to become increasingly concentrated in power generation. The power sector accounts for 57% of the increase in world gas demand over the projection period (Figure 4.3).[1] As a result, the power sector's share of global gas use rises from 39% in 2006 to 45% in 2030. The power sector is the main driver of gas demand in almost all regions, especially in non-OECD countries where electricity demand is projected to rise most rapidly. Despite the recent surge in price, in many cases gas remains competitive with other fuels, especially for mid-load generation and where coal has to

Figure 4.3 ● **Increase in world primary natural gas demand by sector in the Reference Scenario, 2006-2030**

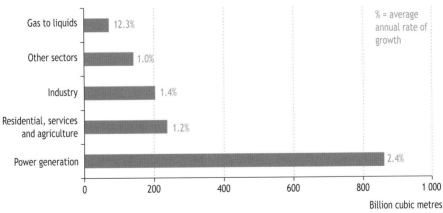

1. The projected growth in global gas use in power generation, while strong, is slower than in last year's *Outlook*, mainly because of less-rapid growth in demand for electricity and an increase in the cost of gas-fired generation relative to other power-generation technologies.

be imported (see Chapter 6). The capital costs of combined-cycle gas turbines, which are much more efficient than coal-based power technologies, are lower than for coal-fired power plants and the construction lead-times shorter. These factors compensate for higher fuel costs. In Europe, carbon penalties give gas an added cost advantage over coal for base-load generation. Nonetheless, renewables-based power technologies are expected to become increasingly competitive against gas over the projection period (see Chapter 7), slowing the rate of construction of gas-fired plants.

Almost all of the rest of the increase in world primary gas demand to 2030 comes from end-use sectors, notably industry and the residential, services and agricultural sectors. Industry remains the single largest gas-consuming end-use sector, with demand projected to grow at 1.4% per year over 2006-2030. Industry's share of total final gas demand rises from 35% in 2006 to 36% in 2030. Nonetheless, the share of gas in total industrial energy consumption falls slightly — mainly due to the increasing penetration of electricity, especially in non-OECD countries. Industrial gas use in the OECD barely increases, due to sluggish growth in heavy industrial production.

As in industry, demand for gas in the residential, services and agricultural sectors grows relatively slowly. In OECD countries, the per-capita use of gas for space and water heating and for cooking is approaching saturation levels. With population growing only very slowly, this holds back the overall increase in gas demand in the residential, services and agricultural sectors to only 0.7% per year over the projection period. Gas consumption in these sectors grows more quickly, by an average of 2.2% per year in the non-OECD countries as a whole. Demand growth is particularly rapid in Asia.

Gas-to-liquids (GTL) plants, which convert natural gas into high-quality oil products (as well as lubricants and petrochemical products), account for a small but growing share of global natural gas demand (Figure 4.4). The consumption of gas in such plants, mainly located in the Middle East and Africa, rises from only 5 bcm in 2006 to 33 bcm by 2015 and over 50 bcm in 2030. There are three commercial-scale GTL plants operating today: Oryx in Qatar, which started up in 2006; Shell's Bintulu plant in Malaysia which came on stream in 1993; and the Mossgas plant in South Africa, which has been

Figure 4.4 ● **World primary natural gas demand by sector in the Reference Scenario**

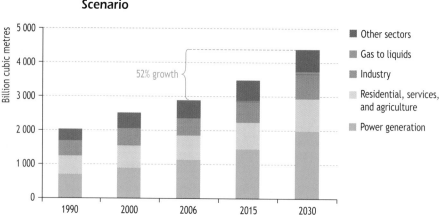

operating since 1990. Two more plants are under construction and others are planned. The long-term prospects for GTL hinge critically on bringing down costs, which have risen sharply in recent years, and on raising the thermal efficiency of the conversion process (see Chapter 11).

Production[2]

The proximity of reserves to markets and the level of production costs will continue to drive regional prospects for gas supply. Gas transportation, whether by pipeline or as liquefied natural gas (LNG), remains very expensive and usually represents a significant share of the overall cost of gas delivered to consumers. A substantial part of the world's gas resources is located far from the main centres of demand and cannot yet be extracted profitably. Those resources are unquestionably large enough to meet the projected increase in global demand in the Reference Scenario. It is assumed here that the necessary investment in the infrastructure required to bring them to market will be made in a timely manner, though this is an area of risk (Box 4.1).

Some 46% of the projected growth in world gas production over the *Outlook* period comes from the Middle East, its output tripling to around 1 tcm by 2030 (Table 4.2 and Figure 4.5). That region holds the largest reserves and has the lowest

Table 4.2 ● **World natural gas production in the Reference Scenario**
(billion cubic metres)

	1980	2000	2006	2015	2030	2006-2030*
OECD	889	1 107	1 117	1 149	1 086	-0.1%
North America	657	763	761	795	765	0.0%
United States	554	544	524	535	515	-0.1%
Europe	219	302	305	282	217	-1.4%
Pacific	12	41	51	72	104	3.0%
Non-OECD	634	1 425	1 842	2 363	3 348	2.5%
E. Europe/Eurasia	480	738	846	963	1 069	1.0%
Russia	n.a.	583	651	712	794	0.8%
Asia	57	247	335	449	540	2.0%
China	14	27	59	104	115	2.9%
India	1	25	28	41	45	2.0%
Middle East	38	204	324	483	999	4.8%
Africa	23	133	197	286	452	3.5%
Latin America	36	104	139	182	287	3.1%
Brazil	1	7	11	17	38	5.2%
World	1 522	2 531	2 959	3 512	4 434	1.7%
European Union	n.a.	262	228	170	99	-3.4%

* Average annual rate of growth.
Note: Historical data for world production differs from demand because of stock changes.

---

2. This section summarises the Reference Scenario projections of global natural gas production, which are described in detail in Chapter 12.

production costs, whether or not the gas is produced in association with oil. Iran, Qatar, Iraq and Saudi Arabia account for most of the increase. About 60% of incremental output is consumed locally, mainly in power stations, while the remainder is exported (see below). Most of the remaining increase in world output is provided by Africa and Eastern Europe/Eurasia (mainly Russia). The latter region remains the largest single producing region in 2030, just ahead of the Middle East. Production rises marginally in OECD North America over 2006-2030, mainly due to non-conventional supplies (notably shale gas), but falls heavily in Europe where North Sea reserves continue to dwindle. Australia accounts for virtually all of the projected increase in OECD Pacific output.

Figure 4.5 ● Natural gas production by region in the Reference Scenario

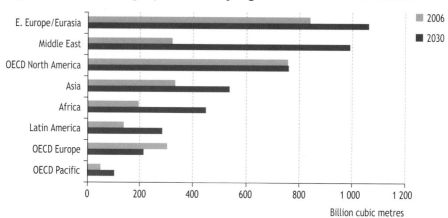

Box 4.1 ● Adequacy of gas-supply infrastructure and risks of shortages

The rigidity of gas-supply chains and the lengthening lead times in building physical infrastructure increase the risk that demand may, at times, outstrip available capacity. As the 2007 issue of the IEA's *Natural Gas Market Review* put it "The world dodged a bullet" in the winter of 2006/2007: delays in bringing new capacity on stream did not lead to shortages in Europe and North America, mainly thanks to warmer-than-normal weather, which dampened demand (IEA, 2007). Yet concerns remain that investment in upstream facilities, LNG chains and long-distance pipelines, in the medium term, may fall short of that needed to meet growing demand, especially if power generators opt to build more gas-fired capacity than the high levels already projected (for example, if gas prices are lower than assumed). It is generally quicker to build gas-fired capacity than the infrastructure required to supply it. Limited spare capacity within the gas-supply system increases the risk of physical shortages occurring due to a sudden supply disruption or an exceptional surge in demand, for weather-related or other reasons.

Box 4.1 ● Adequacy of gas-supply infrastructure and risks of shortages
       (continued)

4

Recent supply problems in several markets have refocused attention on gas-supply security. The loss of US gas-production capacity through hurricane damage in 2005 resulted in a surge in prices that choked off a substantial amount of industrial demand, rebalancing the market. The high degree of inter-connectivity of the North American network enabled supplies to be redirected. In the event, no customer was forced to stop using gas. But other countries that have not liberalised their gas markets to the same degree cannot rely on market forces to bring demand back into balance with supply during a crisis. In the winter of "2005/2006", cold weather and higher-than-usual use of gas for power generation led to a surge in demand in Italy. A lack of cross-border capacity and fixed prices to most customers resulted in physical shortages that could only be addressed through plant closures through administrative decree, the temporary relaxation of environmental standards to allow fuel oil to be used instead of gas and rationing. Commercial disputes with neighbouring countries have recently led to disruptions in Russian gas supplies to Europe. These incidents have highlighted the importance of giving full rein to markets in balancing supply and demand in the event of a crisis, and to the need for timely and adequate investment in transmission and storage capacity.

There are particular concerns about the adequacy of investment in LNG capacity in the medium term. An unprecedented major expansion is underway worldwide in regasification capacities, well in excess of LNG-production capacity. As a result, global regasification capacity is likely to be under-utilised, even though its availability will increase supply flexibility.[3] But liquefaction capacity is not expected to increase as quickly. Although a significant amount of capacity is planned and proposed, many projects have yet to be formally sanctioned. Major delays and cost over-runs afflict many projects that have been given the green light, which has discouraged companies from proceeding to final investment decisions on other projects and has led to some cancellations. The dearth of investment decisions in new LNG projects since mid-2005 means that any new surge of investment is unlikely to result in additional capacity, beyond that due in service by 2012, being available before 2015, given the long lead times involved. Notwithstanding the massive expansion in LNG supply that will undoubtedly occur by 2012, the lag in LNG investment beyond 2012 raises questions about the availability of incremental LNG supply for both OECD and non-OECD importing countries. Shortfalls in the availability of LNG could push up prices and encourage the faster development of indigenous resources in importing regions.

---

3. There has already been an increase in inter-regional swaps of LNG cargoes, particularly from the Atlantic to Pacific regions, facilitated by growing supplies and changing business models in the LNG industry.

Table 4.3 ● Net inter-regional natural gas trade in the Reference Scenario

	2006		2015		2030	
	bcm	% of primary demand*	bcm	% of primary demand*	bcm	% of primary demand*
OECD	**- 353**	**24**	**- 496**	**30**	**- 741**	**41**
North America	- 15	2	- 53	6	- 143	16
Europe	- 241	45	- 333	54	- 477	69
Pacific	- 97	61	- 111	61	- 121	54
OECD Asia	*- 115*	*91*	*- 143*	*97*	*- 179*	*98*
OECD Oceania	*18*	*38*	*32*	*47*	*58*	*58*
Non-OECD	**353**	**19**	**496**	**21**	**741**	**22**
E. Europe/Eurasia	137	16	185	19	224	21
Russia	*198*	*30*	*205*	*29*	*270*	*34*
Asia	46	14	36	8	- 126	19
China	*- 1*	*2*	*- 17*	*14*	*- 106*	*48*
India	*- 8*	*21*	*- 16*	*29*	*- 71*	*61*
Middle East	55	17	105	22	323	32
Africa	99	50	162	57	284	63
Latin America	16	11	8	4	35	12
World	**441**	**15**	**582**	**17**	**1 022**	**23**
European Union	*- 305*	*57*	*- 435*	*72*	*- 582*	*86*

* Production for exporting regions.
Note: Trade between WEO regions only. Positive figures denote exports; negative figures imports.
Sources: IEA analysis and databases; Cedigaz (2008).

Inter-regional trade

Inter-regional natural gas trade (between major *WEO* regions) is projected to more than double over the projection period, from 441 bcm in 2006 to around 1 tcm in 2030 (Table 4.3). Trade rises much faster than demand, due to the pronounced geographical mismatch between resource location and demand. As a result, regional gas markets become more integrated as trade in LNG expands and new long-distance and undersea pipelines enable more gas to be traded between regions.

Imports rise in all the regions (with the exception of non-Russia Eurasia) that are currently net importers of gas, both in volume and as a share of total gas consumption (Table 4.3). The European Union sees the biggest increase in net import volumes, from 305 bcm in 2006 to about 580 bcm in 2030. Its reliance on imports rises from 57% of its total gas needs to 86% over that period. Most of the increase is met by Russia, Africa and the Middle East. North America, which is almost self-sufficient in gas at present, emerges as a major importing region during the projection period as demand outpaces production. Imports from Africa, Latin America and the Middle East, mostly into the United States, reach a combined 140 bcm in 2030. OECD Asia (Japan and Korea) is already highly reliant on imports to meet its gas needs. Its net imports, from non-OECD Asian countries, the Middle East, Australia and Russia (Sakhalin), rise by more than half between 2006 and 2030. Imports into China also increase sharply, covering just under half of the country's gas needs in 2030. India's imports also grow markedly, meeting more than 60% of total gas demand by 2030.

Most of the additional exports over 2006-2030 come from the Middle East and Africa. Together, they account for 59% of total gas exports in 2030. Exports from Africa are projected to almost triple, from 99 bcm in 2006 to over 280 bcm in 2030, while those from the Middle East increase six-fold, from 55 bcm to about 320 bcm. African countries' exports to Europe grow strongly. The Middle East increases its net exports to all the main consuming markets except China: Europe, North America, OECD Asia and India. Most of the additional exports from Africa and the Middle East are in the form of LNG. Russia and the Caspian/Central Asian countries collectively make up the other main exporting region. This region increases its exports to Europe by 14% and starts to export to China and OECD Asia. Russia's total net exports rise from 198 bcm in 2006 to 270 bcm in 2030. Apart from the Sakhalin project, all exports from Russia and the Caspian/Central Asia are via pipeline.

Worldwide, LNG flows have doubled in the past decade and now meet 7% of total world demand for natural gas. The share of LNG in total trade between *WEO* regions continues to grow steadily through the *Outlook* period, from 52% in 2006 to 69% in 2030 (Figure 4.7).[4] The volume of LNG trade reaches 340 bcm in 2015 and around 680 bcm in 2030 — up from only 201 bcm in 2006. LNG accounts for 80% of the increase in inter-regional trade.

---

4. The share of LNG in total international trade is significantly lower, as most intra-regional trade is by pipeline. LNG is generally the cheaper means of transport over long distances.

Figure 4.6 ● Main net inter-regional natural gas trade flows in the Reference Scenario, 2006 and 2030
(billion cubic metres per year)

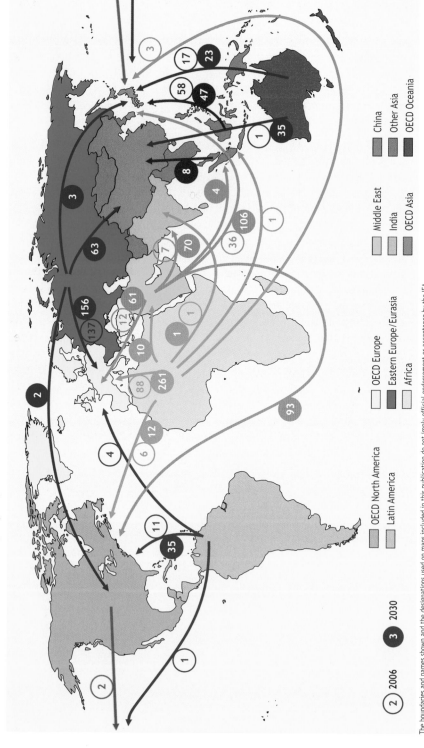

OECD North America
Latin America

OECD Europe
Eastern Europe/Eurasia
Africa

Middle East
India
OECD Asia

China
Other Asia
OECD Oceania

② 2006 ❸ 2030

The boundaries and names shown and the designations used on maps included in this publication do not imply official endorsement or acceptance by the IEA.

Figure 4.7 ● World inter-regional natural gas trade* by type in the Reference Scenario

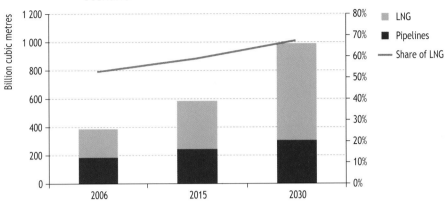

*Trade from major WEO regions, not including international trade within each region.

The pattern of world LNG trade is set to change markedly. Until now, LNG trade has been confined largely to the Asia-Pacific region, with gas sourced within Asia and in the Middle East. Although this market continues to expand, LNG demand from Atlantic Basin markets increases even more over the projection period, so that flows from Africa and the Middle East to Europe and North America quickly overtake those flowing eastwards. OPEC countries, especially in Africa and the Middle East, dominate the growth in supply of LNG through to 2030 (Figure 4.8). At the end of 2007, there were 24 liquefaction terminals in operation worldwide, with a total capacity of 256 bcm per year. An additional 146 bcm/year of capacity is under construction, which will take total capacity to around 400 bcm/year by 2012 (Table 4.4). Another 417 bcm/year of capacity is in the planning stage, though many of the planned projects have been on the table for several years. If only half of this planned capacity is built, total capacity would reach over 600 bcm/year.

Figure 4.8 ● Inter-regional exports* of LNG by source in the Reference Scenario

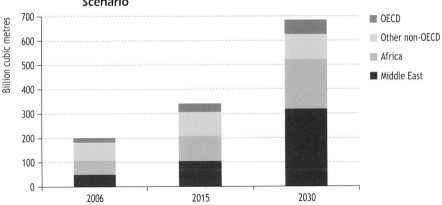

* Net exports of LNG from major *WEO* regions, not including international trade within each region.

Table 4.4 ● **Natural gas liquefaction capacity** (billion cubic metres per year)

	Capacity end-2007*	Capacity under construction**	Projected capacity in 2012***
OECD	23	18	41
Australia	21	13	34
Norway	-	5	5
United States	2	-	2
Non-OECD	233	128	361
Algeria	28	6	34
Angola	-	7	7
Brunei	10	-	10
Egypt	16	-	16
Equatorial Guinea	1	3	4
Indonesia	38	10	48
Libya	1	-	1
Malaysia	31	2	33
Nigeria	25	6	31
Oman	15	-	15
Peru	-	6	6
Qatar	40	65	105
Russia	-	13	13
Trinidad and Tobago	21	-	21
UAE	8	-	8
Yemen	-	9	9
World	256	146	402
OPEC	139	94	233

* Capacity at liquefaction facilities commissioned in 2007 is included in the column *under construction* as they are not yet operated at full capacity.
** Includes ramping up capacity at liquefaction facilities commissioned in 2007 and capacity additions by debottlenecking.
*** Planned and proposed capacity not under construction.
Source: IEA (2008).

CHAPTER 5

COAL MARKET OUTLOOK

H I G H L I G H T S

- Since 2000, global coal consumption has grown faster than any other fuel, despite higher prices, by 4.9% per year between 2000 and 2006. Most of this growth occurred in non-OECD countries. Coal demand is projected to grow by 2% per year over the *Outlook* period, faster than total energy demand. Non-OECD countries account for 97% of the increase in global coal demand over the *Outlook* period, with China alone accounting for two-thirds of the increase and India for a further 19%.

- To meet growing demand, coal production is projected to rise by almost 60% between 2006 and 2030. Around 90% of this increase comes from non-OECD countries. China almost doubles its output, while India's production more than doubles. Russian production jumps by nearly 75%, overtaking that of OECD Europe.

- Proven remaining reserves are more than adequate to meet the growth in coal use projected to 2030. The United States, Russia and China together account for around 60% of world reserves. However, large investments are needed in prospecting (to identify economically recoverable reserves) and in new mining projects.

- Global trade in coal between *WEO* regions rises from 613 million tonnes of coal equivalent today to around 980 Mtce by 2030. Despite a sharp decline in its coal exports, China remains a net exporter at present, but becomes a net importer in the near future, with net imports rising to 88 Mtce by 2030. India's imports grow by 7% per year to 220 Mtce, overtaking Europe to become the world's second-largest net importer after OECD Asia.

- Coal prices have kept pace with increases in oil and natural gas prices in recent years. The spot price of steam coal delivered to ports in Europe and Asia rose to above $100 per tonne in 2007 and continued to rise steeply in 2008. Coal-supply costs have also risen dramatically, due to sharp increases in the cost of materials, equipment, diesel, labour and shipping. Projected cumulative investment in coal-supply infrastructure totals about $730 billion between 2007 and 2030 (in year-2007 dollars), 91% of which is required for mines, and the rest for ports and shipping.

- Carbon dioxide emissions from coal combustion are set to rise from 11.7 gigatonnes in 2006 to 18.6 Gt in 2030, driving up coal's share of total emissions from 42% to 46%. Carbon capture and storage technology has the potential to reduce greatly CO_2 emissions from coal use in the long term, but has only a small impact before 2030 in the Reference Scenario.

Demand

Globally, coal consumption grew briskly between 2000 and 2006, at 4.9% per annum – a rate well above that of total energy demand, which grew by 2.6% per year. Coal demand grew faster even than the use of modern renewables, which rose at a rate of 3.1% per annum (Figure 5.1). Coal is the world's second most important fuel, after oil, accounting for 26% of global energy demand. Global coal demand reached 4 362 million tonnes of coal equivalent (Mtce) in 2006. The world's five largest coal consumers – China, the United States, India, Japan and Russia – account for 72% of total coal consumption. Between 2000 and 2006, coal demand in OECD member countries grew on average by just 0.6% per year, its share of global demand dropping to 37% in 2006, down from 48% in 2000. Preliminary 2007 data shows a renewed increase in OECD demand of 2.1% – twice the rate of growth of total primary energy.

Figure 5.1 ● **Incremental world primary energy demand by fuel, 2000-2006**

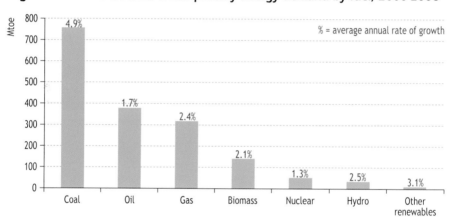

The pace of coal growth is projected to slow over the *Outlook* period, to 3.1% per year on average through to 2015 and 1.3% thereafter to 2030 (Table 5.1). Despite this slowdown as users switch to less carbon-intensive alternatives, coal demand grows faster than overall energy demand. Coal consumption increases by 32% by 2015 and by 61% from 2006 to 2030, reaching 7 011 Mtce. The projected increase in coal consumption to 2030, at 2 649 Mtce, is almost equal to the combined coal consumption of all non-OECD countries today. With this strong growth, the share of coal in total energy supply rises from 26% in 2006 to 29% by around 2025, before levelling off through to 2030 as the growth in other fuels, particularly for power generation, eats into coal's market share.

The detailed analysis in last year's *Outlook* of China and India, two of the world's largest coal consumers, led to a significant increase in projected global coal consumption compared with previous *WEO*s. In comparison, this year's *Outlook* projects lower coal demand in OECD countries, due to recent delays in the construction of coal-fired power plants in the European Union and the United States, for environmental reasons, and because of a shift to natural gas and renewable energy in power generation.

This is offset by slightly higher coal demand in non-OECD countries, driven by a greater emphasis there on economic factors and stronger growth in electricity demand. Overall, projected coal demand in 2030 is slightly lower than in last year's *Outlook*, in line with recent rises in coal prices and the higher coal-price assumptions for the *Outlook* period.

Table 5.1 ● World primary coal* demand in the Reference Scenario
(million tonnes of coal equivalent)

	1980	2000	2006	2015	2030	2006-2030**
OECD	1 373	1 566	1 627	1 728	1 703	0.2%
North America	571	832	839	895	959	0.6%
United States	*537*	*777*	*787*	*829*	*905*	*0.6%*
Europe	657	467	472	491	418	-0.5%
Pacific	145	267	316	342	326	0.1%
Japan	*85*	*140*	*161*	*164*	*153*	*-0.2%*
Non-OECD	1 181	1 714	2 735	4 019	5 308	2.8%
E. Europe/Eurasia	517	295	307	356	386	1.0%
Russia	*n.a.*	*158*	*152*	*201*	*233*	*1.8%*
Asia	572	1 249	2 238	3 415	4 634	3.1%
China	*446*	*899*	*1 734*	*2 712*	*3 487*	*3.0%*
India	*75*	*235*	*318*	*451*	*827*	*4.1%*
Middle East	2	12	13	20	36	4.4%
Africa	74	129	147	174	175	0.8%
Latin America	16	29	31	55	77	3.8%
World***	2 554	3 279	4 362	5 746	7 011	2.0%
European Union	*n.a.*	*459*	*463*	*460*	*372*	*-0.9%*

* Includes hard coal (steam and coking coal), brown coal (lignite) and peat. ** Average annual rate of growth. *** Includes stock changes.

The OECD is projected to see an initial minor increase in coal consumption, from 1 627 Mtce in 2006 to about 1 730 Mtce in 2015, then a drop to just over 1 700 Mtce in 2030. Growth over the projection period averages only 0.2% per year, reflecting policies aimed at reducing carbon-dioxide (CO_2) emissions. The share of coal in total OECD primary energy use drops from 21% today to 19% by 2030, driven mainly by a sharp drop in the share of coal as an input to power generation, from 41% today to 36% by 2030, as natural gas, biomass and waste, and other renewables all increase their share. In contrast with the situation in OECD Europe, the availability of low-cost, indigenous coal in OECD North America favours modest demand growth. The industrial sector in the OECD continues to become less coal intensive, with coal use actually falling by 0.6% per year over the projection period. Most coal use in OECD countries is still used in power generation: the sector's share of total coal use is the same in 2030 as in 2006, at 81%.

Switching from gas-fired to coal-fired power generation remains economically attractive in Russia, leading to a rise in coal demand of over 50% over the projection period, to reach 233 Mtce by 2030. China and India both see strong growth in coal consumption. China alone will account for two-thirds of the global increase in coal demand over 2006-2030, with India accounting for a further 19%. Non-OECD countries in total account for 97% of the global increase in coal demand, mainly to meet rising electricity demand. China consumes 40% of the world's coal today and this share rises to 50% by 2030. Its demand rises at an average rate of 3% per year. India sees the world's second-fastest coal growth of 4.1% per year over the projection period. Although insignificant in global terms, coal demand in the Middle East is forecast to grow strongly by 4.4% per year as coal-fired power generation allows oil and gas to be used for more valuable applications or exported.

Most of the coal consumed today worldwide is for power generation and this is not expected to change. This sector accounted for over two-thirds of global consumption in 2006, a share that remains broadly flat through to 2030 (Figure 5.2). Coal use in power generation increases at 2% per year. This overall average masks the intermediate trend of an increasing share of coal in power generation through to 2020, before falling back to 2006 levels by the end of the *Outlook* period. Industry remains the second largest consumer of coal, though growth in industrial coal use slows dramatically in the second half of the projection period, from 2.9% per year in 2006-2015 to 1.1% per year in 2015-2030. This is caused by the projected levelling out in non-OECD countries, particularly China, of iron production from blast furnaces, which is very coal intensive. Recycled scrap accounts for an increasing share of steel production, particularly from electric arc furnaces, indirectly creating demand for coal in the power sector. Coal use in the residential, services and agriculture sectors as a whole is projected to fall.

Figure 5.2 ● Sectoral shares in coal demand by region in the Reference Scenario

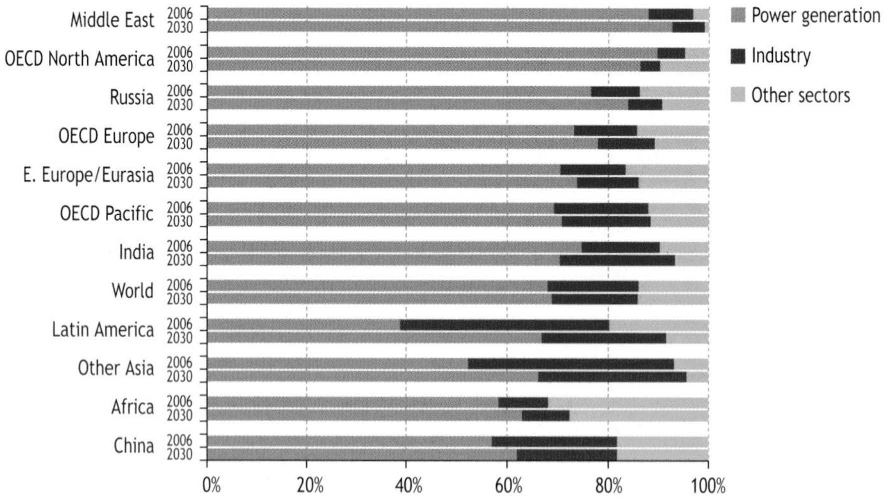

The extent and effectiveness of policy action to reduce the carbon intensity of energy consumption, in order to mitigate climate change, remains the principal uncertainty for future trends in coal demand. Another factor that greatly affects coal's prospects is the cost differential between coal and gas for power generation. While coal is the cheapest way to generate electricity in many regions (see Chapter 6), particularly where it is domestically available, the widespread introduction of a carbon value (such as under the EU Emissions Trading Scheme) could significantly reduce the attractiveness of investing in coal plants, resulting in lower coal demand than projected here.

In 2006, CO_2 emissions from coal use totalled 11.7 Gt, equal to 42% of global energy-related CO_2 emissions (Figure 5.3). This share is ten percentage points higher than the share of coal in total primary fossil-energy use, due to the higher carbon intensity of coal compared to oil and gas. Global CO_2 emissions from coal are projected to rise by 2% per year over the *Outlook* period, reaching 18.6 Gt in 2030. Coal's share of CO_2 emissions rises to 46%. The absolute increase in coal emissions is slightly larger than the level of current emissions from all fossil-fuel use in OECD North America. Coal use also results in emissions of other types of greenhouse gases (see Chapter 16), as well as other toxic and pollutant gases, which can have serious effects on the local environment and human health. Concerted efforts to combat climate change — including switching to lower-carbon fuels and the widespread deployment of carbon capture and storage technology — could lead to much lower emissions than projected in the Reference Scenario (see Part C).

Figure 5.3 ● **World energy-related CO_2 emissions by fuel in the Reference Scenario**

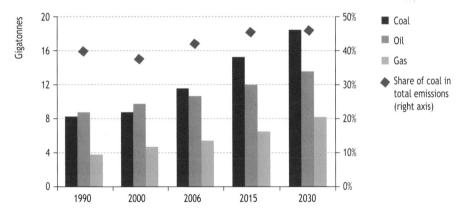

Reserves and production

Coal is the most abundant and geographically dispersed fossil fuel. Proven reserves at the end of 2005 were 847 billion tonnes (WEC, 2007). The United States, Russia and China combined account for 61% of proven reserves (Figure 5.4). Australia, the world's largest coal exporter, has 9% of the world's proven reserves, while the second-largest exporter, Indonesia, has less than 1%. Around half of the world's proven reserves are bituminous coal and anthracite, the grade of coal with the highest energy content. Current reserves are more than adequate to meet projected growth in coal demand through to 2030 in this *Outlook*. However the rapid increase in demand in recent years has seen the global reserves-to-production ratio fall sharply, from 188 years in 2002 to 144 years in 2005 (WEC, 2007 and 2004). This fall can be attributed to the lack of incentives to prove up reserves, rather than a lack of coal resources. Exploration activity is typically carried out by mining companies with short planning horizons, rather than by state-funded geological surveys. With no economic need to prove long-term reserves, the ratio of proven reserves to production is likely to fall further.

Figure 5.4 ● **Proven coal reserves in leading producing countries, 2005**

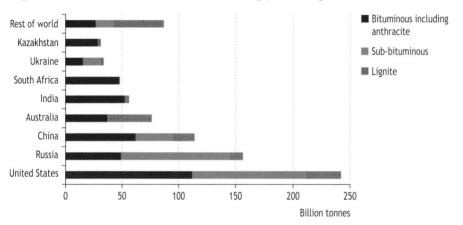

Source: WEC (2007).

Between 2006 and 2030, world coal production is projected to rise by almost 60%, or over 2 610 Mtce (Table 5.2). The United States remains far and away the biggest producer in the OECD, its production rising by 19% between 2006 and 2030. Production in OECD Europe continues its steady decline. The removal of subsidies, notably in Germany, leads to the closure of high-cost mines. Coal output in OECD Pacific is projected to grow at 1.6% per year, almost all of the growth occurring in Australia.

In order to meet domestic coal demand, coal production in non-OECD countries grows significantly, expanding at 2.5% per year. Non-OECD countries account for 91% of the increase in world coal production over the *Outlook* period. China almost doubles its current coal production, though growth slows after 2015. In India, output increases by a factor of 2.1. Robust growth in production in Russia sees it overtake OECD Europe around 2010 and continue to expand thereafter.

The projected growth in coal production and use in China and India in the Reference Scenario hinges on the way those countries address several challenges, including local and global environmental impacts (see Part C). At the local level, the water and other infrastructure demands of coal mining in arid regions of China's northwest will place enormous strains on a delicate ecosystem; in India, the loss of forests and villages, and the displacement of people, make any expansion of its largely open-cast coal industry politically challenging. The Chinese government has identified coal mining as a strategic sector and the industry is currently profitable with ample funds for investment. Proving coal reserves and installing the transport infrastructure to move large volumes of coal over ever-longer distances are practical challenges that China has already demonstrated it can surmount with the development of coalfields in northern Shanxi, Shaanxi and Inner Mongolia. The investment requirements, though large in absolute terms, are small relative to China's whole energy sector. In India, the projected expansion of output assumes that the coal sector, dominated by Coal India, becomes more competitive.

Table 5.2 ● World coal production in the Reference Scenario
(million tonnes of coal equivalent)

	1980	2000	2006	2015	2030	2006-2030*
OECD	1 378	1 384	1 446	1 566	1 684	0.6%
North America	672	835	878	962	1 048	0.7%
United States	*640*	*778*	*824*	*894*	*981*	*0.7%*
Europe	603	306	273	246	208	-1.1%
Pacific	104	243	294	358	427	1.6%
Oceania	*77*	*238*	*293*	*358*	*427*	*1.6%*
Non-OECD	1 196	1 792	2 950	4 180	5 327	2.5%
E. Europe/Eurasia	519	306	357	443	481	1.3%
Russia	*n.a.*	*167*	*205*	*295*	*354*	*2.3%*
Asia	568	1 250	2 316	3 367	4 435	2.7%
China	*444*	*928*	*1 763*	*2 647*	*3 399*	*2.8%*
India	*77*	*209*	*283*	*352*	*607*	*3.2%*
Middle East	1	1	1	2	3	2.2%
Africa	100	187	203	257	271	1.2%
Latin America	9	48	73	110	137	2.7%
World	2 574	3 176	4 396	5 746	7 011	2.0%
European Union	*n.a.*	*306*	*273*	*232*	*180*	*-1.7%*

* Average annual rate of growth.

Figure 5.5 ● World coal production by type in the Reference Scenario

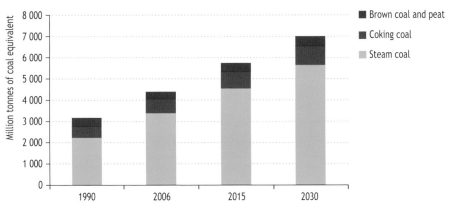

Steam coal, used mainly in power generation, will remain the main type of coal produced worldwide. Output is projected to grow by 2.2% per year and its share of total coal output to rise from 77% in 2006 to 81% in 2030, driven by power generation in Asia. The projected growth of coking coal, at 1.3% per year, is roughly in line with the 1.7% per year coal growth projected in the iron and steel sector (the main consumer) over the *Outlook* period. Use of brown coal and peat also grows slowly, by 1.2% per year.

Box 5.1 ● Alternative energy supplies: underground coal gasification and coal-mine methane[1]

Underground coal gasification (UCG) offers the prospect of bringing more of the world's coal resources to market, not as a solid fuel, but as a clean gaseous fuel. Conventional underground coal mining becomes more difficult and more expensive as mining depth increases. Mining below 1 000 metres is generally not economic. Yet 60% of China's coal resources, for example, lie below 1 000 metres (Pan, 2005). In addition, coal lying offshore is generally not practical to mine, but could be exploited using UCG. Estimates of the coal resources suitable for UCG vary widely, but a conservative estimate suggests that they could yield the equivalent of 146 trillion cubic metres (WEC, 2007) – similar in magnitude to the world's current conventional natural gas reserves.

UCG draws on technologies, developed in the oil and gas industry, to drill into coal seams, introduce an oxidant to combust some coal, and create a hot cavity in which more coal is gasified with steam. The resulting gas (mainly hydrogen and carbon monoxide, with a smaller quantity of methane) is drawn off to fuel a gas turbine for large-scale power generation or as feedstock for chemical or liquid fuel production. UCG was practised on a large scale in the former Soviet Union from the early 1960s, with one site in Uzbekistan remaining in production to supply a 400 MW power plant. Subsequent trials in Europe and the United States, and more recently in China, Australia and South Africa, have not yet led to any commercial UCG projects. But the prospects for UCG are tempting enough to have attracted some private investment, notably by Linc Energy of Australia.

The technical challenge with UCG is to control the hot cavity so that it moves along within the coal seam and converts as much coal as possible into useful fuel gas. Developments in directional drilling over the last decade mean that this challenge can be overcome and an efficient drilling pattern established to recover the maximum amount of energy. The seismic and hydrogeological skills needed to design UCG projects are to be found in the oil and gas industry, though they are in short supply. Environmental concerns relate mainly to the fate of hazardous by-products. In well-designed schemes, these are handled in surface treatment plants or remain immobile within the gasified coal seam. The prospects for UCG are improving, as energy prices rise and technology develops. But until it is demonstrated on a commercial scale, it remains only an interesting prospect: it is not assumed to have a material impact on energy supplies over the *Outlook* period.

---

1. Coalbed methane is discussed in Chapter 12.

Coal-mine methane (CMM) involves capturing methane released from the coal seam and surrounding strata before or during coal mining. In underground mines, ventilation must be sufficient to keep the methane concentration low enough to avoid explosions. Since the build up of methane can slow mining, it is common practice to pre-drill coal seams and draw off methane before mining. The purity of the captured methane, typically of the order of 35% to 75% (Creedy and Tilley, 2003), means it can be used on-site for power generation, sold for local use or purified for sale as pipeline gas, although the latter option is only viable for larger projects. It is also possible to collect methane from the "gob" areas left behind after coal extraction. The methane content of coal can reach 25 cubic metres per tonne, increasing with depth and coal rank. Although the average value might be around 5 m³ per tonne, methane release per tonne of coal mined is much larger, since more coal is disturbed during mining than is actually extracted.[2] An estimated 28 bcm of methane was released in 2005 during coal mining worldwide, or 6% of total global methane emissions from human activity (EPA, 2006).

In developing countries, CMM projects can benefit from Clean Development Mechanism credits under the Kyoto Protocol. This has led to a wave of new projects in China, where the value of avoided methane emissions can be significant. Methane has a global warming potential at least 21 times that of CO_2, so even simple projects that flare rather than vent methane can have a significant environmental and financial value.

Inter-regional trade[3]

Global trade in hard coal between *WEO* regions in 2006 amounted to 613 Mtce, or 14% of total hard coal output (Table 5.3). Trade is projected to grow at 2.0% per year through to 2030, reaching almost 980 Mtce. Trade grows quickest in the period until 2015, at 3.1% per year. Trade grows slightly slower than demand, as most coal continues to be consumed within the region in which it is produced. As a result, the share of global hard coal output that is traded between *WEO* regions remains flat at 14%.

Major demand centres in non-OECD countries, China and India, see rapid growth in imports over the projection period (Figure 5.6). China was a net exporter with a peak of 87 Mtce in 2001, but net exports have declined and China is expected to become a net importer in the near future. Total net imports are projected to reach 88 Mtce by 2030. India's net imports also grow strongly, by 7% per year, resulting in India overtaking OECD Europe to become the world's second-largest net importing region after OECD Asia. Europe's imports rise through to the middle of the projection period, but then fall back by 2030 to a level close to that of today, as coal demand for power generation drops.

Russia is currently the world's third-largest net-exporting country. At the higher prices assumed in this *Outlook* compared with last year, Russian exports are very competitive,

---

2. IPCC (2006) guidelines suggest a range of 10-25 m³ per tonne of coal mined from underground when reporting emissions, before accounting for any methane captured.
3. All the trade figures cited in this section exclude brown coal and peat.

despite the long rail-transport distances from the Kuzbass coalfields of central Russia to ports serving the Atlantic and Pacific markets. There are plans to expand port capacities, with exports to the Far East expected to grow quickly from a low base. Production can easily be expanded to meet both rising domestic demand and export growth.

Table 5.3 ● Net inter-regional hard coal* trade in the Reference Scenario
(million tonnes of coal equivalent)

	1980	2000	2006	2015	2030
OECD	- 19	- 122	- 203	- 162	- 19
North America	80	45	15	67	90
Europe	- 67	- 150	- 202	- 245	- 209
Pacific	- 32	- 18	- 16	16	101
Asia	*- 73*	*- 193*	*- 232*	*- 256*	*- 246*
Oceania	*41*	*175*	*216*	*271*	*347*
Non-OECD	16	119	212	162	19
E. Europe/Eurasia	0	13	52	88	96
Russia	*n.a.*	*10*	*53*	*94*	*120*
Asia	- 2	35	73	- 47	- 199
China	*5*	*58*	*34*	*- 65*	*- 88*
India	*0*	*- 20*	*- 42*	*- 98*	*- 220*
Middle East	- 1	- 10	- 12	- 18	- 34
Africa	26	60	56	83	95
Latin America	- 8	20	42	56	60
World	154	456	613	804	979
European Union	*n.a.*	*- 142*	*- 191*	*- 229*	*- 191*

* Steam and coking coal, and coke.
Note: Trade between *WEO* regions only. Positive figures denote exports; negative figures imports. Inter-regional trade between *WEO* regions differs from total international trade, which includes trade within regions.

Australia remains the world's largest coal-exporting country. Australia, with ample low-cost reserves, has the potential to meet much of the increased demand for internationally traded coal. Infrastructure development will be crucial to realise this potential. Recent announcements of port expansion projects in Queensland and New South Wales are a step in this direction and other projects are likely to follow, including those that boost rail capacity. Given their higher value, coking-coal exports will be particularly important, especially if infrastructure development does not keep pace because of local opposition.

Indonesia's coal sector has repeatedly shown its ability to meet rising international demand for steam coal. Production is expected to continue to increase with modest investment expected in rail infrastructure to access coal resources lying beyond what it is practical to transport with the current combination of trucks and river barges. Nonetheless, net exports grow only modestly, as rapid growth in domestic demand absorbs most of the projected increase in production.

Figure 5.6 ● **Net inter-regional hard coal* trade in the Reference Scenario**

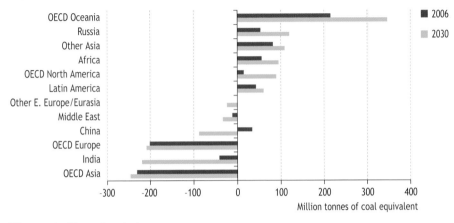

* Steam and coking coal, and coke.

OECD North America remains an important coal exporter throughout the projection period. US coal exports have dwindled since the 1990s, but are now growing strongly in response to very high coking-coal prices and European demand for steam coal. The United States is expected to remain a swing supplier in the international market, helping to meet demand and thus dampening prices. Western Canadian coking-coal producers are enjoying a revival and have a number of new projects planned. Long rail-transport distances from the coalfields to ports mean that Canadian coking coal is likely to remain less attractive economically than Australian coking coal.

Africa remains an important net exporter over the projection period. South Africa is expanding its principal coal-export terminal at Richards Bay to 91 million tonnes (Mt) and producers are optimistic about boosting exports, despite a recent period of limited growth and even decline. Fully utilising this capacity hinges on investment in rail infrastructure, to expand capacity and to extend the network to new producing regions. Domestic coal demand is buoyant with the re-opening by Eskom in 2008 of coal-fired power stations to meet strong electricity demand growth. Consequently, we project only a modest rise in exports to 2030. Mozambique becomes a coking-coal exporter by 2010 with the launch of a project by the Brazilian company Vale. This trend towards upstream coal-supply investment by coal users is also seen amongst some European power utilities. China has also followed this route, with its largest coal producer, Shenhua, now investing in Indonesia.

Colombia is well placed to supply customers in the Atlantic steam coal market, filling demand left unmet by South African producers. It appears likely that the major private coal companies will work closely with government to ensure that new rail infrastructure and roads are built to allow exports to grow to well over 100 Mt per year. Venezuela has the potential to export considerably more than its current 8 Mt per year. A deepwater port, linked to Vale's Socuy project, could see exports grow to 25 Mt. Latin American exports are projected to increase by over 40% between today and 2030.

China's net position in the international coal market is highly uncertain. It has the infrastructure and reserves to export hundreds of millions of tonnes per year and exports did grow sharply during the late 1990s, through to a peak in 2003 of 101 Mtce (net of imports, they peaked at 87 Mtce in 2001). The country is well placed to supply Japanese and South Korean markets. However, to ensure that strong domestic demand is met, the government has imposed export restrictions in the form of taxes and annual quotas on the four companies holding export licences. As China continues its market reforms, the domestic price of coal should better reflect its true value in the global market and allow China's balance of coal imports and exports to reach a natural level. Vietnam has been an important supplier to China in recent years, but rising domestic demand and limited resources will see this trend reverse over the *Outlook* period. Mongolia is already developing mines and infrastructure to meet demand from China. We expect Mongolian coal exports to China to increase rapidly.

Coal prices and supply costs

Coal prices have kept pace with the surge in international oil and gas prices (Figure 5.7), although on an energy basis, coal remains the cheapest fossil fuel. For example, the average price of steam coal imported into the European Union in 2007 was $3 per MBtu, compared with $8.80 per MBtu for imported high-sulphur fuel oil, $7.30 per MBtu for natural gas imported by pipeline and $6.50 per MBtu for liquefied natural gas. During 2007 and 2008, coal prices repeatedly reached historic highs. Asian and European marker prices doubled in 2007 to above $100 per tonne CIF and have risen further during the first half of 2008, to above $200 per tonne in Europe.

While oil and natural gas prices influence coal prices through contractual linkages and opportunities for fuel switching, notably in power generation, there are many other factors which have contributed to higher prices. Supply has been tight during a period of unprecedented demand growth. Unforeseen events in late 2007 and early 2008 have added to this tightness: flooding of mines in Australia, electricity shortages in South Africa and a temporary halt to all Chinese coal exports as the Chinese government sought to ensure that domestic demand was met. Strong demand for steel production and power generation has seen the world's bulk carrier shipping fleet struggle to meet demand to transport iron ore, coking coal, coke and steam coal. Shipping rates rose steeply during 2007 and have been very volatile during 2008, touching an historic high in May. However, freight rates may now fall as the number of new vessels earmarked for commissioning between 2008 and 2013 exceeds projected demand (Rogers, 2007). High coking-coal prices have had a knock-on impact on the price of good-quality steam coal, which can be used as a substitute in some cases. These factors, coupled with rising production costs, have contributed to higher prices in real terms. In fact, the increase has been bigger than that experienced during the mid-1970s to early 1980s, when coal prices last peaked.

Figure 5.7 ● Index of selected fuel prices

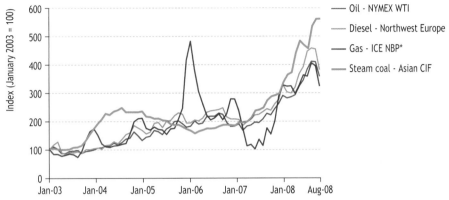

* InterContinental Exchange National Balancing Point.
Sources: Oil, diesel and gas: Platts. Steam coal: The McCloskey Coal Group Ltd, *McCloskey's Coal Report.*

The steam-coal supply-cost curve (Figure 5.8) has shifted up sharply in recent years. Although the curve shows average cash costs (excluding capital depreciation costs) for each of the major coal-exporting countries, individual mine costs can vary widely. For example, Australian exporters operate across a broad range, with costs as low as $20 to more than $50 per tonne. At the high end, steam coal may be sold as a by-product of high-cost deep mines producing coking coal as a primary product. Indonesia, South Africa, Venezuela and Colombia all export coal produced at an average cost of around $30 per tonne, but individual mines range from $20 to $40 per tonne.

The reasons for cost increases in recent years have included escalating material costs (including tyres, explosives, spare parts and steel products), rising labour costs, depletion of the lowest-cost reserves, increased stripping ratios at open-cast mines and, in some cases, longer transport distances (Meister, 2008). Labour costs have risen everywhere, by as little as 5% in the United States to more than 40% in South Africa between 2003 and 2008. Rising oil prices have had a particular impact on open-cast mining, as widely practiced in Australia, Colombia, Indonesia, India, South Africa, Venezuela and the United States. Diesel fuel is essential for open-cast mining, particularly operations that rely heavily on mechanical shovels for extraction and trucks for coal haulage. While open-cast mining costs are generally lower than deep mining, diesel consumption can account for 20% of the total cash cost at open-cast operations. The cost of diesel to mining companies has risen by 100% to 500% in most coal-exporting countries since 2003, with Indonesia at the upper end of this range. Some of the increase in non-OECD countries is due to the removal of subsidies on diesel.

Figure 5.8 ● Coal supply cash-cost curve for internationally traded steam
coal for 2007 and selected average FOB prices for 2007
and first-half 2008

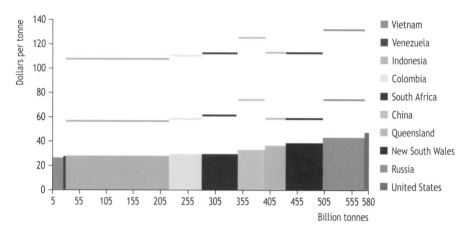

Note: Adjusted for 6 000 kcal/kg. The lower band for prices represents 2007 and the upper band
first-half 2008. FOB is free on board
Source: IEA Clean Coal Centre.

Despite these significant cost increases, a large margin remains between coal prices
and costs, which is attracting new investment into the industry and is stimulating
considerable merger and acquisition activity, notably BHP Billiton's proposed
acquisition of Rio Tinto. This should help overcome one of the factors behind tight
coal supply; but new capacity will take several years to come on line and, with
demand growth remaining strong, prices are expected to remain high in the short
term. Further concentration of the industry, particularly amongst suppliers of coking
coal, works against a competitive investment climate and explains why, while some
coal users are investing upstream, others are turning to competition regulators.

Coal investment

The overall investment needs of the coal industry were examined in detail in
WEO-2003, when it was estimated that $400 billion (year-2000 dollars) would
be required over the period 2001-2030. Since then, capital costs have increased
significantly, with rising steel prices and engineering costs. In *WEO-2003*, the
average mine was assumed to require investment of $34 per tonne of annual
capacity (in year-2000 dollars). In this *Outlook*, we assume a $50 per tonne capacity-
investment cost (in year-2007 dollars) over the projection period. Some projects
announced in 2008 involve much higher costs, of over $80 per tonne, but over the
Outlook period we expect real investment costs to moderate. These cost estimates
have been applied in order to calculate the total investment required in new and
replacement capacity over the *Outlook* period to meet demand in the Reference
Scenario. Investment of $1.20 per tonne produced (in year-2007 dollars) is added

in order to provide for maintaining existing mines during their economic lives, to replace machinery and equipment, and to access new reserves. Increases in port capacity and shipping investment costs have also been taken into account.

Figure 5.9 ● Structure of coal-supply costs for major exporting countries

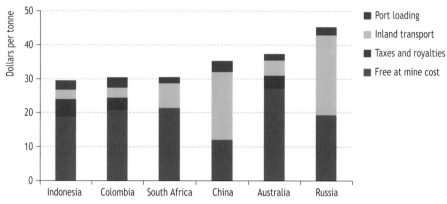

Note: Adjusted for 6 000 kcal/kg.
Source: IEA Clean Coal Centre.

In total, investment in the coal industry over 2007-2030 is now projected to amount to $728 billion (in year-2007 dollars). Some 91% of this is for mines, and the rest for ports and shipping (Figure 5.10). Investment in new capacity includes both surface and underground mine development, new machinery and infrastructure. Projected coal investment is 22% higher than in last year's *Outlook*, reflecting the recent surge in costs as described above. China alone accounts for 44% of this investment. Despite these upwards revisions, coal investment accounts for only 3% of global energy-supply investment requirements.

Figure 5.10 ● Cumulative investment in coal-supply infrastructure by region in the Reference Scenario, 2007-2030

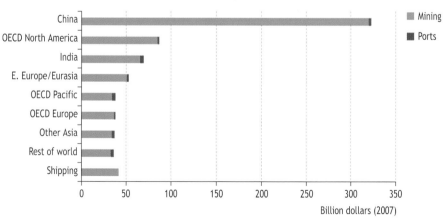

CHAPTER 6

POWER SECTOR OUTLOOK

H I G H L I G H T S

- World electricity demand in the Reference Scenario is projected to grow at an annual rate of 3.2% in the period 2006 to 2015, slowing to 2% per year on average in 2015-2030. This reflects a shift in the economies of non-OECD countries away from energy-intensive heavy manufacturing towards lighter industries and services, as well as saturation effects in the OECD and some emerging economies.

- Most of the projected growth in electricity demand occurs outside the OECD. In the OECD, electricity demand is projected to rise by just 1.1% per year on average, increasing by less than a third between 2006 and 2030. By contrast, demand in non-OECD countries grows by 146%, at an average annual rate of 3.8%.

- Globally, coal remains the main fuel for power generation throughout the period to 2030. Its share in total generation increases from 41% to 44%. Most of the growth in coal-fired generation occurs in non-OECD countries, which are projected to generate over two-thirds of all coal-fired electricity, compared with less than half now. The overall efficiency of coal-fired generation is projected to increase from 34% in 2006 to 36% in 2015 and to 38% in 2030. Plants with carbon capture and storage make only a minor contribution to generation in 2030. Stronger policies would need to be put in place — especially a more generally applied carbon constraint — for a significant amount of CCS capacity to be commissioned before 2030.

- The share of natural gas in the power-generation fuel mix falls, as a result of higher prices. Nuclear power loses market share, dropping from 15% in 2006 to 13% by 2015 and to 10% by 2030. The share of renewables rises considerably: it grows from 18% of total electricity generation in 2006 to 20% in 2015 and 23% by 2030.

- Total capacity additions — including replacement and expansion — amount to about 4 530 GW over the *Outlook* period, of which about 1 690 GW is added in the period to 2015. These additions average around 190 GW per year through to 2030 — about the same as over the past few years. Total cumulative investment in the power sector over the period 2007 to 2030 is projected at $13.6 trillion in year-2007 dollars, just over half of all energy-sector investment.

- The cost of building power stations has increased sharply over the past few years, notably in OECD countries, because of increases in the cost of materials, high energy prices, rising labour costs and supply-chain constraints. Coal and gas prices are assumed to remain high. As a result, the electricity produced in new plants that come on line in the next few years is increasingly costly, pushing up end-user electricity prices.

Electricity demand

Global demand for electricity grew by nearly a quarter between 2000 and 2006, with nearly three-quarters of the increase coming from non-OECD countries (Table 6.1).[1] Demand in OECD countries increased by just 10% during that period, while the increase in non-OECD countries exceeded 50%. China alone saw a doubling of its electricity demand, contributing over 40% of the total increase worldwide. Overall, world electricity demand grew by 3.6% per year in the period 2000 to 2006, following closely the growth in gross domestic product. Electricity demand is projected to grow at an annual rate of 3.2% in the period 2006 to 2015, slowing to 2% per year on average in the period 2015 to 2030. The projected slowdown in demand reflects a shift in the economies of non-OECD countries away from energy-intensive heavy manufacturing towards lighter industries and services, as well as efficiency improvements and saturation effects in the OECD and some emerging economies.

Table 6.1 ● **World final electricity consumption by region in the Reference Scenario** (TWh)

	1980	2000	2006	2015	2030	2006-2030*
OECD	4 740	8 251	9 035	10 177	11 843	1.1%
North America	2 386	4 144	4 413	4 870	5 774	1.1%
United States	*2 026*	*3 500*	*3 723*	*4 045*	*4 723*	*1.0%*
Europe	1 709	2 694	3 022	3 469	3 980	1.2%
Pacific	645	1 413	1 601	1 837	2 089	1.1%
Japan	*513*	*944*	*981*	*1 061*	*1 162*	*0.7%*
Non-OECD	2 059	4 390	6 630	10 580	16 298	3.8%
E. Europe/Eurasia	1 101	1 023	1 165	1 514	1 860	2.0%
Russia	*n.a.*	*609*	*682*	*912*	*1 081*	*1.9%*
Asia	477	2 023	3 669	6 574	10 589	4.5%
China	*259*	*1 081*	*2 358*	*4 554*	*6 958*	*4.6%*
India	*90*	*369*	*506*	*893*	*1 935*	*5.7%*
Middle East	75	371	539	793	1 353	3.9%
Africa	158	346	479	667	997	3.1%
Latin America	248	627	777	1 032	1 498	2.8%
Brazil	*119*	*319*	*375*	*478*	*651*	*2.3%*
World	6 799	12 641	15 665	20 757	28 141	2.5%
European Union	*n.a.*	*2 518*	*2 814*	*3 186*	*3 612*	*1.0%*

* Average annual rate of growth.

1. Electricity demand refers to end-use consumption of electricity in industry, buildings, transport and agriculture. It is less than electricity generation because of losses in transmission and the own use of electricity at power plants.

World demand for electricity grows from 15 665 TWh in 2006 to about 20 760 TWh in 2015 and to about 28 140 TWh in 2030. The level in 2030 is lower than projected in last year's *WEO*, mainly because of slower economic-growth expectations. Higher fossil-fuel prices in this year's *WEO* also depress demand for electricity, as they lead to higher electricity prices. But this effect is partially offset by the improved competitiveness of electricity in end uses against direct use of fossil fuels for space and water heating, as electricity prices rise less rapidly in percentage terms.

Non-OECD countries account for most of the projected growth in world electricity demand. In the OECD, electricity demand is projected to rise by just 1.1% per year on average, increasing by around 30% between 2006 and 2030. By contrast, demand in non-OECD countries grows by 146% over the same period, averaging 3.8% per year. Demand grows fastest in Asia (Figure 6.1). China's electricity demand has been growing at an average annual rate of 14% since 2000. This high rate is expected to slow over time. It drops to 7.6% per year in the period to 2015 and averages 4.6% per year over the entire *Outlook* period. The projected slowdown results primarily from a shift in the economic structure from heavy industry towards less energy-intensive lighter industry and services. Even at lower growth rates, China soon becomes the biggest electricity consumer in the world, leaving behind the United States and the European Union. In Russia, electricity demand is likely to grow at a rate slightly above that of the OECD; growth in demand there is driven by increased electrification in industry and rising household income, which boosts the use of appliances.

Figure 6.1 ● **Electricity demand growth rates by region in the Reference Scenario**

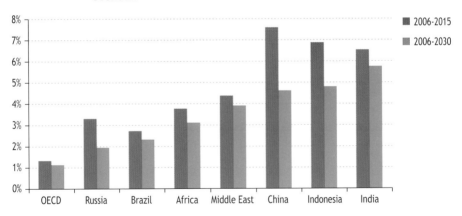

Globally, industrial demand for electricity grows faster than demand for electricity by households and the services sector, driven primarily by rapid industrialisation in non-OECD countries. In OECD countries, demand for electricity in industry grows at a modest 0.6% per year, reflecting a long-term trend toward lighter manufacturing.

Despite strong growth in electricity demand in non-OECD countries, a large number of people living there are not expected to have access to electricity even in 2030. India and Africa have the highest number of people in this category.[2] Per-capita electricity consumption in non-OECD countries doubles by 2030, rising to almost 2 400 kWh per person, but it is still well below the current OECD average of 7 641 kWh per person. There are large differences between countries: in China, per-capita electricity demand rises strongly, from 1 788 kWh in 2006 to 4 776 kWh by 2030, while in Africa, it rises modestly from 518 kWh now to 671 kWh (Figure 6.2).

Figure 6.2 ● **Per-capita electricity demand by selected region in the Reference Scenario**

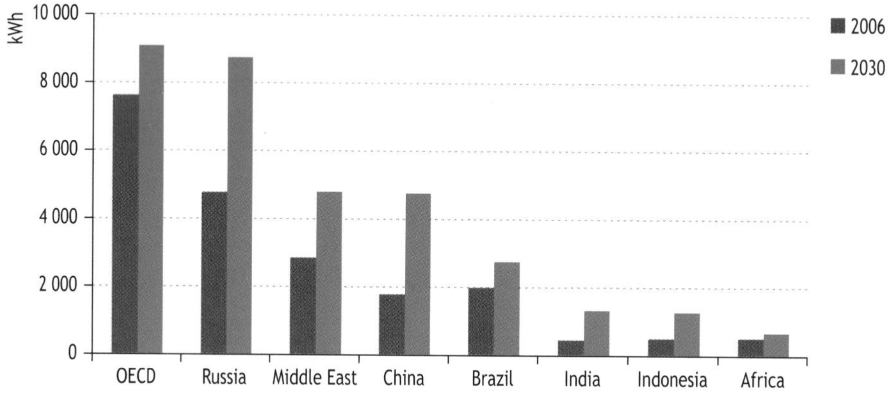

Electricity supply

Outlook for electricity generation

In the Reference Scenario, global electricity generation rises from 18 921 TWh in 2006 to 24 975 TWh by 2015 and to 33 265 TWh by 2030.[3] The largest increase is in non-OECD countries where electricity generation in aggregate matches that of the OECD countries soon after 2010 and by 2030 is almost 50% higher.

Coal remains the main fuel for power generation worldwide throughout the period to 2030. On the back of strong growth in non-OECD countries, its share increases from 41% to 44% (Figure 6.3). The share of natural gas in total generation falls slightly, as a result of higher prices. The share of oil drops to about 2% by 2030, as high oil prices make oil burning extremely expensive. Nuclear power, constrained by the assumption

---

2. Chapter 15 discusses electricity access in resource-rich countries of sub-Saharan Africa.

3. Electricity generation includes final consumption of electricity, network losses and own use of electricity at power plants. Electricity generation figures exceed those for demand (final consumption) because of network losses and own use of electricity at power plants.

of unchanged government policies, also loses market share, which drops from 15% in 2006 to 13% by 2015 and further to 10% by 2030, as nuclear power capacity does not increase as rapidly as demand for electricity. Nuclear electricity generation increases from 2 793 TWh in 2006 to almost 3 460 TWh in 2030. The share of renewables rises considerably, from 18% in 2006 to 20% in 2015 and 23% in 2030.

Figure 6.3 ● World electricity generation by fuel in the Reference Scenario

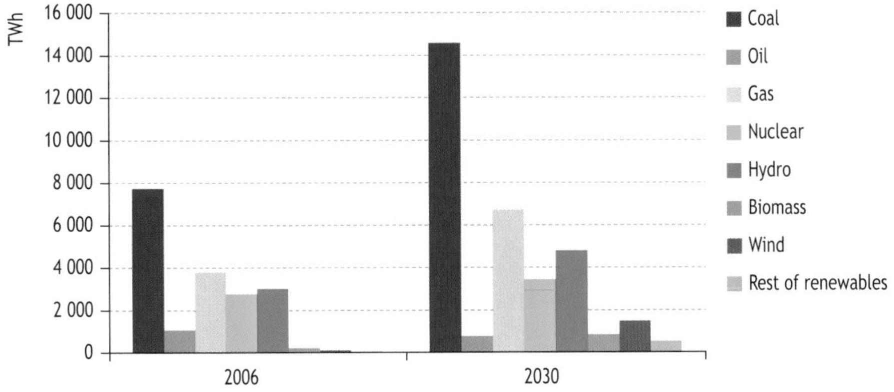

Most electricity is projected to continue to come from centralised power stations, although there is a growing trend towards greater use of distributed generation: as increasing demand for reliable power supply and government policies to encourage the use of combined heat and power (CHP) and renewable energy encourage this solution. Good opportunities exist to provide heat and power for remote rural and urban communities. The use of CHP is projected to increase, based on biomass, natural gas and coal. Generating electricity and heat simultaneously offers an important opportunity to increase the overall efficiency of electricity and heat generation, and to reduce the environmental footprint. Providing for heat capture entails only a modest increase in investment costs and a slight loss of efficiency in electricity generation. Hence, CHP can be very profitable. The challenge is to match the heat supply with the demands of the industrial process. For district-heating systems, demand for heat can be spread across larger areas, but this requires substantial investment in heat-distribution infrastructure.

Over 600 GW of power-generation capacity is currently under construction around the world, which is expected to be operational before 2015. Three-quarters of this new capacity is being built outside the OECD (Figure 6.4). About 200 GW is reported to be under construction in China, although this figure may be largely underestimated. These data provide useful insights into the future patterns of supply. Large amounts of coal-fired and hydropower capacity are set to come on line over the next few years. A smaller increase in nuclear power is in prospect. Gas-fired plants — combined-cycle gas turbines (CCGTs) and open-cycle turbines (OCTs) — which have short construction times (two to three years for a CCGT and one to two years for an OCT) — and land-based wind turbines, which have even shorter construction times (one to two years) may change the picture suggested by Figure 6.4 by 2015. In the OECD, there is more gas-fired capacity under construction than coal. Most of this is being built in Europe, because of tightening CO_2 regulations and because gas is valued for its flexibility.

Figure 6.4 ● Power-generation capacity under construction worldwide

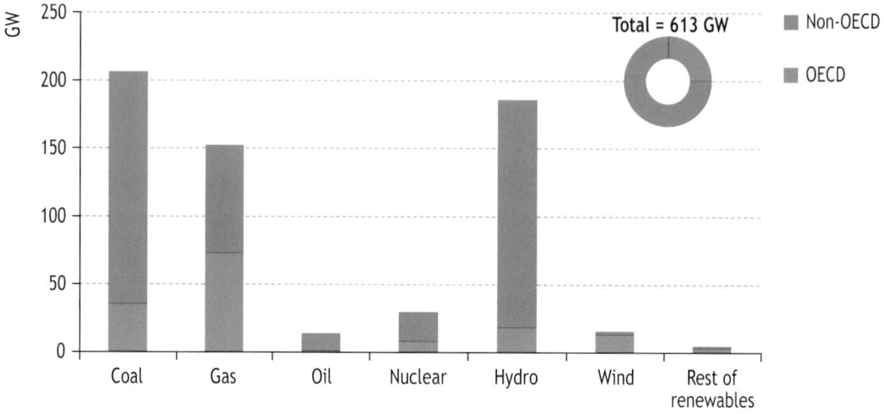

Note: Includes power plants considered as under construction in 2007.
Source: Platt's World Electric Power Plants Database, January 2008 version.

Trends in coal-fired generation

Electricity generation from coal-fired power plants worldwide reached 7 756 TWh in 2006, over 40% of the total. In recent years, most of the growth in coal-fired generation has occurred in non-OECD countries, notably in China, where it more than doubled between 2000 and 2006. Since the beginning of market liberalisation in the 1990s, most new capacity in OECD has been gas-fired, although a large amount of coal-fired capacity was added in the OECD Pacific region. New coal-fired plants with a capacity of 28 GW have come on line since 2000; 18 GW of this capacity was in OECD Pacific, 6 GW in OECD Europe and 4 GW in OECD North America. Sharp increases in gas prices have made the economics of new coal-fired power plants more favourable and many power companies have announced plans to build additional coal-fired capacity. Difficulties have arisen in many cases, however, in moving from the planning phase to construction and some projects have been abandoned, particularly in the United States and Europe, because of local opposition driven by environmental concerns. Some projects have also been abandoned because of rising construction costs and because of regulatory uncertainty about climate policies. A total of 31 GW is now under construction in OECD countries (Figure 6.5).

Figure 6.5 ● Coal-fired capacity under construction in OECD countries

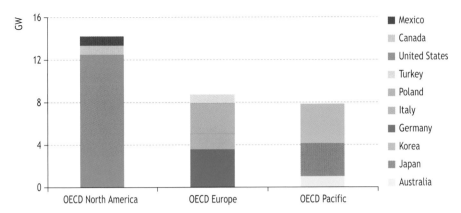

Note: Includes power plants considered as under construction in 2007.
Source: Platt's World Electric Power Plants Database, January 2008 version.

Globally, coal-based electricity is projected to rise to 11 100 TWh by 2015 and to almost 14 600 TWh by 2030, giving rise to significant increases in associated CO_2 emissions (see Chapter 16). Most of the growth takes place in non-OECD countries, which generate over two-thirds of all coal-fired electricity in 2030, compared with less than half now. Coal's share of total electricity generation increases from 41% in 2006 to 44% in 2015 and remains broadly at this level through to 2030. More than half of coal-fired capacity now under construction is based on subcritical technology, while the remainder is mainly supercritical. Over the *Outlook* period, supercritical technology is expected to become the norm, first in the OECD. Ultrasupercritical technology is projected to become more widespread in the OECD after 2020.

Integrated gasification combined-cycle (IGCC) technology is expected to become more widespread after 2020. A small number of plants currently operating were initially built with public funding for demonstration purposes, with the best one achieving 42% electric efficiency (IEA, 2008a). There are plans to build IGCC plants in a number of countries, including the United States, the United Kingdom, Australia, Canada, Germany, the Netherlands, Japan, Poland, Czech Republic, Indonesia, India and China, though not all of them are expected to go ahead. The United States has the largest number of projects but the announced construction costs are high. Under the assumption that construction costs fall, improving the economics of IGCC, a total of 105 GW is projected to be built by 2030.

The average efficiency of coal-fired generation is projected to increase from 34% in 2006 to 36% in 2015 and to 38% in 2030 (Figure 6.6). In the OECD, efficiency increases from 37% to 41%. Although electricity demand there does not increase much, there is a significant opportunity to improve efficiency as old coal-fired power plants are retired. In non-OECD countries, efficiency improves from 31% to 37% because new coal-fired power plants built to meet rapidly growing electricity demand are expected to be far more efficient than existing ones.

Figure 6.6 ● Efficiency improvements in coal-fired generation in the
Reference Scenario

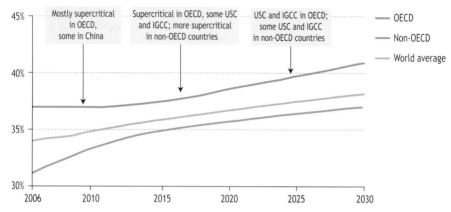

Note: Average efficiency of installed coal-fired capacity. USC refers to ultrasupercritical steam conditions.
IGCC refers to integrated gasification combined cycle.

Trends in gas-fired generation

World gas-fired generation reached 3 807 TWh in 2006, 20% of total electricity
generation. While it is expected to continue to expand in the future, rising to
4 723 TWh in 2015 and to 6 404 TWh in 2030, growth will be constrained by high gas
prices (see Chapter 1). Most of the growth is projected to occur in non-OECD countries,
with the biggest increase in the Middle East. Gas-fired generation is expected to
continue to grow in the OECD, although much more slowly than over the past decade.
Although high natural gas prices are expected to constrain demand for new gas-fired
generation, it still has advantages that make it attractive to investors, notably lower
capital costs and a shorter construction time than most other technologies. Moreover,
the operating flexibility of these plants makes them a very valuable component of the
portfolio of a power company, while the usually high correlation between power and
gas prices in liberalised markets reduces the extent of gas and power price risks.

Gas-fired power plants are expected to be used increasingly for mid-merit order and
peak load, replacing oil to some extent. This implies a need for a large increase in
gas storage capacity. The projected large increase in power from variable renewable
energy sources will require flexible back-up capacity: CCGTs and OCTs are expected to
be used for this purpose, but high gas prices will make back-up power more expensive.[4]
Gas turbines are also expected to be used in decentralised electricity generation. Fuel
cells using hydrogen from reformed natural gas are expected to emerge as a new source
of distributed power after 2020, producing less than 1% of total electricity output in
2030.

---

4. The need to combine variable renewables with gas also has implications for CO_2 emissions.

Trends in oil-fired generation

About 6% of total electricity generation worldwide is based on oil products. This share has been declining slowly, due to high oil prices. In the OECD, the share of oil in total electricity generation was 4% in 2006; but it is much higher in a number of countries, notably in Mexico (22%), Greece (16%), Italy (15%), Japan (11%), Portugal (11%), Ireland (10%), Spain (8%) and South Korea (6%). In most other countries, it is less than 2%. The main oil product used for power generation in the OECD is fuel oil, which accounts for 64% of total oil-fired generation. In 2006, oil-fired generation in the OECD dropped sharply, by about 20%, in response to rising oil prices. In the long run, oil-fired generation in the OECD is projected to fall further, accounting for 1% of total generation by 2030. Use of heavy oil products is expected to fall particularly sharply, the main oil product still in use in 2030 being diesel oil, used for peaking and plant start up and in isolated areas. In non-OECD countries, oil-based electricity generation remains flat in absolute terms, representing a fall in oil's share in total generation. As in the OECD, diesel oil is expected to become the main oil product. Oil-producing countries, notably in the Middle East, are projected to continue to reduce their reliance on oil, so that more can be available for export.

Trends in nuclear power

World nuclear capacity reached 368 GW in 2006. This rose to 372 GW in 2007. About 309 GW of this capacity was in OECD countries. Between 2000 and 2007, about 31 GW of new capacity were added worldwide.[5] In the OECD, new reactors started commercial operation in the Czech Republic, France, Japan, Slovakia and South Korea. Outside the OECD, new reactors were brought on line in Brazil, China, India, Pakistan, Romania, Russia and Ukraine. A total of 8 GW was shut down during the same period: in Bulgaria, Lithuania, Slovakia and Ukraine, following agreements with the European Union (4 GW); in the United Kingdom (16 reactors totalling 2 GW), Spain (the 141-MW Jose Cabrera reactor) and Russia (a 5-MW reactor) as plants reached the end of their operating lives; in Japan, the prototype 148-MW Fugen reactor, because of high operating costs; and in Sweden (a second reactor at the Barseback plant, following one that was shut down in 1999) and Germany (two reactors with a total capacity of 980 MW) in implementation of policies to phase out nuclear power.[6]

Over the past few years, a large number of countries have expressed renewed interest in building nuclear power plants, driven by concerns over energy security, surging fossil-fuel prices and rising CO_2 emissions. Few governments, however, have taken concrete steps to build new reactors, beyond those that have had active nuclear power construction programmes in place for a long time.

A total of 31 GW of nuclear capacity is now under construction in different parts of the world (Table 6.2). The construction of some of these reactors started a number of years ago and was subsequently halted, mainly for economic reasons. In Argentina, the

---

5. This increase in capacity includes uprates (through upgrades of existing reactors).
6. Data are taken from the IAEA's PRIS database, available at www.iaea.org/programmes/a2/.

government recently decided to complete the construction of a second reactor at the Atucha nuclear power plant following energy shortages; construction originally started in 1981 but had been put on hold. In Bulgaria, the government now plans to complete two reactors at the Belene plant, the construction of which had originally started in 1987. In Russia, work has been restarted on three of the seven reactors under construction in the 1980s. In Ukraine, there are plans to complete two unfinished reactors, construction of which started in the mid 1980s. In the United States, the Tennessee Valley Authority plans to complete a second reactor at the Watts Bar plant, on which construction started in 1972. In Iran, one reactor at the Bushehr power plant, which had been abandoned in the 1970s, is now almost complete. In total, these reactors account for a third of the total nuclear capacity under construction.

Table 6.2 ● Nuclear power plants under construction as of end-August 2008

Country	Number of reactors	Capacity (MW)
Argentina	1	692
Bulgaria	2	1 906
China	6	5 220
Chinese Taipei	2	2 600
Finland	1	1 600
France	1	1 600
India	6	2 910
Iran	1	915
Japan	2	2 166
Korea	3	2 880
Pakistan	1	300
Russia	7	4 724
Ukraine	2	1 900
United States	1	1 165
Total	**36**	**30 578**

Note: Installed capacity is net (electricity only).
Source: IAEA PRIS Database (available at www.iaea.org)

Most of the nuclear capacity now under construction is in the Asia-Pacific region. China has the largest amount of capacity under construction in the world. India, Japan and South Korea are planning significant increases in their nuclear power capacity. World nuclear capacity is projected to rise to 397 GW by 2015 and to 433 GW by 2030. Installed capacity in 2030 is 18 GW higher than projected in *WEO-2007* because the nuclear gain from assumed higher fossil-fuel prices offsets the effect of lower global demand for electricity. Most of the increase is in Asia, where China, India, Japan and South Korea are projected to nearly double their installed nuclear capacity, from 75 GW to 142 GW. Prospects for nuclear power have also picked up in the United States. Since 2002, a number of policies have been put in place to address investor concerns and some 17 companies and consortia are actively pursuing licenses for more than 30 nuclear power plants. In the Reference Scenario, installed nuclear capacity in the United States increases from 100 GW to 115 GW. In the European Union, nuclear capacity drops from 131 GW in 2006 to 89 GW in 2030, mainly as a result of phase-out policies in Germany, Belgium and Sweden.

Trends in renewable energy

Higher fossil-fuel prices and increasing concerns over energy security and climate change are expected to encourage the development of renewable energy for electricity production in many parts of the world, particularly where incentives are already in place. Electricity generated from renewable energy sources worldwide amounted to 3 470 TWh in 2006, or 18% of total output. In the Reference Scenario, it rises to 4 970 TWh in 2015 and to over 7 700 TWh in 2030, 23% of total electricity production. Trends in renewable energy are discussed in more detail in Chapter 7.

Trends in CO_2 capture and storage

Carbon capture and storage (CCS) is a promising technology for carbon abatement, even though it has not yet been applied to large-scale power generation. Widespread deployment of CCS depends on developments in legal and regulatory frameworks, financing mechanisms, international co-operation, technological advances and public awareness. Recommendations on how to accelerate the deployment of CCS were developed in 2007 under a joint International Energy Agency-Carbon Sequestration Leadership Forum (IEA-CSLF) initiative, involving wide consultation with interested parties. These recommendations include launching 20 full-scale CCS projects by 2010 and making CCS eligible for funds from the Clean Development Mechanism (IEA-CSLF, 2007). Market mechanisms alone will not be sufficient to achieve the demonstration programme on the scale required. Another challenge is financing the necessary CO_2 transport infrastructure.

Recent legal and regulatory developments include amendments to the London Protocol and the OSPAR (Oslo-Paris) Convention to allow for storage of CO_2 in formations below the international waters that are covered by those treaties. The European Commission's climate change and renewable energy package, released in January 2008, includes a new directive on the EU Emissions Trading Scheme (ETS), which addresses CCS among other matters. It proposes new legislation to encourage CO_2 storage. Also, under the European Union's Zero Emissions Technology Platform, the FLAGSHIP programme will provide guidance on criteria for selecting 10 to 12 demonstration projects covering all the technology blocks of CCS (power plant and capture, and CO_2 transport and storage) for evaluation by the European Commission.[7]

In 2008, the StatoilHydro Snohvit project started injecting CO_2 into a 2 600-metre deep formation, becoming the world's fourth large-scale CCS project. In November 2007, the United Kingdom announced a national competition for government co-funding of a

---

7. The Zero Emissions Technology Platform is a joint initiative between European industry, scientists and NGOs with support from the European Union to accelerate the development of low-carbon power-generation technologies and, in particular, CCS.

post-combustion CCS project, covering as much as 100% of the additional capital and operating costs involved. Several projects have been announced, varying in scale from industrial prototypes to 1 200 MW scale, with target dates between 2010 and 2017 (Table 6.3).

Table 6.3 ● Recent CCS proposals and developments

Company/project	Fuel	Technology	Output	Cost	Start date
BP-Rio Tinto DF4, Abu Dhabi	Gas	NGCC + EOR + Storage in saline aquifer	420 MW		2013
China Huaneng Group (CHNG), GreenGen, China	Coal	IGCC + shift + precombustion	100 MW		2015
E.ON Killingholme, Lincolnshire, UK	Coal	IGCC+shift+precombustion (may be capture ready)	450 MW	£1 bn	2011
Ferrybridge, Scottish and Southern Energy, UK	Coal	PC (supercritical retrofit) + post-combustion capture, retrofit GBP 250 m, capture GBP 100 m	500 MW		2011
E.ON Kingsnorth Kent, UK	Coal	Supercritical retrofit	2 × 800 MW	£1 bn	2012
FutureGen, United States	Coal	IGCC + shift + precombustion	275 MW	$1.5 bn	2012-2017 (under restructuring)
Hypogen, EU	Coal	Pre-combustion + H_2	Approx. 250 MW	€1.3 bn	2014-2016
GE / Polish utility	Coal	IGCC + shift + precombustion	1 000 MW		
Karstø, Norway	Natural gas	NGCC + post-combustion amine, potential storage in the oilfield - EOR	384 MW		2012 (capture)
Mongstad, Norway	Natural gas	CHP with post-combustion CCS Phase 1: Pilot capture Phase 2: Full-scale transport + storage	280 MW 350 MWh		Phase 1: 2010 Phase 2: 2014
Nuon, Eemshaven, Netherlands	Coal/biomass /natural gas	IGCC with option to capture	1 200 MW		After 2011 (decision in 2009)
Powerfuel, Hatfield Colliery, UK	Coal	IGCC + shift + precombustion	Approx. 900 MW		2010
VattenFall, Jänschwalde, Germany	Lignite	New oxyfuel boiler, existing boiler to be retrofitted with post-combustion capture	2 × 250 MW		2015
Stanwell, Queensland, Australia	Coal	IGCC + shift + precombustion, storage in saline reservoir	100 MW		2012

Notes: *Shift* is an essential reaction in IGCC technology using CO_2 capture, involving a catalyst that converts carbon monoxide to carbon dioxide through a reaction with water. *Capture ready* refers to whether an existing plant can be readily converted to a CCS plant. This includes a number of conditions, such as space availability for additional capture equipment and proximity to a CO_2 storage site. *Amine solvents* are used in post-combustion capture.

Source: IEA (2008b).

In the Reference Scenario, CCS makes only a minor contribution. Stronger policies will need to be put in place — especially a widely applicable carbon constraint — if a significant amount of CCS capacity is to be commissioned before 2030 (see Part C).

New capacity and investment needs in infrastructure

Total installed power-generation capacity worldwide in the Reference Scenario is projected to rise from 4 344 GW in 2006 to 5 697 GW in 2015 and to 7 484 GW in 2030. Total gross capacity additions amount to 4 528 GW over the period, with 1 691 GW installed by 2015.[8] This is an average of 190 GW of new capacity per year through to 2030 — about the same as over the past few years.

Cumulative global power-sector investment over 2007-2030, including generation, transmission and distribution, is $13.6 trillion (in year-2007 dollars), just over half of all energy-sector investment. Some $6.8 trillion of investment is required in generation, while transmission and distribution networks together need $6.8 trillion, of which two-thirds goes to distribution. The largest investment requirements, exceeding $3 trillion, arise in China. Investment needs are also very large in OECD North America and Europe. Table 6.4 summarises the capacity additions and investment needs by region over the *Outlook* period.

Table 6.4 ● Projected capacity additions and investment needs in power infrastructure in the Reference Scenario

	Investment, 2007-2015 ($2007, billion)				Investment, 2016-2030 ($2007, billion)			
	Capacity additions	Power generation	Transmission	Distribution	Capacity additions	Power generation	Transmission	Distribution
	(GW)				(GW)			
OECD	514	982	278	656	1 107	2 467	403	922
North America	215	379	121	260	480	1 136	238	512
Europe	221	457	93	281	465	1 048	94	286
Pacific	78	146	65	115	163	283	71	124
Non-OECD	1 177	1 215	589	1 285	1 730	2 177	837	1 793
E. Europe/ Eurasia	137	180	55	183	159	274	51	173
Asia	781	794	433	894	1 170	1 379	596	1 231
China	*574*	*521*	*296*	*612*	*718*	*753*	*299*	*618*
Middle East	78	59	32	67	160	135	71	146
Africa	59	59	28	58	91	159	47	97
Latin America	121	123	41	84	149	230	72	148
World	1 691	2 197	867	1 941	2 837	4 644	1 239	2 716

8. As Figure 6.4 shows, 613 GW of new capacity are now under construction.

Electricity generating costs

Trends in construction costs

There have recently been sharp increases in construction costs of new power plants, particularly in OECD countries. For non-OECD countries, fewer cost data are available, making it difficult to draw firm conclusions on the extent of the increases experienced there. The sharpest increases have been in the United States, where the construction cost of a new supercritical coal plant has doubled over a few years. Companies planning to build nuclear power plants there have announced construction costs at least 50% higher than previously expected. Similar trends, although somewhat less pronounced, are evident in other OECD countries. Table 6.5 provides an overview of these trends as seen by a power plant manufacturer. The main causes of higher costs are as follows:

- *Increases in the cost of materials:* The prices of metals typically used in power plants (iron, steel, aluminium, copper) have substantially increased since 2003/2004 (Figure 6.7) and the prices of some special steels used in power plant manufacturing have increased even faster than the average steel price shown in the chart. Cement prices are also reported to have gone up. These material costs have increased primarily because of high global demand for commodities and manufactured goods, higher production and transportation costs (in part owing to high fuel prices), and a weakening US dollar (The Brattle Group, 2007).

Figure 6.7 • Commodity price indices

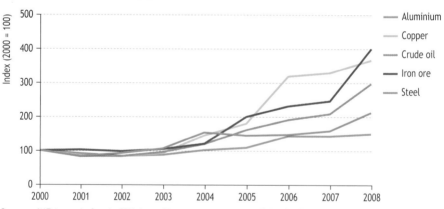

Sources: IMF (www.imf.org); CRU (cruonline.crugroup.com); and IEA databases.

- *Increase in energy costs:* High energy prices affect the manufacturing and transportation cost of power plant equipment and components.
- *Increase in demand:* As their reserve margins are shrinking, OECD countries are entering a new investment cycle. Outside the OECD, strong growth in electricity demand is pushing up orders for new plant.
- *Tight manufacturing capacity:* Reportedly, manufacturers of power plants are often not able to fulfil orders quickly because of a lack of capacity and a shortage of

skilled engineers. Steam boilers, gas turbines, wind turbines and photovoltaic panels are all in short supply. Many manufacturers claim that their order books are full for the next three to five years. At present, the nuclear industry faces bottlenecks in the construction of large steel forgings (an essential component of reactors).

■ *Increases in labour costs:* A shortage of engineering, procurement and construction contractors in some regions and rising labour costs, particularly in non-OECD countries, is pushing up total project costs.

Table 6.5 ● Factors influencing power plant pricing

	Price trend since 2003
Civil engineering	
Construction materials (cement, steel, etc.)	↗
Labour costs (local, international)	↗
Power plant	
Main mechanical components (boiler, generator, turbine)	↑ (approx. + 270%)
Other mechanical equipment (*e.g.* piping)	↑ (+150%)
Electrical assembly and wiring: – cables – transformers	↑ (+150%) (+60%-90%)
Engineering and plant start up	↗
Additional factors	
Transportation and logistic costs	↗
Power plant demand	↗
Cost of capital and inflation	→

Note: A vertical arrow denotes large increases, a slanted arrow moderate increases, and a flat arrow no increase.
Source: Siemens AG.

Cost and efficiency assumptions

The power-plant construction-cost assumptions used in this *Outlook* have been substantially revised upwards (following a revision in *WEO-2006*) to take account of recent trends and industry expectations.[9] Because the uncertainties surrounding future construction costs are so large, our newly revised costs for most types of power plants are generally assumed to apply from the onset and remain constant through to 2030. There are, however, some qualifications to this. Some cost reductions are assumed for new technologies, notably for IGCC and renewables. The construction costs of coal-fired power plants in China now are several times lower than in OECD countries. They are assumed to increase over time, reflecting increases in labour costs and more stringent environmental requirements, though they remain substantially lower than in the OECD even in 2030. China's emergence as a major supplier of coal-fired

---

9. The cost and efficiency assumptions by technology used in this *WEO* are available at www.worldenergyoutlook.org.

power plants to the rest of Asia and markets further afield (such as Russia and Africa) competing with well-established manufacturers in international markets, could drive down construction costs for all regions.

Fossil-fuel prices have soared in recent years and are assumed to remain high. Higher plant construction and fuel-input costs result in much higher levelised generation costs over the projection period than in past *WEOs*. The electricity produced in new plants expected to come on line in the next few years will cost much more in OECD countries than was projected in *WEO-2006*, driving up end-use electricity prices. Generating costs in non-OECD countries are also much higher, but how much final prices are affected will depend on what subsidy-reform policies their governments adopt.

As illustrated in Figure 6.8, by comparison with coal, nuclear or wind generation, gas-fired generation is by far the most expensive in 2015 and 2030 in the United States, the European Union, China and India on the assumption of continuity of present policies.[10]

Figure 6.8 ● **Electricity generating costs in selected regions**

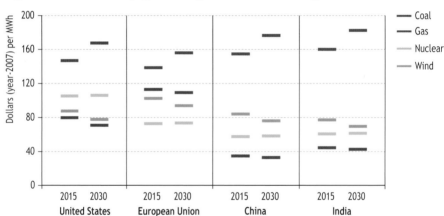

Note: Costs include a carbon value of $30 per tonne of CO_2 in the European Union. In 2015, coal refers to supercritical steam. In 2030, coal refers to IGCC for the United States, ultrasupercritical steam for Europe and China, and supercritical steam for India. Gas refers to CCGT.

Source: IEA analysis.

In the European Union, an assumed carbon value of $30 per tonne of CO_2 adds around $30 per MWh to the generating cost of coal-fired plant and around $15 per MWh to the cost of power from CCGT plants.[11] As a result, the difference in total cost between the two types of generation is small. Coal is the cheapest way to generate electricity

---

10. Wholesale power prices in European and North American markets are already in the same order of magnitude as the costs calculated here.

11. A value of $30 per tonne CO_2 is assumed for ETS over the *Outlook* period. This is equal to €22 per tonne CO_2, assuming an exchange rate of 0.73 euros per dollar (average value in 2007).

in the absence of a carbon value. In the United States, coal is accordingly the cheapest way to produce electricity, followed by wind power. Nuclear power in the United States is more expensive than coal and wind, but expectations about carbon constraints and a large need for firm base-load power are expected to support the development of new nuclear power stations. In China, coal is by far the cheapest way to produce electricity because of low construction costs and cheap fuel. Coal is also the cheapest way to generate electricity in India (as in many other non-OECD countries), though it is more expensive than in China.[12] Generally, gas-fired generation becomes even more expensive over time. Coal-based generating costs fall slightly between 2015 and 2030 because coal prices are assumed to go down after 2015.

6

·· S P O T L I G H T ····························

What are the risks of investing in the power sector?

Projected generating costs (Figure 6.8) are but one criterion used by investors to decide on whether to invest and on the type of technology. Power companies increasingly use portfolio investment-valuation methodologies to take into account risks over their entire plant portfolio, rather than focussing on the technology with the lowest stand-alone projected generating cost. Investors may accept different risk profiles for different technologies, depending on project-specific circumstances.

Concern about both climate change and structural change in the industry have introduced new risks for electricity operators. In relation to climate change, the risk is of uncertainty as to future policy and its implementation. The structural risk is more fundamental, since it involves the transfer of risk from the consumer (or tax payer) to the investor. In the traditional, vertically integrated public service model, the supply company was often a monopoly and could count on recovering the investment and the target return (in practice, governments often imposed price controls, for political reasons).

In the competitive situation now existing in most OECD countries and several non-OECD countries, risks have, to some extent, moved from rate and tax payers to competing market players. This perception of increased risk drives up the investor's required rate of return, a factor influencing the cost assumptions now embedded in the calculations from which our projections derive.

---

12. Coal transport distances in China and India can significantly increase fuel costs, adding to generating costs.

Electricity prices

Electricity prices paid by final customers have increased in real terms in many OECD countries since the beginning of this decade, after falling during the 1990s (Figure 6.9). Sharply higher fuel-input costs, which make up a significant share of the total cost of power supplied to end users, are the principal reason, especially since 2003. The impact of fuel price increases on electricity prices is most direct for gas, which accounts for the largest part of the total costs of generating electricity. Moreover, electricity prices are set by marginal generation costs and — in more and more markets and on more and more occasions — CCGTs are the marginal generation source. Coal and uranium costs have also increased markedly, though in the case of uranium the cost of the fuel accounts for only about 5% of the total cost of generation.

Figure 6.9 ● **Indices of real end-use fuel and electricity prices in OECD**

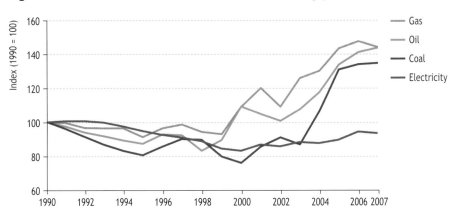

Source: IEA databases.

In the European Union, the Emissions Trading Scheme (ETS) has also contributed to higher electricity prices (Figure 6.10). The price of carbon on the ETS fell sharply in 2006 as it became clear that CO_2 allowances were plentiful for the first phase of the scheme, which ran until end-2007. This price drop was reflected in a marked fall in wholesale electricity prices in several European markets, illustrating the emerging tight interaction between the ETS and wholesale electricity trade. Wholesale prices rebounded in 2007 and 2008 with higher prices for carbon under the second phase of the scheme.

Over the projection period, electricity prices are expected to increase, reflecting fuel price increases and higher construction costs. On average, OECD electricity prices are projected to be 11% higher in 2030 than in 2006.

Figure 6.10 ● European wholesale prices of electricity and EU emission allowances

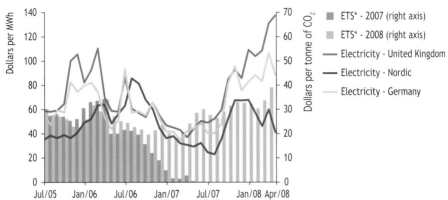

*ETS — European Trading Scheme.

Sources: EEX (www.eex.com/en/); Elexon (www.elexon.co.uk/); Nord Pool (www.nordpool.com/asa/); and PowerNext (www.powernext.fr/).

CHAPTER 7

RENEWABLE ENERGY OUTLOOK

H I G H L I G H T S

- Renewable energy sources are set to expand rapidly. Excluding traditional biomass use, their share of global primary energy demand is projected to climb from 7% in 2006 to 10% by 2030 in the Reference Scenario. This results from lower costs as renewable technologies mature, assumed higher fossil-fuel prices, which make renewables relatively more competitive, and strong policy support. The renewables industry has the opportunity to exploit this development to eliminate its reliance on subsidies and to bring emerging technologies into the mainstream.

- World renewables-based electricity generation — mostly hydro and wind power — is projected to more than double over the *Outlook* period, its share of total electricity output rising from 18% in 2006 to 23% in 2030. Renewables overtake gas to become the second-largest source of electricity, behind coal, before 2015.

- In the OECD, the total projected increase in renewable electricity generation is bigger than the combined increase in fossil fuel-based and nuclear power generation. The share of renewables in electricity generation increases by ten percentage points to 26% over the *Outlook* period.

- Global output of wind power is projected to increase eleven-fold, becoming the second-largest source of renewable electricity after hydro by 2010. The largest increase is in the European Union, where the share of wind power reaches 14% in 2030, accounting for 60% of the increase in total EU electricity generation between 2006 and 2030.

- Biomass, geothermal and solar thermal provided around 6% of total global heating demand in 2006. This share is projected to increase to 7% in 2030. Where resources are abundant and conventional energy sources expensive, renewables-based heating can be very cost competitive with conventional fossil-fuel heating systems.

- The share of biofuels in the total supply of road transport fuels worldwide is projected to rise from 1.5% in 2006 to 5% in 2030, spurred by subsidies and high oil prices. Most of the growth comes from the United States, Europe, China and Brazil. Second-generation biofuels are expected to become commercially viable but still make only a small contribution to total biofuels supply towards the end of the projection period.

- Total cumulative investment in renewable energy supply in 2007-2030 amounts to $5.5 trillion (in year 2007 dollars). The greater part of this investment is for electricity generation. Renewables account for just under half of the total projected investment in electricity generation.

Global trends in the use of renewable energy

The use of renewable energy sources has been expanding rapidly in recent years and this trend is set to continue over the projection period. Investment in renewable energy sources for electricity, heating and in biofuels has increased considerably. However, if traditional biomass is excluded,[1] renewable energy still accounts for a small share of the energy mix. In 2006 it met just 7% of global primary energy needs. The share was around 6% for heat demand (mostly from the direct combustion of biomass) and 1% for transport (biofuels derived from biomass). Renewables accounted for 18% of total electricity generation, the majority of it coming from hydropower plants (16% of total electricity generation). In the Reference Scenario, the share of renewables (including modern biomass) in the global primary energy mix increases from 7% in 2006 to around 10% in 2030.

In the electricity sector, the generating costs of coal- and gas-fired power plants remain high, because of both high fuel prices and high construction costs.[2] Over the projection period, oil, gas and coal prices are assumed to remain high by historical standards (see Chapter 1). While the construction costs of some renewables have also increased recently, the costs of renewable energy systems are expected to fall in the coming decades, mainly as a result of advances in technology and declining capital costs as their use expands.

Demand for renewables for heating and cooling, and demand for biofuels are also expected to be boosted by high fossil-fuel prices. There is a good opportunity during the next decade or so for the renewables industry to prove it can become cost competitive without relying on subsidies and for the technologies to enter the mainstream. A carbon price on fossil fuels would make renewables even more competitive (see Part C).

Despite the improved environment for emerging renewables sources and technologies, many barriers to their deployment remain. These could hold back long-term growth of the sector. They include: the relatively high costs of some technologies in the absence of subsidies; relatively limited research and development until recently; growing concerns about the impact on food availability of the use of crops for energy; a lack of skilled labour and policymaking capacity; regulations that discourage variable and distributed power-generating systems; inadequate investment in networks; and scepticism on the part of some major incumbent players in the energy sector about the viability of renewables.

Biomass (including traditional biomass) is expected to remain by far the single most important primary source of renewable energy for decades to come. In the Reference Scenario, total world demand for biomass rises from 1 186 Mtoe in 2006 to about 1 660 Mtoe by 2030, although its share of world primary energy demand falls slightly from 10.1% in 2006 to 9.8% in 2030. Biomass differs from other renewable energy resources in that it can be a substitute for all fossil-fuel based products, using a wide range of technologies to convert the range of resources into heat, electricity and liquid fuels (Figure 7.1). It can be used directly in traditional ways for heating and cooking, or indirectly using modern conversion technologies. An estimated 60% of current biomass use is in the form of traditional biomass such as scavenged fuelwood, dried animal dung and agricultural residues used on open fires and in crude, low-efficiency stoves to provide basic cooking and heating services.

---

1. The use of fuelwood, dung and agricultural residues in very inefficient stoves or on open fires for cooking and heating.

2. See Chapter 6 for a discussion of recent increases in power plant construction costs.

The quality of data on biomass use is often very poor, making future projections uncertain. Major uncertainties in projecting future demand for biomass for energy purposes include competition for land use (Box 7.1), the rate of improvement in crop yields, water availability for crop production, the effects of climate change and the development of advanced conversion technologies. Most of the biomass consumed in 2030 still comes from agricultural and forest residues, but a growing share comes from purpose-grown energy crops — mainly for making biofuels. A growing share is also projected to fuel combined heat and power (CHP) plants.

Figure 7.1 ● Contribution of biomass to world primary energy demand, 2006

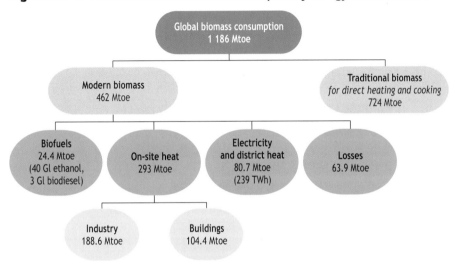

Note: Electricity and district heat and industry include combined heat and power.

Box 7.1 ● Land use required to grow biomass for energy

Of the 13.2 billion hectares (Gha) of the world total land area, more than 10% (1.5 Gha) are currently used to produce arable crops and over a quarter (3.5 Gha) are in pasture for meat, milk and wool production from grazing animals. Annually, around 7 to 8 Mha of forest land is converted to agriculture. Crops grown specifically for biofuels currently utilise around 1% of total agricultural land (FAO, 2008; WWI, 2007). This 1% share is the same in Brazil, where over 40% of the total gasoline demand is provided by ethanol based on sugarcane for feedstock and more is exported. At 38%, however, the land in Brazil, of which only a quarter is currently cultivated, is much higher than the world average of 10%. Other countries in Latin America and Africa also have the potential to expand their agricultural production with the aid of modern farm-management techniques and improved crop varieties, without resorting to deforestation. Shortage of water, either as natural rainfall or irrigation, can be a major constraint on increased energy crop production in some regions. Globally, some of the 1 Gha of marginal and degraded lands unsuitable for food production (due to rising salinity levels, for example, in Australia) could be reclaimed for productive use by growing selected energy crops.

Renewables for electricity

Renewables-based electricity generation is expected to grow substantially over the coming decades, benefiting from high fossil-fuel prices, declining investment costs and government support. In the Reference Scenario, world renewable electricity generation is projected to increase from 3 470 TWh in 2006 to 4 970 TWh in 2015 and to 7 705 TWh in 2030. Before 2015, electricity from renewable energy sources is projected to overtake gas as the world's second-largest source of electricity behind coal, rising from 18% in 2006 to 20% in 2015 and 23% in 2030 (Figure 7.2). The increase is far more substantial in OECD countries, where the share of renewables in electricity generation increases by ten percentage points, to 26%, over the *Outlook* period.

Figure 7.2 ● *Share of total electricity generation from renewables by region in the Reference Scenario*

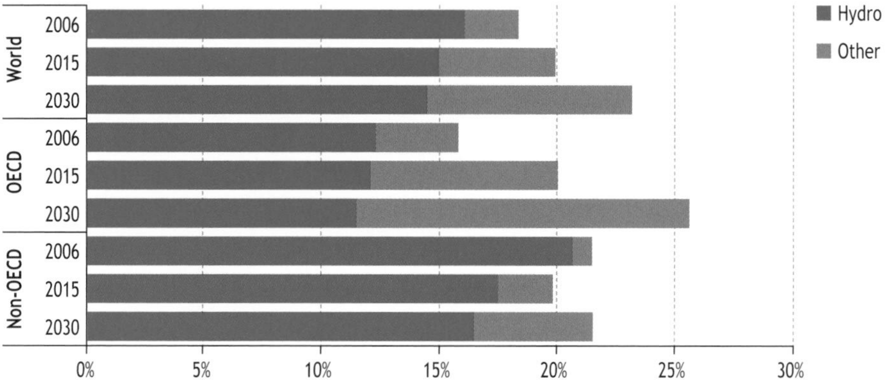

Note: Other includes biomass, wind, solar, tide and wave power.

Hydropower remains the leading renewable source of electricity worldwide (Figure 7.3). But despite the projected large increase for hydropower in absolute terms — it nearly doubles in non-OECD between 2006 and 2030 — its share of total electricity generation falls over the projection period, even in non-OECD countries. The use of other renewables in electricity generation in non-OECD countries increases faster than hydropower. The share of all renewables in electricity generation in non-OECD countries increases from 21% in 2006 to 22% in 2030.

In the period to 2015, most of the increase in renewables generation is expected to come from hydro and onshore wind power. Both continue to grow between 2015 and 2030. Biomass and offshore wind power also grow briskly during this period. Solar power (both photovoltaics and concentrating solar) see their share of electricity output grow in many countries. In the OECD, the total projected increase in renewable electricity generation is bigger than the combined increase in fossil fuel-based and nuclear power generation (Figure 7.4).

Figure 7.3 ● Increase in world electricity generation from renewables in the Reference Scenario

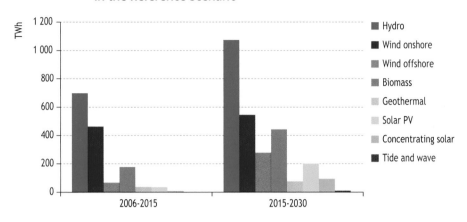

Figure 7.4 ● Increase in OECD electricity generation by energy source in the Reference Scenario

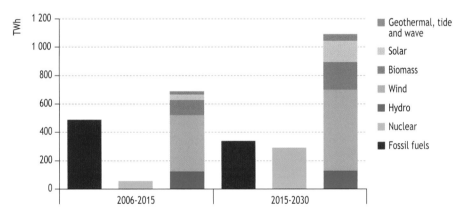

The costs of power generation from renewables are expected to fall over time (Figure 7.5). The main reason is increased deployment, which accelerates technological progress and increases economies of scale in manufacturing the associated equipment, resulting in lower investment costs (Figure 7.6). The costs of the more mature technologies, including geothermal and onshore wind power, are assumed to fall the least. The investment costs of hydropower remain broadly unchanged.

In reality, there is a wide range of generation costs for each technology, based mainly on the assumed lifetime, proximity to demand and local resource availability. Wind power onshore, for example, can be generated for $30 to $40 per MWh in New Zealand, where many good sites near to cities enjoy a high mean annual wind speed, above 10 m/s. This enables wind to compete with hydro and gas without subsidies. Typical sites in Denmark and Germany, however, have mean wind speeds closer to 7 m/s, so that the same wind turbine generates only around half the electricity output per year that it would if built in New Zealand. The resulting relatively high generating costs require supporting policies to enable wind power to compete. In addition, since the generation costs of renewable electricity, other than from biomass, are largely dependent on the investment cost, the choice of discount rate applied adds to the wide cost range.

The different characteristics of the output from different renewable energy technologies must also be taken into account when comparing renewable generating costs and when comparing them with fossil fuels and nuclear.[3] The service provided by large hydro, notably when storage is used, makes it competitive with traditional peak-load and mid-load plants, which have higher generating costs than base-load plants. This increases the value of hydropower. By contrast, supply from wind and solar power depends on the availability of wind and sun. The output from these resources is variable, but if it correlates with peak load (for example, solar energy is available at peak hours in California, Japan and Southern Europe) the value of the electricity produced is higher.

Figure 7.5 ● Projected generating costs of renewable energy technologies in the Reference Scenario

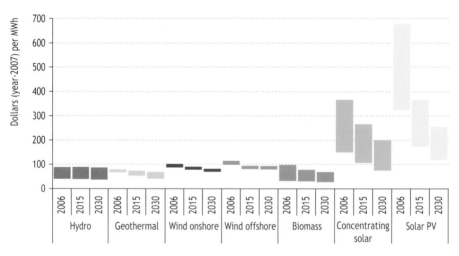

___

3. See Figure 6.8 in Chapter 6 for the generating costs of coal-fired, gas-fired and nuclear power plants.

Figure 7.6 ● Projected investment costs of renewable energy technologies in the Reference Scenario

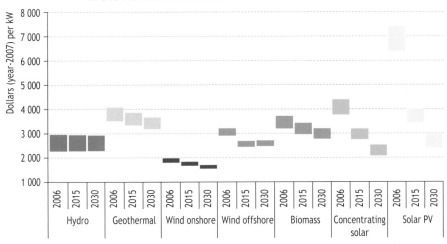

Note: Offshore costs increase with greater depth and distance from the shore.

Hydropower

After two decades of stagnation, hydropower is making a comeback. Some 170 GW of hydropower capacity is under construction worldwide implying a significant increase of generation over the next decade (Figure 7.7). Most of this capacity is being built in non-OECD Asian countries such as China, India and Vietnam. The remaining potential in non-OECD countries is still large. Several non-OECD countries are re-focusing on this domestic source of electricity, driven by rapidly expanding power demand, the high cost of fossil fuels, growing concerns about pollution and greenhouse-gas emissions, and the perceived benefits to supply security by diversifying the electricity-generation mix. In Latin America, however, the amount of capacity under construction falls far short of that sought by government, notably in Brazil. Only 5 GW are being built, whereas the government expects installed capacity of 76 GW to double by 2030 (MME, 2007). We project hydropower capacity in Brazil to reach 104 GW in 2030 in the Reference Scenario.

Interest and support for hydropower projects in non-OECD countries are growing among international lenders and the private sector. In the OECD, many of the best sites have already been exploited and environmental regulations severely constrain new development. Most of the projected increase there comes from large-scale projects in Turkey and Canada. Several other OECD countries are providing incentives for developing small and mini-hydropower projects.

Hydropower generation is projected to increase from 3 035 TWh in 2006 to over 3 730 TWh by 2015 and 4 810 TWh by 2030. Nevertheless, the share of hydropower in total electricity generation continues its downward trend, falling from 16% now to 15% in 2015 and 14.5% in 2030 as other power-generation technologies grow at faster rates.

Figure 7.7 ● Hydropower capacity under construction by region

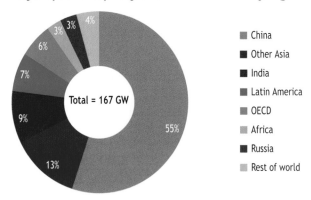

Note: Includes power plants considered as under construction in 2007.
Source: Platt's World Electric Power Plants Database, January 2008 version.

Wind power

Wind power has been growing at around 25% per year over the past few years. Worldwide, installed wind power capacity rose from about 6 GW in 1996 to 74 GW in 2006 and to 94 GW in 2007, with over 60% installed in OECD Europe. Germany has the largest installed capacity in the world, reaching 20.6 GW in 2006 and over 22 GW in 2007. Germany and Spain together account for about two-thirds of installed wind power capacity in OECD Europe. The rapid growth of wind power in these two countries is largely due to feed-in tariff systems,[4] which offer high buy-back rates and guarantee a market for the output from wind farms. Globally, wind power accounts for a very small share of total electricity generation (around 0.7%), but this share is much higher in some countries (Table 7.1).

Table 7.1 ● Top ten wind-power markets, 2006

Country	Installed capacity (GW)	Wind power production (TWh)	Share of total generation (%)
Germany	20.6	30.7	4.9
Spain	11.6	23.0	7.7
United States	11.6	26.7	0.6
India	6.3	8.0	1.1
Denmark	3.1	6.1	13.4
China	2.6	3.9	0.1
Italy	2.1	3.0	1.0
United Kingdom	2.0	4.2	1.1
Portugal	1.7	2.9	6.0
France	1.6	2.2	0.4

Sources: IEA databases; GWEC (2007).

4. A feed-in tariff is the price per unit of electricity that a power company has to pay for the purchase of renewable electricity which it is obliged by law to take from private generators. The tariff rate is fixed by the government, usually at a level high enough to encourage investment in electricity generation from renewables.

The United States has recently emerged as a major growth area for wind power and became the world's second-largest market in 2007. Although incentives have been in place for a long time (a federal production tax credit [PTC] was introduced in 1992), very little growth in wind power was seen until recently. Instability of policy led to the PTC expiring, being extended, then later being renewed several times, heightening uncertainty and risks for investors. The current PTC is again due to expire at the end of 2008, after a one-year extension. The projections in this *Outlook* assume that the PTC will continue to be renewed, as it has been in the past. More recently, state-level incentives and obligations, and rising fossil-fuel prices have encouraged growth in wind power. Most of the growth has been in Texas and California, but wind power is also expected to grow in other states in the future. In the past, many projects in the United States faced siting difficulties, which resulted in them either not obtaining a licence or in very high costs, which made the developers abandon the project. Uncertainties remain about how fast the overall system and transmission network will be upgraded to accommodate large volumes of wind power. At the moment, not enough investment is going into the grid, which is impairing reliability. We assume that some of these difficulties will be overcome in the near future, facilitating the development of wind power.

Outside the OECD, India and China are important growing markets for wind power. India now has the fourth-largest installed capacity in the world and the largest outside the OECD. Wind power is also growing fast in China, where capacity has increased considerably since 2005. Both countries boast flourishing wind-turbine manufacturing industries.

Global wind power output is projected to increase from 130 TWh in 2006 to more than 660 TWh in 2015 and 1 490 TWh in 2030. This increase will make wind the second-largest source of renewable electricity, after hydro, by 2010. Its share in total electricity generation rises from less than 1% in 2006 to 2.7% in 2015 and 4.5% in 2030. The share varies significantly between regions. In the European Union, it reaches 14% in 2030, accounting for 60% of the increase in total electricity generation between 2006 and 2030. In the United States, the share of wind rises ten-fold to 6.2% by 2030, meeting almost 30% of incremental demand for electricity between 2006 and 2030.

Offshore turbines account for only a very small share of total wind-power capacity today, but this share is expected to increase substantially by 2030 as costs decline. Globally, offshore wind power production reaches about 350 TWh in 2030, up from only 3 TWh at present. The most substantial increase occurs in the European Union, where 27% of wind power could come from offshore installations by 2030.

Grid integration of wind power and other variable renewables

The rising share of wind power in electricity generation is posing a challenge for power companies in integrating this capacity into the network where penetration levels are high. Wind power, like electrical power from wave, ocean currents, run-of-river hydro, solar photovoltaics and concentrating solar power systems, is different from conventional generating capacity because of its variability. These power outputs fluctuate according to the prevailing conditions of weather, season and time of day. There are, therefore, additional costs associated with the integration of these technologies into the power-supply system, including those associated with necessary back-up capacity and operation,[5] and grid access (IEA 2008a).[6] These extra costs can add up to $13 per MWh to the generating cost of wind power.

Potential problems due to variability affecting the reliability of an electricity-supply system are manageable when the shares of wind and other variable renewables-based power capacity are small, but they become more pronounced as the shares rise. Technical problems can be largely overcome if the system is sufficiently flexible in responding quickly to large fluctuations in both supply and/ or demand. This can be the case if the system includes a balanced portfolio of power-generation technologies and fuels, substantial hydropower capacity with dam or pumped storage, arrangements for load-shedding to offset both peak demands and periods of lower power supply from variable renewables, good inter-connection between neighbouring systems to reduce balancing requirements, and energy storage facilities (Box 7.2). Nonetheless, in a liberalised power market, higher shares of variable renewables, perhaps above 10% to 15% of total generation, may need some form of government regulation which mandates the integration of a specified share of renewables into the system.

Solar photovoltaics

Worldwide, electricity generation from solar photovoltaics (PV) is still tiny, though the potential is very large. Installed global photovoltaics capacity was around 6 GW in 2006, with most of it installed in Germany (2.9 GW), Japan (1.7 GW) and the United States (0.6 GW).

Electricity generation from PV integrated into buildings is, of course, more econo-mically attractive in areas with abundant sunshine and high electricity prices. PV power is particularly valuable when maximum PV generation — around the middle of a sunny day — coincides with peak electricity demand (such as for air-conditioning). PV is already a cost-effective option in remote off-grid applications, either as a stand-alone system or as a part of a mini-grid.

PV technology has the highest investment cost of all commercially deployed renewable energy sources. Investment costs for a system (including solar collection modules and the other components of the plant), currently range from around $5 500 to

---

5. Alternative generating capacity must be available to meet demand when there is no wind. Due to the current difficulty of accurately predicting wind patterns more than 36 hours in advance as required by some transmission operators, the provision of a reliable supply of power within a system can be complex and costly. Where gate-closure times are only 1 to 2 hours, the problem is largely overcome.
6. Wind turbines can be connected to the local grid at low-voltage levels, a practice that may save grid losses but adds to the complexity of system control and operation.

$9 000 per kW, depending on the type of solar cell, scale of installation and local labour costs. In spite of big falls in module costs in recent years and increases in the efficiency of commercial cells, PV generation remains relatively costly. Further technological advances and ultimately achieving economies of scale will depend on government subsidies. However, new semi-automated PV manufacturing plants, with high annual production capacities of around 300 MW, are bringing down module costs per unit. In the Reference Scenario, the investment cost of a PV system is projected to fall to $2 600 per kW by 2030. There is optimism in the photovoltaics industry that very large cost reductions are in prospect, well before 2030.

Box 7.2 ● Energy storage

Where variable-output renewable energy systems, such as wind and solar, account for a major part of power generation within a system, storing surplus energy to meet later demand is one way to reduce the need for back-up generating capacity: storage avoids the need for power to be generated instantly to meet demand. Currently, storage is rarely the cheapest way of dealing with variability, but it could become increasingly viable as the price of carbon rises.

Electricity cannot be stored directly (except in small capacitors), so it needs to be converted into other forms of storable energy, such as chemical energy in batteries, the potential (gravitational) energy of water in pumped-hydro storage systems, or mechanical energy as compressed air or in flywheels. Advanced systems are under development, such as ultra-capacitors, superconducting magnetic systems and vanadium redox batteries, but they tend to have low energy densities and poor durability, and add high costs to the system.

The capacities of storage systems, the cost of their construction and the overall costs per unit of energy stored vary widely. The capacity of facilities for pumped hydropower and compressed air in underground cavities can reach hundreds of MW. The re-conversion efficiency of pumped storage can be higher than 70%. Flywheels can be more efficient, but generally only at a very small scale. Batteries used either individually or in banks are around 70% efficient with capacities of just a few MW at the most. They tend to be more costly than the other options, at around $20 per MWh. The other key variable of a storage technology is the energy discharge time, which can range from seconds to hours.

Producing hydrogen as an energy carrier from renewable electricity systems − by electrolysis, thermo-chemically from biomass, or by other means − can be another form of storage. This can be at a large scale in aquifers or caverns, or on a small scale involving compressing and storing the gas in cylinders or transmission pipes. The hydrogen can be used to generate electricity in fuel cells on demand but the overall efficiency of the system tends to be low, at around 40%. As a result of this and the high current investment costs for fuel cells, the unit cost is high.

Electricity generation from photovoltaics in the Reference Scenario is projected to reach 42 TWh in 2015 and 245 TWh in 2030, up from just a few TWh in 2006. Most of the increase comes from decentralised systems integrated into buildings where the generation cost competes against the retail electricity price and not the lower wholesale market price. Generous feed-in tariffs and other government incentives, together with falling PV costs and rising grid electricity prices, drive this growth.

Concentrating solar thermal power

Several concentrating solar power (CSP) options are currently available for large-scale electricity generation, though they are at varying stages of development. The parabolic-trough is already commercially available, while the parabolic-dish and central-receiver technologies are still at the demonstration stage. These could eventually achieve higher conversion efficiencies and lower capital costs than the parabolic-trough technology.

Today's oldest commercial parabolic-trough projects were developed in the United States in the early 1980s. CSP installation has been very slow since then, due to the high capital cost of the system. However, following a few parabolic-dish and central-receiver demonstration projects in Australia, Greece, Israel, Spain and Switzerland, as well as in the United States, interest in CSP has started to rise again. Total installed capacity of CSP was 354 MW in 2006. In 2007, a new 64 MW plant came on line in the United States and a 50 MW plant in Spain. Another 255 MW is under construction in Italy and Spain. Several new projects are being planned in other countries, including China, Iran, Jordan and Malta, with over 2 GW of total installed capacity likely by 2010.

CSP generation is projected to reach 11 TWh by 2015 and 107 TWh by 2030. Current power-generating costs under the best conditions are around $150 to $250 per MWh or even less where the sun shines persistently. The lower end of the generation cost range is close to that of gas-fired generation at current gas prices, but CSP is generally more expensive than coal-fired generation (in the absence of a carbon value), nuclear and wind power. The economics are expected to improve in the future, falling to around $100 per MWh in sunny areas by 2030.

Geothermal power

Electricity production from geothermal energy reached 60 TWh in 2006. Although, at the global level, geothermal power production has a very small share of the mix, it meets a significant share of the total electricity demand in Iceland (26%), El Salvador (20%), Philippines (18%), Costa Rica and Kenya (14% each), and Nicaragua (11%). As more fields are exploited, technologies are developed for deeper drilling into high-temperature fields and to enhance geothermal systems (hot dry rocks), power generation is projected to triple to almost 180 TWh by 2030, doubling geothermal's share of 0.3% of the global electricity-generation mix in 2006. Most of the increase is expected to come from projects in the United States and non-OECD Asia.

Tide and wave power

Ocean-energy power systems currently make the smallest contribution of all renewable energy sources. Tidal power stations are in operation in France, Canada, China, Russia and Norway. Wave power and ocean-current technologies are at an early stage of commercialisation, but there is strong interest on the part of several governments to develop them further. The United Kingdom is the leading country in which a specific market-based energy policy has been developed to encourage ocean energy (IEA-OES, 2007). This policy includes capital grants, purchase obligations, tradable certificates, guaranteed prices, and regulatory and administrative rules. In the Reference Scenario, tidal and wave power is projected to reach 14 TWh worldwide in 2030, compared with less than 1 TWh now.

Biomass for electricity

Among all renewable energy sources, biomass is the largest contributor to global primary energy supply, amounting to 1 186 Mtoe in 2006. Of this, around 7% was used to produce 239 TWh of electricity. Approximately 44% of this electricity was generated in electricity-only generation plants, at around 20% conversion efficiency. The remainder was generated in CHP plants, where the heat is either used on-site (as in pulp and paper manufacturing plants) or sold and transported off-site, often for use in district-heating schemes in buildings and by industry.

In the Reference Scenario, biomass use in power generation and heat plants increases by over 5% each year to reach close to 290 Mtoe of primary energy in 2030. Allowing for a projected increase in fuel-to-electricity conversion efficiency over time (typically 18% to 22% for woody biomass electricity-only plants in 2006, rising to 25% by 2030), this will require approximately 1 200 Mt of biomass (approximately 40 million truck loads) to be delivered annually to the generating plants. Over 860 TWh of electricity is projected to be generated by 2030, 60% of it in OECD countries. The share of biomass in global power generation doubles to 2.6%. The biggest increases in generation occur in the United States, Europe and China.

Biofuels

Final demand for biofuels (transport fuels derived from biomass) worldwide reached 24.4 Mtoe (0.6 mb/d adjusted for energy content) in 2006, up from only 10.3 Mtoe in 2000 and 6 Mtoe in 1990.[7] Biofuels represented only around 1.5% of total road-transport fuel demand in 2006. North America is the world's largest biofuels consumer (Table 7.2), followed by Latin America and the European Union, and most of the recent growth in biofuels use has come from the United States. Demand there grew by some 23% per year on average between 2000 and 2006. The United States overtook Brazil as the world's largest biofuels consumer in 2004.

---

7. Preliminary data for 2007 shows biofuels demand at just over 0.8 mb/d (adjusted for energy content).

Table 7.2 ● Final consumption of biofuels by region in the Reference
Scenario (Mtoe)

	2006	2015	2030	2006-2030*
OECD	16.9	49.5	72.5	6.3%
North America	11.3	32.9	46.8	6.1%
Europe	5.5	15.8	24.7	6.5%
Pacific	0.1	0.8	0.9	10.3%
Non-OECD	7.5	24.0	46.0	7.9%
E. Europe/Eurasia	0.0	1.1	1.5	16.8%
Asia	0.8	7.6	17.9	14.0%
Middle East	0.0	0.3	0.8	n.a.
Africa	0.0	0.7	1.1	n.a.
Latin America	6.6	14.4	24.7	5.6%
World	24.4	73.5	118.5	6.8%
European Union	5.5	16.6	25.9	6.7%

* Annual average rate of change.

In the Reference Scenario, world biofuels supply is projected to climb to 118 Mtoe in 2030 (3.2 mb/d), meeting 5% of total road-transport fuel demand[8] (Figure 7.8). The projections for biofuels have been revised upwards substantially since *WEO-2007*, due to new policies in several countries and because of higher oil prices than assumed last year. We assume in the Reference Scenario that the biofuel mandates in China and the European Union will be met after a lag of a few years but that biofuels in the United States in 2030 will attain only about 40% of the very ambitious target in the 2007 Energy Independence and Security Act. Asia and OECD Europe experience faster rates of growth, but in absolute terms these increases trail those

Figure 7.8 ● World biofuels consumption by type in the Reference Scenario

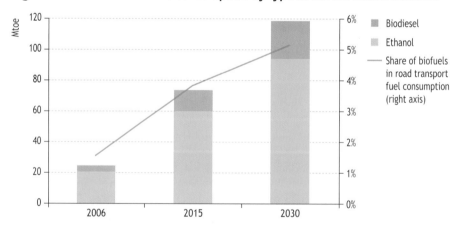

---

8. The biofuels demand projections in this *Outlook* are based on a detailed region-by-region analysis of policy mandates, inter-fuel competition and supply potential. More detail about the prospects for supply to 2013 can be found in the IEA's *Medium-Term Oil Market Report*, released in July 2008 (IEA, 2008b).

in the larger North American market. Biofuels demand in the OECD Pacific region remains modest. Growth in Latin America is moderate, a consequence of the sizeable share of the market in Brazil already held by biofuels. In 2030, about 28% of total Brazilian road-transport fuel demand is projected to be met by biofuels (up from 13% today) and some 8% of the market in the United States (2% today).

Ethanol currently accounts for a much larger share of the global biofuels market than biodiesel. Over the *Outlook* period, demand for biodiesel is set to grow faster than ethanol, so that the share in energy terms of total biofuels coming from ethanol falls from 83% in 2006 to 79% in 2030 (Figure 7.8). The United States and Brazil remain the largest ethanol consumers. The European Union and Asia see the fastest growth in demand for biodiesel. Second-generation biofuels, based on ligno-cellulosic feedstocks using enzyme hydrolysis or biomass-to-liquids gasification technologies, are expected to become commercially viable, but only make a minor contribution in the second half of the projection period. Biofuels are almost entirely used for road transport, but recent demonstration projects in the United Kingdom, Australia and Japan indicate there may be potential for using them on a large scale in aviation and shipping.

7

Several countries have aggressive policies in place for encouraging the production and use of biofuels, including the United States, where the Energy Independence and Security Act 2007 mandates a significant increase in both first- and second-generation biofuels use by 2020. China has a target to 2020 and the European Union has a target for biofuels to meet 10% of road transport demand by 2020. Australia, New Zealand, Colombia, South Africa, Thailand, Japan, Indonesia, Mexico and Canada also have mandates for ethanol blends. Some countries have recently started to reconsider their ambitious biofuels policies, including imported biofuels. This is due to concern about the environmental sustainability of production, overall greenhouse-gas emissions based on life-cycle analysis, and the impact on land use and food prices (see *Spotlight* below). The European Union is reviewing its policies, while India and Indonesia have already scaled back their incentives for biofuels.

········ S P O T L I G H T ·········

To what extent are biofuels driving up the price of food?

Soaring global food prices have recently sparked riots in many countries, including Haiti, Côte d'Ivoire, Ethiopia, Madagascar, Philippines and Indonesia. Food prices accelerated sharply in 2008, with grain prices more than doubling since January 2006. Over 60% of the rise in food prices has occurred since January 2008. Competition from biofuels production is one of many factors contributing to higher food prices. Other factors include:

- increasing dietary demand for meat and milk products, with consequent increased demand for animal fodder;

- high energy prices, which have pushed up the cost of fertilizer and other farm expenses, as well as food processing and distribution costs;

- poor harvests, due to extreme weather events such as droughts and destructive storms;

- the declining value of the US dollar; and

- international and national agricultural policies. The introduction of food-export restrictions by some nations has restricted global supply and aggravated food shortages.

The recent increase in biofuels production has certainly boosted the demand for specific crops and, in some countries, has displaced land that could have been used for growing food. However two of the commodities most often associated with today's food crisis, wheat and rice, are not major sources of biofuel feedstocks. On the other hand, higher prices for crude oil, gas and electricity have greatly affected the cost of producing, processing and transporting food worldwide. The US Government Accountability Office concludes that food aid organisations spend 65% of their budgets on transportation. As a result of the rise in crude oil prices, the cost per food mile worldwide has soared.

While it seems clear that rising biofuels output is contributing to the increase in food prices, there is no consensus on how large this factor is. A US Council of Economic Advisors study found the contribution of biofuels to the price increases of agricultural commodities to be only 3% (CEA, 2008) whereas a recent OECD report holds biofuels production responsible for 15% of the food price increases (OECD, 2008). A study published by the World Bank concludes that recent increases in biofuels production (and related consequences of low grain stocks, large land-use shifts, speculative activity and export bans) explain 70% to 75% of the increase in food prices (Mitchell, 2008). It is very difficult to compare these studies because of different methodologies, different time periods and other factors. More analysis is needed to determine the true impact of biofuels production, because of the very many assumptions and uncertainties involved in assessing its effects on food prices, commodity stocks, oil prices, and direct and indirect land-use change over various time horizons.

Agricultural commodities will see much less competition between food, fibre and biofuels supply if productivity continues to rise at the growth rate seen in the past five decades as a result of better farm management, new technologies and improved crop varieties. Since so much available arable land needs irrigation, increased biofuel production in some regions will have implications for water resources. The uneven global distribution of natural resources results in regional differences, with many countries experiencing major land and water shortages. These differences impact on which countries have a comparative advantage in biofuels production.

Today, global trade in ethanol represents just under 20% of total ethanol demand, but this share has been steadily rising from about 12% in 2002 (F.O. Lichts, 2008). Brazilian exports, including volumes re-exported from countries in the Caribbean Basin Initiative, account for about 45% of global trade. Brazil is the world's largest exporter of biofuels; the United States is the world's largest importer. The Netherlands, Germany and the United Kingdom are the largest importers in the European Union. Biodiesel derived from palm oil, exported from Indonesia and Malaysia to the European Union, accounts for the majority of biodiesel trade. The United States and Brazil also export soybean biodiesel to EU countries.

Numerous life cycle analysis studies have been conducted, but the various benefits of biofuels over conventional oil-based fuels for transport are still uncertain. Methods of allocating the emissions between co-products (such as high-protein animal meal from oilseeds and distillers grain from corn) are being determined. The greenhouse-gas emissions reduction potential per kilometre travelled is variable. It is highest in Brazil for ethanol produced directly from sugarcane because the fossil-fuel needs for processing are lower, as the sugar is fermented directly and the crushed stalk of the plant (known as bagasse) is used to provide heat and power in the production process rather than fossil energy. For each unit of sugar-based ethanol produced, only about 12% of a comparable unit of fossil energy is required (IEA, 2004). Overall, CO_2 emissions calculated on a life-cycle basis are relatively low, at about 10% to 20% those of conventional gasoline.

A recent IEA analysis of 60 studies indicated that the conversion of sugarbeet into ethanol in Europe can yield reductions in well-to-wheels emissions of typically between 40% and 60%, compared with gasoline (OECD, 2008). Estimates for the net reduction in greenhouse-gas emissions that are obtained from rapeseed-derived biodiesel in Europe, compared with conventional automotive diesel, are in a similar range. For corn-based ethanol in the United States, the emission savings are much lower, at only 10% to 30% per kilometre compared with petroleum-based fuels. However, many of these studies do not include emissions resulting from direct and indirect land-use change, which can be significant but are hard to measure.

The successful development of second-generation technologies using non-food biomass feedstocks would allow the use of a much wider array of feedstocks, including dedicated crops such as grasses and fast-growing trees. The reductions in greenhouse-gas and polluting emissions could be significantly higher than those associated with first-generation ethanol and some of the fuels produced may be more suited for aviation, marine and heavy transport applications. Ligno-cellulosic ethanol technologies by bio-chemical conversion using enzymes are the focus of a considerable amount of research into such second-generation biofuels, notably in the United States. Thermo-chemical conversion, by gasification and the Fischer-Tropsch synthesis of the gases into petroleum substitutes, is also under evaluation at a demonstration scale in Germany and elsewhere.

There is no clear consensus about when second-generation technologies will become commercially competitive, even with high oil prices. The key factors in achieving deployment are to prove the optimum technologies at a commercial scale, increase the scale of production, exploit the learning curve, and apply process optimisation and integration techniques. In the United States, Sweden, Canada and elsewhere, demonstration ligno-cellulosic ethanol plants have recently been built. There are also plans to build several small-scale cellulosic bio-refineries over the next 10 to 15 years in the United States. These will produce liquid transportation fuels such as ethanol, as well as bio-based chemicals and other bio-products used in industrial applications. The large Borregaard bio-refinery plant in Norway, employing 900 staff and using spruce logs as feedstock, has been operating for several decades, producing fuel ethanol and other products. The US Department of Energy is providing $385 million between 2007 and 2011 to support the development of six demonstration plants with the aim of making cellulosic ethanol cost-competitive with gasoline by 2012. The capital investment necessary to build cellulosic ethanol facilities, however, is significantly more than that of grain- or sugarcane-based facilities. As a result, the full commercialisation of these technologies hinges on further major cost reductions (IEA, 2008c). In the Reference Scenario, second-generation biofuels are not expected to penetrate the market on a fully commercial scale before 2020.

Renewables for heat

Renewable energy systems directly provided around 300 Mtoe of heat in 2006, excluding the heat supplied from the combustion of traditional biomass or from heating appliances using renewable electricity. Biomass, solar thermal and geothermal currently account for around 6% of total heat demand worldwide. Renewables heating is projected to grow to 516 Mtoe in 2030, boosting its share of total heat demand to about 7% by 2030. This increase comes mainly from increased use of biomass for space and process heating, and greater solar water heating in residential buildings.

Commercial biomass used in boilers and stoves to provide space and process heat in the building and industry sectors amounted to 293 Mtoe in 2006 across all regions. This includes the heat from CHP installations that is consumed on site (mainly in industry). In the Reference Scenario, biomass consumption rises to 453 Mtoe in 2030. Most of the increase occurs in OECD countries, through growth in the number of CHP installations in industrial facilities and increased demand for the heating of buildings. In non-OECD countries, the use of modern biomass increases from 164 Mtoe in 2006 to 241 Mtoe in 2030, leading to the more efficient and sustainable use of the local resource of basic forms of biomass.

There is considerable potential for *solar water heating* to grow in the OECD, since around 20% of total residential energy consumption is for heating water. Over 90% of OECD solar water heaters are installed in the residential sector, which is expected to remain the largest consumer to 2030, although use by the commercial sector will also grow. Those heaters already provide over 7.6 Mtoe of energy for water heating, with a small proportion used for swimming pool and space heating. There is also potential for increasing use of solar water-heating systems in non-OECD countries, since the heaters are often manufactured locally and cheaply. China alone has around 60% of the world's total installed capacity and collected around 3 Mtoe of useful solar heat in 2006. Globally, solar collection used for water and space heating (not including the passive solar heating of buildings) is projected to rise to about 45 Mtoe by 2030, with widespread global distribution.

Geothermal heat, used directly, accounted for around 3 Mtoe of space heating in 2006. The United States, Sweden, China, Turkey and Iceland are the leaders in such direct geothermal heat use.[9] In Iceland it contributes around 45% of the total end-use building

---

9. Geothermal heat use in China is not reported in IEA statistics, but it is estimated to be around 0.5 Mtoe.

heat demand. A third of the energy from this source comes from deep bores and the rest from millions of domestic scale, shallow ground-source heat pumps. Sweden alone has around one third of a million geothermal systems installed and projections show a significant increase will occur worldwide. Direct use of geothermal heat is projected to reach 18 Mtoe in 2030.

The costs of renewable heating technologies vary according to local conditions, particularly the availability of the resource and the size of the market. Where the resources are abundant and conventional energy sources are expensive, they can be very cost-competitive with conventional fossil-fuel or electric-heating systems and require few, if any, government incentives (IEA, 2007). In China, for example, they are a relatively cheap option, particularly in rural areas where gas and electricity are not widely available. There is a large potential to reduce the installed costs of most renewable heating technologies through technological progress, training, mass production (to exploit economies of scale) and improved operating performance. Government intervention can help address some of the barriers to wider deployment, including planning difficulties (see Part C).

Traditional biomass

"Traditional biomass" refers to fuelwood, charcoal, agricultural residues and animal dung. Most of this type of energy is used for lighting and direct heat in poor countries in Africa, Asia and Latin America, especially in rural areas where access to affordable, modern energy services is limited.[10] When used sustainably, the use of traditional biomass is not in itself a cause for concern. However the *World Energy Outlook* has for many years highlighted traditional biomass use because the way in which these resources are used to provide energy services — cooking, heating and lighting — often has a serious impact on health, economic productivity and the environment. More people die prematurely in poor countries from the health impacts associated with indoor air pollution from burning biomass than from malaria. In addition, a great deal of time and effort is devoted to fuel collection, usually by women and children. This restricts them from engaging in more productive activities, such as enrolling in school and running small enterprises. Exploitation of biomass resources can also result in local environmental damage, such as land degradation, deforestation and air pollution. These negative effects can be ameliorated with policies and programmes which promote improved cookstoves with chimneys, proper ventilation in kitchen design, efficient charcoal kilns and fuelwood plantations.

Although accurate and detailed statistics are essential for proper policy and market analysis, very few governments report on the use of traditional biomass at the household level. In order to raise the awareness of household energy consumption in non-OECD countries, the IEA has attempted a global assessment and has estimated the number of people who rely on these fuels, based on national surveys. We calculate that 2.5 billion people in Africa, non-OECD Asia and Latin America rely

---

10. Chapter 15 provides an outlook for the use of modern fuels in oil- and gas-rich sub-Saharan Africa countries. See Chapter 8 in *WEO-2007* for a discussion of household energy demand in China and Chapter 20 for India.

on the burning of biomass resources in inefficient devices to meet their cooking and heating needs. In the absence of new policies, this number of people will rise to 2.7 billion in 2030 (IEA, 2006).

The use of biomass in Africa is mainly in the residential and services sectors for cooking and heating, and it is not expected to decline much over the *Outlook* period. Traditional use of biomass declines in non-OECD Asian countries, as rising incomes enable more households to switch to cleaner-burning fuels. Use of biomass in the residential and services sectors declines in Latin America.

Investment in renewable energy

In the Reference Scenario, total cumulative investment in modern forms of renewable energy in the period 2007 to 2030 amounts to $5.5 trillion (in year-2007 dollars). Most of the investment in renewables — 60% of the total — is for electricity generation, followed by investment in renewables for heat and biofuels, which account for 36% and 4% of the total, respectively. Total investment in renewables for electricity generation in the Reference Scenario from 2007 to 2030 amounts to $3.3 trillion; this provides 1 617 GW of additional capacity, mainly from an increase in hydro and wind capacity.

Average annual capacity additions for renewables-based generation in the period 2007 to 2015 are projected to be 59 GW: some 27 GW for hydro and 32 GW for other renewables. Total annual capacity additions amount to 188 GW over the same period. In 2016-2030, hydropower capacity additions are 24 GW per year and other renewables 49 GW per year, out of a total new generation capacity of 189 GW per year. Annual investment in renewables will climb accordingly. Over the whole of the projection period, the annual investment in new renewable electricity capacity is higher than that in fossil-fuel power plants (Figure 7.9). Renewables-based capacity accounts for 48% of total projected investment in electricity generation between 2007 and 2030.

Figure 7.9 ● **World investment in new power-generation plants by fuel in the Reference Scenario**

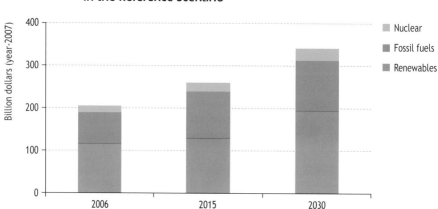

World Energy Outlook 2008 - **GLOBAL ENERGY TRENDS TO 2030**

CHAPTER 8

ENERGY USE IN CITIES

- Cities are a dynamic and vital part of global culture and are the main engines of social, economic and technological development. According to UN projections, by 2030, cities will house 60% of the world's population — equivalent to the total global population in 1986. The geographic distribution of urban population is set to change: while global urbanisation in the first half of the 20th century was dominated by European cities, the majority of urban residents today live in Asia, despite the relatively low proportion there of city residents.

- The scale and pattern of city energy use has significant implications both for energy security and global greenhouse-gas emissions. Alert to the climate-change challenge, some city authorities are actively involved in reducing energy use and CO_2 emissions.

- About two-thirds of the world's energy — an estimated 7 900 Mtoe in 2006 — is consumed in cities, even though only around half of the world's population lives in urban areas. City residents consume more coal, gas and electricity than the global average, but less oil.

- Increases in urbanisation through to 2030 are projected to drive up city energy use to almost 12 400 Mtoe in the Reference Scenario. By 2030, cities are responsible for 73% of the world's energy use. Some 81% of the projected increase in energy use in cities between 2006 and 2030 comes from non-OECD countries.

- Energy use per capita of city residents is slightly lower than the national average in the United States, the European Union and Australasia (Australia and New Zealand). By contrast, city residents in China use almost twice as much energy per capita as the national average, due to higher average incomes and better access to modern energy services.

- The gap between rural and city energy use per capita is assumed to narrow over the projection period in China, but increasing urbanisation pushes up substantially the share of China's energy used in cities.

- By 2030, 87% of US energy will be consumed in cities, up from 80% in 2006. In the European Union that figure will rise from 69% to 75% over the *Outlook* period. Australasian cities' share of energy consumption will rise from 78% to 80% by 2030 and Chinese cities account for 83% of Chinese energy consumption in 2030, up from 80% today.

Why focus on cities?

This chapter analyses the size and pattern of energy consumption in the world's cities and towns today and projected developments through to 2030.[1] Cities (including towns) currently use over two-thirds of the world's energy and account for more than 70% of global CO_2 emissions.[2] Driven by growing urbanisation, city energy use is set to increase significantly through to 2030: in the Reference Scenario, energy use in cities rises to 73% of the global total and CO_2 emissions to 76%. Given the scale of city energy use and CO_2 emissions, if cities and their authorities were to take action to mitigate climate change, this growth could be curtailed.

Cities are a dynamic and vital part of global culture and are the main engines of social, economic and technological development. From the small cities in the Pacific to the large mega-cities of Asia or North America, cities are home to an ever-increasing number of people. But to provide their populations with the myriad of services demanded, cities need large amounts of energy. Today, much of that energy is fossil-fuel based. As the urban population, economic activity and wealth increase, urban energy use is set to grow. In 2008, half of the world's population live in cities. According to UN projections, by 2030, cities will house 60% of the world's population — equivalent to the total global population in 1986. At the same time, the geographic distribution of urban population is set to change: while global urbanisation in the first half of the 20th century was dominated by European cities, the majority of urban residents today live in Asia, despite the relatively low proportion there of city residents (Figure 8.1). Some of the fastest-growing cities are in Africa.

Figure 8.1 ● Regional trends in urbanisation

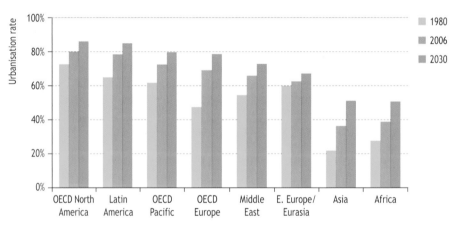

Sources: UNPD, 2007a and 2007b.

---

1. Throughout this chapter, "cities" refers to all urban areas, including towns. The terms "cities" and "urban" are used interchangeably. Box 8.1 describes the ways energy data and projections of energy use in cities were prepared.
2. See Chapter 16 for detailed CO_2 emission projections for cities.

Box 8.1 ● *Methodological issues and city energy data*

There is no international consensus on the definition of a city. For reasons of data availability, in this *Outlook* "city" refers to all urban areas, from "mega-cities" to smaller-scale urban settlements. City energy data are difficult to find, often incomplete and rarely in a format that allows comparisons between cities or with national data. Once data are acquired, analysis requires consideration of city boundary issues – what energy was consumed within the city, how to deal with energy supplied from outside the city (for example, power generation) and transit energy consumption (for example, vehicles passing through a city). Many cities are collecting their own data on energy consumption, but there is a lack of standard reporting methods. Various local government associations, for example the International Council for Local Environmental Initiatives (ICLEI), are attempting to establish more uniform data-collection methods.

The global estimates of city energy use and CO_2 emissions presented in this *Outlook* have been calculated on the basis of the detailed energy-consumption projections for the 21 *WEO* regions in the IEA's World Energy Model. City energy use was calculated using detailed analysis from four regions selected on the basis of the importance of these regions and the availability of city energy data: the United States, the European Union (split into two), Australia and New Zealand combined, and China. These regions account for over half of the world's current energy consumption. For each of these four regions a detailed analysis of 2006 data produced, for each fuel and by end-use sector, a per-capita ratio of city energy use to national energy use. These ratios were used to derive total final consumption in these four regions. The share of electricity consumed in cities was used to apportion national power generation, regardless of whether the electricity was generated in the city or not. This result was then used to calculate the primary energy used in power generation associated with the electricity consumed in cities.[3] Each of the four modelling region's ratios were calculated using methods appropriate to the data available.[4]

In addition to these four detailed regional analyses, selected major cities in other regions for which detailed data were available, such as Tokyo, Moscow and Delhi, were used to further refine the ratios. We applied the most appropriate per-capita ratios, and the UN urbanisation projections, to the energy projections of the 21 *WEO* regions to calculate energy demand in cities at the global level through to 2030. For OECD regions, the differential between rural and urban per-capita energy consumption is assumed to remain constant over the *Outlook* period. For non-OECD regions, we assume that the differential converges over the *Outlook* period towards the urban/rural differential in OECD regions. Energy-related CO_2 emissions were calculated using national carbon factors by sector and fuel (see Chapter 16 for detailed CO_2 emissions projections).

---

3. Based on the assumption that the city power-generation mix and conversion efficiencies are the same as those at the regional level.

4. A detailed definition of regions and a description of the methodology for modelling city energy use are available at www.worldenergyoutlook.org.

The scale and pattern of city energy use has significant implications both for energy security and global greenhouse-gas emissions. Alert to the climate-change challenge, some city authorities are actively involved in reducing energy use and CO_2 emissions. For example, London has an aggressive climate-change policy involving a range of activities, such as working in partnership with private sector companies to design, finance, build, own and operate decentralised, low-energy and zero-carbon projects.

The analysis of global city energy use presented here is, to our knowledge, the most in-depth ever attempted. In view of data deficiencies and methodological challenges, however, the results should be treated as no more than indicative.

Current and projected energy use in cities

Our detailed analysis of current city energy use focuses particularly on four regions: the United States, the European Union, Australasia (defined here as Australia and New Zealand), and China. In the first three, city energy use per capita is roughly the same as the national average (Table 8.1). Cities in the European Union tend to use less energy per capita than US and Australasian cities, because of higher population densities, more extensive urban public transport systems, and more district heating. By contrast, cities in China are significantly more energy intensive per capita than the national average as a result of higher incomes and better availability of energy services compared with rural areas. The recent increase in Chinese national per-capita energy consumption — 8.5% per year between 2000 and 2006 — has been driven partly by urbanisation. During that period the urban population in China grew by 3.2% per year, adding a further 91 million inhabitants to Chinese cities.

Table 8.1 ● Overview of city energy use and urbanisation rate in regions and countries analysed in depth, 2006

Region	Share of city primary energy demand in regional total	Ratio of city per-capita primary energy demand to regional average	Urbanisation rate
United States	80%	0.99	81%
European Union	69%	0.94	73%
Australasia	78%	0.88	88%
China	75%	1.82	41%

Note: Fuel breakdowns for each region are in the regional section.

Based on the results of our analysis of primary energy use in cities in these four regions, we estimate that around 7 900 Mtoe was consumed globally in cities in 2006 (Table 8.2). This equates to 67% of the world's primary energy demand in 2006, or more than four times that of China — the world's second-largest energy consumer. The proportion of global energy consumed in cities is greater than the proportion of the world's population living in cities. This is because city energy use is related to economic activity, as well as city population. A large proportion of industrial and commercial activity, which consume a large proportion of total energy, is located in cities. For example, the majority of commercial buildings are located in cities. Urban energy use is also higher than rural energy use because, in the developing world (with urbanisation rates of 30% to 50%) residential per-capita energy use tends to be significantly higher in cities than in rural areas. This is because energy use is related to income and, as noted above in relation to China, city dwellers in the developing world tend to have higher incomes and better access to energy services. The income effect usually outweighs efficiency gains due to higher density settlement in cities. By contrast, city and rural residents in developed countries tend to enjoy similar levels of energy service access. Because of the rapid growth of cities in the developing world, their pattern of energy use will increasingly shape global energy use, though the rural/urban differential is expected to diminish somewhat.

Table 8.2 ● World energy demand in cities by fuel in the Reference Scenario

	2006		2015		2030		
	Mtoe	Cities as a % of world	Mtoe	Cities as a % of world	Mtoe	Cities as a % of world	2006-2030*
Coal	2 330	76%	3 145	78%	3 964	81%	2.2%
Oil	2 519	63%	2 873	63%	3 394	66%	1.2%
Gas	1 984	82%	2 418	83%	3 176	87%	2.0%
Nuclear	551	76%	630	77%	726	81%	1.2%
Hydro	195	75%	245	76%	330	79%	2.2%
Biomass and waste	280	24%	358	26%	520	31%	2.6%
Other renewables	48	72%	115	73%	264	75%	7.4%
Total	7 908	67%	9 785	69%	12 374	73%	1.9%
Electricity	1 019	76%	1 367	77%	1 912	79%	2.7%

* Average annual growth rate.

Globally, the share of natural gas (82%) and electricity (76%) consumed in cities is higher than the average of all fuels, and much higher than the share of the world's population living in cities. This is due to the more extensive infrastructure in cities for energy distribution and higher appliance-ownership rates in developing cities relative to rural areas. Coal consumption in cities accounts for 76% of the global total, mainly from coal-fired power generation and coal use in urban-based industry in developing countries, such as China. The share of oil consumed in cities (63%) is smaller than the average of all fuels, due to higher penetration of electricity for heating and cooking, and wider use of urban public transport networks. The share of biomass and waste consumption, at 24% globally, is much lower in cities than in rural areas, consisting in OECD cities largely of biofuel consumption and biomass in industry and power generation. In developing countries, traditional biomass and waste is still used for domestic cooking and heating in cities, but consumption is much less per capita than in rural areas. Some 72% of other renewables are consumed in cities, mainly for power generation in OECD countries.

In the Reference Scenario, global city energy use is projected to grow by 1.9% per year (compared to an overall global growth rate of 1.6% per year), to 12 374 Mtoe in 2030. Its share of global energy use rises from 67% to 73% (Figure 8.2). Non-OECD countries account for 81% of the growth in energy use in cities over the *Outlook* period.

Figure 8.2 ● **World and city primary energy consumption in the Reference Scenario**

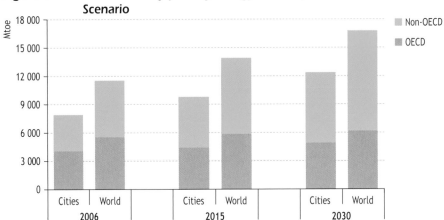

United States

Background

Over the past century, the United States has evolved from a largely industrial economy, dominated by the large cities of the Northeast and Midwest, towards a more dispersed, services-oriented economy. This shift has been characterised by growth in suburban areas and smaller cities, along with the expansion of urban areas in the Southwest which are dependent on cars and air conditioning. The proportion of the US population living in urban areas has increased from 40% in 1900 to over 80% today, with most population growth over the 20th century occurring in urban areas (USGCRP, 2001). Over the next 20 years, urban population in the United States is expected to grow by approximately 1% per year, reaching 87% of the total population by 2030.

The United States contributes just 5% of global population and 8% of urban population, but it is responsible for over 25% of global GDP,[5] nearly 87% of which is generated in metropolitan areas.[6] US energy policy is mainly controlled by the federal government,

5. At market exchange rates.

though state-level authorities are increasingly influential. For example, although the United States has not ratified the Kyoto Protocol, several states have voluntarily set their own targets which meet or exceed Kyoto targets. California aims to reduce its emissions to 80% below 1990 levels by 2050. The Regional Greenhouse Gas Initiative in the eastern part of the United States and the Western Governors' Initiative are multi-state climate change and greenhouse-gas emissions assessment and reduction initiatives.

Three frequent drivers of local policy in the United States are the security of the local energy supply, the affordability of energy services, and the long-term economic prospects of the city. New York City's 2004 Energy Policy Task Force report and 2007 Citywide Sustainability Plan were explicit in warning that the city would soon be unable to meet peak demand for power and in identifying what steps must be taken to remedy the problem. In other cases, such as in San Francisco, local environmental concerns have been pre-eminent, expressed particularly in efforts to force local utilities to reduce power-plant emissions levels. Several large cities, including Los Angeles, Austin and Seattle, actually own and operate the utility providing local gas and electric services, giving them significant influence over the types of fuels used to generate power.

Several mayors, including those of Seattle, New York, Salt Lake City, Chicago and San Francisco, have made climate and energy planning a central tenet of their administrations. They have also been vocal in rallying other cities to join in these efforts. In 2005, the mayor of Seattle spearheaded the formation of the US Conference of Mayors Climate Protection Agreement, an initiative whereby cities pledge to reduce local greenhouse-gas emissions to 7% below 1990 levels by 2012. As of July 2008, 850 mayors across the United States — representing 80 million people — have signed this pledge. In 2007, the mayor of New York hosted the second C40 Large Cities for Climate Protection conference, an international initiative involving 40 of the largest cities around the world. Later that year, the mayor of New York spoke at the Bali Climate Change Conference on behalf of mayors around the world, calling on international climate negotiators to reflect on the role cities can have in global climate-change mitigation efforts.

Reference Scenario projections

City and urban areas account for 80% of total US primary energy demand (Table 8.6) driven by the high rate of urbanisation. This is significantly higher than the global average of around 67%. US cities tend to have slightly lower per-capita energy consumption than the national average. Most urban efficiency gains are attributable to the transportation sector, where each urban resident consumes 11% less transport energy than the average US resident.

---

6. Defined as core urban centres and adjacent surrounding counties (US Census Bureau, 2000; BEA, 2007).

Figure 8.3 ● US energy consumption in cities by state, 2006

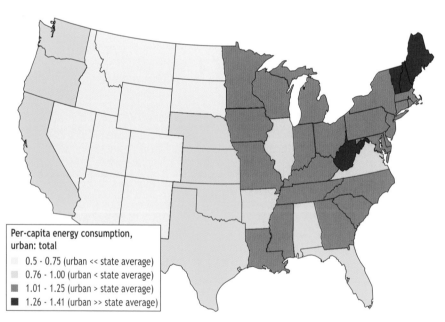

State energy consumption -
urban consumption %

< 30%	61 - 70%
31 - 40%	71 - 80%
41 - 50%	81 - 90%
51 - 60%	> 90%

The boundaries and names shown and the designations used on maps included in this publication do not imply official endorsement or acceptance by the IEA.

Per-capita energy consumption,
urban: total

	0.5 - 0.75 (urban << state average)
	0.76 - 1.00 (urban < state average)
	1.01 - 1.25 (urban > state average)
	1.26 - 1.41 (urban >> state average)

The boundaries and names shown and the designations used on maps included in this publication do not imply official endorsement or acceptance by the IEA.

Source: IEA analysis.

Table 8.3 ● US energy demand in cities by fuel in the Reference Scenario

	2006		2015		2030		
	Mtoe	Cities as a % of national	Mtoe	Cities as a % of national	Mtoe	Cities as a % of national	2006- 2030*
Coal	470	85%	512	88%	577	91%	0.9%
Oil	679	72%	668	75%	683	77%	0.0%
Gas	432	86%	454	89%	478	92%	0.4%
Nuclear	184	86%	199	89%	232	93%	1.0%
Hydro	22	86%	23	89%	24	93%	0.4%
Biomass and waste	68	85%	111	88%	170	92%	3.9%
Other renewables	11	85%	29	88%	65	91%	7.9%
Total	1 865	80%	1 996	83%	2 229	87%	0.7%
Electricity	277	86%	310	89%	376	93%	1.3%

* Average annual growth rate.

Total urban energy consumption in US cities is set to increase from 1 865 Mtoe in 2006 to 2 229 Mtoe by 2030, growing at 0.7% per annum, almost double the 0.4% per annum growth at the US national level. This growth is driven by projected growth of the urban population in the United States, from 81% today to 87% by 2030. However, improvements in energy intensity at the national level result in a drop in per-capita energy consumption of urban residents from 7.6 Mtoe today to 7.0 Mtoe by 2030.

Findings for the United States as a whole mask strong regional variations in urban consumption, driven by large differences in individual city size, levels of urbanisation, climate, density, housing stock and per-capita income (Figure 8.3). In most coastal states, urban energy consumption is over 70% of the total; in many of the densely populated and highly urbanised states of the Northeast, urban energy consumption accounts for over 90% of state consumption. Per-capita consumption tends to be higher in urban areas east of the Mississippi and lower in urban areas west of the Mississippi.

European Union

Background

As one of the early centres of industrial transformation, the area that makes up the European Union is characterised by high levels of population density, urbanisation and energy use. With a current population of almost 500 million, accounting for 8% of the global population, the European Union generates 31% of global GDP.[7] Population projections are flat throughout the *Outlook* period, while urbanisation is projected to continue growing from 73% today to 80% by 2030.

Over the past decade, the European Union has been one of the driving forces behind international policy agreements for binding climate-protection targets. The European Union has set up an internal market for emission trading, which was operational before the Kyoto Protocol came in to force in February 2005.

---

7. At market exchange rates.

Compared with other world regions, the European Union has a distinctive form of multi-level governance uniting 27 member states. It does not have a truly common and comprehensive energy policy, though a growing body of EU legislation does affect the energy sector in member countries. European Union directives cover a range of issues, including co-generation using renewable energy (combined heat and power), internal markets in electricity and gas, and energy efficiency. Additionally, industrial point-source greenhouse-gas emissions are traded in the world's largest multi-national and multi-sector market for emission trading, the European Union Emissions Trading Scheme (see Chapter 17), covering more than 10 000 installations of the energy and industrial sectors. Urban and regional climate-protection strategies operate in parallel with the efforts at the national and supra-national scale.

Arrangements for, and the extent of, energy planning and policy at the urban and regional level vary considerably among member states, reflecting the heterogeneity of the structure of government and the levels of local participation in member states. Some members of the European Union have a federal organisation, with extensive powers exercised at the urban and regional level. Cities like Berlin, Bremen or Hamburg, for example, are federal states (Länder) in their own right, able to decide their individual energy programmes. Communes in the Nordic countries have considerable control over how to spend their tax income; and in the UK many planning decisions are devolved to the local authority or metropolitan level.

European cities have given a lead, internationally, to efforts to mitigate climate change. Almost all EU capitals and large cities have adopted, or are currently discussing, local climate-change action plans and greenhouse-gas emissions reduction targets that are, at times, more ambitious than those at the European and national levels. A specific characteristic of the European institutional framework for energy and climate policy is the importance of city networks, many of them partly financed by the European Union, as a way of sharing ideas and best practice.

Reference Scenario projections

In 2006, urban areas accounted for 1 259 Mtoe, about 69%, of the total primary energy demand of the European Union. Final energy demand on a per-capita basis was about 3.5 Mtoe in urban areas, slightly lower than the EU average of 3.7 Mtoe per capita. Average per-capita consumption in rural areas was even higher, at around 4.9 Mtoe.

Total urban primary energy consumption in the European Union is projected to increase by 168 Mtoe over the projection period, reaching 1 427 Mtoe by 2030 – an average rate of growth of 0.5% per year. This is more than twice the rate of the European Union as a whole, which averages 0.2% per year and is accounted for by the growth in the urban share of the EU population to 80% by 2030 (Table 8.4). Urban energy consumption increases in absolute terms as the urban population rises, because improvements in energy intensity can not keep pace with the rise in population. Per-capita energy consumption increases from 3.5 Mtoe in 2006 to 3.6 Mtoe by 2030 (Figure 8.4).

The fuel mix in cities differs considerably from the EU average. A higher share of grid-based fuels, such as gas, heat and electricity, is consumed in cities, compared with the EU average for all fuels, whereas a lower proportion of coal, biomass and oil is used.

Table 8.4 ● European Union energy demand in cities by fuel in the Reference Scenario

	2006		2015		2030		
	Mtoe	Cities as a % of regional	Mtoe	Cities as a % of regional	Mtoe	Cities as a % of regional	2006-2030*
Coal	207	64%	214	66%	183	70%	-0.5%
Oil	397	59%	388	60%	384	64%	-0.1%
Gas	397	91%	456	92%	536	96%	1.3%
Nuclear	187	73%	171	74%	138	80%	-1.3%
Hydro	19	74%	25	76%	31	82%	1.9%
Biomass and waste	41	45%	61	46%	93	49%	3.4%
Other renewables	10	70%	29	72%	62	76%	8.1%
Total	1 259	69%	1 344	71%	1 427	75%	0.5%
Electricity	176	73%	204	75%	245	79%	1.4%

* Average annual growth rate.

Figure 8.4 ● Per-capita energy demand in the European Union and EU cities in the Reference Scenario

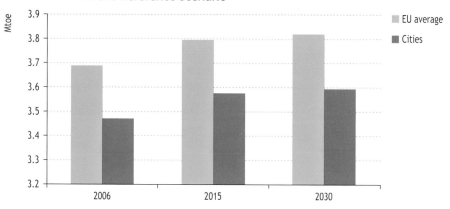

Australasia

Background

Both Australia and New Zealand have developed largely through agriculture and natural resource production, and are now characterised by a few cities that are large relative to the national population. Urbanisation rates have been traditionally high and continue to grow. In 2006, Australia had a population of 20.6 million people, with 13.1 million (63.5% of the total population) living in eight regional capital cities. In 2006, New Zealand's population was 3.9 million people, with 1.9 million (48.5%) living in the three major urban areas. As most of the development of cities in Australia and New Zealand has taken place since the advent of the motor vehicle, the density of the residential urban population, approximately 1 500 people per square kilometre, is low. Cities tend to conform to a spread-out suburban model, with a denser inner ring (around a core that has become denser in the last decade) and gradual reduction of population density as the city expands.

Most major Australian cities are governed by multiple local governments, each of which is responsible for a portion of the urban area. Local governments have the power to enact laws and implement policies relating to planning, transport, building, waste and other local issues relating to energy management and climate change. In general, local governments in Australia can implement policy that affects energy demand, both stationary and mobile, but not energy supply. Their role as the planning authority, with responsibility for approving residential and commercial developments, is their main source of influence in relation to energy consumption and CO_2 emissions.

New Zealand cities are governed by local governments, comprising of 12 regional councils, 74 territorial local authorities and four unitary authorities in total. Each local authority has some degree of control over energy-using activities. Typically, local governments (such as Christchurch and Auckland) have intervened on air quality issues and seek to take climate-change issues into consideration in developing other policies for which they are responsible. This has been particularly important in the development of the Long-Term Council Community Plans. Additionally, as the planning authority for wind farms and hydro developments, local governments have been at the forefront of the development of alternative energy systems. Local governments are not prevented from developing power generation facilities or operating an electricity-supply business but, to date, the focus of policy has been on managing demand through policy implementation or ambitious targets such as the zero net-emissions target of Wellington.

The commercial and services sector together now dominate the Australian economy, accounting for 60% of GDP in 2006. This proportion of the economy has been increasing for a number of years (ABS, 2007). Most commercial activity is office-based and has relatively low energy intensity. Residential energy consumption, on the other hand, has been increasing steadily for many years, driven by increasing appliance-ownership rates. Moving people and goods around sparsely populated countries such as Australia and New Zealand requires a large amount of energy.

Reference Scenario projections

In 2006, the cities in Australia and New Zealand consumed 78% of total energy demand, totalling 109 Mtoe (Table 8.8). Cities consumed 80% of total electricity and almost all natural gas in the end-use sectors, as there is little local distribution of natural gas in rural areas. Energy use per capita in cities is lower than the national average, at 5.0 Mtoe in 2006, compared to 5.6 Mtoe for Australia and New Zealand as a whole.

Table 8.5 ● Australasian energy demand in cities by fuel in the Reference Scenario

	2006		2015		2030		
	Mtoe	Cities as a % of regional	Mtoe	Cities as a % of regional	Mtoe	Cities as a % of regional	2006-2030*
Coal	45	80%	49	82%	47	83%	0.2%
Oil	30	66%	34	67%	35	69%	0.7%
Gas	25	93%	28	95%	34	97%	1.3%
Nuclear	0	n.a.	0	n.a.	0	n.a.	n.a
Hydro	3	80%	3	82%	3	84%	0.8%
Biomass and waste	5	75%	7	77%	10	79%	3.5%
Other renewables	2	70%	3	67%	7	64%	5.9%
Total	109	78%	124	79%	136	80%	0.9%
Electricity	*17*	*80%*	*20*	*82%*	*24*	*84%*	*1.4%*

* Average annual growth rate.

8

The commercial sector is less energy intensive per capita than the residential sector, and industry and transport are the most energy-intensive sectors. Total urban energy demand in Australasia is projected to increase from 109 Mtoe today to 136 Mtoe by 2030, growing at 0.9% per year. This is slightly quicker than the 0.8% per year consumption growth for the region as a whole. In addition to an increased use of oil in the rural residential sector, there is an increase in the use of biomass, due to the proximity of fuelwood sources and lower population density reducing air pollution concerns.

China

Background

China contributes 20% of the global population and 17% of the global urban population. In 2006, China's urban population was 545 million, more than the entire population of the European Union. The UN projections see the current rate of urbanisation in China — around 40% — reaching 60% by 2030. Given that Chinese cities are more energy intensive per capita than rural areas, this will have significant implications for the national energy system and global energy markets.

In China, city governments have some influence over local energy supply and demand. one reason being that public utilities and many industries are still owned by city authorities. However, cities are firmly guided by national policies, which they are responsible for implementing. China's 20% energy-intensity reduction target by 2010, in its 11th Five-Year Plan, illustrates the relationship between national and local government. This target was delegated to provincial level in the form of provincial performance targets. Although regional autonomy was strengthened through reforms in the 1990s, energy remains a strategic sector directed by the central government.

There is intense competition between cities in China to attract investment and, as a consequence, cities act to address concerns about energy security and local air pollution. Interventions by city authorities on energy matters tend to concentrate on four major fronts:

- Clean energy, especially by encouraging greater penetration of natural gas and limiting the use of coal in the household and commercial sectors.
- Action in the energy sector to facilitate economic structural change from primary to secondary industries and towards an enlarged tertiary sector.
- Promoting energy efficiency.
- Improving public and mass-transportation systems.

Climate change is becoming an increasingly important policy priority for both the national government and city governments. A number of energy and environmental policies at the city level have an impact on climate issues. Examples include the local air-pollution control policy associated with the 2008 Beijing Olympics, Shanghai's vehicle-supply control policy, and policies to increase investment in renewable energy. Some Chinese cities have also been involved in international efforts to develop low carbon cities, initiated by organisations such as the World Wildlife Fund and others. New cities are putting greater emphasis on energy and climate issues. Dontang Eco-City, which is being built at the mouth of the Yangtze River close to Shanghai, is one example. Differences in the per-capita energy use and CO_2 emissions of Chinese cities reflect a number of local conditions, of which scale and structure of the local economy are key factors (Figure 8.5).

Figure 8.5 ● **Per-capita energy demand and gross regional product in selected Chinese cities, 2006**

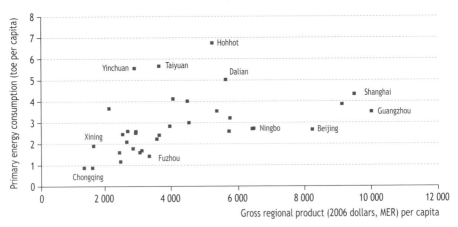

Source: Dhakal, 2008

Reference Scenario projections

The share of cities in China's total primary energy demand in 2006 is estimated at 75% or about 1 424 Mtoe (Table 8.6). The per-capita energy use of urban areas in China is about 80% higher than in the country as a whole. On average, each urban citizen in

China consumes 2.6 Mtoe, compared with 1.4 Mtoe nationally, reflecting higher urban incomes. Coal provides about 87% of urban primary energy. Natural gas use in cities in China is increasing rapidly. Beijing leads this trend, and the share of natural gas has dramatically increased since 2000. Further urbanisation and economic development should lead to a convergence of urban and rural energy intensity. Cities will have an increasing role in shaping the energy profile of China, with urban areas providing great opportunities for large-scale policy interventions for managing the overall energy system. By 2030 cities in China are projected to consume 3 220 Mtoe. The proportionate effect on energy consumption of strong urbanisation growth is partially offset by the fact that increasing energy consumption in rural areas is also expected to grow strongly through the *Outlook* period, with the net result that the share of city energy use in China increases to 83% by 2030. Phasing out of coal, and greater use of natural gas and liquefied petrolum gas, in residential and commercial sectors in urban areas is set to increase.

Table 8.6 ● **Chinese energy demand in cities by fuel in the Reference Scenario**

	2006		2015		2030		
	Mtoe	Cities as a % of national	Mtoe	Cities as a % of national	Mtoe	Cities as a % of national	2006-2030*
Coal	1 059	87%	1 665	88%	2 206	90%	3.1%
Oil	271	77%	428	77%	648	80%	3.7%
Gas	40	81%	84	82%	158	84%	5.9%
Nuclear	12	84%	39	84%	67	87%	7.5%
Hydro	31	84%	52	84%	76	87%	3.8%
Biomass and waste	10	4%	12	5%	37	16%	5.6%
Other renewables	2	45%	9	62%	27	67%	12.2%
Total	1 424	75%	2 289	79%	3 220	83%	3.5%
Electricity	*161*	*80%*	*314*	*80%*	*495*	*83%*	*4.8%*

* Average annual growth rate.

8

PART B
OIL AND GAS PRODUCTION PROSPECTS

How much oil and gas is there in the ground and how much can be economically produced? Over the years to 2030, what investment will be required to exploit these reserves and can we be confident that it will be forthcoming? These are the questions addressed in Part B.

The oil and gas is there, but the sums required to exploit them are daunting. Remaining reserves of oil continue to rise, despite growing consumption, and the gas-reserves position is still more comfortable. But the exploitation costs have risen fast and, as we become increasingly dependent on OPEC countries and their national oil companies, the opportunities for international oil companies diminish. If prices stay high, the depletion policies of some producing countries become increasingly restrictive.

On the basis of a detailed field-by-field analysis of production trends at 800 of the world's largest oilfields and the assessment of the prospects for reserves growth and new discoveries, Chapters 9, 10 and 11 examine in detail the evidence on available resources and the prospects for future supply. The demands are great. Between now and 2015 some 30 mb/d of new production capacity needs to be brought on stream to compensate for the decline in production from existing fields and meet the growth in demand. Chapter 12 similarly reviews the prospects for gas.

Chapter 13 quantifies the investment needed to exploit oil and gas resources on the required scale and, together with Chapter 14, which looks at the structural changes taking place in the upstream industry, assesses whether the prevailing conditions warrant confidence that the investment will be forthcoming.

Finally in this Part B, oil and gas prospects in oil- and gas-rich sub-Saharan Africa are analysed, exposing potential government earnings from oil and gas of some $4 trillion over the years to 2030 — many times more than would be required to bring basic modern energy services to the energy-poor of these countries. But will these government resources be devoted to this cause, which can underpin economic development?

CHAPTER 9

TURNING OIL RESOURCES INTO RESERVES
How much is left to produce?

- The world is far from running short of oil. Remaining proven reserves of oil and natural gas liquids worldwide at the end of 2007 amounted to about 1.2 to 1.3 trillion barrels (including about 0.2 trillion barrels of Canadian oil sands). These reserves have almost doubled since 1980. Though most of the increase has come from revisions made in the 1980s in OPEC countries rather than from new discoveries, modest increases have continued since 1990, despite rising consumption. The volume discovered has fallen well below the volume produced in the last two decades, though the volume of oil found on average each year since 2000 has exceeded the rate in the 1990s thanks to increased exploration activity (with higher oil prices) and improvements in technology.

- Ultimately recoverable conventional resources – a category that includes initial proven and probable reserves from discovered fields, reserves growth and economically recoverable oil that has yet to be found – amounts to 3.5 trillion barrels (leaving aside about 0.5 trillion additional barrels which might come from new sources not yet assessed and the application of new technologies). Only a third of this total has been produced up to now. Undiscovered resources account for about a third of the remaining recoverable oil, the largest volumes of which are thought to lie in the Middle East, Russia and the Caspian region.

- Future reserves growth will depend, to a large extent, on increases in the recovery factor, which is estimated to average about 35% worldwide today. Such increases, through secondary and enhanced oil recovery (EOR) techniques and other factors, could make a big difference to recoverable reserves, prolonging the production life of producing fields and postponing the peak of conventional oil production: a mere one percentage point increase in the average recovery factor at existing fields alone would add more than 80 billion barrels (two years of current consumption) or 6% to the world's proven oil reserves.

- Non-conventional oil resources are also large. Oil sands and extra-heavy oil resources in place worldwide amount to around 6 trillion barrels, of which between 1 and 2 trillion barrels may be ultimately recoverable economically. These resources are largely concentrated in Canada (mainly in Alberta) and Venezuela (in the Orinoco Belt). There is additional potential from oil shales, but their production cost and the environmental impact of their commercialisation are very uncertain.

- The total, long-term potentially recoverable oil resource base, including extra-heavy oil, oil sands and oil shales, is estimated at around 6.5 trillion barrels. Adding coal-to-liquids and gas-to-liquids increases this potential to about 9 trillion barrels. Of these totals, nearly 1.1 trillion barrels have already been produced, for the most part at a cost of up to $30 per barrel in year-2008 dollars (excluding taxes and royalties). The cost of exploiting remaining conventional resources typically ranges from $10 to $40 per barrel, while exploitation of oil sands costs between $30 and $80. EOR costs vary between $10 and $80 per barrel and oil shales from $50 to well over $100.

Classifying hydrocarbon resources

The amount of fossil-hydrocarbon resources (or hydrocarbons initially in place) on the earth is finite. These resources can be categorised according to the degree of certainty that they exist and by the likelihood that they can be extracted profitably. Several different protocols exist for classifying resources, many of them developed by national organisations.[1] This has caused confusion and inconsistency in measuring and comparing resources.

Efforts have been made to achieve a harmonised international approach. The Society of Petroleum Engineers (SPE), the World Petroleum Council (WPC), the American Association of Petroleum Geologists (AAPG) and the Society of Petroleum Evaluation Engineers (SPEE) published jointly in 2007 guidelines on resource definition and classification, called the Petroleum Resources Management System (PRMS). This system is compatible with the 2004 UN Framework Classification for Fossil Energy and Mineral Resources (UNFC), which has been developed by the UN Economic Commission for Europe (UNECE). The PRMS classifies resources and reserves according to the level of certainty about recoverable volumes and the likelihood that they can be exploited profitably (Figure 9.1). The main innovation concerns a shift to a project-based methodology whereby estimated recoverable quantities are related to actual investment. The classification applies to both conventional and non-conventional resources.

Under the PRMS and UNFC systems, "proved reserves" (or 1P reserves) are hydrocarbons that have been discovered and for which there is a 90% probability that they can be extracted profitably (on the basis of assumptions about cost, geology, technology, marketability and future prices). "Proved and probable reserves" (2P reserves) include additional volumes that are thought to exist in accumulations that have been discovered and that are expected to be commercial, but with only a 50% probability that they can be produced profitably. "Possible reserves" (3P reserves) add to the 2P reserves volumes in discovered fields with a 10% probability of being profitable. Estimates of reserves in each category change over time as the underlying assumptions are modified or new information becomes available.

---

1. See Etherington and Ritter (2007) for a detailed outline.

Deterministic and probabilistic methodologies are used to estimate reserves. [
engineers typically apply a number of different formulas involving a range of
and probabilities to test the sensitivity of a preferred approach or set of ass
Increasingly, companies rely on seismic data to map out hydrocarbon reservoir.
the US Securities and Exchange Commission (SEC), which imposes reserves-reporting
standards for companies quoted on US stock exchanges, until now has not allowed
companies to book reserves on undrilled acreage on the basis of seismic data alone:
it also requires evidence from drilling. The price of oil or gas is a key parameter for
assessing the potential profitability of reserves. As prices rise, some reserves that were
previously classified as non-commercial may become potentially profitable and be
moved into the possible, probable or proven category.

Figure 9.1 ● **Hydrocarbon resource classification**

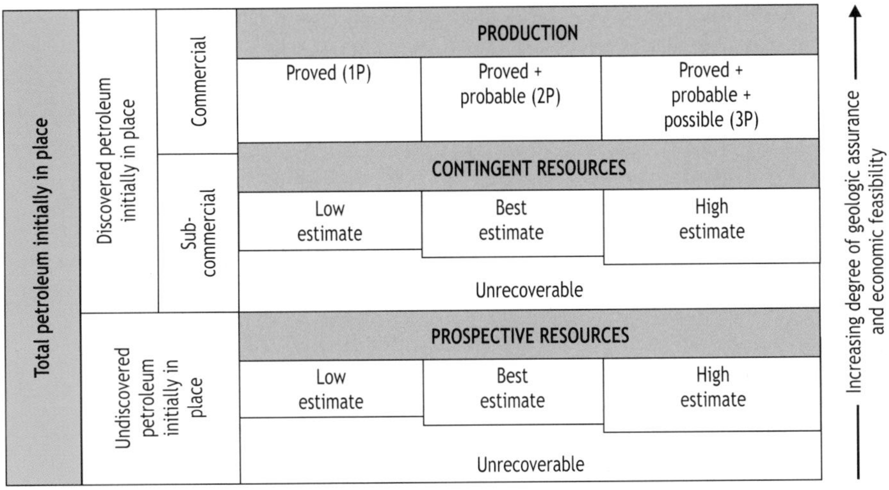

Source: SPE/WPC/AAPG (2007).

While progress has been made in establishing a harmonised system of defining and
classifying resources, the way those resources are measured in practice still differs
widely by country and by jurisdiction. There is no internationally agreed benchmark
or legal standard as to how much proof is needed to demonstrate the existence of a
discovery, nor about the assumptions to be used to determine whether discovered
oil can be produced profitably. This is, in part, because different reporting systems
are designed for different purposes. Standards for financial reporting, such as SEC
rules, are typically the strictest and result in the lowest estimates. In addition, the
extent of the requirements for companies to release information on resources and
reserves differs markedly. Auditing reserves and publishing the results are far from
universal practice. Many oil companies, including international oil companies, use
external auditors and publish the results, but most national oil companies do not.

These inconsistencies have created confusion over just how much oil can reasonably be expected to be produced commercially in the long term. Box 9.1 explains how resources are defined and measured in the *Outlook*.

Box 9.1 ● Defining and measuring conventional and non-conventional hydrocarbon reserves in the *WEO*

The PRMS classification applies to both conventional and non-conventional resources. Unless otherwise stated, in this analysis, non-conventional oil includes extra-heavy oil, oil sands, oil shales, coal-to-liquids and gas-to-liquids. It does not include vegetable oil derived from biomass. But there is also a category of oil which, though considered conventional, can be extracted only using new technologies which are not yet fully developed and/or involves pioneering work in frontier areas, such as ultra-deepwater. Included in this category is oil recovered from as-yet unopened areas of the Arctic and from new deepwater and ultra-deepwater resources, together with additional oil recovered from new enhanced oil recovery projects. There are very large uncertainties about the extent of economically recoverable resources in this category and this *"conventional oil produced by unconventional means"*, which is discussed below, is often not included in estimates of ultimately recoverable resources. For example, it is not included in the latest figures from the US Geological Survey. We make no systematic estimates for each of the various components of this category, but Figure 9.10 in the last section of this chapter gives a broad illustration of their potential size. Additional oil resulting from reserves growth is customarily included in conventional oil, except where the reserves growth derives from the new EOR projects mentioned above.

A number of bodies, including the IEA, UNECE, SPE, WPC, AAPG and the SEC, are working together to try to harmonise the way in which different types of reserves are measured in practice, with the aim of bringing transparency to resource reporting. In particular, there is a need to ensure that financial and accounting standards for hydrocarbon exploration and production are consistent with business and technical practice. In recognition of this, the SEC has itself proposed new rules on reserves disclosure (Box 9.2), and efforts are being made to ensure that harmonised rules on reporting and communicating reserves estimates are implemented as widely as possible. Progress is hampered by the reluctance to accept new standards on the part of countries and industries that have developed their own reporting systems, and difficulties in adapting national systems to a universal system. Some appreciable progress has been achieved in data transparency on oil production, thanks to the Joint Oil Data Initiative (JODI). A similar approach could be considered to improve the quality of the data on reserves. A successful effort to address both concerns would contribute to better decision making by all interested parties.

Box 9.2 • Proposed new SEC reserves-reporting rules

In July 2008, the US Securities and Exchange Commission announced proposed revised oil and gas company reporting requirements aimed at providing investors with a more accurate and useful picture of the oil and gas reserves that a company holds. Reflecting the significant changes that have taken place in the oil and gas industry since the adoption of the original reporting requirements more than 25 years ago, the SEC proposal permits companies to take into account improved technologies and alternative extraction methods, enabling them to provide investors with additional information about their reserves. Specific changes to the rules include the following:

- Allowing for the use of new technologies to determine which reserves may be classified as proved, if those technologies have been demonstrated empirically to lead to reliable conclusions about reserves volumes.

- Permitting companies to disclose their probable and possible reserves to investors. Current rules limit disclosure to proved reserves only.

- Allowing previously excluded resources, such as mineable oil sands, to be classified as oil and gas reserves. Currently these resources are considered to be mining reserves.

- Requiring companies to report the independence and qualifications of the assessor or auditor, based on the criteria of the Society of Petroleum Engineers.

- Where companies rely on a third party to prepare reserves estimates or conduct a reserves audit, requiring these reports to be filed.

- Requiring companies to classify and report oil and gas reserves using an average price based upon the prior 12-month period, rather than year-end prices, to maximise the comparability of reserve estimates among companies by eliminating the distortion of the estimates that can arise through the use of a single pricing date.

Source: SEC (www.sec.gov/rules/proposed/2008/33-8935.pdf).

Latest estimates of conventional oil reserves and resources

Proven reserves

Various organisations compile and report data on oil and gas reserves, using national and company sources. The most widely quoted primary sources of global proven oil reserves (1P) data are the *Oil and Gas Journal (O&GJ)* and the *World Oil Journal*. OPEC compiles data for its member countries, and publishes this together with data for other countries drawn from BP. IHS compiles data for 2P reserves only. Other organisations, including BP, publish their own global estimates based mainly on data from primary sources.

Current estimates of remaining economically recoverable reserves of oil worldwide do not vary greatly, despite differences in the way they are reported. *O&GJ* puts global proven oil reserves (including natural gas liquids, NGLs) at the end of 2007 at 1 322 billion barrels, while *World Oil*, at the other end of the spectrum, reports 1 120 billion barrels (Figure 9.2). The IHS estimate is 1 241 billion barrels, implying a lower figure for proven, 1P reserves. The *O&GJ* estimate includes 173 billion barrels of Canadian oil sands. The totals reported by BP,[2] IHS and *World Oil* exclude Canadian oil sands; *World Oil* also excludes NGLs.

Figure 9.2 ● **Estimated remaining world oil reserves, end-2007**

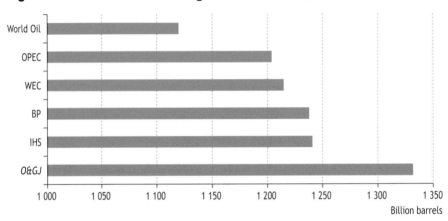

Note: All estimates are for 1P reserves, except the IHS estimate which is for 2P reserves. Oil includes natural gas liquids in all cases except *World Oil*. BP, *O&GJ* and OPEC include oil sands in Canada (BP excludes reserves that are not under active development). The WEC and *World Oil* estimates are for end-2005.

Sources: BP (2008); *O&GJ* (2008); OPEC (2008); WEC (2007); *World Oil* (2006); IHS database.

According to BP, which compiles published official figures, proven reserves worldwide have almost doubled since 1980 (Figure 9.3). Most of the changes result from increases in official figures from OPEC countries, mainly in the Middle East, as a result of large upward revisions in 1986-1987. They were driven by negotiations at that time over production quotas and have little to do with the discovery of new reserves or physical appraisal work on discovered fields. The official reserves of OPEC countries have hardly changed since then, despite ongoing production.

Globally, remaining proven reserves have increased modestly but steadily since 1990, despite continuing consumption growth. According to *O&GJ*, reserves increased by 14.2 billion barrels, or 1.2%, in 2007, mainly thanks to upgrades in Venezuela, Brazil, Saudi Arabia, Kuwait, Iran and Angola. OPEC countries' reserves, at 930 billion barrels based on official data, represent 77% of the world total (using the *O&GJ* estimate). The global reserves-to-production ratio (R/P), based on current levels of production, is in the range of 40 to 45 years, depending on the source and whether non-conventional resources are included. This level has changed little in the last few years.

---

2. In its last two *Statistical Reviews*, BP has included separate estimates of Canadian oil sands. Those reserves are estimated at 152.2 billion barrels at end-2007 (BP, 2008).

Figure 9.3 ● Proven remaining oil reserves by region, 1980-2007 (end-year)

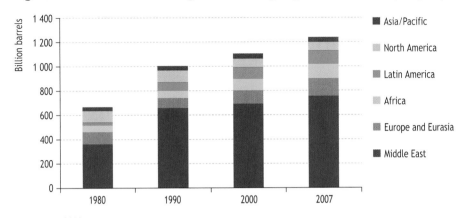

Source: BP (2008).

A growing share of the additions to reserves has been coming from revisions to estimates of the reserves in fields already in production or undergoing appraisal (reserves growth) rather than from new discoveries (see the next section for a discussion of the role of reserves growth). The volume of oil in new discoveries has fallen well below the volume of oil produced in recent years (Figure 9.4). Discoveries dropped from an average of 56 billion barrels per year in the 1960s to 13 billion barrels per year in the 1990s. The *number* of discoveries peaked in the 1980s, but it fell sharply in the 1990s. The fall in both the number of discoveries and the volume of oil discovered has been most acute in the Middle East and the former Soviet Union. By contrast, discoveries rose in Africa, Latin America and Asia. The drop in discoveries worldwide was largely the result of a fall in exploration activity in the regions with the largest reserves (where access by international companies is most difficult) and a fall in the average size of the fields that have been found.

Figure 9.4 ● Oil discoveries* and production, 1960-2006

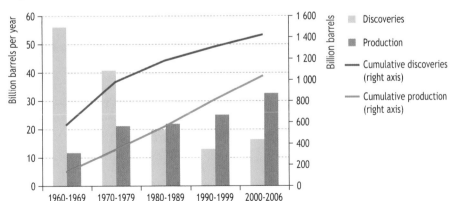

* Additions to proven reserves from new fields.
Sources: IHS and IEA databases.

These factors more than offset the effect of an improved exploration drilling success rate, which has increased by a factor of two in the last 50 years, from one out of six wildcat wells to one out of three today (Harper, 2005). The downward trend in the volume of oil found has reversed slightly in the current decade, thanks to increased exploration activity (with higher oil prices), with an average 16.4 billion barrels per year discovered since 2000. The excess of production over cumulative discoveries over the same period is 400 billion barrels.

Ultimately recoverable resources

Reserves estimates give an indication of how much oil could be developed and produced in the near to medium term. The total volume of oil which might ultimately be produced commercially is known as ultimately recoverable resources. This category includes oil initial proven and probable reserves from discovered fields (including oil already produced), both in production and yet to be developed, reserves growth (see below) and hydrocarbons that are yet to be found. From a larger resource base, more oil is likely to progress into the proven category, deferring the peak in global production and permitting more oil to be produced.

The US Geological Survey, a federal government agency, is the world's leading source of estimates of recoverable hydrocarbon resources. It carried out a major assessment of the world's conventional oil and gas resources in 2000, based on raw data for 1995 (USGS, 2000). Since that time, it has reassessed some basins and assessed some others for the first time. Our current estimates of initial and remaining ultimately recoverable conventional resources are shown in Table 9.1. These take account of the USGS updates, new remaining reserve estimates from IHS and cumulative oil production to the end of 2007, but exclude the "conventional oil produced by unconventional means" discussed later in Box 9.3. On this basis, using the mean figures of the USGS, the world's current ultimate recoverable conventional oil and NGL resources are estimated to amount to just under 3.6 trillion barrels. Of these, cumulative production to date is 1.1 trillion barrels. Remaining resources amount to over 2.4 trillion barrels. Reserves growth accounts for around 400 billion barrels, with the largest contribution to reserves growth (in proportion to the reserves) over the last decade from the Middle East, Latin America and Africa. Remaining recoverable resources are largest in the Middle East, Russia and the Caspian region.

Despite the thoroughness of the assessments, there are considerable uncertainties surrounding the estimates of ultimate recoverable resources — a point highlighted by the USGS itself. In addition to the mean value mentioned above, the USGS provides alternative numbers based on different probabilities, ranging from 2 400 billion barrels with a 90% probability of at least that amount being available to 4 495 billion barrels with a 5% probability (not adjusted for reserves growth since the 2000 assessment was released).

The USGS recently reviewed trends in discoveries and reserves growth in the period 1996-2003, comparing them with their original estimates of the long-term potential (Klett et al., 2007). It found that, based on IHS data, 28% of the estimated additions (mean value) to 2P oil reserves from reserves growth (to 2025) had already been achieved — almost exactly in line with the pace of growth predicted in the 2000 assessment (Figure 9.5). The rate of discovery lagged this figure — 11 % of estimated undiscovered oil volumes had been discovered by 2003 — but the ultimate timescales are not directly comparable. Overall, 71% of the total additions to reserves came from reserves growth and only 29% from discoveries. In all areas except for sub-Saharan Africa and Asia-Pacific, reserves growth outpaced discoveries. For natural gas, a higher proportion of estimated potential from reserves growth had actually been attained (51%) but a smaller share of the potential from discoveries (less than 10%). The share of reserves growth in the total reserve additions between 1996 and 2003 was 79%.

Table 9.1 ● **World ultimately recoverable conventional oil and NGL resources, end-2007** (mean estimates, billion barrels)

	Initial reserves	Cumulative production	Reserves growth	Undiscovered resources	Ultimately recoverable resources	Remaining reserves	Remaining recoverable resources
	[1]	[2]	[3]	[4]	[5 = 1+3+4]	[6 = 1-2]	[7 = 5-2]
OECD	458	363	27	185	670	95	307
North America	368	300	22	95	485	68	185
Europe	77	56	3	80	160	20	103
Pacific	13	7	2	10	25	6	18
Non-OECD	1 911	765	375	620	2 907	1 147	2 142
E. Europe/Eurasia	355	171	67	140	562	184	391
Asia	134	79	20	30	184	55	105
Middle East	986	312	204	257	1 447	674	1 135
Africa	206	102	40	85	331	104	229
Latin America	229	100	44	108	381	129	281
World	2 369	1 128	402	805	3 577	1 241	2 449

Sources: USGS (2000); Klett *et al.* (2007); USGS data provided to IEA; IHS databases; IEA databases and analysis.

Figure 9.5 ● **New field discoveries and reserves growth in 1996-2003 compared with USGS 2000 assessments**

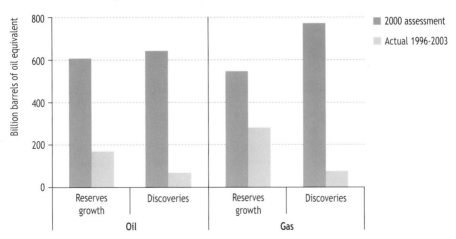

Note: Reserves growth potential in the 2000 USGS assessment is to 2025, while discoveries relate to ultimate resources.

Source: Klett *et al.* (2007).

Arctic resources

The USGS continues to assess global hydrocarbon resources, focusing on particular regions that it judges to be worthy of more in-depth study. In 2005 it launched a major reassessment of the Arctic region (Circum-Arctic Resource Appraisal, CARA), and released the final results in July 2008. Earlier USGS estimates of undiscovered oil and gas in the Arctic, amounting to 25% of total undiscovered resources worldwide, actually included continental areas in Western Siberia below the Arctic Circle.

Box 9.3 ● Potential for exploiting Arctic resources

Oil and gas fields in the arctic frontier area, north of the Arctic Circle, currently account for a small share of the world's hydrocarbon production. But that share could rise significantly in the coming decades as technical challenges are addressed and costs lowered. The Arctic presents many of the high-profile challenges associated with deepwater operating conditions: remoteness, personnel safety, environmental footprints and high costs. An extreme climate and hazards from ice and icebergs add to these difficulties. Significant knowledge of operations in the Arctic was gained in the 1960s and 1970s in Russia, Canada and Alaska. More recently, developments in the Yamal Peninsula, the Snohvit LNG project in the Barents Sea and the offshore Sakhalin projects in Russia, in Arctic-like conditions, have added to that experience. Some prospects are near existing infrastructures such as the North Slope of Alaska and the Pechora Sea in Russia. Other basins are far from areas that have already been explored or where resources have already been exploited.

The ability to drill wells in ice-covered seas will be critical to the efficient development of Arctic resources. There is generally a limited operational window for existing drilling units in ice-covered waters, though the receding ice-cap will increase the size of this window. Fit-for-purpose arctic drillships are being developed in Norway for water depths of more than 80 metres. New technologies such as subsea and sub-ice drilling are being considered. A majority of offshore fields will most likely be developed using subsea technology and well stream transport to land, as was the case with the Snohvit field in Norway (Johnsen, 2008). For easing oil flow at the surface, effective solutions are still to be developed, including fluid conditioning, pressure-boosting and well-intervention technologies. Oil transport by ships is typically done by tankers with a capacity of 100 000 barrels, towed by icebreakers. A tanker being developed by StatoilHydro will be able to carry more than 500 000 barrels of oil (or half as much as a standard very large crude carrier) without the need for icebreakers, except where there are large ice ridges.

Estimates of exploration and production costs in the Arctic vary widely, mainly as a function of the distance from existing fields and the nature of the operating environment. Indicative costs for an offshore arctic production field, including drilling, production facilities, and operating and decommissioning components, are currently about $35 to $40 per barrel for the easiest resources to exploit.

The CARA (USGS, 2008) study covers 31 geological provinces, of which 25 are considered to hold hydrocarbon potential, and 69 assessment units. The new study shows increased potential gas resources — 1 669 trillion cubic feet of gas (30% of the world's undiscovered conventional gas) — but lower quantities of oil — 90 billion barrels (mean value) of undiscovered conventional oil and 44 billion barrels of NGLs (13% of the world's total undiscovered conventional liquids).

Deepwater and ultra-deepwater resources

Estimates of the recoverable conventional oil located in deepwater (water depths between 400 meters and 1 500 metres) and ultra-deepwater (water depths greater than 1 500 meters) lie between 160 and 300 billion barrels (IEA, 2005). Over 70% of these resources are in Brazil, Angola, Nigeria and the United States. Most production to date has occurred in the US Gulf of Mexico, but production is rising in Angola and Brazil (where several large discoveries have been made in the stratum below the salt deposits, the pre-salt layer, Box 9.4). New developments are underway in Mexico, Nigeria, Southeast Asia and the Mediterranean Sea. Other areas of deepwater exploration interest include the UK Atlantic margin, the Black Sea, India and the Arctic. Cumulative global oil discoveries in deepwater offshore areas, plotted against the number of exploration wells, remain on

9

Box 9.4 ● Pre-salt deepwater potential in Brazil

The Santos Basin offshore Brazil is one of the most promising regions for deepwater production. Several discoveries have been made in the pre-salt (or sub-salt) section of the Basin. These include the Tupi and Jupiter condensate/ gas fields in 2007, each with estimated recoverable reserves of up to 8 billion barrels of oil equivalent, and, in 2008, the Carioca field. Brazil's proven oil and gas reserves are expected to be revised sharply upwards once these and other new finds have been appraised. Development plans have already been submitted for some of them. Production testing on Tupi, located in more than 2 000 metres of water and 4 000 metres below the seabed, is due to begin in 2009. Petrobras, which holds a 65% stake in the field, plans pilot production of around 100 thousand barrels per day (kb/d) in 2011-2012 and at least 200 kb/d within 10 to 15 years. Peak output of as much as 1 mb/d is possible. Depending on other deepwater finds, the Santos Basin could contribute the bulk of the increase in Brazil's total oil production over the projection period.

A host of technical difficulties need to be overcome for these pre-salt finds to be developed: the complexity of drilling deviated and horizontal wells through the salt zones, slow drilling rates and the need, in some cases, to hydraulically fracture wells. Secondary recovery, using water or alternated water-gas injection, creates additional challenges. Finally, once the wells start producing, flow assurance requires a careful strategy for preventing the deposition of paraffins and other substances in production lines. Adding to the complexities are the handling of associated natural gas and CO_2, and high pressures.

a linear trend (Figure 9.6), suggesting that more large finds, such as the recent Brazilian Tupi field, are likely to be made in the future. Future prospects are classified here as conventional oil produced by unconventional means.

Figure 9.6 ● **Global offshore oil discoveries to end-2006 versus exploration wells**

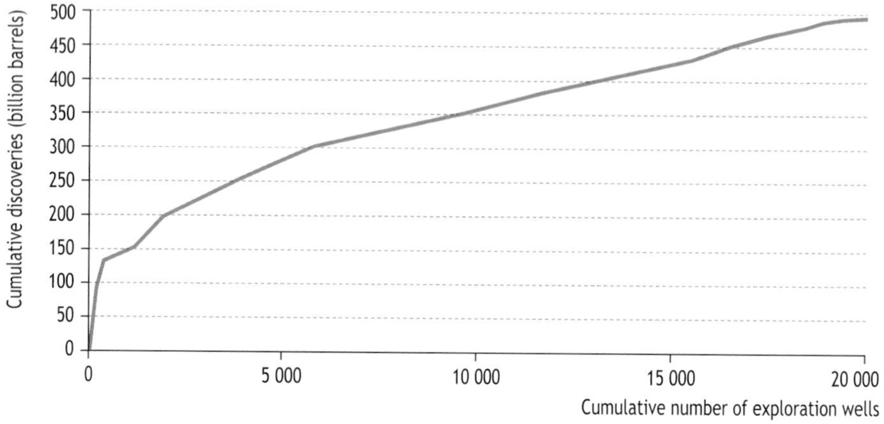

Source: Sandrea and Sandrea (2007a).

The oil and gas industry has made great strides in developing technologies to explore for and produce oil and gas in ever deeper water locations. Total world production from deepwater fields rose from less than 200 kb/d in 1995 to over 5 million barrels per day (mb/d) in 2007. Production from ultra-deepwater fields began only in 2004 and is expected to exceed 200 kb/d by 2010. The average water depth of production wells has more than tripled since the mid-1990s, technical advances having enormously increased the maximum water depth in which wells can be drilled. The 3 000 metres water depth mark for wells drilled was exceeded by the recent Chevron Toledo project in the Gulf of Mexico. A record for the combined depth of water and the well itself was set by another Chevron project, called Knotty Head, also in the Gulf of Mexico. In addition, the time needed to bring deepwater fields into commercial production is shortening (Figure 9.7). Improvements in seismic data gathering and processing technologies that enable images to be prepared of areas located beneath thick layers of salt zones are raising the discovery rate.

Nonetheless, wells drilled in ultra-deepwater locations face major technological challenges, including high underground temperatures and pressures (which require special metals), the behaviour of salt canopies (which can be more than 3 000 metres thick) and near-surface gas zones. In addition, complex hydraulic fracturing may be needed to maintain the structure of the reservoir during production and to avoid the in-flow of sand (Couvillion, 2008). The design of sub-sea production systems needs to evolve to provide assurance of the unimpeded flow of hydrocarbons and to extend the production life of fields.

Figure 9.7 ● Maximum water depth of offshore exploration and production wells worldwide

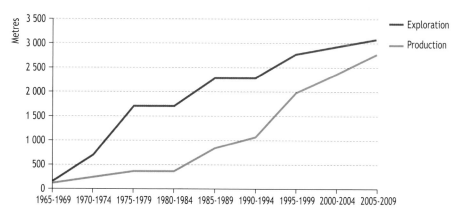

Source: Karlsen (2008).

Although there is thought to be a considerable amount of oil in place in deepwater locations, how much is recoverable will hinge on the balance between development costs and oil prices (as of course, is true of all oil reserves, onshore and offshore). Strong demand for deepwater drilling rigs (semi-submersible platform and drillships, collectively referred to as floaters) has driven up rig rates in recent years (see Chapter 13). At mid-2008, there was a near-record tally of floaters under construction, comprising 44 semi-submersibles and 30 drillships. Most of the new floaters will be capable of drilling in water depths greater than 7 000 feet (2 300 metres), and half of them could drill in more than 10 000 ft (3 300 metres) of water. The majority of the more than 100 offshore rigs built in the 1970s, which are expected to be retired in the next five years, are capable of drilling only in shallow water (less than 400 metres). Investment in deepwater drilling is expected to continue to grow: from $58 billion in 2001-2005 to $108 billion in 2008-2012, with 85% going to the "golden triangle" of North America, Brazil and West Africa, according to recent industry forecasts (Douglas-Westwood, 2007). Asia accounts for a further 10%, with activity in Indonesia, India and Malaysia. Sub-sea wells represent the largest components of capital costs (41%), followed by platforms (32%), pipelines and control lines (16%) and sub-sea hardware (9%). At present, a minimum oil price of $45 in the Gulf of Mexico and $60 in Angola is needed to yield a 12% return on investment.

Reserves growth and enhanced oil recovery

Reserves growth, which refers to the increase in recoverable reserves from a discovered oil or gas field that occurs over the life of the field as it is appraised, developed and produced, is expected to be a major contributor to additions to reserves in the coming decades. It derives from three factors (Klett, 2004):

- *Geological factors*: The delineation of additional reserves through new seismic acquisition, appraisal drilling or the identification (using well-bore measurements), of reservoirs that had been previously bypassed.

- *Technological factors*: An increase in the share of oil in place that can be recovered through the application of new technologies, such as increased reservoir contact, improved secondary recovery and enhanced oil recovery.

- *Definitional factors*: Economic, logistical and political/regulatory/fiscal changes in the operating environment.

The Weyburn field in Canada provides a good illustration of how reserves can grow over time (Figure 9.8). Production started in the mid-1950s with conventional vertical wells. Initial proven reserves at that time were estimated at 260 million barrels. Infill drilling of wells in the mid-1980s added a producible wedge of 20 million barrels. Horizontal wells drilled in the 1990s added a second, additional wedge of reserves of around 60 million barrels. At the end of the 1990s, an enhanced oil recovery scheme — using anthropogenic CO_2 piped in from a coal-gasification plant in North Dakota in the United States — added 120 million barrels more, or one-third, taking initial reserves to 460 million barrels.

Figure 9.8 ● **A case study of oil reserves growth: the impact of technology on oil production from the Weyburn field in Canada**

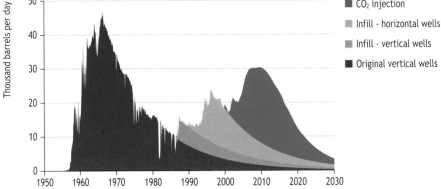

Source: PTRC Weyburn-Midale website (www.ptrc.ca).

The USGS has undertaken a comprehensive analysis of the main factors in reserves growth, based on production series for 186 giant fields outside the United States (133 in OPEC countries) with more than 0.5 billion barrels of reserves for the period 1981 to 2003 (Klett, 2004). Reserves in the OPEC fields increased by 80% in aggregate and in non-OPEC fields by around 30% over this period.

Reserves growth in any given field automatically raises the recovery factor, which is defined as total recoverable reserves (including the oil or gas already produced) expressed as a percentage share of the original hydrocarbons in place. As estimates of both the volume of hydrocarbons in place and how much is recoverable vary as a field is developed and produced, the estimated recovery factor inevitably fluctuates.

Consequently, estimating trends in recovery factors is extremely difficult. The global average recovery factor was recently estimated at 34.5%, based on IHS data (Schulte, 2005). Fields containing more than two-thirds of conventional oil reserves have a recovery factor of less than 40%. Lifting recovery factors could make a big difference to recoverable reserves, prolonging the production life of producing fields and postponing the peak of conventional oil production: a mere one percentage point increase in the average recovery factor would add more than 80 billion barrels (or 5% to 6%) to the world's proven oil reserves (see *Spotlight* below).

Enhanced (or tertiary) oil recovery (EOR) technologies are applied to increase the amount of oil recovered from a reservoir beyond the range that primary and secondary recovery can generally achieve (generally between 20% and 50%). EOR is expected to contribute significantly to future reserves growth. The technologies utilised in EOR aim at altering the properties of the oil and improving its movement from the reservoir to the wellhead. EOR currently accounts for only about 3% of world oil production. There are three main types of EOR techniques in use today: thermal recovery, miscible displacement (using nitrogen, CO_2 or other hydrocarbons — natural gas in the case of EOR), and chemical flooding (with micellar-polymers or alkalines). Other technologies include microbial EOR and foam flooding.

Research and development on EOR technologies, especially those involving miscible displacement and CO_2 injection, which started before 1950, intensified after the first oil shock in the early 1970s. This effort, along with the development of expertise in candidate reservoir screening, EOR project implementation and field management, resulted in the deployment of many of the projects that are currently in operation today, most of which are in the United States. But low oil prices in the 1990s led to a significant loss of expertise amongst oil companies and technology providers. As a result, a renewed effort is needed to improve the prospects for expanding the deployment of EOR in the longer term, particularly in the following areas (NPC, 2007):

- Monitoring and controlling the injection of CO_2.

- Complex multi-lateral wells with control of individual well-branch oil inflow.

- Optimisation of steam-assisted gravity drainage (SAGD).

- Reservoir-scale measurements, including 4-D seismic.

- Smart oil lifting, with re-injection of water in the same well.

Additional production resulting from the use of EOR techniques currently amounts to about 2.5 mb/d, with reliance mainly on thermal processes (in the United States, Canada, Venezuela, Indonesia and China), CO_2 injection (United States), natural gas injection (Venezuela), nitrogen (in the Cantarell field in Mexico) and polymer/ surfactant flooding (China) (Table 9.2). In the Reference Scenario, additional production resulting from EOR techniques (over and above current EOR output) is projected to rise to over 6 mb/d by 2030, with EOR using CO_2 (CO_2-EOR) accounting for most of the increase (see Chapter 11). Worldwide, the prospects for CO_2-EOR, which can be costly, have been boosted by higher oil prices (Box 9.5).

How soon – if ever – could oil recovery factors be raised to 50%?

A 2007 study by the US National Petroleum Council lists advances in technology that offer the potential to improve oil recovery factors. It estimates that the biggest impact would come from technologies that maximise the effective reservoir contact between the well bore and the formation through various techniques, such as controlled multi-lateral drain holes, improvements in the efficiency of secondary and tertiary recovery, better imaging of reservoirs and production management in real-time, and the increased use of 4-D seismic to monitor oil flows, and "smart" injector and producer wells. The commercialisation of some of those technologies may not happen until the end of next decade, but operators are already conducting full-field experiments that could advance the time scale.

In the North Sea's Norne field, the operator StatoilHydro has used new seismic acquisition and processing technologies, and combined them with geological and reservoir models and well-bore measurements to monitor fluid movements across the field (Boutte, 2007). These techniques helped to improve the planning of in-field drilling, to increase the field recovery factor from 40% to 52%, and to extend the life of the field to beyond 2015.

Technologies that improve contact between the well bore and the reservoir show great promise. In Saudi Arabia, the maximum reservoir contact (MRC) approach, used in the development of the Shaybah field, demonstrated that well productivity could be increased significantly by drilling long horizontal and multi-lateral wells. By increasing the length of well in contact with productive areas from 1 km to 12 km, through use of multi-lateral wells, well productivity was increased by a factor of six (Saleri et al., 2003). However, only a limited number of lateral branches can be extended from each mother bore and it is impossible to control the flow from individual sections. This can cause a problem as water production rises. Extreme reservoir contact (ERC), a concept being developed by Saudi Aramco, aims to get around this problem. ERC wells improve on MRC through the development and deployment of new intelligent well completions that improve recovery by means of downhole monitoring and electrically activated downhole control valves, without the use of complex control lines that run from the wellhead. The ERC concept could allow an unlimited number of lateral branches and boost the recovery from heterogeneous carbonate reservoirs. However, the widespread introduction of technologies like these that increase reservoir contact would require a significant increase in footage drilled, which would call for more drilling rigs and personnel — both of which are in short supply at present (see Chapter 13).

It will probably take much more than two decades for the average recovery factor worldwide to be raised from about 35% today to 50%. Achieving this would boost world reserves by about 1.2 trillion barrels — equal to the whole of today's proven reserves (Figure 9.3).

Table 9.2 • **Estimated 2007 incremental production from EOR projects by technology** (thousand barrels per day)

	Thermal	Nitrogen	$CO_2/$ hydrocarbon	Chemical	Total
United States	300	10	340	-	650
Canada	330	-	50	-	380
Mexico	-	500	-	-	500
Venezuela	200	-	170	-	370
China	160	-	5	200	365
Indonesia	190	-	-	-	190
Others	20	-	35	-	55
World	1 200	510	600	200	2 510

Note: Incremental production rate is calculated by deducting the projected rate without EOR from the enhanced production rate with EOR. Current EOR production is included in total crude oil production from existing fields in the projections in Chapter 11.

Sources: Thomas (2008); O&GJ (2008).

Carbon-dioxide enhanced oil recovery (CO_2-EOR)

CO_2-EOR, which involves the injection of CO_2 into oil reservoirs, is receiving increased attention because of the potential availability of CO_2 from anthropogenic sources and the environmental benefits of carbon sequestration. There are currently more than 100 CO_2-EOR projects in the world today, most of them in North America, producing 300 kb/d of additional oil. In most cases, the CO_2 is extracted from produced natural gas. In the United States alone, the contribution from CO_2-EOR has been projected to increase from the current level of 250 kb/d to 1.3 mb/d by 2030 (Caruso, 2007). The economics of CO_2-EOR are attractive, as the injection of one tonne of CO_2 into a suitable reservoir leads to an incremental recovery of between two and three barrels of oil. The value of this oil could be set against the cost of capturing the CO_2 from power plants and transporting it to the injection fields, which is estimated to range from $50 to $100 per tonne (IEA, 2008).

CO_2-EOR was initially deployed in the 1970s and is still used only onshore, with a small inter-well distance. In addition to expanding the use of the technology to new onshore areas, there is considerable potential for using it offshore and in thicker reservoirs. An assessment of the potential in the United States shows that improved CO_2-EOR, in combination with 4-D seismic, advanced well monitoring and control, and reservoir simulation, could add between 20 and 40 billion barrels of economically recoverable oil (ARI, 2006). The worldwide potential for CO_2-EOR is of the order of 160 billion to 300 billion barrels, equal to 7% to 14% of current remaining conventional recoverable oil resources. The Middle East and North America are thought to hold the greatest potential (Figure 9.9). The potential is greatest in fields that have relatively low depletion levels, as the costs of installing the equipment and facilities required are onerous, particularly for offshore fields (Tzimas et al., 2005). Incremental recovery factors with EOR from offshore fields are expected to be lower than onshore fields because of different well configurations and reservoir contacts. CO_2-EOR is now increasingly

Box 9.5 ● **Deploying EOR: when, how and at what cost?**

The applicability of EOR depends on the characteristics of the oilfield and its state of depletion. For a field that is conducive to EOR, there is generally a window of opportunity during which such technology is best applied. Table 9.3 shows the key criteria used for assessing the applicability of EOR technologies. The gravity of the crude oil is generally the first parameter considered: the majority of the miscible flooding techniques work only for light crudes. The second parameter is the amount of oil left in the field. CO_2-EOR can be used when more than 20% of the oil is still recoverable. The oilfield temperature is the next variable: polymer flooding (alkaline and micellar) does not work at temperatures over 95°C.

Hydrocarbon, polymer and surfactant flooding have the greatest potential for increasing recovery factors. Alberta's hydrocarbon miscible flooding projects have achieved recovery factors of more than 70%. A massive polymer flooding project combined with surfactant addition in China's Daqing complex has boosted production by 240 kb/d and the recovery factor by more than 12%.

EOR costs have risen sharply in the last few years, in line with upstream costs generally. Energy feedstock prices for thermal processes and hydrocarbon displacement, increased demand for CO_2, and the impact of higher oil prices on surfactants and polymers have contributed to these higher costs. On the other hand, EOR costs are generally much lower than the cost of other means of reserves replacement, especially in North America. They range from less than $20 to $70 per incremental barrel of oil, excluding the cost offset that might be available through any CO_2 emission credit that might exist.

Table 9.3 ● **Pre-screening criteria for EOR**

Technology	API	Remaining recoverable resources (% of intitial reserves)	Formation type (carbonate/ sandstone)	Depth (metres)	Permeability (md)	Temperature (°C)	Required additional recovery factor (%)
Nitrogen	>35	>40	Carbonate	>2 000	190	-	-
Hydrocarbon	>25	>30	Carbonate	>1 350	-	-	20-40
CO_2	>25	>20	Carbonate	>700	-	-	5-25
Polymer	>15	>70	Sandstone	<3 000	>10	<95	5-30
Surfactant/ Micellar	>18	>35	Sandstone	<3 000	>10	<95	5-30
Thermal/ Combustion	>10	>50	Sandstone	>50	>50	>40	-
Thermal/ Steam	>8	>40	Sandstone	<1 500	>200	-	10-60

Sources: Taber *et al.* (1997); Green (1998); *O&GJ* (2008); IEA analysis.

attractive in the North Sea (OGUK, 2008). While an estimated 15 to 25 years of production life could be added to a number of North Sea fields, some are likely to be dropped from the list of potential candidates by 2010, due to less favourable miscible displacement conditions.

Figure 9.9 ● **Potential additional recoverable oil resources using CO_2-EOR by region**

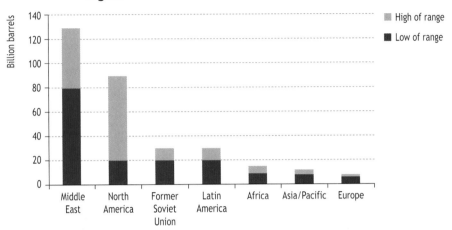

Sources: Khatib (2006); Kuuskraa (2006); IEA estimates based on industry sources.

Non-conventional oil resources

Extra-heavy oil and oil sands

A large share of the world's remaining oil resources is classified as non-conventional.[3] These resources – oil sands, extra-heavy oil and oil shales – are generally more costly to produce, though considerable progress has been made in addressing technical challenges and lowering costs. Oil sands and extra-heavy oil resources in place worldwide amount to around 6 trillion barrels, of which between 1 and 2 trillion barrels may be ultimately recoverable economically. Technically recoverable reserves, defined by the World Energy Council as resources which can be exploited profitably with today's technology, amount to some 1.1 trillion barrels using an average conservative recovery factor of 18% (Table 9.4).

The world's extra-heavy oil and oil sands resources are largely concentrated in Canada (mainly in the province of Alberta) and Venezuela (in the Orinoco Belt). Assuming a potential 20% recovery factor, these two countries would hold more recoverable resources than all the conventional reserves in the Middle East. Alberta alone has proven reserves today of 174 billion barrels (crude bitumen) and an estimated 315 billion barrels of ultimately economically recoverable resources. Nearly 80% of the

---

3. The IEA defines non-conventional oil as oil sands, extra-heavy oil, oil shales, coal-to-liquids (CTL) and gas-to-liquids (GTL). Only the first four are considered here. The prospects for CTL and GTL are discussed in Chapter 11.

proven reserves in Alberta are in the Athabasca Wabiskaw McMurray deposit, while the remaining 20% are split between the Cold Lake Clearwater and the Peace River deposits. A one percentage-point increase in the recovery factor would boost recoverable resources by 60 billion barrels.

Table 9.4 ● **Extra-heavy oil and oil sands resources** (billion barrels)

	Extra-heavy oil			Oil sands		
	Oil in place	Recovery factor	Technically recoverable	Oil in place	Recovery factor	Technically recoverable
North America	184	0.19	35	1 659	0.32	531.0
South America	2 046	0.13	266	1	0.01	0.1
Middle East	650	0.12	78	0	0.00	0.0
Other regions	423	0.13	55	1 135	0.13	120.0
World	3 303	0.13	434	2 795	0.23	651.0

Source: WEC (2007).

Several technologies exist to extract bitumen from oil sands. If the deposit is near the surface, oil sands are mined, using enormous power shovels and dump trucks. The bitumen is then extracted using hot water and caustic soda. The extracted bitumen needs to be upgraded (or diluted) with lighter hydrocarbons before it can be transported to a refinery. Upgrading consists of increasing the ratio of hydrogen to carbon, either by carbon removal (coking) or by adding hydrogen (hydrocracking), resulting in a synthetic crude oil that is shipped to a refinery.

When the heavy hydrocarbon deposit is deeper, drilling is required. When its viscosity is low enough or can be reduced enough for the oil to flow to the surface, long horizontal or multi-lateral wells are used to maximise well bore contact with the reservoir and reduce the drop in pressure in the well bore. This is the technique used for several of the heavy oil deposits in Venezuela's Orinoco Belt. The main drawback of such conventional production techniques is the low recovery factors, typically less than 15%. As a result, the expected amount of extra-heavy oil that could be recovered from the estimated 1 700 billion barrels in place in the Orinoco Belt is less than 250 billion barrels, using current technology.

Much higher recovery factors (up to twice those of conventional production technologies) can be obtained using *in situ* viscosity-reduction techniques. *In situ* technologies are currently used for highly viscous oils: they include cyclic steam stimulation injection (CSS) and steam-assisted gravity drainage (SAGD). Technologies being developed include a vapour extraction process, which uses hydrocarbon solvents instead of steam to increase oil mobility, the use of downhole heaters and hybrid methods. Theoretical recovery factors of 50% to 70% are predicted for SAGD and new *in situ* processes, significantly higher than with CSS (20% to 35%). The steam-oil ratio is also lower with SAGD (2 to 3) than with CSS (3 to 5), so less water would be required. About 20% of Alberta's bitumen can be mined, while 80% requires *in situ* recovery methods (ACR, 2004).

Oil shales: a technological milestone in sight?

Oil shales are rocks that contain a large proportion of solid organic compounds (kerogen) and are found at shallow depths, from surface outcrops to 1 000 metres below ground. Production of shale oil dates back to the 1830s and peaked worldwide in 1980 at around 45 000 tonnes. It fell to only 16 000 tonnes in 2004, with more than 70% coming from Estonia. While resources in place are estimated at 2.5 to 3 trillion barrels, estimates of recoverable reserves vary markedly (see, for example, NPC, 2007 and WEC, 2007). In calculating the long-term, oil-supply cost curve (see below) we have taken a figure of about 1 trillion barrels. The United States has the largest resources (more than 60% of the world total), followed by Brazil, Jordan, Morocco and Russia. Oil shales are not projected to make a significant contribution to world oil supply before 2030, but technological breakthroughs could change this outlook.

Oil shales near the surface can be mined, with the mined rock heated in a process called retorting, which pyrolyses the kerogen into oil. Retort methods are unlikely to provide an environmentally sustainable production process. Deeper deposits require the use of techniques to enhance the productivity of the formation (such as hydraulic fracturing) and an *in situ* mobility-enhancement technology. The processes are very energy intensive. Retorting alone requires nearly 30% of the energy value of the oil produced. In addition, CO_2 emissions generated are in the range of 0.18 to 0.25 tonnes per barrel of oil produced. Production costs currently range from $50 to $120 per barrel, disregarding any potential carbon permitting.

9

The main US resource is the Green River Formation, with four basins in western states. Early experiments in the 1980s were halted due to the unfavourable economics and poor operational performance. Shell is assessing the technical and economic viability of an *in situ* conversion process, using down-hole heaters, at the Mahogany Ridge project (IEA, 2007). The oil produced has an API in the mid 30s, significantly higher than oil produced by surface retort. The process has the advantage of reducing the amount of land used, assuming wells can be drilled as little as 12 metres apart, but it requires the use of both water and of a sufficient amount of energy to heat and cool the relevant areas. A 100-kb/d unit would require 1.2 GW of power. Shell expects gas production from the produced fluid to meet most of the energy needs. Preliminary energy balances indicate, on a life-cycle assessment basis, a ratio of 3-4 to 1 between the energy generated and the energy used. Further technical developments to protect groundwater are required before going to a larger scale demonstration phase. Other companies, including Chevron, EGP and IEL, are testing different *in situ* processes. Shell is not expected to decide on whether or not to proceed with commercialisation of their technology before 2010. If it gets the green light, first production would occur after 2015.

Long-term oil-supply cost curve

We have updated the oil-supply cost curve, which we first produced three years ago (IEA, 2005),[4] based on the latest estimates of resource potential and the estimated range of

---

4. The IEA will be updating in 2009 the *Resources to Reserves* study, first published in 2005 (IEA, 2005), with an extended coverage of resources and technologies.

current costs of production. The curve plots the potential long-term contributions from conventional resources (including those defined above as conventional oil produced by unconventional means) and non-conventional resources (including liquids supply from coal and gas) against their associated current production costs (Figure 9.10). The resource potential is not much different from that estimated in 2005, though technological developments have boosted the recovery potential for some categories of resources, notably ultra-deepwater, EOR and oil sands. But costs have been revised upwards significantly, reflecting the recent surge in costs (see Chapter 13).

Figure 9.10 ● Long-term oil-supply cost curve

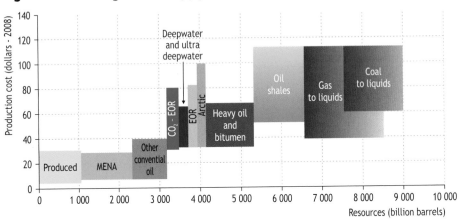

Note: The curve shows the availability of oil resources as a function of the estimated production cost. Cost associated with CO_2 emissions is not included. There is also a significant uncertainty on oil shales production cost as the technology is not yet commercial. MENA is the Middle East and North Africa. The shading and overlapping of the gas-to-liquids and coal-to-liquids segments indicates the range of uncertainty surrounding the size of these resources, with 2.4 trillion shown as a best estimate of the likely total potential for the two combined.

The total long-term potential oil resource base alone is around 6.5 trillion barrels. Adding CTL and GTL increases this potential to about 9 trillion barrels. Of these totals, nearly 1.1 trillion barrels have already been produced at a cost of up to $30 per barrel in year-2008 dollars.[5] Remaining potentially economically recoverable resources are broken down as follows:

- *Conventional resources*, more than half of which are in the Middle East and North Africa, amount to about 2.1 trillion barrels (based on the latest USGS assessments). The cost of exploiting these resources is expected to be much lower on average than the cost of all other sources of supply, with the exception of oil recovered using CO_2-EOR. The cost of exploiting conventional resources (excluding taxes and royalties) typically ranges from less than $10 to $40 per barrel, though some fall outside this range.

---

5. Only a small fraction was produced at a cost of more than $20, mainly in recent years from offshore and North American fields.

- *Additional resources recovered using enhanced oil recovery* has been split according to the use CO_2-EOR and other EOR technologies. The cost of CO_2-EOR ranges from just over $20 per barrel to about $70, compared with about $30 to $80 for other types of EOR. The overall potential from EOR is estimated at between 400 and 500 billion barrels, on the assumption that the introduction of new EOR technologies is accelerated, lowering unit costs.
- *Deepwater and ultra-deepwater* resources could deliver over 160 billion barrels at a cost of up to $65 per barrel.
- *Arctic resources* could amount to 90 billion barrels at a cost of between $40 and $100 per barrel.
- *Extra-heavy oil* and *oil sands* resources total more than 1 trillion barrels and could be produced at costs ranging from over $40 to about $80 per barrel.
- *Oil shales* production costs are estimated to be in the range of $50 to well over $100 per barrel. Because of a lack of major commercial projects, the prospects for improving oil shales production technology are very uncertain. Consequently, we do not expect oil shales to make any significant contribution to world oil supply before 2030. Moreover, a carbon penalty would increase significantly the production cost, as oil shales extraction is extremely energy and carbon intensive.
- *CTL* and *GTL* have a large potential (see also Chapter 11), but they will be in competition for their feedstock with other potential applications (mainly in power generation and final uses). Their costs range from $40 to $120 per barrel at current feedstock prices.

Political, environmental, regulatory and fiscal factors will strongly influence the extent to which this potential is exploited and the costs to oil companies of bringing the resources to market. Production of non-conventional resources, in particular oil sands as well as oil shales in the future, leaves a large environmental footprint, including through the greenhouse gases emitted in the production and use. The widespread introduction of CO_2 emission-reduction incentives would have a major impact on the cost curve, as non-conventional oil would become relatively more expensive and CO_2-EOR potentially cheaper. Technological developments will also continue to change the shape and position of the curve.

9

CHAPTER 10

FIELD-BY-FIELD ANALYSIS OF OIL PRODUCTION
Is decline accelerating?

H I G H L I G H T S

- The future rate of decline in output from producing oilfields as they mature is a critical determinant of the amount of new capacity and investment that will be needed globally to meet projected demand. A detailed field-by-field analysis of historical production trends reveals that the size of reserves and physiographic situation (onshore/offshore) are the main factors in explaining the shape of an oilfield's production profile. The larger the reserves, the lower the peak relative to reserves and the slower the decline once a field has come off plateau. Rates are also lower for onshore than offshore (especially deepwater) fields.

- Based on data for 580 of the world's largest fields that have passed their production peak, the observed decline rate — averaged across all fields and weighted by their production over their whole lives — is 5.1%. Decline rates are lowest for the biggest fields: they average 3.4% for super-giant fields, 6.5% for giant fields and 10.4% for large fields. The average rate of observed post-plateau decline, based on our data sub-set of 479 fields, is 5.8%.

- Observed decline rates vary markedly by region. Post-peak and post-plateau rates are lowest in the Middle East and highest in the North Sea. This reflects, to a large extent, differences in the average size of fields, which in turn is related to the extent to which overall reserves are depleted and their physiographic location. In general, observed decline rates are also higher the younger the field, mainly because these fields tend to be smaller and are more often found offshore. Investment and production policies also affect decline rates, especially in OPEC countries.

- The average size of the fields analysed is significantly larger than that of all the fields in the world, as our database contains all the super-giant fields and most of the giant fields. The decline rates for the fields not included in our dataset are, on average, likely to be at least as high as for the large fields in our database. On this basis, we estimate that the average production-weighted observed decline rate worldwide is 6.7% for post-peak fields.

- The average annual *natural*, or underlying, decline rate for the world as a whole — stripping out the effects of ongoing and periodic investment — is estimated at 9% for post-peak fields. In other words, the decline in production from existing fields would have been around one-third *faster* had there been no capital spending on those fields once they had passed their peak.

- Our Reference Scenario projections imply a one percentage-point increase in the global average natural decline rate to over 10% per year by 2030 as all regions experience a drop in average field size and most see a shift in production to offshore fields. This means that total upstream investment in some countries will need to rise, in some cases significantly, just to offset decline.

Understanding production patterns and trends

An understanding of oilfield production profiles and the impact of various geological and economic variables on the shape of production curves is critically important to projecting future output from fields already in production or from fields that are yet to be brought into production. A major finding of past *Outlooks* is that the future rate of production decline from producing fields aggregated across all regions is the single most important determinant of the amount of new capacity that needs to be added and the need to invest in developing new fields (see, in particular, IEA, 2001 and 2003). In other words, future supply is far more sensitive to decline rates than to the rate of growth in oil demand.[1] Most investment over the projection period will actually be needed to offset the loss of capacity from existing fields as they mature, oilfield pressure declines and – in the absence of new investment – well flow-rates fall (see Chapter 13 for a detailed analysis of investment trends).

For these reasons, we have undertaken a detailed study of historical oilfield production trends, using extensive field-by-field data, with a view to achieving a better understanding of the drivers of decline rates, how they could develop in the future and what that will mean for investment. The results of this study were used to model future production levels to 2030, the results of which are set out in detail in Chapter 11.

The field-by-field study involved building a large database containing the full production history and a range of technical parameters for around 800 of the largest individual oilfields in the world. The database includes, to the best of our knowledge, all the super-giant fields, containing initial proven and probable (2P) reserves[2] exceeding 5 billion barrels; virtually all giant fields, containing more than 500 million barrels, in production today; and the bulk of the world's large fields, containing at least 100 million barrels. Together, these fields account for close to three-quarters of all the initial reserves of all the fields ever discovered worldwide and more than two-thirds of all the crude oil produced globally in 2007 (see Box 10.1 for more details). We believe that this is the most comprehensive study of field-by-field oil production patterns and trends ever made public.[3] We intend to extend and refine this work in the future.

The majority of the fields that have ever been found worldwide have already been brought into production. The share is highest for the biggest fields, both in terms of their number and their overall reserves, mainly because all but a handful of them were discovered several decades ago. Out of an estimated 58 super-giant fields that have been found, all but four[4] are already in production; out of close to 400 giant fields that we have identified, around 80 are either being developed, waiting to be developed

1. See Chapter 11 for the results of an analysis of the sensitivity of oil production and prices to changes in decline rates.

2. All reserves figures cited in this chapter are 2P unless otherwise stated.

3. IHS/CERA prepared a study on oilfield decline rates based on data for 811 fields for private clients in 2007 (CERA, 2007).

4. Azadegan and Ferdows/Mound/Zagheh in Iran, Kashagan in Kazakhstan, and Tupi in Brazil are not yet producing.

or are temporarily shut in.[5] The combined initial 2P reserves of all super-giant and giant fields amount to 1 306 billion barrels, of which an estimated 697 billion barrels remain (equal to about half of the world's remaining reserves of conventional oil — see Chapter 9). In total, an estimated 79% of the world's remaining conventional oil reserves are contained in fields that are already being exploited. Thus, the outlook for production at these fields is critical to world oil supply in the short to medium term.

..................S P O T L I G H T....................

What do rising decline rates mean for oil production and investment?

The production profile of an oilfield reflects a number of different factors, including the techniques used to extract its reserves, the field-development programme, reservoir management practices, geology, national production policies, field-maintenance programmes and external factors, such as strikes and military geopolitical conflicts. The analysis presented below points to a long-term trend towards higher faster decline rates once oilfields have reached their peak, as a result of a shift in the pattern of fields that will be brought on stream in the future. In particular, a growing share of production is expected to come from smaller fields and, in the medium term, from fields located offshore, which tend to decline much more quickly than big, onshore fields because of the way they are developed. This is, in turn, largely a function of technical and economic factors rather than geology. Faster decline rates go hand-in-hand with higher peak-production levels relative to reserves.

Rising decline rates have important implications for development costs and investment needs. In general, the smaller a field, the more expensive it is to develop (and operate), expressed in dollars per barrel per day of capacity and, especially, per barrel of oil produced. Similarly, costs are typically significantly higher for offshore fields, particularly in deep water. Over the projection period, all regions continue to experience a drop in average field size and most see a shift in production to offshore fields as the biggest fields, which are usually found and developed first, decline. This means that total upstream investment in some countries will need to rise, in some cases significantly, just to offset decline (even though total world investment needs are expected to drop, as the share of the lowest-cost producing regions in total production increases). The biggest increases are needed in OPEC countries. It is far from certain that all the required investment will be forthcoming, given the size of these investments and potential barriers (see Chapter 13) — because of so-called "above-ground" factors and not because of geology. These factors are discussed in detail in the next four chapters.

....

---

5. These figures do not include some new fields, including offshore Brazil, as they are yet to be properly appraised.

Current estimates of reserves are derived from the latest estimates of the oil initially in place and the share that can be economically recovered. Yet that share, as well as the rate at which that share can be produced, are far from certain, as the precise behaviour of a given field or reservoir is exceedingly difficult to predict. Moreover, the deployment of new production technologies (including secondary and enhanced recovery techniques) can push up ultimate recovery rates and production levels. Careful analysis of these factors is vital to predicting future recovery and decline rates and, therefore, production.

Box 10.1 • The IEA field-by-field oil production database

The IEA has compiled a database containing the full crude oil production history and a range of key technical parameters for a total of 798 oilfields worldwide. To the best of our knowledge, the database includes all of the world's 54 super-giant fields that have ever produced, as well as the bulk of the giant producing fields (263 out of a total of around 320).[6] Of the remaining 481 fields, 285 are large fields, representing at least half of all the fields in this category in the world and most of the largest ones. The rest of the fields are small fields, containing between 50 and 100 million barrels. The choice of which large and small fields to include in the database was partly driven by data availability. Nonetheless, we believe that the dataset for large fields is reasonably representative of the actual geographic distribution of all such fields in production worldwide today.

For all producing fields, data was compiled on annual oil production over the full life of the field, initial and remaining proven and probable (2P) recoverable reserves, the volume of oil initially in place, lithology (the geological formation of the field), physiographic location (onshore, offshore and shallow/deep water) and the discovery date. For some fields, additional information on reservoir porosity and thickness, as well as the deployment of improved recovery techniques, was also obtained.

The field-by-field data were compiled from a range of different sources. The primary source of data on production and reserves was IHS, without whose assistance we would not have been able to carry out this work. Deloitte & Touche Petroleum Services also provided data on a number of fields. The US Geological Survey and the US Energy Information Administration supplied data for some US fields. Other sources include official statistics, published by the governments of oil-producing countries, international and national oil companies, oil services companies and consulting firms. These organisations assisted us in validating and checking the consistency and veracity of the data, as well as in verifying the results of our analysis. We gratefully acknowledge their contribution.

---

6. The precise number of fields in these categories may differ among data sources, because of differences in the way specific fields are delineated and data discrepancies.

The importance of size

There are currently about 70 000 oilfields in production worldwide. The bulk of crude oil production comes from a small number of very prolific fields, mostly super-giants and giants.[7] Output at the world's ten largest producing oilfields totalled just over 14 million barrels per day (mb/d) in 2007 (Table 10.1), contributing 20% of world conventional production. The 20 largest fields produced 19.2 mb/d, or over a quarter of world production. One field alone – Ghawar in Saudi Arabia – produced 5.1 mb/d, equal to 7% of world conventional oil production (see the next section).

Table 10.1 ● **The world's 20 biggest oilfields by production**

Field	Country	Location	Year of discovery	Peak annual production		2007 production
				Year	kb/d	kb/d
Ghawar	Saudi Arabia	Onshore	1948	1980	5 588	5 100
Cantarell	Mexico	Offshore	1977	2003	2 054	1 675
Safaniyah	Saudi Arabia	On/off	1951	1998	2 128	1 408
Rumaila N & S	Iraq	Onshore	1953	1979	1 493	1 250
Greater Burgan	Kuwait	Onshore	1938	1972	2 415	1 170
Samotlor	Russia	Onshore	1960	1980	3 435	903
Ahwaz	Iran	Onshore	1958	1977	1 082	770
Zakum	Abu Dhabi (UAE)	Offshore	1964	1998	795	674
Azeri-Chirag-Guneshli	Azerbaijan	Offshore	1985	2007	658	658
Priobskoye	Russia	Onshore	1982	2007	652	652
Top 10 total						14 260
Bu Hasa	Abu Dhabi (UAE)	Onshore	1962	1973	794	550
Marun	Iran	Onshore	1964	1976	1 345	510
Raudhatain	Kuwait	Onshore	1955	2007	501	501
Gachsaran	Iran	Onshore	1928	1974	921	500
Qatif	Saudi Arabia	On/Off	1945	2006	500	500
Shaybah	Saudi Arabia	Onshore	1968	2003	520	500
Saertu (Daqing)	China	Onshore	1960	1993	633	470
Samotlor (Main)	Russia	Onshore	1961	1980	3 027	464
Fedorovo-Surguts	Russia	Onshore	1962	1983	1 022	458
Zuluf	Saudi Arabia	Offshore	1965	1981	677	450
Top 20 total						19 163

Sources: IHS, Deloitte & Touche and USGS databases; other industry sources; IEA estimates and analysis.

10

7. In this report, a super-giant is defined as a field with initial 2P reserves of at least 5 billion barrels. A giant is defined as a field with initial reserves of 500 million barrels to 5 billion barrels. A large field contains more than 100 million barrels.

Four of the other fields are also in Saudi Arabia and eight others in other Middle Eastern countries (Iran, Iraq, Kuwait and the United Arab Emirates). Output in 2007 at 16 of the 20 largest fields was below their historic peaks. Production has fallen most in percentage terms at Samotlor in Russia. All of the 20 largest producing fields are super-giants, of which Ghawar, with 140 billion barrels of initial reserves, is by far the largest.

Most of the world's largest fields — by production and reserves — have been in production for many years, in some cases for several decades. The last of the top 20 producing fields to be discovered was Azeri-Chirag-Guneshli in 1985. Priobskoye in Russia was found in 1982, Canterell in Mexico in 1977, and all the others between 1928 and 1968. In 2007, five fields produced more than 1 mb/d and another eight more than 500 thousand barrels per day (kb/d). They make up one-quarter of world crude oil production. Around 110 fields in total produce more than 100 kb/d each. Collectively, they account for just over 50% of world production. A very large number of small fields, each producing less than 100 kb/d at present — approximately 70 000 in total — produce just under half of world production.

$$\frac{110}{7\times10^5} = .00157 = 0.16\%$$ hence $> 50\%$ of oil comes from $< 0.2\%$ of Fields!!

Table 10.2 ● World crude oil production by output and age of field

	Number of fields	Year of first production					Production, 2007	
		Pre-1970s	1970s	1980s	1990s	2000s	mb/d	%
> 1 mb/d	5	4	1	-	-	-	10.6	15
500 kb/d – 1 mb/d	11	8	-	1	2	-	6.7	10
All fields	70 000	n.a.	n.a.	n.a.	n.a.	n.a.	70.2	100

Sources: IHS, Deloitte & Touche and USGS databases; other industry sources; IEA estimates and analysis.

The world's oil supplies remain very dependent on output from big, old fields. Despite the fact that many of them have been in production for decades, output from super-giant and giant fields (holding more than 500 million barrels of initial reserves) has actually grown significantly over the past two decades. The share in world production of all the super-giant fields and those giant fields included in our database rose from 56% in 1985 to 60% in 2007. Surprisingly, fields that came into production before the 1970s still make the largest contribution, amounting to just over 24 mb/d in 2007 — equal to 35% of the world total (Figure 10.1). Indeed, output from these fields has gradually risen since the mid-1980s (it fell sharply in the early 1980s, mainly because of OPEC policies). Only five super-giant or giant fields began producing in the current decade — Ourhoud in Algeria, Grane in Norway, Girassol in Angola, Jubarte in Brazil and Xifeng in the Gansu province of China — and made up a mere 2% of total output from such fields and little more than 1% of world output in 2007.

World Energy Outlook 2008 - OIL AND GAS PRODUCTION PROSPECTS

Figure 10.1 ● World crude oil production from super-giant and giant fields by field vintage

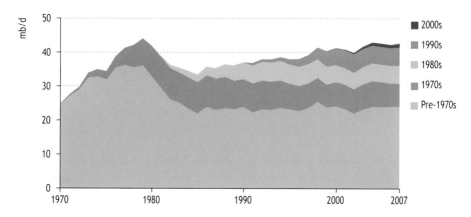

Note: For fields covered by IEA field-by-field oil production database (which includes all the world's super-giant fields and most giant fields). Fields are classified according to the year of first production.

Sources: IHS and Deloitte & Touche databases; other industry sources; IEA estimates and analysis.

Regional differences

10

Big oilfields are unevenly distributed across the world; their share in overall production and their average size vary markedly across regions. The Middle East is characterised by a large number of super-giant and giant fields. With 9 billion barrels of initial reserves, their average size is the highest of any region (Table 10.3).

Table 10.3 ● Geographical distribution of the world's super-giant and giant oilfields (number)

	Super-giants and giants	Of which offshore	Average size of total (billion barrels)
OECD North America	46	11	2.0
OECD Europe	23	23	1.4
OECD Pacific	2	2	1.1
E. Europe/Eurasia	62	5	3.1
Asia	20	5	2.1
Middle East	83	25	8.9
Africa	41	12	1.7
Latin America	40	6	3.4
Total	317	89	4.2

Note: For fields covered by IEA field-by-field oil production database. See footnote 7 for definitions of super-giant and giant fields.

Sources: IHS, Deloitte & Touche and USGS databases; other industry sources; IEA estimates and analysis.

The region holds a quarter of all super-giant and giant fields. Around three-quarters of the world's super-giant and giant fields are located onshore (including fields that straddle land and sea). The share is highest in the Middle East, Asia and the former Soviet Union. In Europe, all big fields are located offshore. Super-giant and giant fields account for the largest share of production in the Middle East, Russia and the Caspian region (Eastern Europe/Eurasia) and Latin America (Figure 10.2). Their share is lowest in Asia, Europe and the Pacific region. Although North America accounts for just over a quarter of all the crude oil ever produced in the world and 13% of current output, there are little more than 50 super-giant and giant fields in that region — a far smaller number relative to output than in any other region.[8]

Figure 10.2 ● Crude oil production by region and size of field, 2007

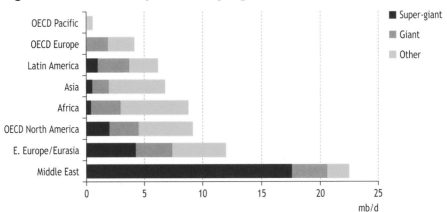

Note: For fields covered by IEA field-by-field oil production database. See footnote 3 for definitions of super-giant and giant fields.
Sources: IHS and Deloitte & Touche databases; other industry sources; IEA estimates and analysis.

There are also big differences, according to their geographic location and their size, in the extent to which reserves have been depleted. Among all fields in production today, the depletion factor — the share of initial reserves that has already been produced — is marginally higher for the super-giant and giant fields. Worldwide, those fields are on average 48% depleted (weighted by total production), compared with 47% for other fields included in our study (Table 10.4). Depletion factors are highest for North America, where most fields have been in production for decades, and Europe, where small fields dominate production. They are lowest in the Middle East.

---

8. The highly fragmented ownership of North American fields means that many large formations are broken down statistically into separate fields, resulting in a smaller number of giants.

Table 10.4 ● Average depletion factor of producing fields* by size, 2007

	Super-giants and giants	Others	All fields
OECD North America	78%	83%	81%
OECD Europe	77%	71%	73%
Middle East	37%	14%	32%
Africa	61%	44%	50%
Total	48%	47%	48%

* Based on the full IEA dataset of 798 fields.

Note: The depletion factor is cumulative production divided by initial 2P reserves.

Sources: IHS, Deloitte & Touche and USGS databases; other industry sources; IEA estimates and analysis.

Oilfield production profiles and characteristics

Every oilfield follows a unique production profile, according to the natural characteristics of the reservoirs within it, the manner in which it is developed and production-management policies. Typically, an oilfield goes through a build-up phase, during which production rises as newly drilled wells are brought into production, a period of plateau production, during which output typically is broadly flat as new wells are brought on stream offsetting declines at the oldest producing wells, and a decline phase, during which production gradually falls with reservoir pressure.

In practice, oilfields rarely follow a smooth, predictable production path. Commercial and policy considerations affect how a field is developed. And reservoirs behave in different ways at different stages of depletion for geological and technical reasons. In addition, production rates can fluctuate sharply as new phases of a field's development are launched, often to combat the "natural" or underlying decline in output. In general, with larger fields, the build-up period is long and development is pursued in phases. Some fields can build up over several decades: the Zakum field in the United Arab Emirates, for example, began producing in 1967 and hit record output of 790 kb/d only * in 2002 — a level that is expected to be exceeded in the future. Periodic maintenance programmes (scheduled and unplanned) and deliberate shut-ins for policy reasons (for example, to comply with national production quotas) can also upset the underlying trend in production.

* Table 10.1 contradicts this, w/ peak 795 in 1998

Standard production profiles

Distinguishing the impact of the inherent technical characteristics of specific types of fields from the effect of how those fields are developed and managed over time is crucial to understanding historic production trends and assessing the long-term prospects for output — both for fields that are already producing and those that are yet to be developed. For this reason, we have identified standard production profiles for different types of oilfields and assessed how those profiles differ according to a number of technical variables. This analysis is based on a sample of 725 fields from our oilfield database, with an average production history of just under 22 years and total initial reserves of 1 358 billion barrels (Table 10.5) The oldest field, Balahani-Sabunchi-

Ramani in Azerbaijan, started producing in 1871. The full dataset could not be used, because of a lack of data on certain technical parameters. Nonetheless, almost all super-giant and giant fields are included, together with most large fields.

Table 10.5 ● **Initial reserves of oilfield dataset for production profiling**

	Number of fields	2P reserves (billion barrels)
By location		
Onshore*	400	1 120
Offshore shelf	294	213
Offshore deepwater	31	25
By lithology		
Carbonate	145	716
Sandstone	473	613
Chalk	12	6
Unknown	95	23
Total	**725**	**1 358**

* Includes fields partially offshore.

Sources: IHS, Deloitte & Touche and USGS databases; other industry sources; IEA estimates and analysis.

The analysis revealed that the size of reserves and the physiographic situation (onshore/offshore) are the most important variables in explaining the shape of the production profiles (Box 10.2). Lithology — essentially whether the field is carbonate or sandstone — does not appear to influence to a significant degree the shape of the production profile, everything else being equal. The results show that small fields reach their peak sooner, produce a higher share of initial reserves by peak and decline more rapidly than large fields (Table 10.6 and Figure 10.3). It takes about twice as long for big fields to get to peak. Everything else being equal, peak production relative to reserves at offshore (shelf) fields is higher than at onshore fields, reflecting the need for developers to recover more quickly the higher costs usually associated with offshore fields. Deepwater fields, although usually big, behave in a similar way to small offshore fields with peak production reached after five years. On average, 7% of reserves are produced in that year, with cumulative production reaching 22% of reserves. The production curve for deepwater fields is, thus, highly skewed to the left, with less than a quarter of reserves produced in the relatively brief pre-peak period. Generally, offshore fields tend to have fewer wells but more highly productive horizontal wells. Spacing between wells is also much wider for offshore fields, because of the higher cost of drilling wells.

The notional average productive life of each category of field (on the assumption that cumulative production equals total initial reserves when the field is abandoned) differs markedly, from 27 years for deepwater fields to 110 years for fields holding more than 1.5 billion barrels. In practice, however, the tail of production at mature fields is strongly influenced by the prevailing economic conditions. The water cut (the share of water contained in the mixture of hydrocarbons and water that flows from the well) tends to rise towards the end of a field's life, pushing up processing costs. For as long as total operating costs are below the market value of the oil recovered, production can be sustained at relatively low levels for a long time. Since the behaviour of heavily depleted fields varies, the estimates presented here should be considered indicative only.

Box 10.2 ● Oilfield production-profiling methodology

The analysis of oilfield production profiles seeks to explain the shape of standardised profiles according to a number of technical variables, namely:

● Total crude oil reserves.

● Physiographic situation (onshore, shallow offshore and deep water).

● Lithology (carbonate, sandstone and chalk).

● Permeability, thickness and porosity of the reservoir and the API gravity of the liquids present (for fields holding initial reserves of at least 1 billion barrels). These parameters were amalgamated into a single indicator of the transmissibility of the fluid in the reservoir rock, by multiplying permeability and thickness with each other and dividing the result by gravity.

The analysis revealed that the size of reserves and the physiographic situation were the most important variables in determining the shape of the production profile. Therefore, normalised production curves (plotting annual production against cumulative production, both expressed as the share of initial 2P reserves) were first estimated according to the size of reserves for three categories: over 1.5 billion barrels; between 500 million and 1.5 billion barrels; and less than 500 million barrels. Using statistical techniques, the degree of influence of the other technical variables in explaining the shape of the normalised production curves was then estimated.[9] The results were used to produce mean normalised curves for each size category of field according to different variants of the technical variables. The mean curves were then extended to show how each category of field would be expected to behave through to full depletion of reserves. This was done by assuming an exponential rate of change.

10

Table 10.6 ● Production characteristics of sample oilfield dataset for production profiling

	% of initial reserves produced in the peak year	Cumulative % of initial reserves produced in the peak year	Number of years of production at plateau*	Estimated average total number of production years**
Onshore, < 500 Mb	3.9	21	7	75
Shelf, <500 Mb	9.7	25	4	60
Onshore, 500 Mb – 1.5 Gb	2.3	17	10	90
Shelf, 500 Mb – 1.5 Gb	3.5	20	8	65
All, > 1.5 Gb	1.7	15	13	110
Deepwater	7.0	22	5	27

* Defined as the period during which production is more than 85% of that in the peak year.
** Over the full life of the field, assuming that cumulative production strictly equals initial reserves.

Sources: IHS, Deloitte & Touche and USGS databases; other industry sources; IEA estimates and analysis.

9. A detailed explanation of the procedures used can be found at www.worldenergyoutlook.org.

Figure 10.3 ● Standard oilfield-production profiles by category of field

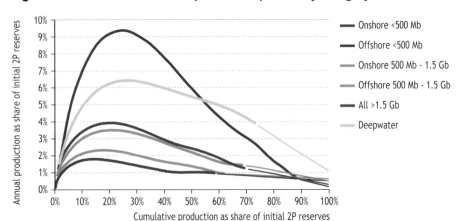

Note: The thick lines are derived from observed data; the thin lines show the trajectory assuming full depletion of the field.

Focus on giant fields

We extended further the analysis of the oil-production profiles of super-giant fields and those giants in our sample holding initial reserves of more than 1 billion barrels. For these fields, we collected additional data on porosity, permeability and thickness of reservoirs, as well as the gravity of the oil, to test the influence of these factors on the shape of the standard production profiles. The results show that the size of the field is still the dominant variable, with transmissibility (permeability and viscosity) playing a less important role. Porosity and lithology do not seem to have any influence.

We identified distinct differences in the standard profiles for fields holding between 1 and 2.8 billion barrels and those holding more than 2.8 billion barrels. For the first set of fields, transmissibility is a more important determinant of the shape of the production profile than the physiographic situation of the field. Those fields with high transmissibility tend to reach a higher plateau sooner and to be produced more rapidly: 68% of reserves are produced after about 30 years, while the corresponding figure for low transmissibility fields is only 57% (Figure 10.4).

The impact of all technical variables other than the size of reserves on the production profile of fields holding more than 2.8 billion barrels was not found to be statistically significant. This may be explained by the influence of non-technical factors, such as production quotas and geopolitical factors, especially in the Middle East, where many of the largest fields are found. In addition, the development of large fields tends to occur in phases, according to long-term technical, economic and political objectives. As a result, they are less likely to conform to standard profiles.

Figure 10.4 ● Standard oilfield-production profiles of giant fields

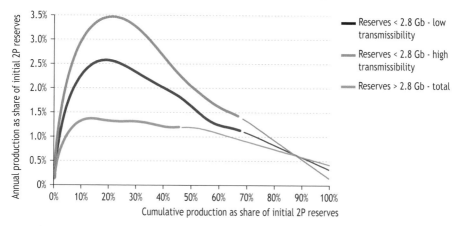

Note: the thick lines are derived from observed data while the thin lines show the trajectory assuming full depletion of the field.

Changes in production profiles over time

The standard production profiles for the six categories of field analysed above (Figure 10.3) are derived from production data for fields that came into production at different times over several decades. Three-quarters of the fields with reserves of more than 1.5 billion barrels in this dataset started to produce in the 1970s or earlier. More than 60% of medium-sized fields, both onshore and offshore, also started producing in the same period. The smallest fields were generally developed later: half of small onshore fields and more than three-quarters of small offshore fields started to produce in the last 15 years.

Analysis of production profiles by vintage shows that fields developed in recent years tend to build up more quickly to a higher plateau (relative to reserves), maintained over a shorter period of time, than fields developed before the 1990s. For example, Hassi Berkine Sud, a medium-sized Algerian field brought into production in 1998, recently reached plateau production equal to around 6% of reserves compared with a typical peak of little more than 2% for all onshore fields of similar size in our dataset (Figure 10.5). This finding is not particularly surprising: advances in production technology have made it financially attractive to introduce improved and enhanced recovery techniques earlier in a field's life. In addition, the pressure from investors on private companies to minimise the payback period and so maximise the net present value of future cash-flow, has increased in recent years.

Measuring observed production decline rates

Approach and definitions

While each phase of an oilfield's life is important, the rate at which production from oilfields declines once it has reached peak production is critical to determining the need for additional capacity, either through further development work at existing fields or by bringing new fields into production. At a global level, the faster the rate of decline, the greater the need for additional capacity for a given level of demand. The actual rate of decline, how it has changed and how it could evolve in the years to come have assumed enormous importance in the current debate about the medium- and long-term prospects for oil supply. For this reason, we have carried out an in-depth, field-by-field analysis of decline rates in order to improve understanding about the topic and gain insights into future production trends.

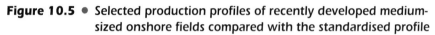

Figure 10.5 ● *Selected production profiles of recently developed medium-sized onshore fields compared with the standardised profile*

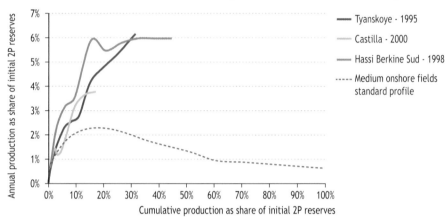

Discussions about decline rates are often confused by a failure to make clear what is meant by the term and exactly how they are calculated. It is important to understand that, at any given moment, some oilfields will be ramping up to peak production, others will be at peak or plateau, and others will be in decline. Averaging rates across a group of fields does not, therefore, reveal by itself any clear information on the decline rate of fields at different stages of their production life. Only a field-by-field analysis of production trends can shed light on this. In this section, we use our field-by-field database to quantify decline rates in detail and analyse long-term trends. The subsequent section looks at how decline rates could evolve over the projection period. The precise definitions and methods used to measure decline rates are described in Box 10.3.

Of a total of 798 producing fields in our field-by-field database, we prepared a dataset of 651 fields with initial reserves of at least 50 million barrels in order to carry out our analysis of decline rates. Of this set, 580 fields were found to have passed peak production (Table 10.7). In other words, for each of these fields, production over the latest year of production is below the maximum level ever achieved in any one year. These fields produced a total of 40.5 mb/d in 2007, or 58% of world crude oil production. Their initial reserves total 1 241 billion barrels, equal to 52% of the world total. Of the post-peak fields, a total of 479 were found to be in the post-plateau phase. Of these, 362 fields are in decline phase 3 (with annual production at less than

Box 10.3 ● How do we define and calculate decline rates?

Peak production is the highest level of production recorded over a single year at a given field.

An oil field is in **decline** when aggregate production in the latest year (2007 for most fields in the dataset used for this analysis) is below production in the peak year, even if the field attains other lower peaks in the interim. **Plateau production** is when annual production is more than 85% of peak production. A field is in the **post-plateau phase** when it has fallen below plateau. For the purposes of our decline rates calculations, only fields with production in the last year of production that is below the level of the first year of post-plateau production are included.

The full period of production decline after peak is broken down into three distinct phases for the purposes of measurement: **decline phase 1** is the period from peak annual production to the last year of plateau production; **decline phase 2** is from the first year at which production falls below plateau through to the last year in which production is above 50% of peak; and **decline phase 3** is the period after which production is consistently below 50% of peak.

The **observed decline rate** is the cumulative average annual rate of change in observed production between two given years (for example, between peak production and the latest year).

The **natural decline rate**, sometimes called the underlying decline rate, is the notional rate of decline in production between two given years had there been no investment beyond that associated with the initial development of the field. The methodology used to estimate this rate by region is described in Figure 10.9 below.

Unless otherwise mentioned, all the decline rates referred to in this chapter are **production-weighted**. In other words, the average for a particular group of fields (by type or region) takes into account the level of production of each field in the total. Cumulative production over the full life of the field was used to weight decline rates for fields currently in production and in the post-peak phase.

Generally, historical observed decline rates were calculated using the full production history of each field. Of course, these vary greatly in length: the oldest field in our dataset has been producing for 137 years and the youngest for two years (the minimum period for which calculating a decline rate is possible). Solely for the purposes of measuring long-term trends, decline rates were also calculated on a year-by-year basis, with the decline rates for each field weighted by the actual production in the given year.

half that at peak). A larger share of super-giant fields are in the post-plateau phase, as most of them have been in production for several decades. Nonetheless, the world's biggest field by far — Ghawar — is not among the post-plateau fields, as production in 2007 was still less than 15% below the peak of 5.6 mb/d reached in 1980 (Box 10.4).

Table 10.7 ● Number of oilfields in dataset for decline rate calculations

	Super-giant	Giant	Other	All fields
By location				
Onshore*	43	185	159	387
Offshore shelf	11	61	147	219
Offshore deepwater	0	17	28	45
By lithology				
Carbonate	32	69	59	160
Sandstone	22	189	268	479
Chalk	0	5	7	12
By grouping				
OPEC	40	97	48	185
Middle East	33	41	8	82
Other	7	56	40	103
Non-OPEC	14	166	286	466
By region				
OECD	3	68	150	221
North America	3	43	56	102
Europe	0	23	89	112
Pacific	0	2	5	7
Non-OECD	51	195	184	430
E. Europe/Eurasia	10	52	14	76
Asia	1	19	73	93
Middle East	33	50	18	101
Africa	1	40	53	94
Latin America	6	34	26	66
Total	**54**	**263**	**334**	**651**

* Includes fields partially offshore. The dataset includes all post-peak fields in our database.
Sources: IHS, Deloitte & Touche and USGS databases; other industry sources; IEA estimates and analysis.

Results of the analysis

The observed post-peak decline rate averaged across all fields on a production-weighted basis is 5.1% using raw data. That is equal to 3.6 mb/d per year, based on the 2007 level of global crude oil production. As the standard production profiles suggest, decline rates are lowest for the biggest fields: they average 3.4% for super-giant fields, 6.5% for giant fields and 10.4% for large fields (Table 10.8). Rates are also lowest for onshore fields and highest for deepwater offshore fields, reflecting the different ways in which they are developed (as described in the previous section). On average worldwide, production has declined yearly by 4.3% at onshore fields and 7.3% at offshore fields, with deepwater fields declining by 13.3%. Sandstone fields have declined significantly faster than carbonate fields, 6.3% versus 3.4%, but this largely reflects the fact that the latter tend to be much larger and are more often located in the Middle East (where decline rates have been tempered by historically conservative production policies);

Box 10.4 ● The Ghawar field: the super-giant among super-giants

The Ghawar field — the world's largest — was discovered in 1948 and started producing in 1951. The area of the field — more accurately described as a collection of oil-bearing formations — is partitioned into six geographical areas, from north to south: Ain Dar, Shedgum, Farzan, Hawiyah, Uthmaniyah and Haradh. Oil is produced from the Jurassic formations, namely Arab, Dhruma and Hanifa, while gas and condensate are extracted from the deeper and older reservoirs, in the Khuff, Unayzah and Jawf formations. Ghawar crude, which has an average gravity of around 34° API and sulphur content of 1.8%, accounts for most of the Saudi Arab Light export blend.

Ghawar is a large anticline structure, 280 km long by 25 km wide, with about 50 metres of net oil pay. Initial oil in place is 250 billion barrels, of which initial recoverable reserves are estimated at 140 billion barrels (implying an expected ultimate recovery rate of 56%). Cumulative production reached 66 billion barrels in 2007, so remaining reserves are about 74 billion barrels. Ghawar produced 5.1 mb/d of crude oil in 2007, down from a peak of 5.6 mb/d in 1980 (when the field's capacity was fully utilised in response to the loss of Iranian production following the revolution) and a recent peak of 5.3 mb/d in 1997. The observed post-peak decline rate is, thus, a mere 0.3% per year. Ghawar is still at the plateau phase of production on our definition (Box 10.3).

Reservoir pressure is maintained through the use of peripheral water flooding, whereby seawater is injected into the reservoir in the oil layer just above the tar mat that separates the oil layer from the aquifer. The water pushes the oil inwards and upwards, towards the producing wells. This secondary recovery technique, first used at Ghawar in 1965, typically results in lower flow rates than the more commonly used pattern water flooding, but tends to result in a higher recovery rate and allows for plateau production to be maintained for longer (see IEA, 2005 for more details). Nonetheless, as the field has matured, maintaining reservoir pressure and sustaining production has become more difficult and costs have risen. The water cut — the share of water in the liquids extracted — increased sharply in the 1990s, reaching 37% in 2000. However, recent development work has succeeded in reducing the water cut to 27% at present, according to Saudi Aramco, the field operator.

Ghawar has been developed in distinct stages, which have progressively raised the field's capacity and kept the field at plateau. The most recent project, involving the Haradh area in the southern part of the field, was completed in 2006, tripling capacity there to about 900 kb/d. This has helped to offset natural declines in other parts of the field. The overall capacity of Ghawar is sustained by infill drilling and well work-overs to maintain flow pressure in various parts of the field. Reports suggest that enhanced oil recovery techniques are being used to boost capacity in the mature zones of the Shedgum and Uthmaniyah areas, where extensive drilling programmes have recently been undertaken (Sanford Bernstein, 2007).

lithology does not appear to be a major determinant of decline rates (see the previous section). Regardless of location or lithology, decline rates are, in most cases, lower the bigger the field. Similarly, the rates of post-plateau decline are usually slightly higher than the rate of post-peak decline, confirming the results of the production-profiling analysis (Figure 10.6).[10] Worldwide, the average rate of observed post-plateau decline is 5.8% for the 479 fields that are in the post-plateau decline phase out of the 580 post-peak fields and the total of 798 fields in our database.[11]

Table 10.8 ● Production-weighted average observed decline rates by size and type of field

	Post-peak				Post-plateau			
	Super-giant	Giant	Large	Total	Super-giant	Giant	Large	Total
Onshore	3.4%	5.6%	8.8%	4.3%	4.9%	5.5%	9.4%	5.3%
Offshore	3.4%	8.6%	11.6%	7.3%	1.2%	9.0%	11.7%	7.2%
Shelf	3.4%	7.7%	11.2%	6.6%	1.2%	8.6%	12.2%	6.7%
Deepwater	-	13.1%	14.2%	13.3%	-	10.8%	12.6%	11.2%
Carbonate	2.3%	6.6%	8.9%	3.4%	2.7%	6.9%	9.3%	4.3%
Sandstone	4.8%	6.5%	10.9%	6.3%	5.5%	6.5%	11.1%	6.6%
World	3.4%	6.5%	10.4%	5.1%	4.3%	6.6%	10.7%	5.8%

Sources: IHS, Deloitte & Touche and USGS databases; other industry sources; IEA estimates and analysis.

Decline rates also vary markedly by region. Rates are lowest in the Middle East and highest in the North Sea (Table 10.9). This reflects, to a large extent, differences in the average size of fields, which in turn is related to the extent to which reserves are depleted and their location onshore or offshore. North Sea fields tend to be much smaller than Middle East fields, while almost all significant North Sea fields are located offshore. North Sea fields (which make up all the European fields in our dataset) have declined on average by 11.5% per year since peak and 13.3% since plateau. The relatively low decline rates of Middle East fields, which have averaged less than 3% per year, is also explained by the

---

10. The average post-peak decline rates calculated using the standard production profiles for different categories of field by size are, unsurprisingly, of a similar magnitude to the rates calculated using raw data that are presented in this section.

11. The observed decline rates shown in this chapter differ from those for non-OPEC countries described in the IEA's most recent *Medium-Term Oil Market Report*, published in July (IEA, 2008). This is because of methodological differences, associated with the different time horizons of the two reports. The *MTOMR* estimates decline rates on a year-by-year basis, rather than over the full production life of the field. The *MTOMR* also adjusts raw field-by-field production data for temporary reductions in output caused by unexpected events such as weather-related outages, strikes and security-related disruptions. Nonetheless, the results are similar.

disruptions to the standard production profile caused by short-term production-management policies (notably in support of OPEC targets) and geopolitical conflicts. The dominance of Middle East countries and the heavy weight of super-giant fields in the population of OPEC fields contribute to the much lower average post-peak decline rates for OPEC compared with non-OPEC countries.

Figure 10.6 ● **Production-weighted average post-peak and post-plateau observed decline rates by field size**

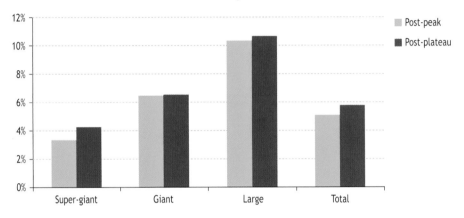

Sources: IHS, Deloitte & Touche and USGS databases; other industry sources; IEA estimates and analysis.

Table 10.9 ● **Production-weighted average annual observed decline rates by region**

	Post-peak				Post-plateau			
	Super-giant	Giant	Large	Total	Super-giant	Giant	Large	Total
OPEC	2.3%	5.4%	9.1%	3.1%	2.9%	4.8%	8.3%	3.6%
Middle East	2.2%	6.3%	4.4%	2.6%	2.8%	6.5%	6.4%	3.4%
Other	4.8%	5.0%	10.2%	5.2%	3.8%	4.1%	8.8%	4.3%
Non-OPEC	5.7%	6.9%	10.5%	7.1%	6.0%	7.4%	10.9%	7.4%
OECD North America	6.4%	5.4%	12.1%	6.5%	4.5%	6.0%	12.3%	6.0%
OECD Europe	-	10.0%	13.5%	11.5%	-	13.1%	15.5%	13.3%
OECD Pacific	-	11.1%	13.2%	11.6%	-	10.4%	12.6%	11.1%
E. Europe/Eurasia	5.1%	5.0%	12.1%	5.1%	5.3%	5.1%	12.4%	5.3%
Asia	2.1%	8.3%	6.6%	6.1%	2.5%	5.7%	6.7%	5.2%
Middle East	2.2%	6.5%	7.4%	2.7%	2.8%	7.0%	9.8%	3.7%
Africa	1.5%	5.2%	8.8%	5.1%	1.2%	5.2%	9.3%	5.0%
Latin America	8.4%	5.2%	6.9%	6.0%	9.5%	5.3%	6.8%	6.1%
World	3.4%	6.5%	10.4%	5.1%	4.3%	6.6%	10.7%	5.8%

Sources: IHS, Deloitte & Touche and USGS databases; other industry sources; IEA estimates and analysis.

The impact of field age and maturity

In general, observed decline rates are higher the younger the field. For example, the average decline rate for all the non-OPEC fields in our dataset that have come on stream since the start of the current decade is 14.5%, compared with 11.6% for post-peak fields that started producing in the 1990s and only 5.9% for fields that started producing no later than 1969 (Table 10.10). This pattern applies to both OPEC and non-OPEC fields (Figure 10.7). The very low average decline rate for the pre-1970s vintage of OPEC fields — less than 3% — is influenced strongly by the very low observed post-peak decline rate of the Ghawar field (0.3%). The fall in the decline rate for OPEC fields that came into production since 2000 is explained by the fact that most of them, while past their initial peak, are still at plateau.

Table 10.10 ● Production-weighted average post-peak observed decline rates by vintage*

	Pre-1970s	1970s	1980s	1990s	2000s	Total
OPEC	2.8%	3.5%	4.6%	7.5%	5.0%	3.1%
Non-OPEC	5.9%	6.8%	8.3%	11.6%	14.5%	7.1%
World	3.9%	5.9%	7.9%	10.6%	12.6%	5.1%

* First year of production.
Source: IHS, Deloitte & Touche and USGS databases; other industry sources; IEA estimates and analysis.

As explained in the previous section, advances in production technology and changes in commercial practice mean that fields developed today tend to build up more quickly to a higher plateau, maintained over a shorter period of time, than fields developed before the 1990s. The growing importance since the 1970s of offshore fields (which normally reach a higher peak as a share of reserves than onshore fields) also explains this trend. It follows that the post-peak decline rate from such shorter and accelerated production profiles is higher.

Figure 10.7 ● Production-weighted average post-peak observed decline rates by type of producer and year of first production

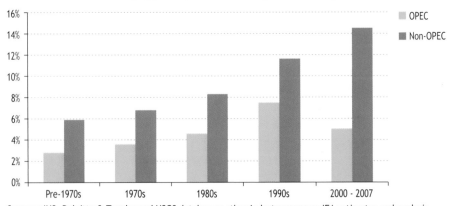

Sources: IHS, Deloitte & Touche and USGS databases; other industry sources; IEA estimates and analysis.

Decline rates show some variation according to the decline period (Box 10.3 for definitions), though the differences are less marked than for other factors including field size. For all post-peak fields still in decline phase 1 (*i.e.* whose production in the most recent year is still more than 85% of peak), the average decline rate is 1.4% (Table 10.11). The decline rate rises to 3.6% for those fields in decline phase 2 and to 6.7% in decline phase 3. For all three decline periods, rates are always lowest for the super-giant fields, with those still in decline phase 1 registering an average decline rate of only 0.8%. Once again, the large weight of the Ghawar field in this group of fields helps to lower the overall decline rate. The rise in the observed decline rate as a field reaches the end of its life is probably explained by the increase in the rate of decline in pressure.

Table 10.11 ● Production-weighted average annual observed decline rates by decline phase

	Decline phase 1 (peak to end of plateau)	Decline phase 2 (plateau to 50% of peak)	Decline phase 3 (50% of peak to latest year)	Total
Super-giant	0.8%	3.0%	4.9%	3.4%
Giant	3.0%	3.7%	7.6%	6.5%
Large	5.5%	7.2%	11.8%	10.4%
World	1.4%	3.6%	6.7%	5.1%

Note: See Box 10.3 for precise definitions of the decline periods. Fields were sorted according to the period in which they currently lie (based on the last year of production data). Of the 580 post-peak fields included in our analysis, 101 were in decline phase 1, 117 in phase 2 and 362 in phase 3.

Source: IHS, Deloitte & Touche and USGS databases; other industry sources; IEA estimates and analysis.

Trends in observed decline rates

For individual fields, observed decline rates would be expected to change over time, because of changes in well productivity, as pressure drops, and in production policy, and because of investment in field re-development. At any given moment, fields will be at different stages of their production life, so the rate of observed decline averaged over all fields in decline inevitably changes over time. We have calculated the *year-on-year* change in production, averaged across all the post-peak fields in our dataset (all the decline rates shown up to this point correspond to the average over the life of each field). For each year, only those fields that were in decline were included in the calculation. The results show that the production-weighted average rate of fall in production has fluctuated significantly over time, but has been relatively more stable since the 1980s, at around 5% to 12% per year (Figure 10.8).

Short-term fluctuations appear to reflect the impact of the production policies of OPEC countries and cyclical changes in investment in existing fields, resulting from policy, geopolitical factors and fluctuations in oil prices and fiscal terms. The very rapid fall in production in 1980 is explained primarily by the collapse in output at several fields in Iran following the Iranian revolution in late 1979, while the invasion of Kuwait, which led to the loss of all of the country's production for several months, caused the drop in output to accelerate in 1990 and 1991. The acceleration in the year-on-year rate of fall in production in the late 1990s was the result of a downturn in upstream investment, in response to a slump in prices, while the fall in the rate of decline since 2000 (with the exception of 2006, when production constraints in OPEC countries caused average rates of decline to accelerate) appears to have resulted from higher capital spending on re-developing existing fields.

Figure 10.8 ● **Year-on-year change in the production-weighted average production from post-peak fields**

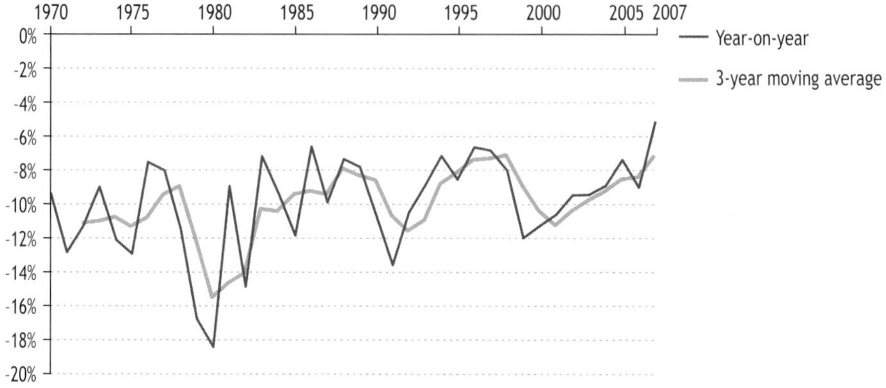

Note: In contrast to the decline rates shown in the preceding tables and figures, which are based on the average decline rate of each field over a period of time determined by its peak or plateau, the rates of change shown here are calculated using simple year-on-year changes in each field's production. For each year, the dataset is adjusted to include only those fields that were in the post-peak phase and that were in decline in that year. As a result, the sample size diminishes going backwards in time. For example, the number of fields that were post-peak in 1970 was 36 compared with 580 in 2007. The decline rates may therefore be considered less representative of all rates for all the world's producing fields for the earliest years than for 2007.

Sources: IHS, Deloitte & Touche and USGS databases; other industry sources; IEA estimates and analysis.

Deriving an estimate of the average global observed decline rate

Our field-by-field analysis of decline rates allows us to obtain a reasonable estimate of the average decline rates for all the fields in the world, weighted by production. All the decline rates presented so far in this chapter are based on field-by-field production data from our database, covering 798 fields. The average size of these fields — predominantly super-giants and giants — is significantly larger than the average size of *all* the fields in the world. The 580 fields included in our analysis of post-peak decline rates produced 40.5 mb/d of crude oil in 2007 — equal to 58% of world production. Yet these fields make up less than 1% of all the producing fields in the world.

It is impossible to know precisely what the observed decline rates are for these other fields. Nonetheless, it is reasonable to assume that the decline rates are, on average, at least as high as these of the large fields in our database. In reality, they are likely to be somewhat higher, given that we have detected a clear correlation between field size and the observed decline rate. In order to derive an indicative estimate of the overall decline rate for *all* the world's oilfields, we have assumed that the average rate for the fields not included in our database is the same as that for the large fields (which averages 10.4% worldwide). This is a somewhat optimistic assumption, as the differences in decline rates between the three categories of fields we assess here suggest that smaller fields are likely to have higher decline rates than large fields. On this basis, we estimate that the average observed decline rate worldwide is 6.7%. Were that rate to be applied to 2007 crude oil production, the annual loss of output would be 4.7 mb/d. The adjusted decline rate is higher in all regions, markedly so in North America, because our sample for that region is dominated by super-giant and giant fields (Table 10.12).

Table 10.12 ● Estimated production-weighted average annual observed post-peak decline rates for all fields worldwide by region

	Based on 580 field dataset	All fields
OECD North America	6.5%	9.7%
OECD Europe	11.5%	11.9%
OECD Pacific	11.6%	12.6%
E. Europe/Eurasia	5.1%	5.8%
Asia	6.1%	6.7%
Middle East	2.7%	3.4%
Africa	5.1%	6.8%
Latin America	6.0%	6.6%
World	**5.1%**	**6.7%**

Sources: IHS, Deloitte & Touche and USGS databases; other industry sources; IEA estimates and analysis.

10

Trends in natural decline rates

Estimating historical trends

Observed decline rates are an important indicator of the performance of oilfields across regions and over time, but, by themselves, they do not reveal underlying trends in field production behaviour. This is because observed rates are heavily influenced by on-going and periodic investment in fields already in production, aimed at maintaining well pressure and flow rates, and improving recovery of oil reserves. In reality, few oilfields are left to produce without further field-development work involving significant amounts of capital expenditure once the initial set of wells has been drilled. This further investment can take the form of infill drilling (to target pockets of oil that prove to be inaccessible from existing wells), well work-overs (major maintenance or remedial treatments, often involving the removal and replacement of the well casing), secondary recovery programmes such as water flooding (the injection of water to push the oil towards producing wells) and gas injection and enhanced oil recovery techniques, such as CO_2 injection. Such activities can arrest the natural decline in pressure and production from a field and may even boost output to a significant degree. It is necessary to estimate the underlying, or *natural* decline rate — the rate at which production at a field would decline in the absence of any investment — in order to ascertain how much capital needs to be deployed to sustain production or limit observed decline to a particular rate.

To arrive at the natural decline rate, therefore, one needs to strip out the effect of new investment beyond the initial capital spending involved in bringing the field into production. We have developed a top-down methodology for estimating historical natural decline rates, based on the estimated impact of the actual investment that has gone into existing fields over the past five years (summarised in Figure 10.9). This approach required detailed estimates of the amount of new capacity coming into production each year over 2003-2007, the associated capital expenditure and the unit cost of incremental capacity at existing fields, based on generic (region-by-region) estimates of finding and development costs and reserve life estimates (drawing on the results of our analysis of investment in Chapter 13). The results were calibrated against our estimates of observed decline rates for all fields worldwide. Inevitably, a degree of judgment was involved, in consultation with industry, in estimating these parameters, given data deficiencies. The results must, therefore, be considered as indicative only.

Figure 10.9 ● **Methodology for estimating natural decline rates**

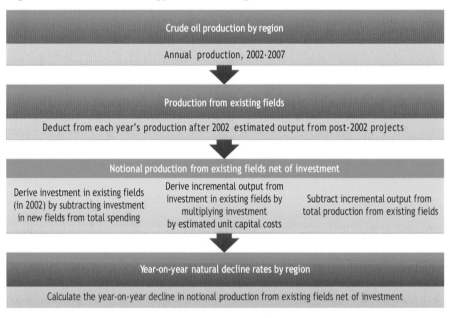

The production-weighted average annual *natural* decline rate for the world as a whole is estimated at 9.0% — some 2.3 percentage points higher than the *observed* decline rate for post-peak fields. In other words, the decline in production from existing fields would have been around one-third faster had there been no capital spending on those fields once they had passed their peak. Natural decline rates are highest for OECD Europe and Pacific (Australia), and Asia. The rate is lowest for the Middle East. The difference between observed and natural decline rates varies in both absolute and proportionate terms across regions (Figure 10.10). Nonetheless, the ratio of observed to natural decline rates, which averages about 1:1.3, is broadly similar across all regions, suggesting that these estimates are reasonably robust. The smallest difference between observed and natural rates is for Europe (North Sea). This appears to reflect the relatively limited remaining scope for infill drilling compared with other parts of the world.

Figure 10.10 ● *Indicative natural decline rates by region*

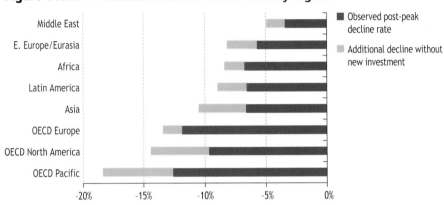

Discerning a trend from the short time period we used to estimate natural decline rates is risky. Nonetheless, a clear rising trend does emerge from our analysis: the worldwide average natural decline rate (year-on-year) rose from 8.7% in 2003 to 9.7% in 2007 (the average rate is 9% for the period 2003-2007 as a whole). This result is in line with expectations, as over that period, a growing share of crude oil production came from younger, smaller and offshore fields, which have inherently higher decline rates. Smaller and offshore fields typically exhibit higher observed decline rates, because of the more limited potential for infill drilling, as mentioned in the previous section. But natural decline rates would also be expected to be higher too, as these fields tend to be developed in such a way as to maximise and bring forward peak production in order to improve cash-flow and amortise the large up-front investment as quickly as possible. Development programmes for larger fields typically are less likely to be driven by purely financial considerations and are more likely to be effected by a policy of maximising ultimate recovery rates.

Other recent studies support the finding that natural decline rates have been rising. For example, the natural decline rates of fields operated by 15 major oil companies rose on average from 10.6% to 13% between 2001 and 2006 (Goldman Sachs, 2007). The higher rate for these companies is to be expected, since a relatively large share of their production comes from OECD regions (notably North America) and West Africa, where decline rates are highest. The increase in the overall rate of natural decline, based on our analysis, is far from negligible: based on world crude oil production of 70.2 mb/d in 2007, this increase represents an additional annual loss of capacity through natural decline of around 700 kb/d. The implication is that an additional 700 kb/d of gross capacity — the equivalent of almost one-and-a-half projects the size of Khursaniyah in Saudi Arabia — had to be brought on stream in 2007 simply to offset the higher rate of natural decline compared with five years before.

Case studies of how individual fields have behaved in the absence of any major investment provide a way of verifying the extent to which natural decline rates deviate from observed rates. In reality, there are few cases where a field has been left to decline over a long period without any capital spending whatsoever. Some cases can, nonetheless, be identified. The collapse of the Soviet Union caused upstream investment virtually to dry up for several years in the first half of the 1990s and led to a precipitous drop in oil production. During 1990-1995, the production-weighted average annual decline rate for the 19 largest Russian fields (with reserves in excess of 1 billion barrels) that were in decline at that time was close to 14%, though decline rates were certainly exaggerated by a lack of spending on operation and maintenance, too. Among those fields, Samotlor — the world's sixth-largest in terms of initial reserves — experienced a year-on-year production decline of more than 16% over the same period.

Among all the North Sea fields in our dataset, we have identified only nine that were not subject to any major development programme over a period of at least three years (the majority of fields have been developed in a continuous fashion, with sustained capital spending over much of the life of the field). The (arithmetic) average decline rate is 13.7% for all the fields in this sample (Table 10.13), which is very close to the natural decline rate we estimate for all North Sea fields (which make up virtually all of Europe's production) based on 2002-2007 data. Decline rates among the nine fields range from under 6% to over 20%.

Table 10.13 ● **Average year-on-year decline rates for selected North Sea oilfields**

Field	Country	Initial oil reserves (million barrels)	Period of production without significant investment	Average decline rate*
Fulmar	UK	583	1997-2006	13.2%
Miller	UK	345	1998-2000	23.1%
Murchison	UK	332	1985-1989	20.3%
Ninian	UK	1 310	1994-1996	13.2%
Tern	UK	287	2003-2007	13.9%
Thistle	UK	433	1996-2002	12.0%
Auk	UK	197	1998-2003	5.7%
Skjold	Denmark	298	2004-2007	11.9%
Rijswijk	Netherlands	275	1969-1976	10.2%
Average (arithmetic)				13.7%

* Calculated as the cumulative average annual rate of decline between the first and last year of production over the specified period without significant investment.

Source: Official government data; IEA analysis.

The apparent inverse relationship between field size and the natural decline rate mirrors that between the rate of depletion of recoverable reserves (measured by the ratio of remaining reserves to production, R/P) and the decline rate. The R/P ratio is inversely correlated with the natural decline rate at the regional level, even though we have only eight regional data points. The four regions with the lowest R/P ratio — OECD North America, Europe and the Pacific, together with Asia — have the highest natural decline rates, while the Middle East, with the highest R/P ratio, has the lowest decline rate (Figure 10.11). In short, the natural decline rate appears to rise over time as a producing region matures and the R/P ratio drops.

Figure 10.11 • **Natural decline rates and reserves-to-production ratios by region, 2007**

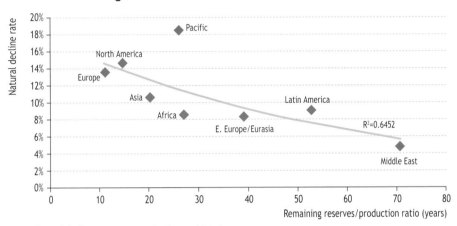

Note: Natural decline rates are production-weighted.

Sources: IHS databases; IEA databases and analysis.

Long-term prospects for natural decline rates

The scale of upstream investment required to match oil production to demand in the medium to long term hinges critically on the evolution of natural decline rates. The rate and type of investment, both in existing oilfields and in new fields, that will come on stream over the projection period will determine the extent to which observed decline rates diverge from natural rates.

There is little reason to suppose that, for a given type and size of field in a specific location, the natural decline rate will change significantly in the future. However, a change in the mix of fields that will be developed in the future, including a shift towards smaller reservoirs and offshore deepwater fields, would be expected to drive up natural decline rates over time in all regions. On the other hand, a larger share of new field developments over the projection period is expected to come from onshore locations in the Middle East, where natural decline rates are the lowest (mainly because the average size of fields is high). This factor will offset, at least partially, the effect of declining field size on the weighted-average natural decline rate worldwide.

We have assessed, by region, how average natural decline rates weighted by production could change in the future, using our Reference Scenario projections of crude oil and NGLs production, and additions to proven and probable reserves through reserves growth and discoveries (described in detail in Chapter 11). The correlation between the R/P ratio and the natural decline rate is applied to the projected R/P ratio in each region to derive an estimate of how the natural rate in each case might evolve between 2007 and 2030 (Figure 10.12). The results suggest that natural decline rates will tend to rise in all regions. At the world level, the increase in the production-weighted average decline rate over the projection period is about 1.5 percentage points, taking the rate to around 10.5% per year in 2030. The increase is particularly pronounced in North America, where the natural decline rate increases from about 14% to 17%, while the R/P ratio falls to about 10 years (as remaining reserves fall even faster than production).

Figure 10.12 ● **Projected change in natural decline rates and reserves-to-production ratios by region, 2007 to 2030**

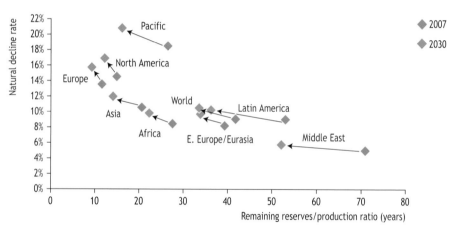

Note: Natural decline rates are production-weighted.

Sources: IHS databases; IEA databases and analysis.

CHAPTER 11

PROSPECTS FOR OIL PRODUCTION
Running faster to stand still?

H I G H L I G H T S

- In the Reference Scenario, world oil production (not including processing gains) rises by 26%, from 82.3 mb/d in 2007 to 103.8 mb/d in 2030. The share of OPEC countries in global output increases from 44% in 2007 to 51% in 2030. Saudi Arabia remains the world's largest producer throughout the projection period, its output climbing from 10.2 mb/d to 15.6 mb/d.

- Worldwide, conventional crude oil production increases only modestly between 2007 and 2030 — by 5 mb/d — as almost all the additional capacity from new oilfields is offset by the decline in output at existing fields. Output from known oilfields that are already being developed or are awaiting development expands through to 2020, but then begins to drop, as few such fields are left to be brought into production and many of them enter their decline phase. Fields that are yet to be found account for about a quarter of total crude oil production by 2030.

- The bulk of the net increase in total oil production comes from natural gas liquids (NGLs), driven by the relatively rapid expansion in gas supply, and from non-conventional resources and technologies. Enhanced oil recovery, predominately from CO_2 injection, makes a growing contribution.

- The regional breakdown of world oil production does not change dramatically over the projection period, but there are some important country-level changes. Saudi Arabia sees the largest incremental increase in oil production, followed by Canada. Brazil and Kazakhstan see large increases in output, while production in Russia falls. NGLs in Saudi Arabia and crude oil in Iraq dominate the increase in OPEC output.

- Non-OPEC production of crude oil and NGLs declines from 44.8 mb/d in 2007 to 43.5 mb/d in 2015 and then falls further to 42.9 mb/d in 2030 in the Reference Scenario. Non-OPEC non-conventional oil production, in contrast, rises from 1.5 mb/d in 2007 to 7.9 mb/d in 2030.

- OPEC crude oil and NGL production increases from 35.9 mb/d in 2007 to 44.0 mb/d in 2015 and to 52.0 mb/d in 2030, on the assumption that there are no major disruptions in supply and that the requisite investment occurs. The increase in crude oil and NGL output comes mainly from onshore fields: offshore production falls after 2015, despite rising output in Angola and Nigeria. The average size of onshore fields in Middle East OPEC countries declines over the *Outlook* period, especially after 2015.

- These projections call for huge investments to explore for and develop more reserves, mainly to combat decline at existing fields. An additional 64 mb/d of gross capacity — the equivalent of six times that of Saudi Arabia today — needs to be brought on stream between 2007 and 2030. A faster rate of decline than projected here would sharply increase upstream investment needs and oil prices.

Global oil-production trends

Summary of projections in the Reference Scenario

In the Reference Scenario, world oil production rises (not including processing gains) by 26%, from 82.3 mb/d in 2007 to 103.8 mb/d in 2030. Declines in crude oil production at existing fields (those already in production in 2007) are more than compensated for by output from fields under or awaiting development and, mainly in the last decade of the *Outlook* period, fields that are yet to be found (Figure 11.1). Worldwide, production of conventional crude oil alone increases only modestly, from 70.2 mb/d to 75.2 mb/d over the period. The share of natural gas liquids (NGLs) and enhanced oil recovery (EOR), predominately from CO_2 injection, in total oil production rises considerably, from 13% in 2007 to 25% in 2030. The contribution of non-conventional oil also rises substantially, from 2% in 2007 to 8.5% in 2030, with a marked spurt in the decade commencing now. Cumulative conventional oil production (crude and NGLs), which stood at 1.1 trillion barrels in 2007, is projected to rise to over 1.8 trillion barrels by 2030. Its share of currently estimated ultimately recoverable resources would, therefore, rise from slightly less than a third today to around one-half by 2030, though any increase in resources, for example, brought about by advances in technology, would result in a smaller increase in that share.

Figure 11.1 ● **World oil production by source in the Reference Scenario**

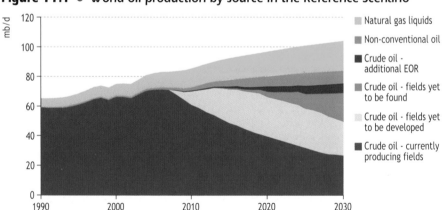

The projections take account of build-up and decline rates at existing fields and those that will come on stream over the projection period, new capacities from current, sanctioned and planned upstream projects, and potential discoveries over the projection period based on our country-by-country assessment of ultimately recoverable reserves (Box 11.1). Assumptions about decline rates are based on the analysis of Chapter 10.

The share of world oil production from member countries of the Organization of the Petroleum Exporting Countries (OPEC), particularly in the Middle East, grows significantly, from 44% in 2007 to 51% in 2030. Their collective output of crude oil and NGLs grows from 35.9 mb/d in 2007 to 44.0 mb/d in 2015 and 52.0 mb/d in 2030 (Table 11.1). The contribution of NGLs to total conventional output in OPEC countries (and to a lesser extent elsewhere), rises quickly over the projection period, reaching 25% of OPEC output in 2030, compared with 13% in 2007. Saudi Arabia remains the world's largest oil producer throughout the projection period, its production climbing from 10.2 mb/d in 2007 to 15.6 mb/d in 2030.

Table 11.1 ● **World oil production and supply in the Reference Scenario**
(million barrels per day)

	2000	2007	2015	2030
Crude oil*	66.0	70.2	73.0	75.2
OPEC	29.0	31.1	35.9	38.9
Of which offshore	6.7	9.2	10.8	7.4
Non-OPEC	37.0	39.1	37.1	36.3
Of which offshore	15.9	15.2	15.4	16.3
NGLs	7.8	10.5	14.4	19.8
OPEC	3.0	4.7	8.1	13.2
Non-OPEC	4.9	5.7	6.4	6.6
Non-conventional oil**	1.2	1.6	4.6	8.8
OPEC	0.2	0.1	0.4	0.9
Non-OPEC	1.1	1.5	4.2	7.9
Total production	75.0	82.3	92.0	103.8
OPEC	32.1	35.9	44.4	52.9
Non-OPEC	42.9	46.3	47.6	50.9
Processing gains	1.7	2.1	2.3	2.6
World oil supply	76.8	84.3	94.4	106.4
OPEC market share	43%	44%	48%	51%

* Including condensates.
** Extra-heavy oil (excluding Venezuela), oil sands, chemical additives, gas-to-liquids and coal-to-liquids. Biofuels are not included.

Non-OPEC production increases much more slowly, from its current level of 46.3 mb/d to 47.6 mb/d in 2015 and 50.9 mb/d in 2030. Crude oil production alone is projected to decline slowly, from 39.1 mb/d in 2007 to 36.3 mb/d in 2030, as output from offshore fields is unable to fully compensate for a steady drop in onshore production. The share of non-OPEC countries in world oil production declines by 7 percentage points, from 56% now to 49% in 2030. The reduction in non-OPEC production would be even more pronounced were it not for the growing contribution of oil from enhanced oil recovery (EOR) projects, which rises from 0.4 mb/d in 2007 to 3.6 mb/d in 2030.

Box 11.1 • Modelling oil production in *WEO-2008*

For *WEO-2008*, trends in oil production to 2030 are modelled using a bottom-up methodology, making extensive use of the IHS database of worldwide proven and probable reserves and discovered fields, and country-by-country estimates of ultimately recoverable resources from the US Geological Survey (USGS). The methodology aims to replicate investment decisions in the oil industry by analysing the profitability of developing reserves at the project level (Figure 11.2).

In the model, production in countries that are assumed to be open to private companies is separately derived, according to the type of asset in which investments are made: existing fields, new fields, non-conventional projects and exploration. Standard production profiles are applied to derive the production trend for existing fields and for those new fields (by country and type of field) which are brought into production over the projection period (see Chapter 10). Cash available for investments is a function of past production, the international oil price (taking account of the government take in oil revenues) and the investment policies of oil companies. Investment is made only in profitable projects. New projects generate cash, which is then spent on future profitable projects.

The profitability of each type of project is based on assumptions about the capital and operating costs of different types of projects, the hurdle price (expressed as a proportion of the actual oil price assumed in the Reference Scenario) and the discount rate, representing the cost of capital. The net present value of the cash-flows of each type of project is derived from a standard production profile, which is determined by the size of the field and its location onshore or offshore. Projects are prioritised by their net present value and available cash is spent on the most potentially profitable projects, with total capital spending constrained by the total available cash-flow of the industry.

Investment in exploration, which is assumed to absorb a fixed share of total cash-flow, determines the number of exploration wells drilled (based on assumptions about the cost of drilling). For each country, the amount of oil discovered (onshore and offshore) each year is based on an historical analysis which allows us to determine the relationship between the cumulative number of exploration wells and the total amount of oil found (known as a "creaming curve").

It was further assumed that total discoveries equal the ultimately recoverable resources, as estimated by the USGS.

The main assumptions used in the model are the international oil price, exploration and development costs, the marginal tax take of the host country, and the rate of re-investment of cash-flows by oil companies. The price used to evaluate the profitability of projects is assumed to be a function of the assumed international market price. We assumed the current fiscal regimes and the average rates of re-investment observed by the oil industry in 2007 to remain constant over the projection period. We also assume in the Reference Scenario that upstream costs level off in 2009 and remain flat thereafter in real terms.

The oil-supply projections for countries which are considered to be closed to international investments are based on exogenous assumptions about investment, on a country-by country basis, derived from announced plans and policies, as well as our judgment of the feasibility of the investment being made. Here, too, we apply standard production profiles to the fields which are assumed to be developed. The countries in question include Saudi Arabia, Kuwait, Iran, Iraq, Qatar, United Arab Emirates, Mexico and Venezuela — all of which, bar Mexico, are members of OPEC.

11

The projected growth in global oil production is significantly lower than in last year's *Outlook* (but so, too, is demand). Total oil production in 2030, including non-conventional supplies (but not biofuels) is almost 10 mb/d lower than in *WEO-2007*. This reflects the slower economic growth assumption and the impact on demand of the large upward adjustment in our oil-price assumption. This oil price is, in turn, based on a re-assessment of the prospects for upstream investment in the main resource-rich countries, in light of the large escalation of project costs (see Chapter 13). It now looks much less likely that the key producing countries, in particular, will be willing and able to expand capacity as much and as quickly as previously assumed. Thus, this year's Reference Scenario resembles closely the Deferred Investment Scenario of *WEO-2005* (IEA, 2005). As a result, a bigger share of production will need to come from non-OPEC countries, where decline rates and development costs are generally much higher (see Chapters 10 and 13). Combined with sharp increases in upstream capital and operating costs, higher prices will be needed to bring forth the investment needed to expand capacity and to balance supply with demand. As always, future investment and decline rates are uncertain. The results of an analysis of the sensitivity of global oil markets to changes in these factors are presented in the last section of this chapter.

Figure 11.2 ● Architecture of the Oil Supply Model

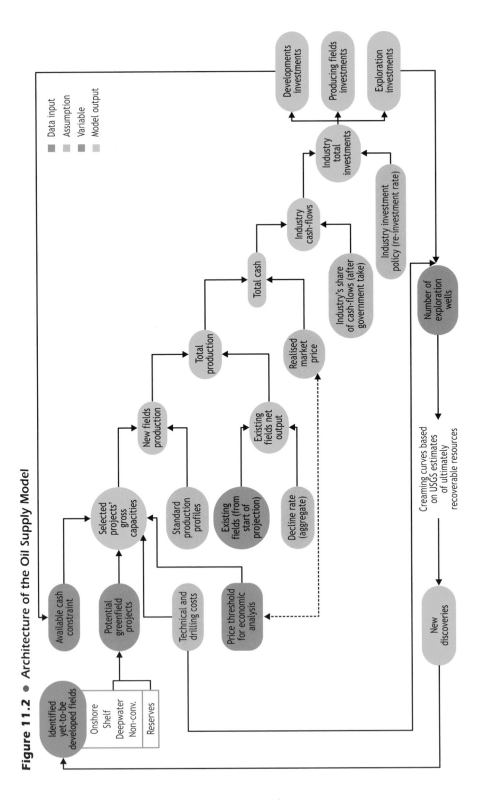

World Energy Outlook 2008 - **OIL AND GAS PRODUCTION PROSPECTS**

Crude oil output at existing fields

Our oil-production projections are based on a rigorous analysis of trends in output at existing fields (defined as those that were producing in 2007), which is also applied to known fields yet to be developed and fields yet to be found. Among existing fields, some are still building up, some are at plateau and the rest are in decline (see Chapter 10). Thus, the average year-on-year fall in the aggregate production of these fields will tend to accelerate over time, as more and more of them enter their decline phase. In the Reference Scenario, we assume that the decline rate (year-on-year) for all oilfields, once they have passed their peak, is constant for given types and sizes of fields in each region. However, the expected shift in the sources of crude oil, in terms of region, location and field size, means that the average production-weighted observed post-peak decline rate tends to rise, from 6.7% at the start of the projection period to 8.6% by the end.[1]

In total, output of crude oil from existing oilfields (not including non-conventional projects) drops from 70 mb/d in 2007 to 51 mb/d by 2015 and 27 mb/d by 2030 – a fall of 43 mb/d (excluding projected production using EOR). As a result, 64 mb/d of new capacity, in gross terms, needs to be brought on stream between 2007 and 2030 in order to maintain capacity at the 2007 level and meet the projected 21 mb/d increase in demand. The gross new capacity required by 2015 is about 30 mb/d. Oil production from existing oil sands and extra-heavy oil projects typically declines much less rapidly, as output is largely determined by the accessibility of the deposits and the intensity of mining or steam injection (see Chapter 9).

Production from existing offshore fields declines much more rapidly than that from onshore fields, for the reasons outlined in Chapter 10. On average, output from existing onshore fields falls at a year-on-year rate of 3.2%, from 46 mb/d in 2007 to 22 mb/d in 2030. Output drops much more quickly at existing offshore fields, by an average of 6.3% per year, from 24 mb/d to 5 mb/d. The overall average annual fall in output at existing fields is proportionately much smaller in OPEC countries, at 3.3%, than in non-OPEC countries, where it is 4.7%, reflecting the fact that most OPEC fields are onshore. Production at existing fields falls by 17 mb/d in OPEC countries over 2007-2030, compared with 26 mb/d in non-OPEC countries (Figure 11.3).

The biggest fall in crude oil output from existing fields, in absolute terms, occurs in the Middle East, where some 11 mb/d of capacity needs to be replaced (Figure 11.4). This simply reflects the fact that this region is, by far, the biggest single producing region: the *rate* of the overall fall in production – an average of around 3% per year – is actually lower than that in any other region. In OECD Europe and OECD Pacific, offshore fields account for most of the loss of oil output; in Asia and Africa, the losses are evenly spread between offshore and onshore fields. Russian and other eastern European/Eurasian countries account for 17% of the overall 43 mb/d fall in output.

---

1. See Chapter 10 for detailed estimates of decline rates.

Figure 11.3 ● Crude oil production from existing fields in OPEC and non-OPEC countries in the Reference Scenario

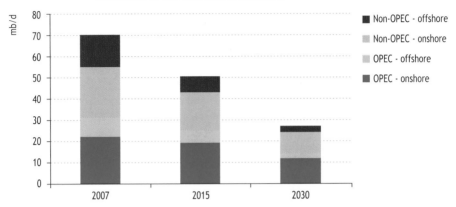

Figure 11.4 ● Crude oil production decline of existing fields by region in the Reference Scenario, 2007-2030

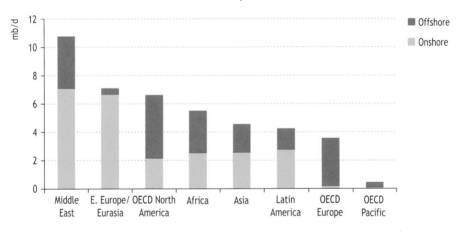

Contribution of new fields to crude oil production

Despite continuing investment in the world's existing fields, their aggregate output begins to decline already in 2008, as declines at mature fields outweigh increases at fields recently brought on stream. Output from new conventional oilfields, not yet in production, makes the biggest contribution to compensating for this loss of capacity and meeting rising global oil demand, with the remainder coming from non-conventional sources and from enhanced oil recovery (at both existing fields and those that will be developed during the projection period).

New conventional oil production will come both from known fields (included in proven and probable reserves) that are awaiting development and from fields that have yet to be found (as a result of exploration) but that are expected to be developed before 2030. The contribution of production from fields now awaiting development is projected to be the larger of the two, even in 2030, but their share of gross capacity additions falls quickly towards the end of the projection period. Overall output from those fields peaks soon after 2020 as more and more of them are brought on stream, mature and enter their decline phase. By contrast, the contribution from fields yet to be found grows quickly after 2015, as more of them are found and are selected for development, in some cases ahead of yet-to-be-developed known fields (Figure 11.5). By 2030, output from yet-to-be-found fields (19 mb/d) approaches that from known but yet-to-be-developed fields (23 mb/d).

Figure 11.5 ● World crude oil production from new fields in the Reference Scenario

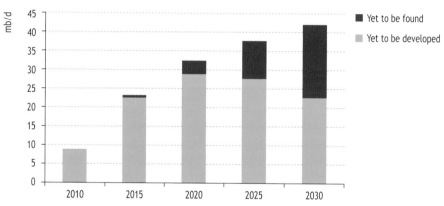

Known but yet-to-be-developed fields

At the end of 2007, world conventional oil reserves in fields that have been discovered but not yet developed amounted to an estimated 257 billion barrels.[2] OPEC countries held 133 billion barrels, or just over half. About 65% of OPEC's undeveloped conventional reserves are located onshore. In non-OPEC countries, onshore reservoirs account for only 38% of total reserves. Over half of the world's undeveloped reserves are in the Middle East and Russia. The Middle East alone holds 99 billion barrels, nearly 40% of the world total.

Production from these yet-to-be-developed fields is projected to rise steadily to a peak of 29 mb/d just after 2020 and then fall back to around 23 mb/d in 2030 (Figure 11.6). This means that 220 billion barrels out of the 257 currently identified, or 86%, are produced over the projection period. By 2030, the contribution from onshore fields is twice as large as that from offshore fields, although offshore production dominates until about 2020. In non-OPEC countries, known yet-to-be developed fields contribute 11 mb/d in 2030, after peaking at 16 mb/d. Offshore production represents over two-thirds of total output from these fields until about 2020. In OPEC countries, yet-to-be-developed fields produce 11 mb/d in 2030, slightly down on the peak of 14 mb/d.

---

2. IEA analysis based on IHS data.

Figure 11.6 ● Crude oil production from yet-to-be-developed fields in OPEC and non-OPEC countries by location in the Reference Scenario

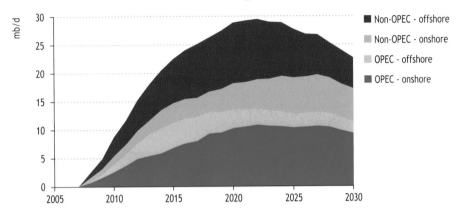

Onshore yet-to-be-developed reserves are concentrated in the Middle East and Russia. Together, they account for three-quarters of all onshore fields awaiting development. Offshore reserves are more equally distributed worldwide (Figure 11.7). The majority of the fields awaiting development in Africa, North America and eastern Europe/Eurasia and nearly all of them in Latin America and OECD Europe and Pacific are offshore.

Figure 11.7 ● Conventional proven and probable crude oil reserves in yet-to-be-developed fields by region, end-2007

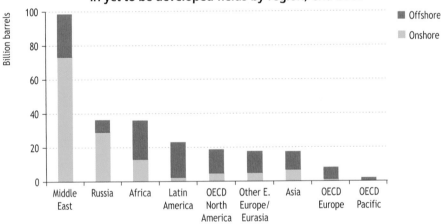

The 257 billion barrels of yet-to-be-developed conventional oil reserves are distributed in 1 874 fields, 971 of which are onshore and 903 offshore (Figure 11.8). Two-thirds of these fields are in non-OPEC countries. Africa holds 21% of them, roughly evenly distributed between offshore and onshore. All but six of the 141 fields awaiting development in OECD Europe are offshore. Some 93% of Russia's yet-to-be-developed fields are onshore.

Figure 11.8 ● Number of yet-to-be-developed oilfields by region and location, end-2007

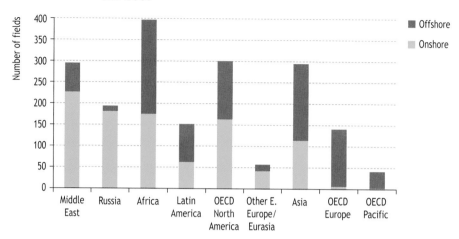

The average size of yet-to-be-developed fields tends to be much larger in the Middle East, at 335 million barrels, compared with the three OECD regions, Asia and Africa (Table 11.2). The average size of offshore fields in the Caspian region is high, because of the Kashagan field in Kazakhstan, which is due to come on stream in 2014. The average field size in OPEC countries is twice that of fields in non-OPEC countries.

Table 11.2 ● Average size of yet-to-be-developed oilfields by region, end-2007 (million barrels)

	Onshore	Offshore	Overall average
OECD North America	28	102	62
OECD Europe	64	52	53
OECD Pacific	33	48	47
Russia	160	570	187
Other E. Europe/Eurasia	116	854 (228*)	310 (142*)
Asia	58	60	59
Middle East	324	368	335
Africa	74	104	91
Latin America	36	232	152
OPEC	213	182	201
Non-OPEC	84	119	103

*Excluding Kashagan.
Sources: IEA analysis based on IHS data.

Yet-to-be-found fields

Conventional oil production from yet-to-be-found fields is projected to reach 19 mb/d in 2030, based on the projected discovery of 114 billion barrels of reserves worldwide over the projection period. Almost 11 mb/d comes from offshore fields (Figure 11.9). Onshore production comes mostly from OPEC countries — 8 mb/d out of a total of

8.7 mb/d in 2030 — as most undiscovered resources in the Middle East are onshore (USGS, 2000). By contrast, the bulk of production from yet-to-be-found offshore fields comes from non-OPEC countries: they produce 7.9 mb/d out of a total of 10.7 mb/d in 2030. Non-OPEC offshore yet-to-be-found fields are about equally divided between Russia and other Eurasian countries, Africa and OECD North America.

Enhanced oil recovery (EOR)

Production using EOR technology is projected to contribute an additional 6.4 mb/d [3] to world oil supply in 2030, with most of the increase occurring after 2015 (Figure 11.10). Three-quarters of this increase comes from just four countries: the United States, Saudi Arabia, Kuwait and China (in ranked order). Cumulative production in 2007-2030 amounts to 24 billion barrels, out of an estimated potential of about 300 billion barrels — of which one-third is in Saudi Arabia (see Chapter 9).

Most of the new EOR projects that are expected to be implemented during the projection period involve CO_2 injection. In total, about 9.8 gigatonnes of CO_2 is captured and stored in CO_2-EOR oil projects over the projection period.[4] These projects are exclusively onshore, as the technology for offshore CO_2-EOR is not expected to be sufficiently advanced for it to be deployed before the end of the projection period. Current EOR technology typically recovers about an additional 10% of oil in place. A bigger and more widely applied carbon penalty than assumed in the Reference Scenario (see Chapter 1) would significantly increase the potential for EOR.

Figure 11.9 ● **World crude oil production of yet-to-be-found oilfields in OPEC and non-OPEC countries by location in the Reference Scenario**

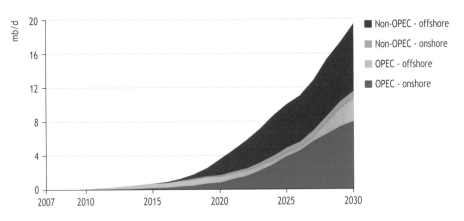

---

3. Over and above the estimated 2.5 mb/d of EOR production from existing fields — see Chapter 9 (Table 9.2).
4. This projection assumes that about 2.5 barrels of oil are recovered per tonne of CO_2 injected.

Figure 11.10 ● Enhanced oil recovery by country in the Reference Scenario

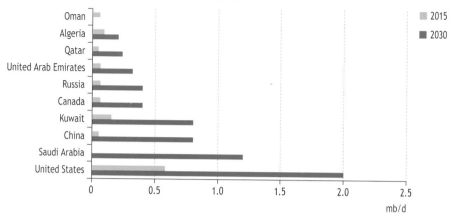

Natural gas liquids (NGLs)

Output of natural gas liquids – light hydrocarbons that exist in liquid form underground and that are produced together with natural gas and recovered in separation facilities or processing plants – is expected to grow rapidly over the Outlook period. Global NGL production is projected to almost double, from 10.5 mb/d in 2007 to just under 20 mb/d in 2030. This increase is driven by the steady rise in natural gas output (see Chapter 12). The bulk of the increase comes from OPEC countries, where gas production (to supply local markets and new LNG projects) is projected to expand quickest. OPEC NGL production almost triples, from 4.7 mb/d in 2007 to over 13 mb/d in 2030. The Middle East accounts for four-fifths of this increase. Non-OPEC NGL production increases by about 1 mb/d, to close to 7 mb/d in 2030 (Figure 11.11). These projections assume that the average NGL content of gas production is constant over the projection period.

Figure 11.11 ● World natural gas liquids production by OPEC and non-OPEC countries in the Reference Scenario

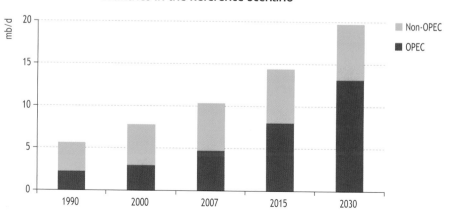

Non-conventional oil

Non-conventional oil — extra-heavy oil (excluding Venezuela), oil sands, chemical additives, gas-to-liquids and coal-to-liquids — is expected to play an important role in offsetting the decline in production from existing fields and supplementing supplies from new conventional oilfields and NGLs. The global supply of non-conventional oil is projected to increase from 1.7 mb/d in 2007 to 8.8 mb/d in 2030 (Figure 11.12). Canadian oil-sands projects make, by far, the largest contribution, increasing by 4.7 mb/d, followed by coal-to-liquids (CTL) projects in the United States and China, which together increase by 1 mb/d. Output from gas-to-liquids (GTL) projects expands from about 50 kb/d in 2007 to 650 kb/d in 2030. These projections need particular qualification, especially those for gas- and coal-to-liquids, given the uncertainties about future choices of technology and the resulting mix of fuels, the evolution of the technologies, how production costs will develop relative to alternative ways of exploiting the resources and future environmental constraints.

Figure 11.12 ● **World non-conventional oil production by type in the Reference Scenario**

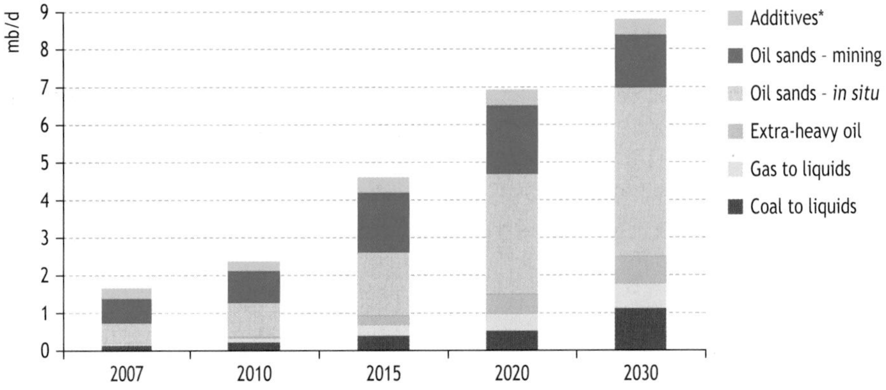

*Methyl tertiary butyl ether (MTBE) and other chemicals.

Oil sands and extra-heavy oil

Production of oil from Canadian oil sands is projected to increase from 1.2 mb/d in 2007 to 5.9 mb/d in 2030. Total proven recoverable oil-sands reserves are estimated at 175 billion barrels, of which 35 billion barrels can be mined and 140 billion barrels can be produced *in situ* (see Chapter 9). All the mineable reserves are projected to be developed over the projection period, with production from mining projects reaching about 1.4 mb/d in 2030. Current mining techniques are not economic if the depth of the oil sands exceeds about 75 metres; since most oil-sands reserves lie at depths which require the use of *in situ* steam-assisted production techniques, almost all of the projected increase in oil-sands production comes from *in situ* projects. Of the more than 50 billion barrels that are projected to be developed to 2030, only about 30 billion barrels derive from projects that are already sanctioned, planned or at the feasibility study stage. Our projections of oil-sands production are inevitably uncertain in view of the environmental challenges, notably water needs and CO_2 emissions (see Chapter 9).

Extra-heavy oil production projects are expected to be concentrated in Venezuela (such as the Carabobo project), as this country holds the major part of the relevant world resources. However, due to the IEA practice of classifying extra-heavy oil in Venezuela as conventional oil, Venezuelan extra-heavy oil production is not included here. Production of extra-heavy oil outside Venezuela is projected to occur mainly in Kuwait and in a few isolated projects in Brazil, Vietnam and Italy, and may reach more than 0.7 mb/d in the last decade of the projection period.

Gas-to-liquids (GTL)

GTL technology involves converting natural gas into liquid fuels with longer-chain hydrocarbons, such as diesel fuels that can be directly used to fuel diesel-engine vehicles, naphtha and chemical feedstock. GTL technology generally uses the principles of the Fischer-Tropsch (F-T) process, in which methane-rich natural gas is transformed, via steam-reforming or partial oxidation, into a mixture of carbon monoxide and hydrogen, called "syngas". Catalytic conversion converts the syngas into diesel fuels. While the F-T process was developed in the 1920s, significant progress has been made on the design of catalysts. The trend is to move from iron to cobalt and other metals.

Three plants — Sasol's Mossel plant in South Africa, Shell's Bintulu plant in Malaysia and the Oryx plant in Qatar (a joint venture between Qatar Petroleum and Sasol) — account for the bulk of the 50 kb/d of GTL capacity currently in operation worldwide. Two plants are under construction: Shell's 140-kb/d Pearl project in Qatar, the first train of which is due on stream by the end of the current decade and the second by 2012, and Chevron/ Nigerian National Petroleum Corporation's 34-kb/d Escravos project in Nigeria, expected on stream by the beginning of the next decade. They will bring total world capacity to above 200 kb/d by around 2012. All these plants will produce primarily diesel, together with smaller volumes of naphtha.

The long-term prospects for GTL hinge critically on costs. Costs have dropped sharply in the past, from $120 000 per barrel per day of capacity in the mid-1950s to less than $40 000 in 2000 — partly due to economies of scale. But costs have rebounded in recent years, with the surge in capital and operating costs that has afflicted all sectors of the oil and gas industry and the higher cost of the gas feedstock. At present, each barrel of diesel produced requires 8 000 to 10 000 cubic feet of gas. Current GTL production costs per barrel are now in the range of $40 to $90, depending on the price of the feedstock gas. GTL plants generate between 0.2 and 0.25 tonnes of CO_2 per barrel produced. If a CO_2 penalty of $50 per tonne were introduced, production costs would rise by $10.00 to $12.50 per barrel of synfuel. How the industry might develop in the longer term is uncertain. Recent sharp increases in construction costs, technical difficulties in commissioning the Oryx plant and a tightening of LNG supply in the near to medium term may lead to a shift in strategy towards LNG in many gas-producing countries. GTL is a highly capital-intensive chemical process, involving more complex engineering and operation, compared with LNG.

In the Reference Scenario, fewer GTL projects are brought on stream than in last year's *Outlook*. Planned plants in Egypt and Australia are assumed to proceed, but others, including that proposed in Qatar but delayed because of a moratorium on new gas projects, do not proceed. World GTL production reaches 650 kb/d in 2030.

11

Coal-to-liquids (CTL)

CTL — a well-established technology that transforms coal into oil products — is expected to play a small but growing role in meeting the world's fuel needs. The CTL process requires access to coal of stable quality, but has been given a new lease of life by technical improvements and by higher oil and gas prices. Global production of CTL is projected to grow from a mere 0.13 mb/d today to 1.1 mb/d in 2030. In addition to one plant that has been operating in South Africa for many years, a number of projects are assumed to be developed in China and the United States, because of their abundance of low-cost resources. India is not assumed to begin production of CTL before 2030, though plans to do so have been discussed for several years. The uncertainties surrounding CTL prospects are very large, because of technical, economic and environmental considerations.

There are two main types of CTL technology in use or under development (IEA, 2006):

■ The two-stage liquefaction process, which uses gasification of coal to produce syngas and then a F-T process to generate the fuel. It has been commercially used in South Africa since 1955. The Secunda plants there currently produce the equivalent of 130 kb/d of fuels and chemicals, using three different types of catalyst (low-temperature iron, high-temperature iron and low-temperature cobalt). The plants generally produce 20% to 30% of naphtha, along with 70% to 80% of diesel, kerosene and fuel oil. The process uses 0.35 to 0.45 tonnes of coal per barrel of oil produced. New plants have an overall energy efficiency of around 40%.

■ The more energy-efficient direct liquefaction process involves the dissolution at high temperature and pressure of a high percentage of coal in a solvent, followed by catalysed hydrocracking. The chemistry of this process is more complex. Output includes 20% to 30% of naphtha and 70% to 80% of diesel and liquefied petroleum gas. The first commercial project using the technology is the 20-kb/d Shenhua project located in Inner Mongolia (China), now nearing completion, with a planned capacity expansion to 100 kb/d. The process uses 0.3 to 0.4 tonnes of coal per barrel of oil produced.

Average CTL capital costs for a 50-kb/d unit are estimated at around $85 000 per barrel per day of installed capacity (Rahim, 2008), with the gasification unit representing the largest cost component (30% of the total cost). Scale matters as both unit operating and capital costs fall by more than 30% with an increase in capacity from 10 to 80 kb/d. Cost factors vary regionally: costs in China are about 30% lower than the United States. Current costs for a plant in China with 1 million tonnes (Mt) per annum production capacity are $40 to $60 per barrel of oil produced.

A big drawback with CTL processes is their very high CO_2 emissions: each barrel of oil produced gives rise to 0.5 to 0.7 tonnes of CO_2. A 50-kb/d plant, accordingly, generates an average 11 Mt of CO_2 per year. On this basis, a penalty of $50 per tonne of CO_2 would add $20 to $30 per barrel to production costs. Large CTL projects will need access not only to large coal reserves (typically at least 2 billion tonnes), but also to CO_2 storage sites if CCS is deployed.

Plans to produce up to 30 Mt per year (around 600 kb/d) of fuels from CTL in China by 2020 have been announced. But environmental concerns, including emissions and access to water, along with spiralling costs and coal prices, have led the Chinese government to impose stricter rules for plant construction and operation. In the United States, several CTL projects have been announced, totalling more than 300 kb/d, but more are still at the feasibility study stage.

Crude oil quality

There has been a small shift in the average quality of crude oil produced over the past decade towards slightly heavier and higher-sulphur grades (Eni, 2006). The shift towards heavier crudes is expected to continue in the longer term, but not as fast as projected in previous WEOs. Indeed, average API gravity[5] is expected to rise through to 2011, mainly due to increased supplies of condensate and a preponderance of lighter (and sweeter) crudes coming from Saudi Arabia's capacity-expansion programme (IEA, 2008). The fall in the average API gravity of world crude oil production resumes in 2012 and accelerates after 2015. The share of light and ultra-light grades (with an API gravity of at least 35°) in total crude oil production is projected to fall from 26.1% in 2005 to 24.4% in 2015 and 22.7% in 2030. The share of medium grades (with an API gravity of between 26° and 35°) increases by one percentage point from 53.7% in 2005 to 54.6% in 2030. Heavy grades (with an API gravity of 10° to 26°) account for 16.1% of world production in 2030, up from 12.8% in 2005. The average sulphur content of crude oil worldwide is expected to rise appreciably in the longer term, from the current levels of close to 1.14%.

Figure 11.13 ● Crude oil quality worldwide in the Reference Scenario

Source: IEA analysis based on Eni (2006).

The near doubling of production of NGLs over the projection period helps to offset, in part, the projected modest fall in the average gravity of crude oil. NGLs include a mixture of propane, butane, pentane, ethane and other light hydrocarbons in widely varying proportions. The average API degree of these liquids is typically at least 60°.

---

5. The American Petroleum Institute gravity, or API gravity, is a measure of the relative density of petroleum liquids compared with water, expressed in degrees. The higher the degree, the lighter the oil.

Outlook by country and region

There is no dramatic shift in the regional breakdown of world oil production over the projection period in the Reference Scenario, but there are some important changes at the country level (Figure 11.14). Saudi Arabia sees the largest incremental increase in oil production, followed by Canada. Eurasian countries, notably Kazakhstan, see a large increase in crude oil output, while production in Russia declines. Saudi Arabia and Iraq dominate the increase in OPEC (and Middle East) production, with most of the additional capacity coming from NGLs in Saudi Arabia and from crude oil in Iraq. In the United States, an increase in the production of non-conventional oil largely offsets a decline in conventional crude oil production.

Figure 11.14 ● **Change in oil production by country/region, 2007-2030**

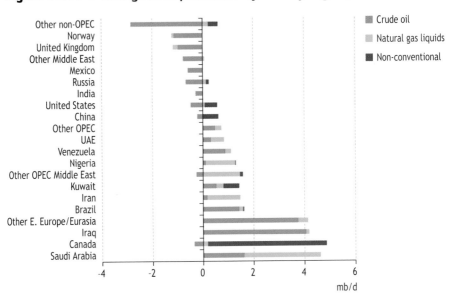

Non-OPEC production

Non-OPEC production of crude oil and NGLs in the Reference Scenario declines from 44.8 mb/d in 2007 to 43.5 mb/d in 2015 and then falls further to 42.9 mb/d in 2030 (Table 11.3). Non-conventional oil production, in contrast, rises from 1.5 mb/d in 2007 to 7.9 mb/d in 2030. Most of the decline in conventional production is a result of falling output levels in OECD countries, but that same group accounts for three-quarters of the increase in non-conventional oil output.

Investment in exploration will be crucial to increasing production in non-OPEC countries. The majority of the existing offshore fields in non-OPEC countries will be in the final decline phase of their production profile by 2030, resulting in a 12-mb/d drop in output compared with today. In the medium term, the shortfall is met from known but yet-to-be-developed fields, but output even from those fields is expected to start to decline in aggregate by around 2020, from a peak of about 16 mb/d to about 11 mb/d in 2030. Output from offshore fields that are yet to be found starts to fill the gap from 2015 and reaches 8 mb/d in 2030.

Table 11.3 ● Non-OPEC oil production in the Reference Scenario
(million barrels per day)

	2000	2007	2015	2030
Crude oil and NGLs	41.8	44.8	43.5	42.9
OECD	20.9	18.0	15.0	14.1
North America	13.3	12.5	11.1	11.4
Canada	*2.1*	*2.1*	*1.9*	*1.9*
Mexico	*3.5*	*3.5*	*2.4*	*3.0*
United States	*7.7*	*6.9*	*6.8*	*6.5*
Europe	6.8	4.9	3.3	2.1
Norway	*3.3*	*2.6*	*2.0*	*1.3*
United Kingdom	*2.7*	*1.7*	*0.9*	*0.5*
Pacific	0.9	0.6	0.6	0.6
Non-OECD	20.9	26.8	28.5	28.9
E. Europe/Eurasia	8.1	12.9	14.3	16.5
Kazakhstan	*0.7*	*1.4*	*2.4*	*4.3*
Russia	*6.5*	*10.1*	*10.4*	*9.5*
Asia	5.6	6.4	5.8	5.1
China	*3.2*	*3.7*	*3.3*	*3.5*
India	*0.7*	*0.8*	*0.8*	*0.5*
Middle East	2.1	1.7	1.4	1.1
Africa	1.9	2.3	2.0	1.7
Latin America	3.2	3.5	5.0	4.5
Brazil	*1.3*	*1.8*	*3.5*	*3.4*
Non-conventional*	**1.1**	**1.5**	**4.2**	**7.9**
OECD	0.9	1.3	3.6	6.7
Canada	*0.6*	*1.2*	*3.3*	*5.9*
United States	*0.3*	*0.1*	*0.3*	*0.6*
Non-OECD	0.2	0.2	0.5	1.2
Total	**42.9**	**46.3**	**47.6**	**50.9**
Of which NGLs	4.9	5.7	6.4	6.6
OECD	*3.7*	*3.7*	*3.9*	*3.9*
Non-OECD	*1.2*	*2.0*	*2.5*	*2.8*

* Extra-heavy oil, oil sands, chemical additives, gas-to-liquids and coal-to-liquids. Biofuels are not included.

Onshore production in non-OPEC countries, excluding EOR, is also projected to fall, from 24 mb/d in 2007 to 16 mb/d in 2030 (Figure 11.15). Known but yet-to-be-developed fields contribute about 6 mb/d and yet-to-be-found fields 1 mb/d by the end of the projection period. NGLs rise modestly from 5.7 mb/d in 2007 to a little under 7 mb/d in 2030, reflecting flat gas production in non-OPEC countries.

Figure 11.15 ● Non-OPEC oil production by type in the Reference Scenario

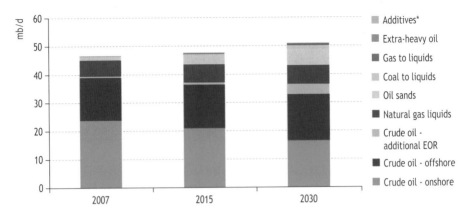

* Methyl tertiary butyl ether (MTBE) and other chemicals.

Offshore fields account for most of the gross additions to conventional oil capacity in non-OPEC countries over the *Outlook* period. About 180 sanctioned, planned and proposed projects, to develop an estimated 65 billion barrels of proven and probable reserves, are projected to yield new production capacity over the next five to six years. Most of the offshore projects are small: only 44 of them concern fields holding more than 300 million barrels. The bulk of non-OPEC offshore production in this period, including both shallow offshore and deep water, comes from a few major projects, including Tupi in Brazil, the fifth phase of Sakhalin in Russia, Kashagan in Kazakhstan, Jidong Nanpu in China and ACG in Azerbaijan. Brazil and the United States (Gulf of Mexico) are the only non-OPEC countries with more than two major projects in the pipeline. Other smaller-scale offshore developments include Ku Maloob Zaap in Mexico, Kikeh and Gumusut-Kakap in Malaysia and Moho-Bilondo in the Republic of Congo. The overall paucity of projects in the near term is mostly due to the current high costs of developing offshore fields, low levels of investment in exploration over the past decade and unfavourable regulatory and fiscal frameworks.

In the longer term, most of the additional offshore production will come from about 150 known fields, each holding between 50 and 600 million barrels of proven and probable reserves. In total, they hold about 20 billion barrels, in both shallow offshore and deep water. Again, Brazil has the largest offshore potential, with more than 50 fields containing a total of some 8 billion barrels — equal to 40% of total non-OPEC known offshore undeveloped reserves. Continuing active exploration, notably in the pre-salt layer of the Santos Basin, is likely to boost Brazil's proven reserves substantially in the coming years. The United States has about 15 undeveloped fields, holding a total of 1.5 billion barrels. Kazakhstan holds about 1 billion barrels in 5 fields, each of more than 50 million barrels. Mexico, Malaysia, Norway and the United Kingdom together hold similar potential of about 1 billion barrels in about 5 to 7 fields. They also possess about 30 other discovered fields with reserves of less than 50 million barrels. The potential for offshore oil production in Russia is limited both by the number of known fields (less than 10) and by volume (less than 1 billion barrels in total). Several discoveries have been made in Australia, Canada, Republic of Congo, Gabon, India, Thailand and Vietnam; but the average size of the fields is well below 100 million barrels, so their potential contribution to non-OPEC offshore production is limited at the prices assumed in the Reference Scenario and at current costs. Developing groups of small fields simultaneously could lower costs and make more of them economically viable.

In contrast to the relative abundance of viable offshore projects, prospects for onshore projects in non-OPEC countries, outside of Russia, are very poor. Beyond 2015, the majority of known but yet-to-be-developed onshore fields with reserves of more than 100 million barrels are located in Russia, where the physiographic location of the fields complicates their exploitation considerably. Mexico and China hold most of the rest of the onshore potential in non-OPEC countries in fields holding more than 100 million barrels. As for smaller fields holding between 50 and 100 million barrels, fewer than 100 await development. Exploration will undoubtedly yield many new discoveries, but the maturity of the resource base in most non-OPEC regions suggests that the potential for finding fields that are large enough to be exploited profitably is fairly limited. In the Reference Scenario, yet-to-be-found onshore fields in non-OPEC countries contribute less than 1 mb/d in 2030, compared with 8 mb/d from offshore fields.

Oil production in the *United States* is expected to pick up slightly in the next few years, mainly thanks to a surge in output in the Gulf of Mexico. About 5 billion barrels of proven and probable reserves in the Gulf are expected to be developed before 2015. A major project, Thunder Horse, came on stream in the third quarter of 2008 – about three years later than originally planned. It is projected to produce over 200 kb/d at peak by the beginning of the next decade. Other fields, such as Atlantis, Kaskida, Tahiti, Shenzi, Great White, Puma and Cascade, add another 400 kb/d by 2015. The average size of these fields is about 200 million barrels – about 50% of the average field size in Brazil. They are located in deep water and, therefore, are likely to have high post-peak decline rates (see Chapter 10). Onshore, the Nikaitchuq field with about 200 million barrels of reserves, is also expected to be developed. The additions to US output from these projects compensate only temporarily for declines at existing fields in Alaska and in the lower 48 states. Production in the longer term is expected to resume its long-term downward trend, reaching 6.5 mb/d in 2030. The lifting of the moratorium on offshore drilling proposed by the current administration – not assumed in the Reference Scenario because Congress had not yet approved it at the time of writing – would temper the decline, but only marginally.

Canadian production will become increasingly dominated by oil sands in Alberta. Conventional crude oil production is projected to continue to decline, but this is largely offset by increased output of NGLs; the combined output edges down from 2.1 mb/d in 2007 to 1.9 mb/d in 2030. Oil-sands output, in contrast, jumps from 1.2 mb/d to 5.9 mb/d.

Mexico's proven oil reserves have fallen continuously over the past two decades, mainly because of under-investment in exploration. In 2007, Mexico produced around 3.5 mb/d of oil. Production at Cantarell, Mexico's largest field and the third-largest

11

offshore field in the world by initial reserves, is falling sharply. Year-on-year declines averaged only 5% per year between the field's peak in 2003 and 2007, but output has reportedly dropped precipitously since 2007: at end-2007, it was 16% down on the beginning of the year. According to Pemex, the national company and sole operator of all Mexican fields, output at Cantarell is set to fall by a further 16% by end-2008. Total Mexican crude oil production is projected to bottom out at around 2.4 mb/d by 2015, as the Ku Maloob Zap and Chicontepec fields build up and reach their plateau. It then recovers gradually to more than 3 mb/d in the last decade of the projection period. Mexico holds 3 billion barrels of reserves in onshore fields which are yet to be developed and the above figures are boosted by output from new offshore discoveries — on the assumption that exploration is stepped up.

In *OECD Europe*, production from mature North Sea basins will continue its long-term decline. Output is projected to drop to 3.3 mb/d by 2015 and 2.1 mb/d in 2030. Despite higher oil prices, European exploration and development have declined sharply in the last few years, as the prospects for discovering significant new reservoirs have deteriorated. Of more than 28 projects planned in the North Sea, only a handful hold more than 100 million barrels. The larger ones include the Lochnagar and Callanish/Brodgar fields in the United Kingdom, which are projected to produce a bit less than 100 kb/d until 2015, and the Goliat, Tyrihans, Alvheim and Skarv/Idun fields in Norway, with aggregate production of slightly less than 200 kb/d. Most of the other fields being developed are extensions to earlier developments.

Prospects for finding more oil in *Australia* are good. Projected output growth there is supported in the short term by production from the Angel and Pyrenees fields, and in the medium term by the Vincent and Enfield fields. Total production levels off at about 0.5 mb/d in 2015, but grows to 0.6 mb/d in the second half of the projection period with new discoveries, although on average they are modest in size.

In *Russia*, production is expected to level off in the near term. The most significant onshore projects are Vankorskoye (with 3 billion barrels of proven and probable reserves), Priobskoye (1.6 billion barrels), Verkhne-Chonskoye (1.2 billion barrels) and Talakanskoye (900 million barrels). All of these fields are due to start producing oil before 2013, adding a total of 1.1 mb/d from around 2015. They start to decline by around 2020. Other important fields holding significant reserves in the region of 500 to 600 million barrels are also expected to be developed, including Tagulskoye and Suzunskoye (660 million barrels), Vladimir Filanovski (600 million barrels), Yurubcheno-Tokhomskoye (560 million barrels), Salym (500 million barrels) and Khylchuyuskoye Yuzhnoye (480 million barrels). The additional contribution from those fields is close to 500 kb/d between 2015 and 2020. Beyond 2015, Russia has a substantial potential to develop new projects, with numerous fields reported to hold between 200 and 500 million barrels. Russia has more large onshore fields than any region bar the Middle East. Nonetheless, relatively rapid declines in mature fields in western Siberia and the Volga-Ural region are expected to offset the production increases from new developments. Long-term production prospects depend to a large extent on government licensing and fiscal policies, as well as on how quickly investment in pipeline and export infrastructure is forthcoming. Recent fiscal changes are expected to stimulate more upstream investment, but are not sufficient to sustain production growth in the longer term. We project total Russian oil output to drop to 9.5 mb/d in 2030, after peaking at 10.4 mb/d around 2015.

In other Eurasian countries, new export routes are expected to stimulate production growth. In *Kazakhstan*, there is potential for growth at the three main fields, Tengiz, Kashagan and Karachaganak. Capacity expansions at the Tengiz and Karachaganak fields, with combined reserves of more than 3 billion barrels, add about 500 kb/d of peak capacity. When the Kashagan field comes on line (at the earliest in 2013), combined production from these three fields reaches more than 1.5 mb/d, with Kazakhstan entering the small group of countries producing more than 2 mb/d.

Production from new oilfield developments in *China* will not be sufficient to offset declining production from mature onshore areas, including the super-giant Daqing field, which has been in production since the 1960s. Production from the Changqing area, Tarim Basin and Xinjiang is expected to remain flat or grow modestly in the near term. Chinese production dips to 3.3 mb/d in 2015 but rebounds to 3.5 mb/d by 2030.

Output is expected to be broadly flat in the rest of Asia through to the end of the current decade and to decline thereafter. Recent discoveries in *India*, however, including the Mangala (430 million barrels), Bhagyama (150 million barrels) and Aishwariya (105 million barrels) fields, delay the decline until 2015. These three fields produce between 100 and 150 kb/d from 2012 to 2020. Rehabilitation of the Bombay High field in India will also contribute. Some new developments are expected in Vietnam, Malaysia and Thailand, boosting their collective output marginally.

Prospects for non-OPEC African countries are good to 2010, but production declines thereafter, to 1.7 mb/d in 2030, down from 2.3 mb/d today. Côte d'Ivoire, Republic of Congo, Equatorial Guinea and Sudan are expected to achieve higher output through to 2010 (see Chapter 15). The most significant project in these countries is the Moho-Bilondo in Republic of Congo, which is projected to produce about 100 kb/d at plateau in the next three years. Further production growth will depend on the success of exploration and appraisal drilling in firming up reserves, and on how favourable the investment and legislative frameworks are.

Production in *Latin America* is projected to grow from 3.5 mb/d in 2007 to 5 mb/d in 2015 and then to fall to 4.5 mb/d in 2030. Brazil, the region's largest non-OPEC producer, has proven oil reserves of 8.5 billion barrels (not including some large recent finds that have yet to be officially confirmed) and huge potential for further discoveries. After a first pilot phase, which is projected to see production reaching about 100 kb/d before 2015, the giant Tupi field discovered in 2006 is assumed to reach plateau production of 1 mb/d before 2020, assuming that the technical challenges in producing oil from the sub-salt layer can be overcome (see Chapter 9). Ultimate capacity could be higher, depending on ultimate recoverable reserves (currently estimated tentatively at 5 to 8 billion barrels). Other fields, including the Jupiter and Carioca fields announced in 2008, could add to production eventually, though further appraisal work is needed before formal development plans can be prepared. In the shorter term, 13 fields, including the Papa-Terra, Marlim Leste, Marlim Sul, Jubarte, Cachalote and Jabuti, holding between 300 and 700 million barrels, are currently

11

being developed. Each of these fields is due to start producing between 50 kb/d and 200 kb/d before 2015. They add about 1.3 mb/d to Brazilian production around 2015. Brazil alone holds more than 20% of the total non-OPEC offshore reserves that are expected to be developed over the medium term.

OPEC production

OPEC crude oil and NGL supply increases from 36 mb/d in 2007 to 44 mb/d in 2015 and to 52 mb/d in 2030 (Table 11.4). These projections assume that oil prices remain high by historical standards. By 2030, OPEC countries account for 51% of world oil production. Crude oil production increases from 31.1 mb/d in 2007 to 38.9 mb/d in 2030. EOR projects contribute 2.8 mb/d to this increase: 1.2 mb/d in Saudi Arabia, 800 kb/d in Kuwait, 320 kb/d in the United Arab Emirates, 240 kb/d in Qatar and 210 kb/d in Algeria. EOR is projected to provide one-third of the net increase in OPEC crude oil output. Offshore OPEC production declines, from around 9 mb/d in 2007 to 7.4 mb/d in 2030, after peaking at just below 11 mb/d around 2015. Onshore production (including EOR) is projected to increase from 22 mb/d in 2007 to 32 mb/d in 2030.

Table 11.4 ● **OPEC oil production in the Reference Scenario**
(million barrels per day)

	2000	2007	2015	2030
Crude oil and NGLs	32.0	35.9	44.0	52.0
Middle East	21.3	23.6	30.3	37.1
Iran	*3.8*	*4.4*	*4.5*	*5.4*
Iraq	*2.6*	*2.1*	*3.0*	*6.4*
Kuwait	*2.2*	*2.6*	*2.9*	*3.3*
Qatar	*0.9*	*1.3*	*2.0*	*2.5*
Saudi Arabia	*9.3*	*10.2*	*14.4*	*15.6*
UAE	*2.6*	*3.1*	*3.7*	*3.9*
Non-Middle East	10.7	12.2	13.6	15.0
Algeria	*1.4*	*2.2*	*2.0*	*2.3*
Angola	*0.7*	*1.7*	*2.3*	*2.6*
Ecuador	*0.4*	*0.5*	*0.3*	*0.2*
Indonesia	*1.4*	*1.0*	*0.8*	*0.3*
Libya	*1.5*	*1.9*	*2.0*	*2.2*
Nigeria	*2.2*	*2.3*	*3.4*	*3.7*
Venezuela	*3.1*	*2.6*	*2.7*	*3.6*
Non-conventional*	0.2	0.1	0.4	0.9
Total	32.1	35.9	44.4	52.9
Of which NGLs	3.0	4.7	8.1	13.2
Middle East	*1.8*	*3.0*	*6.0*	*9.8*
Non-Middle East	*1.2*	*1.7*	*2.0*	*3.4*

* Extra-heavy oil (not including Venezuela), oil sands, chemical additives, gas-to-liquids and coal-to-liquids. Biofuels are not included.

In OPEC countries, a decline occurs in output from existing fields of about 17 mb/d, from 31 mb/d in 2007 to less than 15 mb/d in 2030 (excluding the impact of EOR). Output from existing onshore fields drops by one-half and from offshore fields by three-quarters. These production losses are made good mainly by output from known fields yet to be developed. Production in these fields, however, is expected to peak at about 14 mb/d in 2020 and to fall back to 11 mb/d by 2030. Yet-to-be-found fields produce about 1 mb/d in 2015 and 11 mb/d in 2030. Whether the investment needed to bring these fields into production will be made is one of the biggest uncertainties in this *Outlook*.

Output of OPEC NGLs is projected to triple, from almost 5 mb/d in 2007 to over 13 mb/d in 2030, reflecting huge upstream gas developments to meet rapidly rising domestic demand and to supply new LNG projects. Non-conventional oil is expected to remain very limited. Excluding extra-heavy oil in Venezuela,[6] total output is projected to grow from 0.1 mb/d to 0.9 mb/d in 2030. The main contribution to non-conventional OPEC oil production comes from Middle East countries, specifically extra-heavy oil in Kuwait (0.6 mb/d) and GTL in Qatar (about 0.2 mb/d).

Figure 11.16 ● OPEC oil production by type in the Reference Scenario

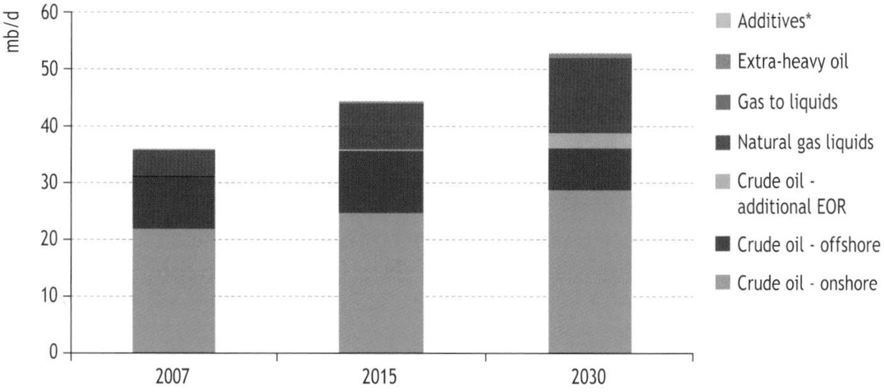

* Methyl tertiary butyl ether (MTBE) and other chemicals.

There are 101 upstream oil projects currently under development and planned in OPEC countries as a whole, involving an estimated 48 billion barrels of proven and probable reserves. Of these projects, 56 are onshore, involving about 28 billion barrels of reserves. The largest element of new production is due to come from Saudi Arabia, which will bring four new onshore fields into production (see below). In the longer term, there is considerable potential for other known onshore fields to be brought into production — in stark contrast to the situation in most non-OPEC countries. There are more than 100 onshore fields awaiting development, each holding more than 100 million barrels and with combined reserves of more than 50 billion barrels. The bulk of them are in just three countries: Saudi Arabia, Iran and Iraq. Two-thirds of those reserves are concentrated in about 30 giant fields (each holding more than

6. In this *Outlook*, extra-heavy Venezuelan crude oil is categorised as conventional oil.

500 million barrels), including Sharar, Niban, Jaladi, Dhib and Lugfah fields in Saudi Arabia, Halfayah, Hamrin, Tuba and Ratawi fields in Iraq, and Hosseinieh, Kuskh and Kuh-I-Mand fields in Iran. We project that 70 fields in these three countries will be brought into production before 2030. Their development costs per barrel of production are on average the lowest in the world.

Over the next five to six years, 45 offshore projects are either under development or firmly planned in OPEC countries, totalling 20 billion barrels. The largest project by far is the Manifa field in Saudi Arabia, accounting for one-quarter of these reserves. This field is expected to come on line in 2012 and will produce close to 1 mb/d when the plateau is reached about three years later. Angola and Nigeria together account for two-thirds of the remaining 15 billion barrels. Nigeria ranks second in terms of total reserves developed over the medium term, with about 5 billion barrels in 11 projects, all of which involve more than 500 million barrels of reserves. Other large projects include Corocoro (450 million barrels) in Venezuela, Reshadat and phases 9 & 10 of South Pars in Iran (400 million barrels each), phase 2 of the Al Khaleej project in Qatar (380 million barrels) and Jeruk 2 (280 million barrels) in Indonesia. No new developments in the United Arab Emirates are expected in the medium term but expansions of existing fields such as Upper Zakum, Lower Zakum, Umm Shaif and Rumaitha are planned there. Several other offshore fields that are awaiting development could be brought on line before 2030. The offshore fields in OPEC Middle East countries generally are more economic to develop than those in other OPEC countries as they are mainly in shallow water and their average size is high (about three to four times higher than in Angola and Nigeria).

Saudi Arabia will continue to play a vital role in balancing the global oil market. Its willingness to make timely investments in oil-production capacity will be a key determinant of future price trends. Five major onshore projects, Khurais, Khursaniyah, Hawiyah, Shaybah and Nuayyim, which collectively hold 13 billion barrels of reserves, are all in the final phases of development and are projected to provide a total gross capacity addition of close to 3 mb/d by 2015. Expansions of the Zuluf, Safaniyah and Berri fields could give further momentum to Saudi Arabian production.[7] There are 6.2 billion barrels of reserves in 11 other known fields in Saudi Arabia that have yet to be developed — the highest in the world. Each of them holds reserves of at least 150 million barrels and the average is 450 million barrels. The largest known undeveloped field, Hasbah 1, holds 1.8 billion barrels. Part of the increase in gross capacity will be offset by the decline in capacity at existing fields. Saudi Arabia aims to maintain spare capacity in the range of 1.5 mb/d to 2 mb/d in the long term.

The prospects for oil production in *Iraq* remain very uncertain. Output is beginning to recover following the war in 2003. Iraqi production has always been low relative to the size of the country's reserves. Iraq holds the world's third-largest remaining oil reserves, after Saudi Arabia and Iran, with 115 billion barrels, according to OPEC. Iraq undoubtedly has the potential to increase its production capacity by several

---

7. At the Jeddah Summit of 22 June 2008, Oil Minister Al-Naimi said Saudi Arabia could expand capacity to more than 15 mb/d, subject to future market conditions. This increment was centered on five key fields: Zuluf, Safaniyah, Berri, Khurais and Shaybah.

million barrels per day. On the assumption that security across the country continues to improve, we project production to rise steadily from 2.1 mb/d in 2007 to around 3 mb/d in 2015 and to accelerate to 6.4 mb/d in 2030. This projection implies a five- to six-fold increase in investment in the upstream oil sector. Achieving this will hinge on political stability and providing opportunities for foreign oil companies on satisfactory commercial and fiscal terms.

Oil and NGL production potential in *Iran* is also very large. Output falls to 4.1 mb/d in 2010, largely because of delays in implementing new projects, but recovers to 4.4 mb/d by 2015 and jumps to 5.4 mb/d in 2030. A total of 15 onshore projects is due to come on stream over the next five to six years. Leaving aside the Pars 12 and Darkhovin III fields, which have reserves of more than than 600 million barrels, the 13 other projects have reserves between 150 and 300 million barrels. Five additional projects are reported to hold less than 100 million barrels. The sum of the reserves being developed in these 20 projects ranks second among OPEC countries, with exploitation of more than 4.5 billion barrels due to start in this period. Total production from the projects, which are at or close to the final phase of development, is projected to reach about 1 mb/d on average in 2010-2020. It is nonetheless very uncertain that these production levels will be achieved, given limitations on investment and geopolitical factors.

Developments in *Kuwait* are concentrated on the Sabriyah and the Umm Niqa fields, where a total of 50 kb/d of natural gas liquids capacity is being added, with completion expected in 2011. Another project at the Sabriyah field adds 160 kb/d of crude oil production by 2015. The reserves being developed are estimated to total 2.5 billion barrels. A water treatment project at the Greater Burgan field — the second largest in the world — is expected to boost gross capacity by 120 kb/d by 2009. Beyond 2020, we project Kuwait to develop about 6 billion barrels of heavy and extra-heavy oil resources. In addition to the 3.3 mb/d from conventional sources in 2030, the extra 0.5 mb/d from those projects are counted as non-conventional in our Reference Scenario. Total Kuwaiti oil production is projected to reach 3.8 mb/d in 2030.

Outside the Middle East, *Venezuela* has the largest reserves among OPEC countries and the greatest long-term potential for expanding production. Several large onshore projects underway involve extra-heavy oil, including the Carabobo project, which we project to start producing by around 2015. This project produces close to 1 mb/d when it reaches full capacity between 2018 and 2020. Other projects, in the Junin, Petro Cedeno and Machete areas, target reserves of around 1 billion barrels each. Over the longer term, there is strong potential for new extra-heavy oil projects like Carabobo, if investment can be mobilised. The prospects for developments of conventional oilfields are much more limited. The La Ceiba onshore and Corocoro offshore fields together are projected to produce around 100 kb/d by around 2020.

Nigeria's proven oil reserves are estimated at 25 billion barrels. The country produced 2.3 mb/d of oil in 2007. In addition to the Agbami field, which started producing this year, several fields are currently under development, the most important of which are the Bonga Southwest/Aparo, Akpo, Bonga Northwest and Usan and Egina — all of them in deep water. They are projected to add 1.2 mb/d of gross capacity by 2015, boosting total production to around 3.6 mb/d (taking account of declines at existing fields). Investment risk in Nigeria is high, because of political instability and corruption.

Nigeria is seeking an increase in its share of the OPEC production ceiling. Considering its huge potential and recent government reforms to oil and gas legislation, we expect the country to produce some 3.7 mb/d by 2030.

Angola is leading the momentum in developing offshore production. Some 15 projects are expected to come on line before 2015. All but one is located in deep water. The combined reserves of these projects are 5.5 billion barrels. Except in the case of the Pazflor, which alone holds some 1 billion barrels, other projects usually include several neighbouring fields, such as Gindungo/Canela/Gengibre and Plutao/Saturno/Venus/Marte. Total production from this group of projects is projected to reach 1 mb/d around 2012-2013. It then inches up to a bit less than 1.5 Mb/d in 2015 and dips below 1 mb/d beyond 2020. Offshore potential from Angola lies in 26 fields, with more than 50 million barrels each and total reserves of 3 billion barrels. Unless some of those fields are geographically close enough to be developed simultaneously, their average size of about 110 million barrels makes their development uncertain from an economic point of view, as most of them are located in deep waters.

Libya is considered a highly attractive oil province because production costs are low, it is close to Europe and it has well-developed infrastructure. Libya produces high-quality, low-sulphur crude oil. Two major projects are underway: the re-development of the Sirte basin and an expansion of the Nafoora field. Ten smaller projects over the next four to five years have an average reserve level of 120 million barrels. Oil output in Libya is projected to increase from 1.9 mb/d now to 2.2 mb/d by 2030.

Algeria and *Indonesia* have the fewest and, on average, smallest current projects among the OPEC countries. In both countries, the biggest project involves the development of about 350 million barrels of reserves. There are just two projects underway in Indonesia and three in Algeria, with combined reserves of less than 1 billion barrels.

Sensitivity of oil output to decline rates

The production decline rate that will prevail over the projection period will determine the extent of the need to make new investments in existing fields and new fields: the faster the decline-rate, the bigger the investments that will need to be made, and *vice versa*. Our Reference Scenario decline-rate assumptions are derived from a detailed bottom-up approach, examining the situation in each country separately on a field-by-field basis, and drawing on extensive consultation with the oil industry, as well as assumptions about production and investment policies. Nonetheless, the level of present decline rates and of future trends is extremely uncertain. Decline rates could deviate significantly from assumed trends, with major implications for oil markets.

In order to demonstrate the importance to oil-production prospects of the decline rates of existing fields, and to quantify the extent to which changes in decline rates affect investment needs and oil prices, we have developed two variants of the Reference Scenario: a high decline-rate case, in which the decline rate for all fields producing in 2007 is assumed to be one percentage point higher than in the Reference Scenario throughout the projection period, and a low decline-rate case, in which the rate is assumed to be one percentage point lower. All other exogenous variables are assumed to be unchanged, including the decline-rates and production profiles of new fields. Crucially, we have assumed that the level of global oil supply and demand is unchanged over the *Outlook* period, in order to be able to quantify the change in price that would correspond to a higher or lower decline rate, and the consequent change in investment needs: for example, in the high decline-rate case, higher prices would be needed to make more projects profitable and bring forth more investment.

The differences in the international oil prices and investment in the two cases, *vis-à-vis* the Reference Scenario, are large. In the high decline-rate case, the oil price in 2030 is almost $20 per barrel higher than in the Reference Scenario, reaching more than $140 (Table 11.5). Cumulative investment in the upstream oil industry over the whole projection period, at $6.1 trillion, is over $1 trillion, or one-fifth, higher than in the Reference Scenario. The gap is already significant in the period to 2015, as more exploration and development spending is needed to compensate for the faster drop in production from existing fields.

Table 11.5 ● **World cumulative investment in the upstream oil sector under different decline-rate assumptions for existing fields, 2007-2030**

	Oil price* in 2030 ($2007/barrel)	Investment (billion $2007)		
		2007-2015	2016-2030	2007-2030
Reference Scenario	122	1 819	3 217	5 036
High decline-rate case	141	2 179	3 923	6 102
Low decline-rate case	100	1 817	2 531	4 349

* Average IEA crude oil import price.

In the low decline-rate case, there is a very small difference in 2015, compared with the Reference Scenario, as most of the investment over that period has already been sanctioned. Over the projection period, however, as the gap widens between production from existing fields and demand, the marginal cost of producing each barrel of new supplies rises, so that investment needs increase faster than the additional capacity needs. As discussed in detail earlier in this chapter, this reflects the change in the composition of the supply base in the longer term, as more offshore fields and more fields smaller in size than those today need to be developed.

NATURAL GAS RESOURCES AND PRODUCTION PROSPECTS
Who will supply the world's growing gas demand?

H I G H L I G H T S

- Global proven reserves of natural gas at the end of 2007 stood at close to 180 trillion cubic metres — equal to around 60 years of current production. Like oil, gas resources are highly concentrated in a small number of countries and fields. Three countries — Russia, Iran and Qatar — hold 56% of the world's reserves, while just 25 fields hold almost half. OPEC countries also hold about half.

- Remaining reserves have more than doubled since 1980, with the biggest increases coming from the Middle East. Reserves have risen by more than 15% even since 2000, despite rising annual production. As with oil, the bulk of the increase in reserves in recent years has come from upward revisions for fields that have been producing or have been undergoing appraisal and development work. Although the size of gas discoveries has been steadily declining in recent decades (in the same way as for oil), discoveries continue to exceed production.

- The USGS estimates remaining ultimately recoverable resources of conventional natural gas, including proven reserves, reserves growth and undiscovered resources, at 436 tcm. Cumulative production to 2007 amounts to 13% of total initial resources.

- Non-conventional gas resources — including coalbed methane, tight gas sands and gas shales — are much larger, amounting perhaps to over 900 tcm, with 25% in the United States and Canada combined.

- Worldwide, gas resources are more than sufficient to meet projected demand to 2030. The outlook for production by region depends largely on the proximity of reserves to markets, which primarily determines the cost of supply. Much of the world's gas resources is located far from the main markets, so that only a small proportion of the economic potential has yet been exploited.

- In the Reference Scenario, world natural gas production is projected to rise from just over 3 tcm in 2007 to 4.4 tcm in 2030. Production expands in all major regions, with the exception of OECD Europe, where production is already in decline, and in OECD North America, where output begins to dip in the second half of the *Outlook* period.

- Output grows most strongly, in both volume and percentage terms, in the Middle East, tripling between 2007 and 2030 to 1 tcm per year. Most of this increase comes from Iran and Qatar. Production in Latin America and Africa also grows briskly. It is very uncertain whether all of the investment needed to achieve the projected production levels in these regions, especially the Middle East and Russia, will materialise.

Gas resources and reserves

Conventional gas

Global resources of natural gas that can be economically extracted are of a similar magnitude (on an energy-equivalent basis) to those of oil. Proven reserves[1] at the end of 2007 stood at 179 trillion cubic metres according to Cedigaz, an international centre for gas information, and 175 tcm according to the *Oil and Gas Journal (O&GJ)* — equal to around 60 years of current production. Other sources show similar estimates.[2] OPEC countries hold about half and OECD countries well under 10%. Remaining reserves have more than doubled since 1980, with the biggest increases coming from the Middle East (Figure 12.1). Reserves have risen by about 12% since 2000, despite rising annual production.

Figure 12.1 ● Proven reserves of natural gas

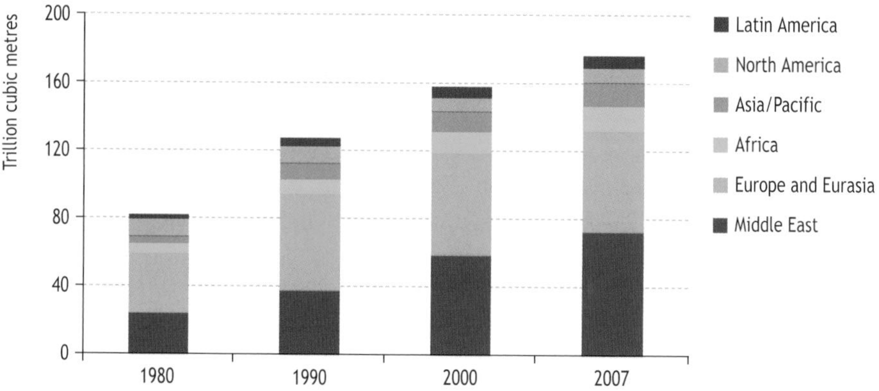

Source: BP (2008).

Natural gas reserves, like those of oil, are unevenly dispersed across the world, being highly concentrated in a small number of countries and fields. Three countries — Russia, Iran and Qatar — hold 56% of the world's remaining proven reserves, while just 25 fields contain 48% of the global total. The Middle East as a whole holds 41% of reserves and Russia alone one-quarter. Regional shares in global production are very different from shares in reserves: the Middle East, for example, accounts for only 11% of world production. North America holds only 4.5% of the world's reserves, but 26% of production (Figure 12.2). These disparities largely reflect differences in the proximity of reserves to markets and the investment climate.

---

1. For definitions, which are the same as those for oil, see Chapter 9.
2. BP (2008) shows a figure of 177 tcm.

Figure 12.2 ● Regional share in natural gas production and proven reserves, 2007

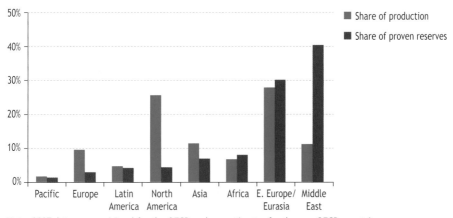

Note: 2007 data are provisional for the OECD and are estimates for the non-OECD countries.
Sources: Reserves - Cedigaz (2008); production - IEA databases.

As with oil, the bulk of the increase in proven reserves in recent years has come from upwards revisions for fields that have been producing or have been undergoing appraisal and development work. Nonetheless, newly discovered volumes remain large. Although the size of gas discoveries has been steadily declining in recent decades, unlike oil, volumes discovered continue to exceed production (Figure 12.3).

Figure 12.3 ● Natural gas discoveries* and cumulative production, 1960-2006

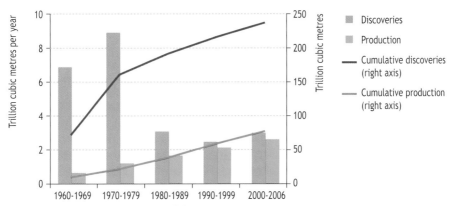

* Additions to proven reserves from new fields.
Sources: IHS and IEA databases.

Estimates of ultimately recoverable conventional resources, including cumulative production, remaining proven and probable reserves, reserves growth and undiscovered resources, vary widely. In its 2000 assessment, the US Geological Survey estimated ultimately recoverable resources at at 436 tcm in its mean case (USGS, 2000). Adjusted for cumulative production and changes in reserves since that assessment, remaining resources (including proven reserves, undiscovered resources and reserves growth) at end-2007 are estimated at 380 tcm (2 240 billion barrels of oil equivalent), of which about half have already been proven (Table 12.1). Cumulative production to 2007 amounts to 13% of total initial conventional gas resources (compared with 33% for conventional oil). These numbers do not take account of the latest USGS estimates of the resource potential of the Arctic region, released in July 2008 (USGS, 2008). According to that assessment of 25 Arctic provinces, the mean undiscovered gas resources are about 46 tcm (excluding NGLs), and more than 70% of the overall undiscovered gas potential is in three provinces (West Siberian Basin - 18 tcm; East Barents Basins - 9 tcm; and Arctic Alaska - 6 tcm).

Table 12.1 ● Remaining proven reserves and mean estimates of ultimately recoverable conventional resources of natural gas, end-2007

Region	Remaining proven reserves (tcm)	Proven reserves share (%)	Ultimately recoverable resources (URR) (tcm)	Reserves as share of URR (%)
OECD North America	8.0	4.5	62.5	12.8
Latin America	7.7	4.3	24.5	31.5
Europe	6.2	3.5	25.5	24.3
Former Soviet Union	53.8	30.1	132.2	40.8
Africa	14.6	8.2	33.9	43.1
Middle East	73.2	41.0	134.8	54.2
Asia-Pacific	15.2	8.5	29.9	50.8
World	178.7	100.0	443.3	40.3

Sources: Reserves — Cedigaz (2008); resources — USGS (2000); IEA estimates.

Recovery rates — the share of the estimated amount of hydrocarbons initially in place that is economically recoverable — are significantly higher for conventional gas fields than for oil fields. They are thought to range from 30% to close to 100%,[3] averaging around 61%, based on IHS data (Laherrere, 2006).[4] Average rates are likely to increase with technological improvements, such as the increased use of well-stimulation techniques that target stranded and bypassed pockets of gas. Use of enhanced gas recovery (EGR) with the injection of CO_2 from anthropogenic sources is another option, but this technology is in its infancy compared with enhanced oil recovery (EOR). The world's first pilot project of CO_2-EGR is currently being operated by GDF Suez in the offshore K12B field in the Netherlands.

---

3. Extremely tight gas reservoirs may have recovery factors lower than 10%.
4. The 61% recovery rate was calculated from a sample of 8 560 fields in 2006. An earlier study by the same author, using 1997 data, yielded a recovery rate of 75%.

Box 12.1 ● Sour gas reserves: a costly nuisance?

Sour gas reservoirs contain, in addition to methane, significant quantities of hydrogen sulphide (H_2S) and/or carbon dioxide (CO_2). More than 40% of the world's gas reserves are estimated to be sour (Table 12.2). In the Middle East, 60% of proven gas reserves are sour. Southeast Asia's largest gas reservoir is the Indonesian Natuna field, with 1.3 tcm of gas reserves, but it has a CO_2 content as high as 71%. Technical difficulties have delayed Natuna's development for more than two decades.

The presence of H_2S or CO_2 poses a number of challenges for drilling and production. The majority of the completion components need to use special alloys to prevent corrosion. A bigger problem is dealing with the gases produced and avoiding their release to the atmosphere. In the case of CO_2, re-injection and underground storage is a potential solution that has been successfully implemented. The Norwegian Sleipner project and the Algerian In-Salah project each store over 1 million tonnes of the gas each year. In 2008, the Snohvit project started injecting 0.7 million tonnes of CO_2 per year into storage, while the planned Australian Gorgon project plans similar procedures to avoid emissions of more than 3 million tonnes of CO_2-equivalent per year by 2010. Carbon capture and storage (CCS) in gas production is a near-term opportunity to demonstrate the CCS technology, as the cost of capture of CO_2 from natural gas streams is significantly lower than from the flue gases of power stations (IEA, 2008). The cost of separating (from gas production), compressing, transporting and re-injecting CO_2 is site-specific (generally in the range of $5 to $20 per tonne of CO_2).

12

Table 12.2 ● World proven sour gas reserves, end- 2006

	High H_2S only	High CO_2 only	High H_2S and CO_2	Total	
	(tcm)	(tcm)	(tcm)	(tcm)	% of total reserves
Mexico & Latin America	0.3	1.1	0.3	1.7	21
Europe	0.1	0.7	0.3	1.1	19
Former Soviet Union	0.8	10.1	7.3	18.2	34
Africa	0.0	0.5	0.5	1.0	8
Middle East	2.6	0.4	40.9	44.0	60
Asia-Pacific	0.3	4.4	2.3	7.1	46
World	4.2	17.2	51.6	73.1	43

Note: Excludes North America. High H_2S is more than 100 parts per million; high CO_2 is more than 2%.
Source: Bourdarot (2007).

Non-conventional gas

Non-conventional gas embraces a set of gas resources that are generally contiguous in nature, sometimes referred to as "resource plays" in the industry, that require special drilling and stimulation techniques to release the gas from the formations in which they occur. Non-conventional gas includes coalbed methane, tight gas sands and gas shales. Such resources are widespread worldwide, but their development has generally been limited so far to North America. Determining the amount of gas in place in non-conventional reservoirs is a complex task, due to the heterogeneous structure of the reservoirs and of the production profiles, which can differ significantly from conventional wells. Total worldwide non-conventional gas resources are estimated at over 900 tcm, with 25% in the United States and Canada combined, and 15% each in China, India and the Former Soviet Union.

Non-conventional gas accounts for a significant and rising share of US gas production. Eight of the ten largest onshore gas fields discovered in the United States in the 1990s were non-conventional reservoirs, including the 1-tcm Newark East Barnett Shale and the Powder River coalbed methane deposits. The US Energy Information Administration projects that the share of gas production from non-conventional resources in total domestic production will increase from 40% in 2004 to 50% in 2030, with this gas making up 28% of the US natural gas supply increase between 2004 and 2030 (DOE/EIA, 2007).

Tight gas sands

Tight gas sands are generally defined as natural gas reservoirs with a continuous accumulation system[5] and low permeability. World tight gas sand recoverable reserves are estimated at 200 tcm, with the largest quantities in the Americas (38%), Asia-Pacific (25%), the Former Soviet Union (13%), the Middle East and North Africa combined, and sub-Saharan Africa (11% each). The United States (principally) and Canada have been the leaders in tight gas sands development. In the United States in 2006, tight gas sands accounted for 40% of all the gas wells drilled and nearly 30% of total gas production. Although the number of tight gas sands wells drilled per year and production have been rising rapidly over the last decade in the United States (Figure 12.4), productivity, measured by gas reserves per well, has fallen by half. As a result, drilling activity needs to continue to rise if production is to be sustained. That factor, compounded by increasing upstream costs (see Chapter 13), has led to a near-quadrupling of production cost per unit of gas in the last five years.

Coalbed methane

The majority of the world's coal resources, estimated at 86 to 283 tcm (Creedy and Tilley, 2003), are found at depths where coal cannot be mined. Coalbed methane is the methane contained in coalbeds that, due to the deposit's depth or the coal's poor quality, cannot be mined. In operating coal mines, methane gas is generally considered to be a hazard, as well as creating an environmental problem if vented to

---

5. An accumulation that is pervasive through a large and continuous area.

Figure 12.4 • Tight gas drilling in the United States

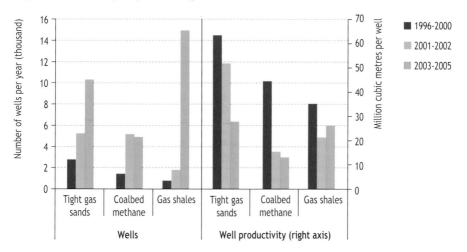

the atmosphere. Coalbed methane can be produced with well-bore technologies that are similar to those used for conventional hydrocarbons. However, production can be difficult where the formations are tight, requiring techniques such as hydraulic fracturing to enhance well productivity. Water in the porous space needs to be removed before the gas can be extracted, which may also complicate the production process, increasing capital costs and giving rise to environmental concerns.

Despite these difficulties, the contribution of coalbed methane to natural gas supply is growing rapidly in the United States. Commercial coalbed-methane production started there in the late 1980s, spurred by tax incentives, and grew with new technologies and expansion to new basins. Advances in seismic technology, horizontal well drilling, hydraulic fracturing and basin modelling have helped reduce uncertainties over the assessment of reserves and their commercial exploitation. US production has expanded from the original San Juan Basin to several new basins in Colorado, New Mexico and Wyoming, reaching 1.8 trillion cubic feet (tcf) (50 bcm) in 2006 and accounting for nearly 10% of US non-associated gas production.

Coalbed-methane production is also expanding outside the United States. In Canada, large resources are located in the Mannville, Ardley and Horseshoe Canyon formations. Over 10 500 wells had been drilled by early 2007 and production is expected to exceed 0.3 tcf (8.5 bcm) in 2008, making up more than 5% of Canada's total gas production. In Australia, commercial production started in Queensland in 1998 and in 2005 supplied more than 7% of the country's total gas needs. It is projected to provide 35% to 50% of Eastern Australia's gas needs by 2020 (Geoscience, 2008). International oil companies, including Shell, Petronas and BG, have acquired coalbed-methane assets in Australia, some with the intention of exporting the gas as LNG. India is expected to produce up to 0.1 tcf (2.8 bcm) by 2010, accounting for nearly 5% of total Indian gas production. The Indonesian government hopes to develop the country's coalbed-methane resources, offering better terms for production-sharing agreements than for conventional natural gas projects.

Coalbed methane has been slower to take off in China, even though the country has the world's third-largest reserves and despite the large amounts of methane released through venting from coal mines (estimated at over 0.2 tcf, or 5.7 bcm, per year) and the associated safety and environmental risks. Increasing production is a priority in China's 11th five-year national plan (2006-2010), with the stated objective of producing nearly 0.3 tcf − 8.5 bcm − by 2010. Russia has over 80 tcm of recoverable coalbed-methane reserves, including more than 10 tcm in the Kuzbass basin, located at a depth of less than 1 200 metres. A few experimental projects have been started by Promgaz, a subsidiary of Gazprom, but production remains negligible. Other countries interested in developing their coalbed-methane reserves include Ukraine and Romania.

Box 12.2 ● **CO_2-enhanced coalbed methane (ECBM) production: a dual benefit?**

The injection of CO_2 into deep unmineable coal seams − a technology known as CO_2-enhanced coalbed methane (ECBM) − can produce a double benefit: it can enhance production of coalbed methane and store CO_2. The first application has been under consideration, along with nitrogen injection, for more than a decade. CO_2 is preferentially adsorbed[6] in coal (compared to CH_4), because fractures in the structure of the coal can absorb twice as much CO_2 as the methane it initially contained. Recent studies have shown that some low-quality coals in the United States could store five to ten times as much CO_2 as the initial methane (Mastalerz, 2004).

Estimates for CO_2 storage using ECBM range from 150 to 220 gigatonnes of CO_2 (Table 12.3). The potential is biggest in the United States and Australia. Between 0.1 and 0.2 tonnes of methane are expected to be recovered for each tonne of CO_2 injected. Commercial-scale injection of CO_2 for ECBM has been undertaken in the US San Juan Basin, recovering 77% to 95% of the methane in place. Other experimental ECBM projects have also been launched in Canada, China, Japan and Poland. A number of technical questions need to be addressed before this technology can become commercial, including the interaction of CO_2 with the formation rock, which can reduce permeability and lower productivity.

---

6. Adsorbtion refers to the formation of a thin film on a surface through condensation.

Table 12.3 ● Enhanced coalbed-methane CO_2 sequestration potential by country/region

Country	Potential (Gigatonnes)
United States	35-90
Australia	30
Indonesia	24
Former Soviet Union	20-25
China	12-16
Canada	10-15
India	4-8
South Africa & Zimbabwe	6-8
Western Europe	3-8
Central Europe	2-4
Total	**146-228**

Sources: Gale (2004); Reeves (2003).

Shale gas: a neglected resource becomes valuable

Significant volumes of natural gas are sometimes contained in layers of shale rock, often hundreds of metres thick, in regions with conventional oil and gas resources. Until recently, producing the gas from such formations, usually discovered when drilling for oil and gas at deeper levels, was not profitable because of the low permeability of the rock. Shale gas can also occur in areas without commercial oil and gas resources. As exploration in those areas has been minimal, those resources may be significantly larger than currently thought.

Natural gas can be stored in shales through different storage mechanisms: free gas in the pores of fractures and adsorbed gas. Due to the very tight nature of the shale, production requires stimulation (hydraulic fracturing): in shallow reservoirs, fluids mixed with nitrogen are often used; in deeper formations, low-viscosity fracturing fluids *(slickwater)* have replaced more expensive treatments (Frantz and Jochen, 2006). New methods of completing the wells involve the combined use of horizontal wells and a series of staged hydraulic fractures. The recent take-up of those techniques has made possible the development of the Barnett Shales in the United States. Recovery factors are expected to increase from an estimated 12% up to 50% during this decade.

Global shale-gas reserves are estimated at 450 tcm, with 35% in the Americas, 35% in the Asia-Pacific region and 15% in the Middle East (Rogner, 1997). The United States is currently the only large-scale producer, with output reaching 20 bcm in 2005. This is expected to rise to 28 bcm by 2010, accounting for nearly 5% of total US gas production. An economic analysis is underway of the potential development of shale gas in British Columbia, Canada: early tests with a horizontal well have achieved production rates of 5 million cubic feet per day per well; there are plans to drill up to 20 additional wells by the end of 2008.

12

Gas hydrates: are we getting closer to commercial exploitation?

Methane or gas hydrates are the most abundant source of hydrocarbon gas on earth. They are crystal-like solids that are formed when methane is mixed with water at low temperature and moderate pressure. They occur at relatively shallow depths, usually offshore or in Arctic regions. Various estimates of the total amount of natural gas in place in the hydrate accumulations have been made. The most recent estimate put the range for the volume of gas trapped between 2 500 tcm and 20 000 tcm, or up to 50 times conventional reserves (see, for example, NPC, 2007).

While the volume of hydrates contained in marine environments is several orders of magnitude higher than the volume in arctic permafrost regions, their concentration is higher in the latter. However, there are no commercial techniques yet available to recover them from either source. The costs could also be very high: in an offshore environment, capital and operation costs for a hydrate well could be at least twice as high as those for conventional gas (RPS, 2008). For these reasons, we do not expect commercial production of gas hydrates to begin on a significant scale before 2030. Experimental options to exploit gas hydrates include either a decrease of reservoir pressure below the level at which the gas would separate out and heating the formation to the temperature at which the same effect would occur (but the latter would require too much energy). Commercial exploitation of hydrates with minimal environmental impact requires a good understanding of the processes by which they were laid down, technologies to identify accumulations, and analysis of the interaction between their production and the rock structure.

Arctic hydrates are mostly found beneath and within permafrost in the Canadian Arctic, the North Slope of Alaska and Siberia. Their presence offshore has been confirmed, through multi-party efforts such as the International Offshore Drilling Program, principally in the Americas, Norway, Russia and Japan (Figure 12.5). R&D on hydrates development and production has been carried out principally in Japan, Canada, Korea, the United States, China and India, and involves expenditure of some $200 million per year. In an experimental programme in the Nankai Trough, offshore Japan, measurements have been carried out to determine the properties of gas hydrates and the sediments where they are found. A joint Japanese/Canadian/US project in the MacKenzie Delta in the Canadian Arctic, launched in the late 1990s, led to the world's first consistent and steady flow of gas following the depressurisation of gas hydrates. In March 2008, the Mallik well in northern Canada produced methane for six days, at a rate comparable to a coalbed-methane well (2 000 to 4 000 cubic metres per day).

China and India have also been conducting active hydrate research and development programmes. In 2007, a 2- to 15-metre layer of gas hydrate was discovered under the seabed of the South China Sea by the Chinese Guangzhou Marine Geological Survey. It may be possible to exploit this gas using conventional technologies, including the use of CO_2 to displace methane. A major national programme in India has led to the discovery of a 130-metre thick layer of methane hydrates in the Krishna-Godavarie basin.

Figure 12.5 ● Location of gas-hydrate resources

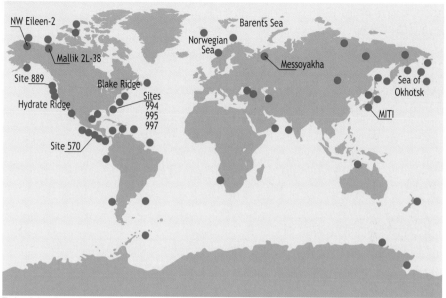

The boundaries and names shown and the designations used on maps included in this publication do not imply official endorsement or acceptance by the IEA.

Gas production prospects

Worldwide, natural gas resources are more than sufficient to meet projected demand to 2030. Nonetheless, it is uncertain whether the entire infrastructure needed to develop those resources and transport the gas from the resource-rich countries to the main centres of demand can be built in the face of economic, geopolitical and technical barriers — often referred to as "above-ground risks" (see Chapter 13). The first determinant of potential production by region is the size of the resource base and its proximity to markets, which affects the cost of supply. Gas transportation, whether by pipeline or as LNG, is very expensive when compared with oil or coal, and has become even more so in recent years with rampant cost inflation. Transport usually represents the largest share of the total cost of gas supply, especially to small consumers. Much of the world's gas resources are located far from the main markets, so that only a small proportion can as yet be exploited profitably.

In the Reference Scenario, world natural gas production is projected to rise from just under 3 tcm in 2006 (and just over 3 tcm in 2007, according to provisional data) to 4.4 tcm in 2030 (Table 12.4). Production expands in all major *WEO* regions, with the exception of OECD Europe, where production is already in decline, and in OECD North America, where production begins to fall over the second half of the *Outlook* period. Output grows most strongly in both volume and percentage terms in the Middle East, tripling between 2006 and 2030 to 1 tcm. Most of this increase comes from Iran and

Qatar, which, alongside Russia, hold the largest reserves. Indeed, Iran sees the biggest volume increase of any country in the world (Figure 12.6). Most of the incremental output in the Middle East will be exported to North America, Europe and Asia, where indigenous output will not keep pace with demand. Production in Latin America and Africa also grows strongly.

Table 12.4 ● **Natural gas production in the Reference Scenario**
(billion cubic metres)

	1980	2000	2006	2015	2030	2006-2030*
OECD	**889**	**1 107**	**1 117**	**1 149**	**1 086**	**-0.1%**
North America	657	763	761	795	765	0.0%
Canada	*78*	*182*	*188*	*196*	*164*	*-0.6%*
United States	*554*	*544*	*524*	*535*	*515*	*-0.1%*
Europe	219	302	305	282	217	-1.4%
Norway	*26*	*53*	*89*	*121*	*127*	*1.5%*
United Kingdom	*37*	*115*	*84*	*44*	*10*	*-8.4%*
Pacific	12	41	51	72	104	3.0%
Australia	*9*	*33*	*43*	*64*	*96*	*3.4%*
Non-OECD	**634**	**1 425**	**1 842**	**2 363**	**3 348**	**2.5%**
E. Europe/Eurasia	480	738	846	963	1 069	1.0%
Kazakhstan	*n.a.*	*12*	*26*	*40*	*48*	*2.5%*
Russia	*n.a.*	*583*	*651*	*712*	*794*	*0.8%*
Turkmenistan	*n.a.*	*47*	*64*	*92*	*103*	*2.0%*
Asia	57	247	335	449	540	2.0%
China	*14*	*27*	*59*	*104*	*115*	*2.9%*
India	*1*	*25*	*28*	*41*	*45*	*2.0%*
Middle East	38	204	324	483	999	4.8%
Iran	*4*	*58*	*104*	*139*	*313*	*4.7%*
Qatar	*3*	*28*	*49*	*124*	*169*	*5.3%*
Africa	23	133	197	286	452	3.5%
Algeria	*14*	*86*	*92*	*106*	*142*	*1.8%*
Nigeria	*2*	*13*	*29*	*64*	*127*	*6.3%*
Latin America	36	104	139	182	287	3.1%
Argentina	*10*	*40*	*45*	*49*	*60*	*1.1%*
Brazil	*1*	*7*	*11*	*17*	*38*	*5.2%*
Trinidad & Tobago	*3*	*13*	*31*	*46*	*61*	*2.8%*
Venezuela	*15*	*28*	*25*	*33*	*70*	*4.4%*
World	**1 522**	**2 531**	**2 959**	**3 512**	**4 434**	**1.7%**

* Average annual rate of growth.

Figure 12.6 ● *Change in natural gas production by country/region, 2007-2030*

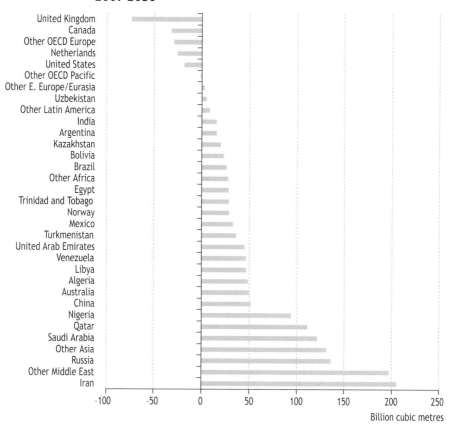

Note: Based on provisional data for 2007.

Regional trends

OECD North America

Canada and the United States form the largest integrated natural gas market in the world, with Canada providing about a quarter of their combined production, while there is a limited amount of trade between Mexico and the United States. Proven reserves in the entire region are currently estimated to be 8 tcm or 4.5% of the world total.[7] The North American market is very mature, with the proven reserves equal to about only 10 years of production at current rates. In total, the region's combined gas production is projected in the Reference Scenario to peak by

---

7. Unless otherwise stated, all of the figures for proven reserves cited in this section are from Cedigaz (2008) and correspond to end-2007.

around the middle of the next decade and then decline gradually through to 2030. A steady rise in Mexican production is insufficient to offset declines in Canada and the United States.

Canada's production, 60% of which is exported to the United States, appears to be close to reaching a plateau. Conventional gas reserves in Western Canada represent almost a third of the remaining resource base and the National Energy Board of Canada expects this region to be the source of almost 80% of projected Canadian natural gas production in the medium term. The region also contains significant non-conventional natural gas resources, estimated at 15% of the national total, including coalbed methane, tight gas and shale gas (see section above). Further reserves in frontier areas, including the Arctic, account for more than half of Canada's remaining ultimately recoverable gas resources. However, it is unlikely that these frontier reserves will contribute to production before 2030. Significant volumes of discovered gas are associated with offshore oil projects close to Newfoundland, but this gas is expected to be used to maintain reservoir pressure until oil production reaches an uneconomically low level.

In the *United States*, proven remaining reserves of gas have increased almost every year for the last decade and, at 6 tcm, now cover almost 11 years of production at current rates. Recent drilling trends point to continued growth in reserves, with a stronger concentration on non-conventional resources, notably shales and coalbed methane. Shale formations in the lower 48 states are widely distributed, large, and contain huge resources of natural gas (as discussed in the previous section). Commercial development began only recently, yet just one field in Texas – the Barnett Shale – already contributes more than 6% of all production from the lower 48 states, a volume bigger than that from Louisiana, a traditional large producer state.

The combination of improved technology and higher gas prices has stimulated production of deepwater and non-conventional resources, which have previously been too difficult and costly to extract. Sustained high gas prices in the last few years have resulted in higher levels of gas drilling and a trend away from drilling simple vertical wells to horizontal wells. These trends have helped to compensate for a continued decline in production from shallow-water areas in the Gulf of Mexico – output fell in 2007 for the sixth consecutive year – and falls in production in some other major producing states, including New Mexico and Louisiana. Thanks to big increases in output in Texas and Oklahoma, production in the first quarter of 2008 was 9% up on a year earlier. In the Reference Scenario, assumed high prices drive modest increases in US gas production in the medium term, but rising costs and dwindling reserves lead to a gradual decline in output over the second half of the projection period. The emergence of Alaska as a significant producing region, on the assumption that a pipeline to connect with the network in western Canada and the United States is built, is not sufficient to compensate for lower output in the lower 48 states. Nor can imports from Canada make good the remaining shortfall, so imports from outside the region (in the form of LNG) and possibly from Mexico grow through the projection period (Figure 12.7).

Figure 12.7 ● US natural gas balance

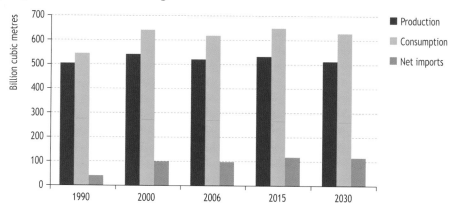

OECD Europe

European gas production peaked in 2004 at close to 330 bcm and is now in long-term decline. Continued growth in Norway has not been sufficient to offset a rapid decline in output in the United Kingdom, for many years Europe's largest producer, despite a recent surge in drilling for gas in the North Sea. In aggregate, production in OECD Europe in the Reference Scenario is projected to decline steadily from 305 bcm in 2006 to 282 bcm in 2015 and 217 bcm in 2030 – a fall of one-third on current levels.

Norway is Europe's leading gas producer and the sixth-largest in the world – though it holds just 3 tcm, or 1.7% of the world's remaining proven reserves. The ultimate recoverable resource potential is thought to be large, however, as large parts of continental shelf have yet to be explored, especially the Barents Sea. The Norwegian Petroleum Directorate estimates that ultimately recoverable resources are in the range of 3.4 tcm to 6.6 tcm. However, despite their obvious potential, northern Norwegian reserves present a significant challenge, firstly due to their remoteness and the arctic conditions but also to the distance from the existing transport infrastructure and traditional markets. Production of natural gas started on the Norwegian shelf simultaneously with oil production in 1971 and exports began in 1977. Norway currently has capacity to export about 120 bcm per year, though marketed production in 2007 reached only 91 bcm, according to preliminary estimates. Output is projected to continue to grow, to over 120 bcm by 2015, and then level off at close to 130 bcm in 2030.

Large-scale extraction of oil and gas from the *United Kingdom* Continental Shelf began in the late 1970s. Production of both, however, is in decline and the United Kingdom became a net importer of gas on an annual basis in 2004. Output has already dropped by a third from its peak of 113 bcm in 2001. Proven reserves, at just under 650 bcm, would support production at current rates for less than 12 years. In recent years, the UK government and industry have launched a number of initiatives to help increase investment in long-term offshore projects, from improving access to pipelines and other infrastructure to ensuring activity in all areas under licence. These are proving successful. For example, the 2005 licensing round evoked more interest than any other round since gas production started in 1964. Monthly data shows a slowing of the rate of decline in production in early 2008. Nonetheless, increased drilling is expected only to slow, rather than halt, the long-term downward trend in production. We project output to reach 44 bcm in 2015 and then fall to only 10 bcm in 2030.

The *Netherlands* holds the second-largest gas reserves in western Europe (1.25 tcm), the bulk of them in the Groningen gas field. Around two-thirds of its production, which amounted to 77 bcm in 2007, is exported. Proven reserves have been in gradual decline for several years: as Groningen has depleted, the portfolio of small fields has matured and discoveries have dropped off. In order to reverse this downward trend and to extend the life expectancy of the highly flexible (and valuable) Groningen field, the Dutch government has adopted several measures, including imposing a ceiling on output over discrete periods. Over the period 2006-2015, the field is allowed to produce 425 bcm. The government has also tried to stimulate exploration and production activity by improving access to information, tackling the issue of "sleeping" licences (for which no detailed development plan has been put forward) and making active approaches to exploration companies. These measures, together with higher prices have led to increased exploration, which is expected to temper the decline in output in the next few years. Nonetheless, production falls progressively more quickly through the projection period, reaching little more than 50 bcm in 2030 — a third down on 2007.

OECD Oceania

Natural gas reserves in Australia and New Zealand stand at 2.5 tcm, the bulk of which are located in remote locations in offshore Western Australia. In addition to conventional natural gas, Australia has extensive deposits of coalbed methane. *Australia* is fast becoming an important LNG player in the Asia-Pacific region, helping to compensate for Indonesia's declining role as an exporter of LNG. Australia's Santos recently announced its proposed Gladstone LNG project is for a 3 to 4 million tonnes per year LNG processing train and associated infrastructure, based on coalbed methane from Queensland's Bowen and Surat Basins, the first of its kind. The project aims to export its first shipment by 2014. Total Australian production is projected to double by 2030, to close to 100 bcm from less than 50 bcm in 2007. *New Zealand* production is expected to remain modest.

Eastern Europe/Eurasia

Russia has 48 tcm of proven gas reserves, one-quarter of the world total and the largest share of any country. The USGS estimates undiscovered recoverable conventional resources, not including reserves growth, at 80 tcm, including an estimated 37 tcm located north of the Arctic Circle (USGS, 2000 and 2008). Russia is the world's largest natural gas producer and exporter, and is the second-largest natural gas consumer after the United States. Russian exports meet almost a quarter of OECD Europe's gas needs, directly to Finland and Turkey, and via transit pipelines through Ukraine or Belarus.

Russia's resources are unquestionably large enough to support continuing long-term growth in production. But there are doubts about the cost of developing those resources and the speed with which Gazprom, the dominant gas producer, and independent companies can proceed. Gazprom reported reserves replacements in 2007 of 585 bcm – 6% more than it produced and the third year in a row in which it was able to replace all its production. But during the previous ten years, the reserves replacement ratio was only around 50% to 70%. The Russian gas industry is at a cross-roads as production shifts from the super-giant fields that have accounted for most of the country's output for decades – notably Urengoye, Yamburg, Medvezhye and more recently Zapolyarnoye – to fields located in new, more difficult-to-develop regions, needing new transportation infrastructure.

Gazprom has begun development work on the 4-tcm Bovanenkovskoye field, the first to be brought into production on the Yamal peninsula in northern Siberia. Production is due to begin around 2012, with output expected to reach 115 bcm per year once a new pipeline is built to link the field to the national transmission system. Other Yamal fields are lined up for development. Yamal presents major technical challenges because of its extreme climate and permafrost, making it difficult to stabilise infrastructure. The annual operational window for getting equipment to the construction site is also very tight. Furthermore, new warmer climate trends are affecting construction plans, often requiring new project design, which needs to be tested before being put in place, causing delays to project timelines. Given these difficulties and the scale of the project, many industry observers believe that the project may not be commissioned on time.

Gazprom, in partnership with Total and StatoilHydro, also plans to bring the 3.8-tcm Shtokman field, which is located offshore in the Barents Sea, into production by 2012. Production is planned to reach 40 bcm per year at plateau in the first two phases of the field's development and 70 bcm after one or two more phases. Development of this field also faces major technical hurdles, as the field is located 550 kilometres offshore in water prone to ice-floes. A long-distance pipeline to European markets will also need to be built. Total development costs have ballooned to more than $40 billion for the first two phases. We assume that first gas comes after 2015.

In the Reference Scenario, Russian gas production is projected to rise from 680 bcm in 2007 to about 710 bcm in 2015 and just under 800 bcm in 2030 – an overall increase of just under one-fifth. There are enormous uncertainties about the mobilisation of the massive investments needed to develop these new fields and build pipelines to connect them to the domestic network and export systems. Gazprom has increased its capital spending programme for 2008 to around $35 billion, of which about $22 billion is earmarked for the upstream sector and pipelines. It plans to invest a total of $140 billion over the five years to 2012. A growing share of gas investment in Russia is expected to come from independent gas producers, on the assumption that their access to Gazprom's transmission system is made easier. Gazprom will nonetheless remain the dominant producer for the foreseeable future.

Caspian region producers are expected to make a major contribution to the growth in gas production in the Eastern Europe/Eurasia region (Figure 12.8). The contribution of the Caspian region to global gas supply will depend on the level of investment in

Figure 12.8 ● Natural gas production in Eastern Europe/Eurasia

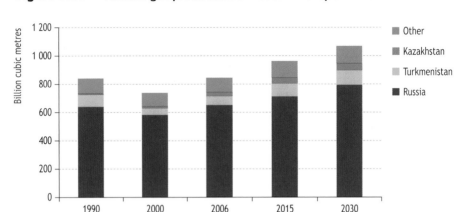

exploration and production, and on the availability on commercial terms of reliable routes to international markets. Volumes available for export will also depend on the region's own demand for gas, which has been growing strongly on the back of heavy subsidies; gas is used very inefficiently across the region.

Turkmenistan has ambitious plans to increase production and exports. Turkmenistan is the largest producer in Central Asia, with output of 72 bcm in 2007; its relatively small population (4.9 million) means that large volumes are available for export. Russia is currently the main importer of Turkmen gas, with smaller volumes going to Iran. Estimates of Turkmenistan's natural gas reserves vary considerably, introducing a large element of uncertainty into projections of its future contribution to global gas supply. Official sources have put gas reserves in the country at more than 20 tcm, an amount approaching the range of proven reserves in Iran or Qatar — and far more than the 3 tcm of proven reserves reported elsewhere (for example, BP, 2008 and *O&GJ*, 2007). The government announced in April 2008 an international audit of Turkmenistan's gas reserves. The Turkmen government aims to raise production to 250 bcm per year by 2030, but there is considerable uncertainty that the known resource base would support such an increase or that sufficient investment will be forthcoming. Major investment is required to develop new reserves to compensate for declining output from the mature fields that provide most of the country's output now. We project annual production to rise to over 100 bcm by 2030.

Uzbekistan is a major gas producer, with production of 65 bcm in 2007, of which 11 bcm is exported, mainly to Russia. Following signs of a slowdown in oil and gas output in 2005, Uzbekistan has sought to increase investment in exploration and production to stem the decline in output at its mature fields and has concluded a number of new production-sharing agreements, predominantly with Russian and Asian companies. Output is projected to remain broadly flat through to 2030. Russia is likely to remain the most significant export market, but the construction of a gas pipeline from Turkmenistan through Uzbekistan (and Kazakhstan) to China will open up the possibility of gas trade with China when it is completed in 2011 (though most of the gas that will flow through the line is likely to come from Turkmenistan).

Production is projected to increase moderately in *Kazakhstan*. Almost all of the gas produced there is associated with oil production, notably from the Tengiz and Karachaganak projects in the west of the country. Much of this gas is re-injected, in order to maintain reservoir pressure and enhance oil output, or flared for lack of infrastructure to transport it to market. Most of the gas produced in Kazakhstan is consumed domestically. Annual gas production is projected to increase from 26 bcm in 2006 to around 40 bcm by 2015 and close to 50 bcm by 2030. Gas production in *Azerbaijan* is also set to grow, with the offshore Shah Deniz field making a sizable contribution, providing up to 20 bcm per year for export to Turkey and other European countries from the middle of the next decade.

Non-OECD Asia

Asia is a small producer and consumer of gas relative to the size of its population and its overall energy use. The region as a whole is a net exporter, though some countries — including China and India — need to import some or all of the gas they consume. Asian gas production — most of which is consumed locally — amounted to 341 bcm in 2007 (little more than half that of Russia), having grown by 95 bcm, or 39%, since 2000. Annual output rates are projected to expand further, to around 450 bcm in 2015 and 530 bcm in 2030.

Indonesia has the largest proven gas reserves in the region, estimated at 3 tcm, and is the largest producer. Reserves grew sharply in 2006 and 2007, with new discoveries (resulting from a spurt in the issue of new exploration licences) and increased appraisal drilling. Production has nonetheless continued to drift lower as output from the main fields, which have been producing for many years, declines. Total output stood at 70 bcm in 2007. Indonesia's difficulties in meeting its contractual commitments and extending existing contracts as they expire have been an important factor in the run-up in LNG prices in the Pacific region in recent years. There is a major geographical mismatch between the main demand centres in Indonesia, in Java and Bali, and the main reserves. Pipelines connect these demand centres to procuring areas on Natuna Island and South Sumatra, but other resource-rich areas, such as Kalimantan and Papua, are not connected because of their remoteness. Due to this mismatch, LNG import terminals are being considered in East Java, West Java and North Sumatra.

Exports to Southeast Asia and further afield, together with rising domestic demand, are expected to stimulate a modest rebound in Indonesian production through to 2030. There are already pipelines to its neighbours, including from West Natuna to Singapore and Malaysia, and from South Sumatra to Singapore. The government plans to make more gas available to the domestic market to replace oil, which will drive up demand (especially in power generation). It hopes that moves to speed up the approval process for new upstream projects and more transparent tenders will encourage greater participation by international and domestic players in exploration and appraisal activities. We project Indonesia's production to rise to 90 bcm in 2030.

China's proven reserves of natural gas amount to 2.7 tcm, about a fifth of which are associated with oil and 90% located onshore. Most production to date has come from onshore associated reserves; onshore non-associated gas reserves are largely untapped.

12

Production has been rising swiftly in recent years, reaching an estimated 68 bcm in 2007 — more than 60% higher than in 2004. Only a small number of gas fields have reached their production peak and several fields with large reserves have yet to be developed, so there is significant potential to boost output in the short to medium term. In the Reference Scenario, China's annual production is projected to reach more than 100 bcm by 2015 and 115 bcm by 2030, by which time output is expected to be in decline.

Middle East

The Middle East holds around 40% of world gas reserves with Iran, Qatar, Saudi Arabia and United Arab Emirates holding the largest volumes. Gas reserves in Iran and Qatar alone account for nearly 30% of the world total. Yet, despite a rising trend in production in recent years, these two countries together account for only 5% of global production and the region as a whole for less than 11%, suggesting strong potential to boost supply in the long term, particularly in Iran. Production in the Middle East is expected to grow more than in any other region. In the Reference Scenario, we project Middle East output will jump from 318 bcm in 2007 to 480 bcm in 2015 and to 1 tcm in 2030.

Iran remains the region's biggest gas-producing country in the Reference Scenario, its production rising from an estimated 107 bcm in 2007 to over 350 bcm in 2030 — on the assumption that the required investment can be mobilised. The lion's share of the country's reserves, and the expected source of much of the production growth in the medium term, is in the Iranian part (South Pars) of the South Pars/North Dome gas/condensate field. The combined structure is the world's largest gasfield, with 40 to 50 tcm of reserves. More than one-third of these reserves are in the Iranian sector. South Pars currently accounts for about one-quarter of Iran's total gas production and just under half of the country's 28 tcm of proven reserves.

The government has, for many years, had ambitious plans to boost production from South Pars and other fields to supply the rapidly growing domestic market and to export (by pipeline and as LNG), but developments have been delayed for technical and political reasons. New upstream awards have slowed markedly since 2004, due to changes in political priorities and the international isolation resulting from trade embargoes imposed in response to the country's nuclear programme. A growing proportion of well-head gas supplies has been re-injected to maintain oil production in some old fields which are faced with high natural decline rates (see Chapter 10). As a result, production growth is likely to slow significantly through to the middle of the next decade. Boosting capacity thereafter will depend on a resurgence in awards and the clearance of other obstacles in the next few years. A large-scale internal pipeline construction programme is underway to accommodate higher production to meet domestic demand.

Increasing domestic demand for re-injection, power generation and end uses, however, is likely to mean further delays in planned gas-export initiatives. In mid-2008, Iran officially postponed two of the three LNG developments at South Pars planned for the 2010-2013 period, leaving only the domestic LNG development in place. Shell and Total are now discussing the prospect of LNG development linked to later phases of the South Pars field. China's CNOOC and Malaysia's SKS have held intermittent talks on LNG development of other fields, but no firm investment commitments have been made as yet. In addition, prolonged negotiations about gas deliveries to the Iran-Pakistan-India (IPI) pipeline mean that the start date for this project is now 2013 or beyond, rather than the original date of 2011.

Qatar, with proven reserves of 26 tcm, is far and away the biggest gas exporter in the Middle East and the region's fastest-growing producer. We project its production to rise from 54 bcm in 2007 to almost 170 bcm in 2030, driven mainly by LNG exports. Projects currently being developed by Qatar Petroleum with foreign partners will boost the country's LNG export capacity to 105 bcm per year by 2011, up from 40 bcm at end-2007 (Table 12.5). Qatar became the world's biggest LNG exporter in 2006 and looks set to retain that title well into the future. The world's largest trains, of 10.6 bcm per year each, are under construction in the Qatargas and Rasgas ventures, as well as the world's largest gas-to-liquids plant at the Shell/Qatar Petroleum Pearl project (70 kb/d). The world's biggest GTL plant, Oryx, with a capacity of 34 kb/d, was commissioned in Qatar in 2006. The current raft of projects, however, has been hit by technical problems and cost escalation, resulting from difficulties in securing materials and services. This has contributed to delays of more than six months in the commissioning of the first train at Qatargas 2 and the postponement of Rasgas 3 to early 2009 (delays which are by no means unique to Qatar). Project participants believe that this will have a knock-on effect through the project chain.

Table 12.5 ● **Qatari LNG projects**

Trains	Project	Start date (previous target)	bcm per year	Partners
Qatargas			55.4	
1-3		1997-1998	12.9	QP, ExxonMobil, Total, Marubeni, Mitusi
4	Qatargas 2	Q2 2008 (Q1)	10.6	QP, ExxonMobil
5		2009 (2008)	10.6	QP, ExxonMobil, Total
6	Qatargas 3	2010 (2009)	10.6	QP, ConocoPhillips, Mitsui
7	Qatargas 4	2011 (2010)	10.6	QP, Shell
RasGas			49.4	
1-2		1999	9.0	QP, ExxonMobil, Kogas, Itochu, LNGJapan
3	RasGas 2	2004	6.4	QP, ExxonMobil
4		2005	6.4	QP, ExxonMobil
5		2007	6.4	QP, ExxonMobil
6	RasGas 3	2009 (2008)	10.6	QP, ExxonMobil
7		2010 (2009)	10.6	QP, ExxonMobil
Total capacity in 2011			104.8	

Source: IEA (2008).

The prospects for further growth in Qatari gas production beyond 2012 are clouded by the uncertainty created by a moratorium on new export projects, which was imposed in 2005 while the effect of existing projects on North Field reservoirs was studied.

Rather than make early commitments further to boost exports, in the form of LNG, GTL or pipeline gas (gas is already exported to the United Arab Emirates through the Dolphin pipeline), Qatar may seek first to prove up more reserves through additional exploration and appraisal, perhaps first at greater reservoir depths in the North Field. The government is also concerned about ensuring adequate supplies to domestic users, including a burgeoning petrochemical sector. In 2007, gas blocks at the North Field assigned to a cancelled GTL project (a joint venture between Qatar Petroleum and ExxonMobil) were reassigned to the domestic Barzan project, which will supply the domestic industrial sector.

Gas production in the *United Arab Emirates* is projected to grow less rapidly than in neighbouring states, from 46 bcm in 2007 to 72 bcm in 2030. Surging energy demand from industrial projects, power generation and desalination plants has led to shortages in the Emirates of Abu Dhabi and Dubai. Although reserves are large, totalling over 6 tcm, most existing production is earmarked for re-injection at oilfields and for LNG exports from the country's only plant, at Das Island in Abu Dhabi. Rising international gas prices have made it more attractive to develop the country's reserves, but gas-quality problems are holding back investment. For example, although two sour gas fields at Shah and Bab have been put out to tender for development with foreign contractors, negotiations on the Shah field have been hampered by high costs — estimated at between $4 and $5 per MBtu — because of the difficulties in accessing the reserves and the high sulphur content. Bab, together with an integrated gas project and the sour gas development at the Hail field, are expected to provide additional volumes, but much of these will be required for re-injection to boost production at the country's ageing oilfields.

In *Saudi Arabia,* Saudi Aramco's upstream exploration programme has continued to prioritise exploration for non-associated gas. Most of the 67 bcm of gas it produced in 2007 was associated with oil. It has laid out plans to increase reserves, which now stand at 6 tcm, by an average 142 bcm per year over the next ten years. Some successes have been reported, although efforts with foreign partners in the Empty Quarter have not yet yielded any new reserves. Development plans are currently focused on the offshore Karan field, which is now due to supply some 16 bcm per year into the national gas-gathering system from the end of 2011 — 5 bcm per year more than originally planned. The switch to fuel oil and crude oil in some power stations will make more gas available for domestic uses in the medium term. However, Saudi Arabia remains unlikely to consider any export of natural gas until it is certain that its own increasing needs are assured. We project Saudi gas production to reach almost 190 bcm in 2030.

Africa

Three countries — Algeria, Egypt and Nigeria — account for over 90% of all the gas produced in Africa. In aggregate, production is projected to more than double from 206 bcm in 2007 to over 450 bcm in 2030 in the Reference Scenario — the largest increase in volume terms of any region bar the Middle East. The three main producers account for the bulk of this increase in volumetric terms, but the share of other countries, notably Libya and Equatorial Guinea, grows over the projection period.

Nigeria is expected to overtake Algeria to become the region's biggest producer by 2030. With an estimated 5.2 tcm of proven natural gas reserves — the fifth largest in the world and the largest in Africa — output is projected to reach close to 130 bcm in 2030, up from just over 35 bcm in 2007. More than half of the country's marketed output is exported as LNG, with the remainder flared (see Chapter 15) or used for power generation and in industry (there is no public distribution network for the residential sector). A large share of total output is used for oil extraction. Future production growth will be driven by both export projects and rising domestic demand, particularly for power generation.

With the launch of Train 6 in December 2007, the Nigeria LNG (NLNG) project, located on Bonny Island in the Niger Delta, reached a total LNG production capacity of 31 bcm per year, overtaking Algeria and becoming the largest-capacity LNG facility in the Atlantic Basin. NLNG is investigating the possibility of adding huge seventh and eighth trains, of 10.9 bcm per year each, though a final investment decision has yet to be made. Other projects are planned. In total, capacity could reach over 60 bcm per year by 2015. Nigeria has also developed projects to export natural gas via pipelines. The West Africa Gas Pipeline project will carry natural gas from Nigeria to Benin, Togo and Ghana. The 678-km line was completed in December 2007 but commercial operation is not expected to begin until 2008, a delay of more than one year from the original target date at the time of the construction decision.

Algeria, with 4.5 tcm of proven gas reserves, has the potential to continue to expand its production to meet growing domestic demand, particularly for power generation and water desalination, and for export. Output is projected to rise from almost 90 bcm in 2007 to over 140 bcm per year by 2030. The state-owned company, Sonatrach, which dominates the industry, aims to achieve gas exports (by pipeline to Europe and as LNG) of 85 bcm in 2012 and 100 bcm in 2015, up from 62 bcm in 2007. Gas reserves in the Berkine Basin, as well as more difficult reserves from the southwest of the country, are expected to feed these projects. They will require large infrastructure investments around Hassi R'Mel, the country's largest single gasfield. Further supplies are envisaged from recent exploration successes, which included 20 oil and gas discoveries in 2007. Algeria resumed licensing rounds for upstream acreage in 2008, after a hiatus caused by revisions to the hydrocarbon law in 2005 and 2006. Sonatrach is negotiating partnerships in upstream projects with companies in importing countries in Europe, in return for direct access to those companies' domestic markets. Alliances have also been pursued with other producers, including Norway's StatoilHydro, with an eye to joint developments, cargo swaps and market access (on this occasion) to StatoilHydro's capacity at the US Cove Point terminal.

Egypt, with 2.1 tcm of proven gas reserves, raised production from 22 bcm in 2000 to 52 bcm in 2007. Most of the increase has gone to the domestic market, but exports have grown too, quadrupling between 2004 and 2007, following the opening of the Arab gas pipeline to Jordan and the commissioning of three LNG trains. Egypt does not permit export commitments to exceed one-third of the reserve base, in order to ensure adequate domestic supplies for future generations. Two new export outlets were opened up in early 2008, in the form of a pipeline to Israel and the extension of the Arab gas pipeline from Egypt through Jordan into Syria. That pipeline will be linked

12

into the Turkish grid in the next phase of development, although there will be limited volumes of gas available for onward delivery in the near term. A final investment decision is still pending on a second train at the Damietta LNG plant.

Other countries are set to emerge as major producers and exporters. In *Libya*, the emphasis is on export markets: domestic consumption is expected to increase rapidly, but from a small base, due to the limited population and small industrial base. A 2004 deal with Shell could lead to a new LNG project, if sufficient reserves were to be found. BP has also undertaken exploration commitments, with a view to locating feedgas for an LNG facility. ExxonMobil is actively searching for potentially exportable gas offshore. At the end of 2007, the only current gas exporter, Eni, committed to a ten-year deal which includes the further development of its Libyan fields to supply an additional 3 bcm of gas through the 8 bcm Greenstream pipeline to Italy and construction of a new 5 bcm per year LNG export plant at Mellitah. The LNG deals are unlikely to yield significant gas exports before 2013, but do make Libya an expected player in regional export growth in the latter half of the next decade. The country held its first upstream licensing round focused specifically on gas in 2007, with a view to more than doubling its existing proven reserve base of 1.3 tcm.

Some other African countries are also aiming to develop LNG projects. *Angola*, with large associated gas reserves, is building its first LNG liquefaction plant in the *Zaire* province with capacity of 7 bcm per year. It is expected to be completed by early 2012. *Equatorial Guinea* began exporting LNG in 2007 from a 4 bcm per year plant.

Latin America

Gas production and consumption in Latin America remain highly concentrated. Argentina, Bolivia, Brazil, Colombia, Trinidad and Tobago, and Venezuela account for almost all the region's production, most of which (with the exception of that from Trinidad and Tobago, which exports LNG) is consumed within the domestic market. Although the region has plentiful gas reserves, estimated at 7.7 tcm, the recent surge in producing countries of resource nationalism and government policies that discourage upstream investment has led some importing countries to turn to imported LNG from outside the region, rather than rely on overland pipeline imports from neighbouring countries. Today, several LNG receiving terminals are either being built or are at the planning stage – three in Brazil, two in Chile, one in Argentina and one in Uruguay. If all are built, Latin America could be importing as much as 14 bcm per year of LNG by the end of the decade, reaching 27 bcm per year by the end 2012.

All the main gas-resource holders are expected to see rapid growth in production. Venezuela, which has enough gas resources to overtake Argentina as the leading producer in Latin America, has proven reserves of 5.1 tcm accounting for two-thirds of the total for the whole continent. We project its output to jump from only 25 bcm in 2007 to 70 bcm in 2030, though the above-ground risks to this projection are high. Exports of LNG are likely to drive much of the growth in the latter part of the *Outlook* period. Brazil's output, all of which will be needed to meet domestic demand, is projected to more than triple, to 38 bcm by 2030, with a sharp increase in output expected to come from recent offshore pre-salt finds (see Chapter 9).

CHAPTER 13

UPSTREAM INVESTMENT PROSPECTS

Are we spending enough?

H I G H L I G H T S

- Worldwide investment in the upstream oil and gas industry has surged in nominal terms in recent years, partly due to soaring costs and higher oil prices, which have strengthened incentives to explore for and develop reserves in some regions. Total upstream investment more than tripled between 2000 and 2007, from an estimated $120 billion to $390 billion. Most of this increase was due to higher unit costs: in cost-inflation adjusted terms, investment in 2007 was about 70% higher than in 2000.

- Based on the plans of the companies surveyed for this *Outlook*, global upstream oil and gas investment is expected to rise to just over $600 billion in nominal terms by 2012 — an increase of more than half over 2007. If costs level off, as assumed, real spending in the five years to 2012 would grow by 9% per year — about the same rate as in the previous seven years. Spending on exploration will remain small compared with that on field development.

- The bulk of upstream investment will continue to be made by the international companies. Over the period 2000-2007, the five super-majors alone accounted for 29% of all the upstream investment made by the companies surveyed for this *Outlook* and other international and private upstream companies for a further 31%. These shares will not change much over the next five years or so. Much of the increase in this upstream spending will go to meeting rising unit costs of developing dwindling resources in non-OPEC regions, where the bulk of their investment is directed.

- Worldwide, upstream unit costs rose on average by an estimated 90% between 2000 and 2007 and by a further 5% in the first half of 2008, based on the IEA Index of Upstream Capital Costs. Most of the increase occurred in 2004-2007. Exploration and development costs have risen at roughly the same rates. Taking account of these cost increases, overall *physical* upstream activity over the seven years to 2007 grew by about 70%, or 8% per year.

- Current projects are expected to add more than enough capacity to meet demand growth and counter declines at existing fields through to 2010. But many more projects will need to be sanctioned (mostly within the next two years) to bridge the gap between the total gross capacity addition of 30 mb/d needed by 2015 and the actual projected addition of 23 mb/d from current projects. If actual capacity additions fall short, spare production capacity would diminish and oil prices would undoubtedly rise.

- The Reference Scenario projections imply a need for cumulative investment in the upstream oil and gas sector of around $8.4 trillion (in year-2007 dollars) over 2007-2030, or $350 billion per year. That is significantly *less* than is currently being spent. But there is a major shift in where that investment is needed. Much more capital needs to go to the resource-rich regions, notably the Middle East, where unit costs are lowest. It is far from certain that these countries will be willing to make this investment themselves or accept sufficient foreign investment to make it up.

Recent investment trends and near-term outlook

Worldwide investment in upstream oil and gas has surged in nominal terms in recent years and, on current plans, is set to rise further in the coming years. This reflects a combination of higher oil prices, which have strengthened incentives for oil and gas companies to explore for and develop reserves in some regions, soaring cash-flow and rising costs. The prices of cement, steel and other materials used in building production facilities, the cost of fuel used in construction, the cost of hiring skilled personnel and drilling rigs, and the prices of oilfield equipment and services have soared, especially since 2003, though there are signs that costs may now be levelling off. Between 2000 and 2007, capital spending grew at an average rate of 18% per year. In 2007, total upstream investment reached an estimated $390 billion, up from $120 billion in the year 2000 — a more than three-fold nominal increase. The increase has been particularly strong since 2004 (Figure 13.1). This trend is broadly in line with data reported by other organisations. Most of the increase in spending since 2000 was needed to meet higher unit costs: in cost-inflation adjusted terms, investment in 2007 was 70% higher than that in 2000. Box 13.1 describes the methodology used to analyse investment trends.

Figure 13.1 ● World investment in oil and gas exploration and production

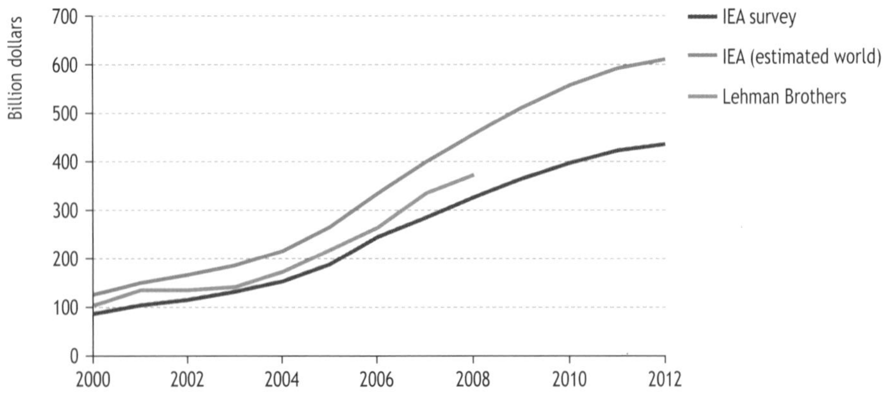

Sources: IEA databases and analysis; Lehman Brothers (2007).

Based on the announced investment plans or forecasts by the 50 companies surveyed for this *Outlook*, total upstream oil and gas investment is expected to rise to just over $600 billion in nominal terms by 2012 — an increase of more than half over 2007. If this expectation is realised, annual investment in nominal terms would be on average two-and-a-half times higher in 2008-2012 than in 2000-2007. Upstream investment as a share of total oil and gas industry investment (including refining, oil pipelines, liquefied natural gas chains and gas-to-liquids) is expected to rise slightly from 68% in 2000-2007 to 70% in 2008-2012. In cost-inflation adjusted terms, upstream spending is set to grow by around 50% between 2007 and 2012, assuming unit costs level off in 2008. This equates to 9% per year. There is little scope for the industry to increase real spending faster than this, even if major new investment opportunities arise, because of a lack of skilled labour and equipment. These investment trends should be treated as indicative only, as they are based on current plans, which could change were oil prices and costs to differ markedly from our assumptions.

Box 13.1 ● Approach to assessing the outlook for upstream investment

Our outlook for upstream investment is assessed both bottom-up and top-down. The former involves a detailed analysis of the plans and prospects for oil and gas industry investment over the period 2000 to 2015, with the aim of determining whether the industry is planning to invest more in response to higher prices and to a growing need for new capacity and of assessing the resulting additions to production capacity. This analysis is based on two main elements:

● A survey of the capital-spending programmes of 50 of the largest upstream oil and gas companies (national and international companies and pure exploration and production companies), covering actual capital spending from 2000 to 2007 and their plans or forecasts of spending through to 2012 (Table 13.1). Companies were selected on the basis of their size as measured by their production and reserves, though geographical spread and data availability also played a role. The surveyed companies account for close to 80% of world oil production and 79% of oil reserves, 66% of gas production and 71% of gas reserves. Total industry investment was calculated by adjusting upwards the spending of the 50 companies, according to their share of world oil and gas production for each year.

● A review of all major upstream projects worldwide — sanctioned (approved by the company board) and planned — which are due to be brought on stream before 2015. This review covers over 570 projects, each involving a capacity addition of more than 5 thousand barrels of oil per day (kb/d). Projects include conventional oil and gas production, non-conventional oil sands and coal- and gas-to-liquids.

Data was obtained from companies' annual and financial reports, corporate presentations, press reports, trade publications and direct contacts in the industry.

The top-down determination of overall upstream investment needs to 2030 was derived from the *WEO* oil- and gas-supply models. These models determine the rate of development of new projects, based on assumptions — derived from our review of upstream projects — about unit capital costs which take into account the impact of technological change and country-specific factors. The results are presented in year-2007 dollars. With this approach, capital spending is attributed to the year in which the plant in question becomes operational, because of the difficulties in estimating lead-times and how they might evolve in the future.

For both the near-term and longer-term assessments, investment is defined as capital expenditure only. It does not include spending that is usually classified as operation and maintenance.

The bulk of upstream investment will continue to be made by the international companies. Over the period 2000-2007, the five super-majors[1] alone accounted for 29% of all the upstream investment of the companies surveyed for this *Outlook* and other international and private upstream companies for a further 31% (Figure 13.2). Their combined share is projected to drop by just one percentage point to 59% over 2008-2012. The share of national companies is set to rise from 40% to 41%. More than half of total upstream investment over the next five years will, as before, continue to go to maintaining output at oil and gas fields already in production. Spending on exploration is expected to remain small compared with that on the development of existing and new fields (Figure 13.3).

Figure 13.2 ● **Upstream investment of surveyed companies by type of company**

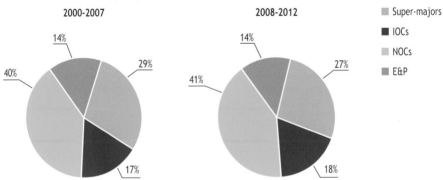

Note: For 50 surveyed companies. IOC = international oil company; NOC = national oil company. E&P = exploration and production; breakdown by type of company.
Source: IEA database and analysis.

---

1. ExxonMobil, Shell, BP, Total and Chevron.

Table 13.1 ● Companies in investment survey, 2007

Company	Type	Oil production (mb/d)	Gas production (bcm)
Saudi Aramco	NOC	10.9	68.4
NIOC	NOC	4.4	106.7
Pemex	NOC	3.5	56.0
Adnoc	NOC	2.7	22.5
ExxonMobil	Super-major	2.6	97.0
KPC	NOC	2.2	12.0
BP	Super-major	2.4	84.2
PDVSA	NOC	2.6	25.0
CNPC	NOC	2.8	57.8
Rosneft	NOC	2.0	15.7
INOC	NOC	2.3	4.3
Lukoil	IOC	2.0	14.0
Shell	Super-major	1.9	84.9
Petrobras	NOC	1.9	23.7
LNOC	NOC	1.9	10.9
Chevron	Super-major	1.8	51.9
Sonatrach	NOC	1.6	90.0
Total	Super-major	1.5	50.0
TNK-BP	IOC	1.4	8.5
NNPC	NOC	1.4	18.3
StatoilHydro	NOC	1.1	34.7
ConocoPhillips	IOC	1.1	52.6
Eni	IOC	1.0	42.3
Qatar Petroleum	NOC	1.0	42.9
Gazprom	NOC	0.9	548.5
Petronas	NOC	0.8	57.3
Sinopec	NOC	0.8	8.0
Sonangol	NOC	0.7	0.8
ONGC	NOC	0.5	22.3
Repsol YPF	IOC	0.5	32.3
Occidental	E&P	0.4	7.3
CNOOC	NOC	0.4	5.8
Anadarko	E&P	0.3	19.7
Apache	E&P	0.3	18.6
CNR	IOC	0.3	14.0
Hess	E&P	0.3	6.9
PetroCanada	IOC	0.3	6.1
BG	IOC	0.2	26.6
Devon	E&P	0.2	24.5
Talisman	E&P	0.2	10.5
Marathon	IOC	0.2	9.6

13

Table 13.1 ● Companies in investment survey, 2007 (continued)

Company	Type	Oil production (mb/d)	Gas production (bcm)
Nexen	E&P	0.2	2.0
EnCana	E&P	0.1	37.7
XTO	E&P	0.1	15.0
Pertamina	NOC	0.1	10.6
PTT	NOC	0.1	9.6
Woodside	E&P	0.1	5.9
Plains	E&P	0.1	0.8
Pioneer	E&P	<0.1	4.4
Chesapeake	E&P	<0.1	18.6
Total		65.8	1 997.5

Note: NOC = national oil company; IOC = international oil company; E&P = exploration and production company.

Source: IEA databases.

Figure 13.3 ● Upstream oil and gas investment of surveyed companies by activity

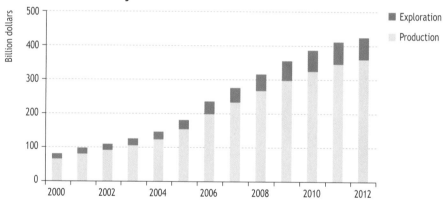

Note: For the 50 surveyed companies (see Table 13.1).
Source: IEA database and analysis.

Capital spending on oil and gas exploration has increased substantially since 2004, but continued to decline as a share of total upstream spending until 2006 (Figure 13.4). In 2007, the share fell back again, to just over 15%, down slightly on 2006 and well below the level of almost 20% in 2000 – despite dwindling reserve-replacement rates and a surge in the value of reserves. This reflects several factors: an emphasis on developing proven reserves in order to profit from high prices, the limited opportunities for the international companies to explore for hydrocarbons in highly prospective regions (see Chapter 14) and shortages of rigs and manpower. The credit squeeze, as yet, has had little impact on upstream financing (Box 13.2).

Box 13.2 ● Impact of the credit crunch on upstream financing

The upstream oil and gas industry has weathered the credit crunch better than most other sectors — largely because most capital spending is financed out of cash-flow and because those companies that do need to borrow are able to secure loans against healthy balance sheets. Many national companies are also largely immune from tighter lending standards because of credit guarantees and favourable borrowing terms from their state owners. Nonetheless, smaller private companies have experienced an increase in the cost of borrowing in recent months, which has encouraged some — most recently, Imperial and Cairn India — to raise cash through rights issues in order to limit interest charges. Others, including Tullow Oil, have disposed of non-core assets in order to raise funds for upstream developments.

In addition, project finance, commonly used for mid-stream activities such as LNG chains and oil and gas pipeline projects, has become more costly and harder to secure as a result of diminishing liquidity and increased risk-aversion among lenders — especially for smaller projects. Such projects are increasingly making use of export credit guarantees to facilitate access to long-term credit. This tendency stems partly from an increase in the sheer size of projects and partly from increased uncertainty and risk. Should there be any delays and cancellations resulting from tougher credit terms, these will inevitably affect the scale of development of upstream projects.

Figure 13.4 ● Investment in oil and gas exploration of surveyed companies

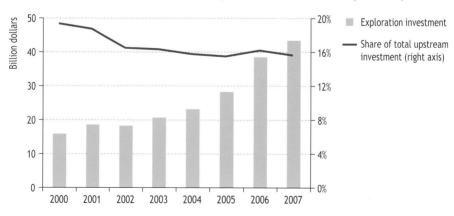

Note: For the 50 surveyed companies.

Source: IEA database and analysis.

New upstream projects

The last few years have seen a big increase in nominal spending on large oil and gas projects (mainly new fields), particularly in the Middle East. As with overall investment, this largely reflects higher costs. We have identified more than 570 projects that are due to come on stream over the period 2008-2015, involving total investment of about $1.4 trillion (Table 13.2). The three biggest projects currently in development — Kashagan (phase 1 and 2) in Kazakhstan and Sakhalin 2 and Shtokman in Russia — involve total investment of $114 billion. Some of the sanctioned and planned projects will undoubtedly encounter delays due to shortages of equipment and manpower. The average slippage in project completion has risen to more than a year (IEA, 2008). Examples of major projects that are falling behind schedule include Thunder Horse in the US Gulf of Mexico and Sakhalin-2, both of which are now expected to be completed only in 2008 — more than two years later than originally planned. Development of the Kashagan oilfield in Kazakhstan has been delayed by at least five years, with first production now due in 2013 at the earliest.

Some 41% of the investment in current projects, all of which are due to come on stream by 2015, will go to developing fields located in OECD countries (Figure 13.5). Less than a quarter will go to projects in OPEC countries, altough they hold two-thirds of the world's resources. Oil and gas companies based in OECD countries continue to dominate global upstream investment. They will account for 70% of investment in new projects over 2008-2015. The share of total project investment made by the national oil companies of OPEC countries is very small, at only 9%, while those of Middle East OPEC countries account for 6%. Unit development costs in the Middle East are much lower than in most other regions.

Figure 13.5 ● **Investment in new upstream oil and gas projects, 2008-2015**

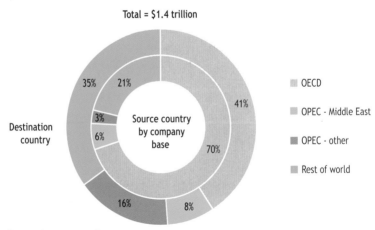

Note: Based on projects surveyed.

Source: IEA database and analysis.

Capital-cost trends

The cost to oil companies of exploring for and developing new fields and boosting output at existing fields has increased considerably since the beginning of the current decade. This is mainly due to the soaring unit cost of all the inputs to upstream activities, including drilling and oilfield services, skilled labour, materials and energy. The fall in the value of the US dollar, which has pushed up the cost of materials, equipment and labour sourced in countries with currencies not tied to the dollar, has been a major contributor to the overall surge in costs in dollar terms. A shift in spending towards more technically complex projects in locations where no infrastructure exists, especially deepwater fields, and to smaller fields, where unit costs tend to be higher, has also contributed. These factors have more than offset the impact of new technology, which had helped to lower average unit costs in the 1990s (IEA, 2001).

Finding and development costs per barrel − defined as exploration and development expenditure divided by additions to reserves − have rebounded in all regions in dollar terms. According to official US data for upstream companies covered by the financial reporting system, the three-year moving average of finding and development costs jumped by almost half between 2005 and 2006 (Figure 13.6). The biggest increase occurred in Europe, where costs doubled, partly because of the sharp rise in the value of the euro against the dollar. Expressed in local currencies, cost escalation in many regions has been much less marked, though still substantial.

Figure 13.6 ● **Finding and development costs for US FRS companies**

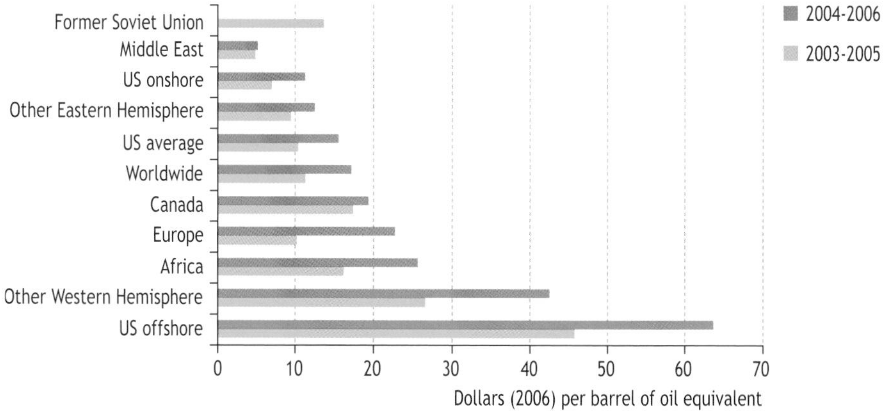

Note: FRS is Financial Reporting System. Three-year weighted averages of exploration and development expenditures (excluding expenditures for proven acreage), divided by reserve additions (excluding net purchases of reserves). Natural gas is converted to equivalent barrels of oil at 178.1 barrels per thousand cubic feet.

Source: DOE/EIA (2007).

Table 13.2 • New upstream oil and gas projects,* 2008-2015 (ranked by cost)

Project	Country	Operator	Date of first production	Peak capacity addition Oil (kb/d)	Peak capacity addition Gas (mcm/year)	Capital cost ($ million)
Conventional oil						
Kashagan - Phase 1	Kazakhstan	Eni	2014	370	0	29 000
Kashagan - Phase 2	Kazakhstan	Eni	2015	450	0	25 000
Sakhalin 2 Oil Expansion	Russia	Sakhalin Energy (Shell)	2008	220	0	20 000
Khurais expansion	Saudi Arabia	Saudi Aramco	2009	1 200	4 341	11 000
Tengiz Stage 3 (extension)	Kazakhstan	Chevron	2013	260	0	9 500
Manifa	Saudi Arabia	Saudi Aramco	2012	900	1 240	9 000
Kuwait North Redevelopment	Kuwait	KPC	2012	450	0	8 000
Usan (PSC)	Nigeria	Total	2012	180	0	8 000
Marlim Leste P 53 FPSO	Brazil	Petrobras	2008	180	2 191	7 000
Marlim Sul Module 2 P51 FPSO	Brazil	Petrobras	2008	180	2 191	7 000
Thunder Horse - Phase 1	USA	BP	2008	210	1 912	6 300
Vankor Oilfield (Vankorneft)	Russia	Rosneft	2008	200	0	6 000
Gjoa	Norway	StatoilHydro	2010	50	3 390	5 400
Jidong Nanpu	China	PetroChina	2012	200	0	5 200
Skarv / Idun	Norway	BP	2012	85	5 168	6 380
Goliath	Norway	Eni	2012	100	0	5 040
Roncador Module P-55	Brazil	Petrobras	2013	180	2 191	5 000
BC-10 (Sugar Loaf)	Brazil	Shell	2010	100	0	5 000
Verkhnechonsk Oil and Gas Expansion	Russia	BP-TNK	2009	150	0	5 000
Tahiti	USA	Chevron	2009	125	723	4 700
Agbami	Nigeria	Chevron	2008	250	0	4 000

Table 13.2 ● New upstream oil and gas projects,* 2008-2015 (ranked by cost) (continued)

Project	Country	Operator	Date of first production	Peak capacity addition		Capital cost ($ million)
				Oil (kb/d)	Gas (mcm/year)	
Ku-Maloob-Zaap (KMZ Extension)	Mexico	Pemex	2010	465	1 240	4 000
Banyu Urip (Cepu Phase 1 & 2)	Indonesia	ExxonMobil	2009	165	207	3 800
Landana (Tombua Landana)	Angola	Chevron	2009	100	0	3 800
Pazflor (Acacia, Zinia, Hortensia, Perpetua)	Angola	Total	2012	200	0	3 740
Alvheim / Klegg / Vilje	Norway	Marathon	2008	120	0	3 980
Kizomba C - Mondo/Saxi-Batuque	Angola	ExxonMobil	2008	200	0	3 500
Corocoro - Phase 1	Venezuela	PDVSA	2008	75	0	3 500
BS-500	Brazil	Petrobras	2013	175	5 685	3 300
Bonga SW	Nigeria	Shell	2012	150	775	3 000
Non-conventional oil						
Fort Hills - Phase 1 (oil sands)	Canada	PetroCanada	2012	140	0	13 200
Athabasca Oil Sands (Scotford Upgrader) Exp. 1	Canada	Shell	2010	100	0	10 000
Muskey River Mine - Phase 2	Canada	Chevron	2010	100	0	10 000
Surmont - Phase 2	Canada	Conoco Phillips	2012	65	0	8 600
Kearl Lake - Phase 1	Canada	ExxonMobil	2010	100	0	8 000
Horizon - Phase 1	Canada	CNR	2008	110	0	7 600
Pearl GTL - Phase 2	Qatar	Shell	2012	70	0	7 500
Pearl GTL - Phase 1	Qatar	Shell	2011	70	0	7 500
Hebron	Canada	PetroCanada	2015	140	0	7 000
Carabobo1 (Orinico Belt)	Venezuela	PDVSA	2015	200	0	7 000

13

Table 13.2 ● New upstream oil and gas projects,* 2008-2015 (ranked by cost) (continued)

Project	Country	Operator	Date of first production	Peak capacity addition		Capital cost
				Oil (kb/d)	Gas (mcm/year)	($ million)
Northern Lights	Canada	Synenco Energy	2011	115	0	4 400
Long Lake - Phase 1	Canada	Nexen/OPTI Canada	2008	60	0	3 500
CTL project (Inner Mongolia)	China	Shenhua Group	2008	20	0	3 150
Natural gas						
Shtokman - Phase II	Russia	Gazprom	2015	0	50 000	25 000
Shtokman - Phase I	Russia	Gazprom	2014	0	22 490	15 000
Natuna D-Alpha	Indonesia	Pertamina	2015	0	10 306	15 000
D1 & D3 Block - (KG - Gas)	India	Reliance	2008	0	14 470	8 840
MA-1 Field (D6 block)	India	Reliance	2008	40	3 617	8 840
Ferdows	Iran	SKS Ventures	2014	70	9 095	6 000
Laggan / Tormore	UK	Total	2011	0	5 581	5 300
North Pars	Iran	CNOOC	2013	0	49 611	5 000
Krishna Godavari Basin	India	ONGC	2012	0	4 362	5 000
Vietnam Gas Development	Vietnam	Chevron	2012	0	5 147	4 000
Gendalo Hub (includes Gehem)	Indonesia	Chevron	2013	0	7 752	3 100
Al Khaleej Gas - Phase 2	Qatar	ExxonMobil	2009	0	12 920	3 000
Karan (Gulf Karan field)	Saudi Arabia	Saudi Aramco	2011	0	10 336	3 000
Sub-total				9 090	236 943	428 670
Other projects						931 330
Total projects worldwide						1 360 000

* For which data is available. These projects are thought to account for the bulk of all projects currently sanctioned and planned worldwide.

Source: IEA database.

Drilling is the single largest component of upstream capital spending, accounting for over half of the total (including exploration and development wells). Drilling costs have risen particularly rapidly in recent years. The average dollar cost of drilling a well more than doubled between 2000 and 2007, reflecting both an increase of around 90% in the cost per foot drilled, and a 15% increase in the average depth drilled per well (Figure 13.7).

Figure 13.7 ● Worldwide upstream drilling cost indices

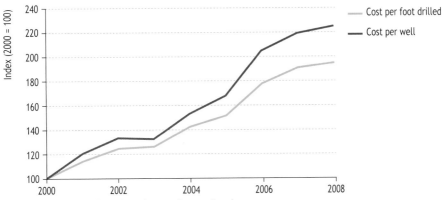

Note: Based on dollar-denominated costs. Covers oil and gas.

Sources: Spears and Associates (2007); IEA analysis.

A surge in day-rates for drilling rigs,[2] caused by strong demand from oil and gas field operators, has been the principal reason for increased drilling costs (Figure 13.8). Day-rates typically make up about half of the total cost of drilling a production well. Day-rates in all regions rose strongly in 2005 and, in most parts of the world, in 2006 and 2007 too, but they have levelled off in recent months in most places. In the US Gulf of Mexico, day-rates for jack-up rigs have been declining steadily since the middle of 2006, but rates for deepwater rigs have continued to rise strongly. In mid-2008, ultra-deepwater drillships were under contract for more than $650 000 per day. Rates for semi-submersible rigs were approaching $500 000/day, compared with $130 000/day at the turn of the decade.

2. Day-rates are the daily cost to the operator of renting the drilling rig and the associated costs of person-nel and routine supplies. They usually do not include capital goods, such as casing and well heads, or special services, such as logging or cementing, but may include the cost of fuel.

Figure 13.8 ● Day-rates for drilling rigs

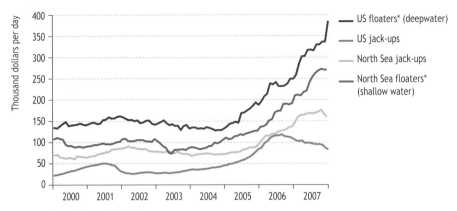

* Semi-submersibles and drillships.
Source: ODS-Petrodata.

Utilisation rates for both land and offshore rigs are at, or close to, 100%, as demand for rigs has grown. Demand for rigs and day-rates have been boosted by higher oil and gas prices (Figure 13.9), which have boosted returns on upstream investment. Higher drilling costs have, in turn, driven up the cost of developing new supplies and lent support to forward prices. To a large extent, the surge in day-rates for drilling rigs simply reflects the short-term rigidity of supply in the face of rapidly rising demand. Consequently, rig-owners have seen their profits rise strongly. But some of the underlying costs typically included in day-rates for drilling services (such as labour) and other costs for services not included in day-rates (notably cement, well-

Figure 13.9 ● Drilling rig day-rates and the average IEA crude oil import price, 1995-2007

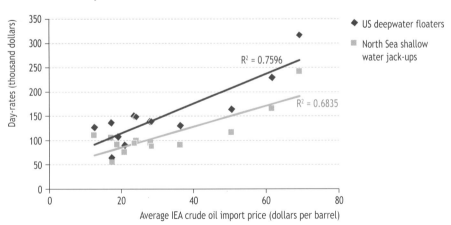

Sources: IEA database and analysis; ODS-Petrodata.

casings and specialist drilling services) have also risen strongly. The international price of steel has almost tripled since 2001, while the price of aluminium has doubled, driven by booming demand from China and other developing countries. The costs of hiring skilled personnel have also risen sharply.

Figure 13.10 • *Average capital cost of upstream projects under development*

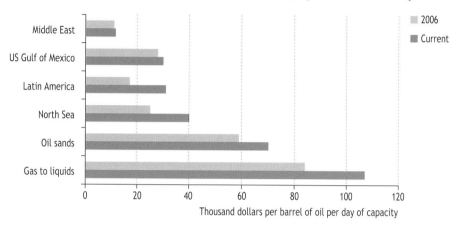

Source: IEA database and analysis.

Cost inflation has hit upstream projects in all regions. The average capital cost of projects (weighted by production) under development is estimated to have risen by about 50% since 2006 (Figure 13.10). At present, the cost of new capacity is highest for gas-to-liquids plants, at close to $110 000 per barrel per day. The Middle East remains the lowest-cost region, with an average capital cost for all projects of just over $10 000/b/d. Worldwide, upstream costs rose on average by an estimated 90% between 2000 and 2007 and by a further 5% in the first half of 2008, based on the IEA Upstream Investment Cost Index, or UICI (Box 13.3 and Figure 13.11). Most of the increase occurred in 2004-2007. Exploration and development costs have risen at roughly the same rates. Costs have risen most for materials, products, hiring land rigs and project-management fees, all of which have more than doubled since 2000.

The outlook for upstream costs remains very uncertain. The extent to which the run-up in upstream costs is the result of structural rather than cyclical factors is unclear. Few people in the business expect costs to fall back to the levels prevailing at the beginning of the current decade, though some expect costs to retreat to some degree as physical capacity in the oil services and drilling industries expands in the coming years. Many others expect costs to continue to rise in dollar terms — barring a sharp revaluation of the currency — if not at the rapid pace of the last few years. What is clear is that, over the longer term, costs will continue to swing in response to marginal imbalances in the supply of and demand for drilling services and equipment.

13

Box 13.3 ● IEA Upstream Investment Cost Index

We have prepared an overall index of upstream capital costs worldwide in US dollars, based on disaggregated data for the different cost components, back to 2000. The aim is to determine the average annual rate of increase in underlying costs incurred directly by operating companies for both exploration and production, stripping out the effect of shifts in spending on different types of upstream projects and regions as well as the impact of changes in drilling productivity (*e.g.* average well depth). These costs include the acquisition of seismic data, project management, rig hiring, drilling services and the construction of production facilities (including treatment and processing plant, compressors, generators and gathering pipelines). The underlying costs of labour, materials and equipment are incorporated in charges for drilling, related services and facilities.

Indices for exploration and production are calculated by weighting the contribution of each component within those activities. Costs for onshore and offshore developments (broken down by shallow and deep water) are assessed separately, so that the index is not distorted by a shift in spending over time between these locations. The overall Upstream Investment Cost Index (UICI) is the average of the two separate indices for exploration and production, weighted by capital spending (based on the results of our survey of upstream investment). Our approach differs from that used by IHS/CERA[3] in preparing its Upstream Capital Costs Index, which tracks the costs of equipment, facilities, materials and personnel used in the construction of a geographically diversified portfolio of 28 onshore, offshore, pipeline and LNG projects. The IEA and IHS/CERA indices report similar increases in costs between 2000 and 2007.

Figure 13.11 ● IEA Upstream Investment Cost Index by activity

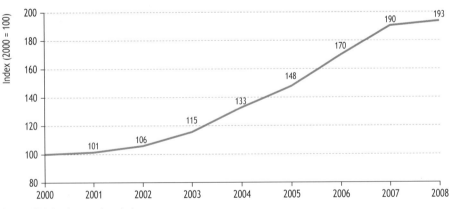

Source: IEA database and analysis.

---

3. More details can be found at www.cera.com.

There are signs that the pace of upstream cost-inflation is slowi. result of new capacity coming on line and a slowing of growth in der services and related materials. This is partly because some companies high costs and are delaying investment decisions in the hope that cos later. Day-rates for jack-up rigs in the United States, for example, have down from peaks reached in mid-2006 (Figure 13.8, above). The surge recent years has prompted a new wave of construction of rigs, especial drilling (Figure 13.12). Around 160 offshore rigs were under construction in mid-2008, compared with close to 140 in 2007 and fewer than 20 in 2004. Utilisation and day-rates are nonetheless likely to remain at historically high levels: all of the deepwater rigs that will come to market between now and 2010 have already been assigned to projects that are under development, leaving no free rigs for any new opportunities that may emerge in the next few years (see the *Spotlight* below).

The discovery of Tupi and other large deepwater fields in Brazil has led to an increase in demand for heavy-duty rigs: Petrobras has announced its intention to order 26 such rigs in the next decade. On the other hand, new land and offshore rigs being brought into operation generally use more efficient technologies (such as rotary steerable systems), cutting the number of days needed to drill a well. This will reduce the number of rig-days needed to find and develop hydrocarbons in the coming years. In the light of these uncertainties, we have assumed that costs stabilise in 2009 and remain flat in real terms (adjusted for consumer price inflation) thereafter.

Figure 13.12 ● **Offshore rigs under construction and effective utilisation rates**

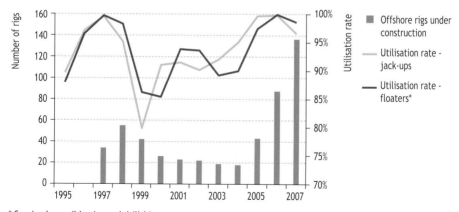

* Semi-submersible rigs and drillships.

Sources: Baker Hughes rig count (www.bakerhughesdirect.com); Spears and Associates (2007); IEA database and analysis.

Although nominal upstream investment in dollar terms increased by about 220% between 2000 and 2007, we estimate that around two-thirds of this increase has been absorbed by cost inflation. In other words, overall physical upstream activity (actual spending adjusted for cost inflation using the IEA UICI) over the seven years to 2007 grew by about 70%, or 8% per year. Activity, or *real investment*, was actually flat in 2004 (Figure 13.13). On the assumption that costs increase on average by 3% in 2008 (assuming that costs levelled off in the second half of the year at the levels reached in the first half) and then stabilise, current oil-company investment plans imply an increase in real investment of about 50% between 2007 and 2012 – again, growth of 8% per year. Growth in real and nominal investment begins gradually to decline over that period.

·····················S P O T L I G H T····················

Is strong demand leading to more drilling capacity?

Increased capital spending on exploration and production in recent years, resulting largely from higher oil and gas prices, has led to a surge in demand for drilling rigs, especially for offshore activities. The world fleet of offshore rigs, including jack-ups (fixed platforms supported by rigid legs for shallow-water drilling), semi-submersibles (floating vessels supported by large pontoon-like structures submerged below the sea surface and anchored with cables to the seabed in deeper water) and drillships (used in very deep water), has been operating at close to 100% of capacity for most of the last three years and backlogs of orders have grown. At present, existing ultra-deepwater rigs are on average contracted through to 2012, with several rigs committed to beyond 2015.

Strong demand for rigs has stimulated a sharp increase in the construction of new offshore rigs. Most of the current rig fleet of 614 vessels (the majority of which are jack-ups) were built in the 1970s and early 1980s: more than 450 rigs were delivered between 1970 and 1985. Another 40 or so were added over the next 12 years. Deliveries picked up at the end of the 1990s (over 40 rigs were added in 1998-2000 alone) and, after stalling during the first half of the current decade, have begun to climb rapidly once again. In mid-2008, 147 rigs (half of them jack-ups) were under construction, all of which are expected to be delivered before end-2010. Between 2000 and 2004, the average number of rigs under construction rarely exceeded 25. About 60 existing vessels are currently undergoing modification. Were this number to remain constant, the fleet of active offshore rigs would rise from 560 at end-2007 to about 700 at end-2010 – an increase of one-quarter. Delays in obtaining materials may, however, slow this increase, as will retirement of older rigs. Almost all the new deepwater rigs under construction have already been contracted, in some case for several years.

Sources: IEA databases; www.rigzone.com

Figure 13.13 • Year-on-year change in world upstream investment and dollar-cost inflation rate

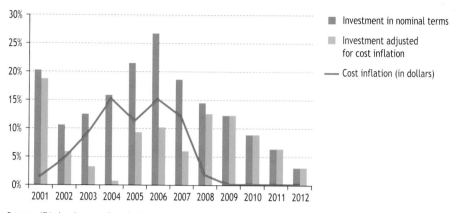

Source: IEA database and analysis.

The historic trends in real spending implied by nominal spending and the IEA UCCI are broadly in line with various indicators of upstream activity (Figure 13.14). That is, physical activity has increased much less quickly than nominal spending. For example, the worldwide land rig count (number of active rigs) was lower in every year from 2003-2007 than in 2000, while the offshore rig count was only marginally higher in 2007 than in 2000. Total footage drilled worldwide nonetheless rose by close to 80% between 2000 and 2007, implying a significant increase in the average depth of wells drilled. Most of the increase in footage drilled occurred in North America, which accounted for two-thirds of all drilling in 2007. Production added per foot drilled in North America is far lower than in the rest of the world.

13

Figure 13.14 • Indicators of upstream activity

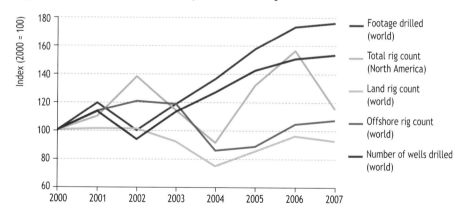

Sources: Baker Hughes rig count (www.bakerhughesdirect.com); Spears and Associates (2007); IEA database and analysis.

Implications for oil-production capacity

The more than 570 upstream projects currently under construction (sanctioned) and planned — most of them involving new fields — will add in total around 28 mb/d of new peak oil-production capacity in the period to 2015, on the assumption that their completion is not delayed. Even though spending by their national companies amounts to under 10% of the global total, the largest capacity additions come from Middle East countries (Figure 13.15), notably Saudi Arabia (3.10 mb/d), Iran (0.99 mb/d) and the UAE (0.43 mb/d). The Saudi capacity increments will come from the Khursaniyah (500 000 b/d in 2008), Shaybah (250 000 b/d in 2008), Nuayim (100 000 b/d in 2009), Khurai (1.2 mb/d in 2009) and Manifa (900 000 b/d in 2011) fields. The other regions that will contribute the bulk of the gross capacity additions are North America (mainly Canadian oil sands and US Gulf of Mexico), Africa and Latin America.

Figure 13.15 ● **Gross peak-oil production capacity additions from current projects by region, 2008-2015**

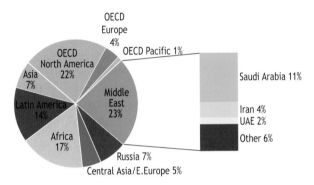

Source: IEA database and analysis.

The gross capacity additions from current projects will, of course, be offset to a large degree by production declines at existing fields as their reserves are depleted — despite continuous large-scale investment (see Chapter 11). In the Reference Scenario, the decline in global production at existing fields is expected to total 21 mb/d between 2007 and 2015, even allowing for new investment in existing fields. World oil demand is projected to grow by 9 mb/d between 2007 and 2015. Thus, an additional 30 mb/d of capacity over and above that currently being built or planned will need to be built to match the loss of production through decline and the increase in demand to 2015.

Although the aggregate peak capacity of current projects totals 28 mb/d, they reach peak at different times and then decline, so the actual gross cumulative capacity addition in any given year will inevitably fall some way short of the aggregate. In 2010, gross capacity additions are expected to reach about 6.5 mb/d, slightly exceeding projected demand growth.[4] But the additions to capacity from 2011 onwards begin to fall short of net projected demand, as fewer projects are brought on stream, and new projects peak and then decline. Taking account of project slippage, we estimate that the actual addition to capacity in 2015 (over and above the 2007 level) from these projects, based on the observed decline rates by region reported in Chapter 10, amounts to 23 mb/d.[5] This means that other projects beyond those currently in development – most of which would need to be sanctioned within the next two to three years given current lead-times – would need to add a further 7 mb/d of capacity to offset decline and match the net growth in demand. In practice, new projects will undoubtedly be sanctioned. But it is by no means certain that all of the necessary additional capacity will be forthcoming. If actual capacity additions fall short of this amount, at the very least spare production capacity would be squeezed and oil prices would rise.

Outlook for investment to 2030

In the longer term, upstream investment will hinge on market conditions and the policy and regulatory environment. While access to capital is unlikely to constitute a major hurdle to investment, there is considerable uncertainty about future costs, the level of prices needed to make new investments attractive, changes in regulatory and fiscal regimes, and the willingness of resource-rich countries to undertake new investment.

In the Reference Scenario, oil production is projected to rise from 85 mb/d in 2006 to 106 mb/d in 2030 and gas production from 3.0 tcm to 4.4 tcm, taking account of the economic viability of developing new reserves and various constraints on investment in each region. These projections imply a need for cumulative investment in the upstream oil and gas sector of around $8.4 trillion (in year-2007 dollars) over 2007-2030, or $350 billion per year. Oil accounts for $5 trillion and gas for $3.3 trillion (Table 13.3).

Oil and gas investment falls in the second half of the projection period: the average annual rate of upstream oil and gas investment in 2007-2012, derived from our bottom-up analysis, is estimated at over $500 billion (in year-2007 dollars). This rate is projected to dip to about $300 billion in 2016-2030, mainly because of the projected shift in output to lower-cost regions, notably the Middle East – by far the world's lowest cost region. In short, the opportunities for international companies to invest in non-OPEC regions will diminish as the resource base contracts, eventually leaving the national companies to take on a larger responsibility for investment where the remaining oil and gas reserves are much cheaper to develop. Projected upstream investment is nonetheless considerably higher in this *Outlook* than in last year's edition, reflecting the recent continued increase in unit costs and the assumption that they stabilise in 2008, rather than fall back as previously assumed (see above).

13

---

4. Effective spre OPEC production capacity is projected to rise 2.5 mb/d in 2008 to over 4 mb/d in 2009 and 2010 – equal to around 5% of global demand, according to the July 2008 edition of the IEA *Medium-Term Oil Market Report* (IEA, 2008).
5. This assessment assumes that project slippage, caused by shortages of labour, materials, rigs and other equipment, remains a major problem. Project delays are currently running at around one year, while delays at 20 major projects (excluding Kashagan and Thunder Horse, which have been subject to very long delays already) are estimated at around 15 months (IEA, 2008).

Table 13.3 ● Cumulative upstream investment by region in the Reference Scenario, 2007-2030 ($ billion in year-2007 dollars)

Region	Conventional oil	Non-conventional oil	Total oil	Gas	Total oil and gas
North America	644	268	913	1 044	1 957
Europe	224	1	225	349	574
Pacific	70	-	70	121	192
OECD	**939**	**269**	**1 208**	**1 514**	**2 722**
E. Europe/Eurasia	982	-	982	535	1 516
Russia	*487*	*-*	*487*	*407*	*893*
Asia	391	89	480	431	910
China	*180*	*88*	*268*	*151*	*419*
India	*49*	*-*	*49*	*46*	*95*
Middle East	807	24	832	297	1 128
Africa	824	8	832	360	1 192
Latin America	662	42	703	186	889
Non-OECD	**3 665**	**163**	**3 829**	**1 808**	**5 637**
World	**4 604**	**432**	**5 036**	**3 322**	**8 358**

Around two-thirds of global cumulative upstream investment to 2030 is projected to be made in non-OECD countries (Figure 13.16). Investments in OECD countries are large, despite the small and declining share of these countries in world oil and gas production. In contrast, investment in Middle East countries represents only 13% of total investment, because of low unit costs in this region. The share of this region in world oil supply rises from 30% in 2007 to 37% in 2030, while its share of gas supply increases from 11% to 23%.

Figure 13.16 ● Cumulative upstream investment by region in the Reference Scenario, 2007-2030

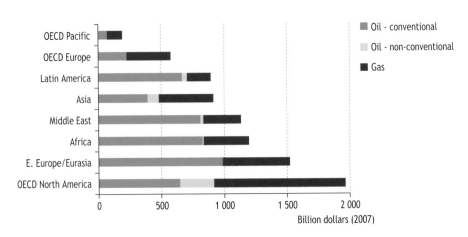

Potential barriers to upstream investment

Over the period to 2012, the total amount of investment that will be made in upstream oil and gas facilities is known with a reasonable degree of confidence. Investment plans may change in response to sudden changes in market conditions and some projects may be cancelled, delayed or accelerated for various reasons. But the actual gross additions to production capacity and the net additions (taking account of estimated decline rates at existing fields over that period) are unlikely to depart much from those projected in this *Outlook*. However, beyond the next five years or so, there is considerable uncertainty about the prospects for upstream investment, costs and, therefore, the rate of capacity additions. Few investment decisions that will determine capacity additions after 2012 have yet been taken, with the exception of some very large projects, such as the Kashagan development in Kazakhstan (where production is now expected to start up only in 2014 at the earliest, peaking later at around 0.8 mb/d).

In our judgment, the policies, regulatory frameworks and prices assumed in the Reference Scenario could together create an investment environment conducive to stimulating the amount of investment projected above for 2007-2030 at the unit costs assumed. Nonetheless, the opportunities and incentives for private and publicly owned companies actually to undertake all of this investment are still very uncertain. In reality, investment in particular regions may fall short of that required to meet the projected level of supply — not least because prices and costs could turn out to be markedly different from those assumed. Host government policies, including licensing and fiscal arrangements, could shift and the overall investment and business climate may deteriorate, making upstream investments riskier and less attractive. Uncertainty about future climate-change and other environmental policies adds to investment risk (see Part C). Moreover, logistical, practical and technical factors may constrain the ability of oil and gas companies to launch upstream developments in a timely way. Not all of the uncertainties are on the down-side: in the longer term, technological advances, lower input prices and a more favourable policy environment could open up new opportunities for investment and help lower costs. Nonetheless, there is a regional dimension to this issue. Were investment in the lowest-cost regions — notably the Middle East — to fall short of that projected in the Reference Scenario, investment in other regions would need to be much higher, because of the higher costs, thus increasing overall upstream capital spending and requiring higher oil prices. The main potential barriers to upstream investment are reviewed below.

Depletion policies of resource-rich countries

The depletion policies of the small number of countries that hold the bulk of the world's remaining oil and gas reserves will be critical to investment and future capacity expansions — whether carried out by national or international companies. Paradoxically, the surge in oil prices in the past five years and the prospect of prices remaining at historically high levels may make it more likely that some of those countries will decide to deplete their resources more slowly, simply because they have less need for additional revenue in the near term and may prefer to keep resources in the ground to benefit future generations. Were the oil-supply curve to bend backwards in this way, a vicious circle might emerge of lower investment leading to tighter supply, which could in turn push up prices and revenues even more and further reduce the incentive to invest, eventually forcing the world to shift the pattern of consumption away from oil.

Higher prices have transformed the economic well-being of those hydrocarbon-producing states for which oil and gas export earnings represent a large share of national income. Most such hydrocarbon-dependent states are members of OPEC. The total annual oil and gas export revenues (the value of total exports at prevailing international prices) of OPEC countries more than doubled between 2000 and 2007 in real terms, to a record $732 billion (Figure 13.17). In the Reference Scenario, OPEC revenues are projected to continue to grow, reaching a total of just over $2 trillion in 2030. Oil remains by far the biggest contributor to OPEC revenues, but the share of gas grows. The share of total OPEC revenues in world GDP (at market exchange rates) rises from 1.3% in 2007 to around 2% in 2030. Six Middle East countries — Saudi Arabia, Iran, Iraq, Kuwait, Qatar and the UAE — accounted for over 70% of these revenues in 2007, a share that is projected to remain broadly constant through to 2030. In these countries, much of the increase in revenues has been used to pay off external debt and acquire external assets, mostly financial. Russia's oil and gas revenues also grow, from about $229 billion in 2007 to just over $400 billion in 2030.

Figure 13.17 ● OPEC oil and gas export revenues in the Reference Scenario

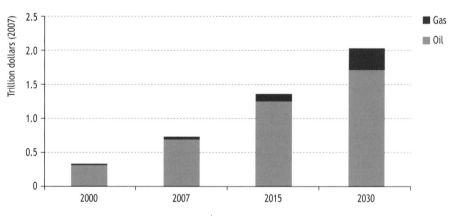

Note: Revenues are the economic value of net exports (production minus domestic consumption) at prevailing international prices.

Source: IEA database and analysis.

Unlike in the 1970s and early 1980s in the aftermath of the first two oil shocks, government spending has increased much less quickly than the growth in revenues. This reflects, partly, caution about how long higher prices will persist, but also the limited capacity of these economies to absorb the additional revenues without stoking up inflation in the non-tradable goods sector. As a result, the government budgets in all these countries have swung heavily into surplus. Most countries have long-term investment funds for short-term stabilisation purposes or to ensure income for future generations, and have rules that limit public spending to revenue generated under very conservative price assumptions.

Concern that over-investment in the upstream sector may lead to lower prices is also likely to temper capital spending. The oil price required by OPEC countries to balance the external account has risen sharply in recent years, reflecting increased domestic spending (private and public) and rising import costs — partly the result of the fall in the dollar. According to a recent report, the price per barrel of oil equivalent to West Texas Intermediate ranges from $4 in Qatar to $94 in Venezuela (PFC, 2008). The price is projected to rise further in 2009, on the assumption of unchanged domestic policies (Figure 13.18).

Figure 13.18 ● OPEC countries' external account price thresholds to balance the external account

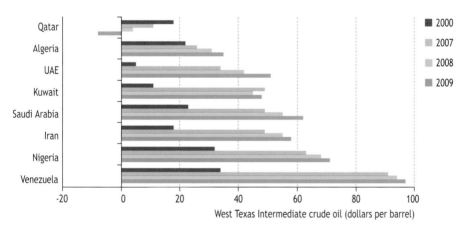

West Texas Intermediate crude oil (dollars per barrel)

Source: PFC (2008).

There are signs that higher prices and revenues are blunting, rather than boosting, incentives to invest more in upstream developments in some countries — even though the increase in revenues is generally more than sufficient to cover the capital required for new projects and the potential net present value of those projects has risen sharply. King Abdullah of Saudi Arabia announced in April 2008 that he wants new oil discoveries to be kept in the ground to preserve some of the Kingdom's oil wealth for future generations. Other Arabian Gulf countries, including Qatar, have scaled back plans to boost oil and gas production capacity, citing the need to preserve resources for the long term. Uncertainty about the future call on OPEC oil supplies in the face of much higher prices and the risk of investing in capacity that may not be needed (especially if consuming countries were to take strong action to curb demand growth) are also, somewhat perversely, encouraging producers to take a "wait and see" approach to major new investments. Thus, there is a real and growing risk that upstream investment in hydrocarbon-rich countries will falter once the current wave of projects has come to an end.

Profitable opportunities for international companies to invest

Most investment in dollar terms continues to be carried out by privately owned international oil and gas companies. Yet the opportunities for them to invest in new developments have diminished in recent years, as a growing number of resource-rich countries have imposed restrictions on foreign participation in favour of national companies. This factor is discussed in detail in Chapter 14. Even where it is, in principle, possible for international companies to invest, the licensing and fiscal terms or the general business climate may be a deterrent. The objective of all host governments is to strike the right balance between maximising their share of the rent — the difference between the cost of production and the selling price of the oil produced — and maintaining investment at their chosen strategic level. But, in practice, short-term revenue needs may over-ride the longer-term considerations: exploiting investment already made, the government may raise taxes and royalty rates to increase revenues quickly, at the expense of new investment.

The average tax take — the share of all taxes and royalties in the wholesale price of oil and gas produced — has risen significantly in most countries in recent years, reflecting the surge in prices and rents. In some cases, the government take has risen to such an extent that new investment has been discouraged. Investment in gas drilling slumped in 2007 in Alberta in Canada, in response to proposals by the provincial government to raise royalty rates. Similarly, in Venezuela, a sharp increase in royalty rates in 2007 and plans in 2008 to introduce a windfall tax on exports made by private operators appear to have dampened interest in investing in new upstream projects. The slump in drilling and decline in Russian oil production since the end of 2007 is largely due to earlier changes in the tax regime that effectively ensure that the government takes the bulk of the additional rent that accrues as prices rise, dampening incentives to invest. A more recent change reduced taxes in order to stimulate upstream investment and production.

The stability of the upstream investment regime is a critical factor in oil companies' evaluation of investment opportunities. Retrospective increases in taxes, applied to sunk investments, tend to lead investors to raise their hurdle rates of return when evaluating future investments to accommodate the higher perceived risk. Changes in environmental regulations can also prevent or deter investment. Growing concerns over the ecological impact of drilling in the Amazon jungle in Peru, for example, are likely to hamper efforts to boost investment and production. The discussion or actual introduction of taxes or penalties on carbon emissions from oil and gas production or on gas flaring also affects the attractiveness of new investments. Norway already has in place a tax on carbon emissions, while Nigeria recently announced that it will impose penalties on gas flaring from 2009. Australia is actively discussing taxing carbon emissions, which would affect gas investment.

Political constraints

Internal political and broader geopolitical factors may hold back upstream investment in many countries, in spite of favourable official policies and strong economic incentives. Several OPEC countries, notably Kuwait and Iran, have struggled to reach agreement on how best to attract the investment needed to meet official targets for production capacity, with the result that expansion projects have been delayed or cancelled. Investment in Iran continues to be impeded by US and European sanctions and political pressure from other countries related to Iran's nuclear activities. Political resistance to changes in the upstream regime in Mexico that would give private companies a bigger role in exploration and development have impeded efforts to expand investment in order to offset the decline in production from existing fields.

War or civil conflict is a powerful deterrent in certain regions. No major oil company has yet decided to invest in Iraq, though the new government is negotiating exploration and development deals with several international companies. How soon large-scale investment in Iraq could begin and how quickly it could increase depend on political factors and a continuing improvement in security in the country, both of which remain highly uncertain. The possibility that heightened geopolitical tensions in other parts of the Middle East and in other regions may discourage or prevent inward investment in upstream developments and related LNG and export-pipeline projects can never be discounted. The long-term prospects for investment in Nigeria, for example, remain extremely uncertain in view of the worsening conflict in the Niger Delta, which holds the bulk of the country's remaining oil and gas resources.

Availability of people and equipment

Shortages of skilled labour and equipment have already contributed to the surge in upstream costs and project delays in recent years, and may continue to place a physical constraint on the rate at which the upstream industry is able to invest in and develop reserves. Labour shortages could be the biggest obstacle, given the long lead-times in recruiting and training suitable staff. The upstream labour force has contracted since the 1990s as a result of reduced recruitment and lay-offs, partly due to a cost-cutting drive, and — more recently — to a surge in retirements as the average age of oil-company employees has risen. In the United States, the average oil-company employee is approaching 50 years old and more than half of all employees are due to retire within the next decade (NPC, 2007a). At the same time, staffing needs for new projects will rise. For example, the 160 offshore rigs currently being built will need to be staffed by about 30 000 people, though some will come from rigs that will be retired.

Labour shortages are currently most acute among the most specialised workers, such as design engineers, who take longest to train. This has led to a widening of the gap between the demand and supply for mid-career technical staff (NPC, 2007b): in North America and Europe, the shortfall is expected to exceed 15% of demand by 2012 (Figure 13.19). Recent studies by Schlumberger Business Consulting predict a severe shortage of university gradates in petroleum-related disciplines in North America,

13

Russia and the Middle East, though surplus graduates in other regions — notably southeast Asia — could, in principle, bridge the gap to the extent that linguistic, cultural and legal barriers can be overcome (Rostand, 2005 and 2006).

Not surprisingly, oil companies are responding to these labour shortages by offering incentives to staff to delay retirement, by re-hiring retired employees and by recruiting overseas staff. In Canada's Athabasca oil-sands region, a large number of engineers and labourers have been recruited from countries as far away as China. The Canadian government has even offered citizenship to foreigners working on oil-sands projects as an incentive to attract and retain skilled workers. Saudi Aramco has launched an initiative to create domestic engineering, procurement and construction (EPC) companies to operate as joint ventures with existing international operators. The aim is two-fold: to establish a ready source of EPC capability that can quickly respond to Aramco tenders for new projects at more predictable costs and to stimulate local employment and economic development.

Figure 13.19 ● Demand for and supply of mid-career petrotechnical professionals aged 30 to 39 in North America and Europe

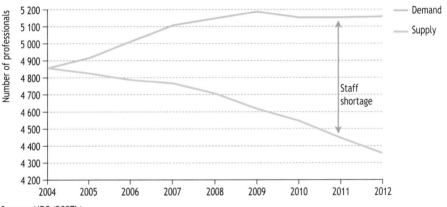

Source: NPC (2007b).

Although demand for labour and equipment will undoubtedly increase in the coming decades, current high salaries and day-rates would be expected to stimulate increased capacity in the longer term, as more students opt for petroleum-rated disciplines and trades, and service companies invest in new equipment (including rigs). There are signs that the number of university students studying petroleum-related disciplines and the training of lower-skilled workers, such as pipe welders and drilling labourers, is already on the rise. Many of the new graduates entering the field are in China and India. The latter country is conveniently located for migration to the Middle East, Russia and Central Asia, where much of the increase in oil and gas supplies is expected to occur. Several oil companies have stepped up their in-house training programmes and have strengthened their ties with universities. The construction of new rigs and related drilling equipment has also picked up strongly in recent years (see above).

The question is whether that increase in capacity will be big enough to meet rising demand. The upstream industry is inherently cyclical, as each period of scarcity in oil-services capacity has been followed by a period of over-supply. It is likely that the industry will enter at least one period of over-capacity of labour and equipment, such as in the 1980s and 1990s, at some point over the projection period; but when that will occur and how long it will last are difficult to predict. Many in the industry believe that labour and equipment shortages will persist well into the next decade, even if the rate of cost inflation tempers in the near future. The credit crunch, which has reportedly led to the cancellation of some orders to build new rigs, may exacerbate such shortages.

13

CHAPTER 14

THE STRUCTURE OF THE UPSTREAM INDUSTRY

Who will do what?

H I G H L I G H T S

- A new world order is emerging in the upstream oil and gas industry. National oil companies control most reserves, but account for a much smaller share of current production. This is set to change. In the Reference Scenario, their share of world oil production rises from about 57% in 2007 to 62% in 2030, accounting for about 80% of total incremental oil production.

- In most of the countries with the largest oil and gas reserves, national companies dominate the oil and gas industry; foreign companies are either not allowed to own and develop reserves, or are subject to restrictions. Higher oil prices and a growing conviction among political leaders that national companies serve the nation's interests better than private and foreign oil companies have boosted the confidence and aspirations of national companies, some of them rivalling the international companies in technical capability and efficiency.

- The international oil companies, which have traditionally dominated the global oil and gas industry, are increasingly being squeezed by the growing power of the national companies and by dwindling reserves and production in mature basins outside OPEC countries. The super-majors have been struggling to replace their proven reserves and expand production. The share of their cash earnings that is returned to shareholders has been growing.

- How the structure of the global oil and gas industry evolves in the coming decades will have important implications for investment, production capacity and prices. The increasing dominance of national companies may make it less certain that the investment projected in this *Outlook* will actually be made. The long-term policies of the major resource-rich countries may favour slower depletion of their resources. And while some national companies, like Saudi Aramco, are strong in most areas, others may be less well placed to address financing, technical and managerial challenges in bringing new upstream capacity on stream.

- Stronger partnerships between the national and international oil companies could help ensure adequate supplies in the long term. The mutual benefits that could accrue are compelling: the national companies control most of the world's remaining reserves, but in some cases lack the technology, capital and/or skilled personnel to develop them efficiently; the international companies are opportunity-constrained, but have the finance and management skills, and technology to help national companies develop their reserves.

- The governments of producing and consuming countries have a role to play in encouraging this development: producer governments through institutional, regulatory and fiscal reforms aimed at attracting foreign participation and at getting the national companies to operate more commercially; and consumer governments through high-level dialogue and multi-lateral trade and development agencies.

The emergence of a new world order for oil

The last decade has seen a rapid transformation in the structure of the upstream oil and gas industry, involving in particular a wave of mergers and acquisitions among the international and private domestic oil companies, and a renaissance in the market power of state-owned national oil companies. Higher oil and gas prices and efficiency gains throughout their supply chains have bolstered the profits and free cash-flow of the international oil companies. Yet they face increasing difficulties in obtaining access to profitable new investment opportunities and maintaining production levels. The national oil companies in the leading resource-holding countries are increasingly taking on the task of developing new fields themselves, often with the help of oilfield-services companies. They are, in many cases, seeking to expand internationally. The increasing ambitions of the national companies reflect a trend in emerging economies towards greater direct state control over natural resources, a phenomenon commonly referred to as "resource nationalism". There are few signs of any reversal of this trend on the horizon.

The evolution of the structure of the global upstream industry matters, because the corporate objectives, technical competences, operational capabilities and financial resources of the various players differ markedly — both among and between the national and international companies. This has implications for the scale and types of investment that will be made and the way producing assets are managed. There are concerns that the national companies may, in general, be less willing than the international companies to develop and produce remaining oil and gas reserves on the scale required to meet global demand (see Chapter 13). They may also be less well placed financially and technically to develop reserves in an efficient manner. These concerns have already contributed to tensions on international oil markets and will grow as upstream developments become more technically challenging and expensive. They could have implications for the long-term security of the world's oil and gas supplies.

On the other hand, national companies are becoming more technically proficient and better able to handle challenging new developments with the help of the oilfield-services companies. New forms of partnership between the national and international companies could evolve. The evolution of the interplay between the national oil companies in resource-rich countries, the oilfield-services companies and the international companies will, therefore, be central to investment and production prospects going forward.

National oil companies currently account for 51% of world oil and gas production, the super-majors for 12%; other integrated international oil companies and wholly upstream companies account for the rest (Figure 14.1). The national companies' share of world proven reserves is much higher, at 71%. For oil alone, the super-majors own only 3% of reserves, yet produce 12% of the world's supply. This imbalance suggests that the share of the national companies in world oil and gas production could grow markedly over the longer term, though much will depend on the policy of host governments on the appropriate rate of depletion of national assets and the benefits of working with international companies through partnerships, production-sharing agreements or other types of co-operative arrangements. The national companies' share of production has risen in recent years, partly because of production-sharing deals that reduce the allocation to foreign partners as the oil price rises.

Figure 14.1 ● World oil and gas reserves and production by company, 2007

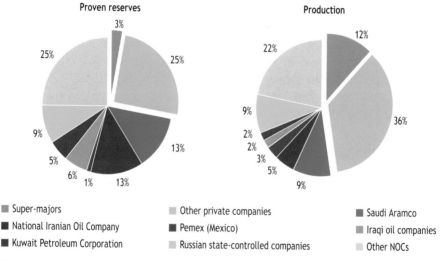

Note: Production shares are based on preliminary data for gas for 2007. The super-majors are ExxonMobil, Shell, BP, Total and Chevron.

Sources: *O&GJ* (2007); IEA databases and analysis.

In most of the countries with the largest oil reserves, national companies dominate the oil and gas industry; foreign companies are either not allowed to own and develop reserves, or are subject to restrictions under prevailing laws and regulations (Figure 14.2). Such restrictions have been put in place both for constitutional and operational reasons: some host governments are obliged by law and local political expectation to retain direct control over their natural resources and some prefer to exercise short-term management control over the reservoirs in order to maintain flexibility in their depletion policies. Among the 20 leading countries for oil reserves, only four – Brazil, Canada, Norway and the United States – give foreign companies unrestricted access to reserves. In four countries – Iran, Kuwait, Mexico and Saudi

Arabia — no foreign company is allowed to explore for or develop oil other than as a sub-contractor or supplier of technical oilfield services to the national companies or other local firms.[1] Iraq effectively remains closed to foreign investment until parliamentary approval is secured to a proposed oil law that would open up the upstream and security is improved, though the Iraqi government is currently negotiating service contracts with foreign companies, which would be remunerated in cash or oil. Several countries permit foreign investment only in the form of production-sharing deals, whereby ownership of and control over reserves remains with the national company.

Figure 14.2 ● Foreign company access to proven oil reserves, end-2007

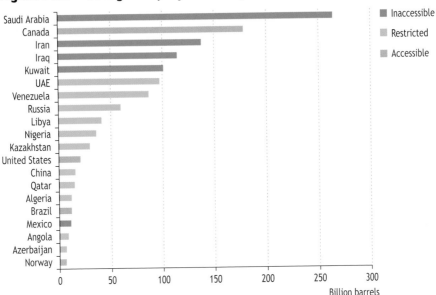

Sources: *O&GJ* (2007); IEA databases and analysis.

The resurgence of the national oil companies

The last decade has seen a dramatic revival of the financial health and market power of national oil companies,[2] helped by a combination of rising oil prices and a growing conviction among some political leaders that such companies serve the nation's interests better than private and foreign oil companies. The national oil companies,

---

1. In these countries, no foreign contractor is allowed to "book" oil reserves, *i.e.* declare ownership of any reserves they find or help to produce under stock market regulations listed in the United States, Canada or Europe. Up to now, Kuwait has permitted international companies to provide technical services to the Kuwait Petroleum Corporation (KPC), but only under short-term contracts. KPC is reportedly negotiating with those companies longer-term contracts that would, for the first time, link technical and commercial arrangements to performance — an approach favoured by the international companies.
2. The term refers here to any oil and/or gas company involved in upstream activities that is wholly or majority owned by the state.

the largest of which are based in the Middle East, Russia and Venezuela, increasingly dominate world oil and gas supply: of the top 25 producing companies, 17 are national companies (Table 14.1). Most of them continue to focus on domestic operations – often along the entire supply chain and often including both oil and gas – though some companies are increasingly investing outside their national borders. In some countries, there is more than one national company, one or more of which may be partially privately owned, for example in Russia and China.[3] In each of the 13 OPEC countries, there is a single, wholly state-owned company with exclusive or special rights over most upstream activities and, in some cases, downstream operations, too.[4] With the exception of Iran, Kuwait and Saudi Arabia, all OPEC national companies participate in joint ventures with foreign companies to develop domestic resources. Norway, Mexico and Turkey are the only OECD countries that still have national companies with upstream operations of any size: StatoilHydro is 62.5% owned by the Norwegian state, while Mexico's Pemex and Turkey's TPAO are both wholly state-owned. All the major *producing* countries outside the OECD have national companies.

In several resource-rich countries, tentative moves to open the upstream sector to direct investment by international oil companies have either been reversed, as in Venezuela, or have stalled, as in Kuwait. Saudi Arabia dropped a scheme to open up the gas sector to large-scale exploration and development in 2003, following difficult negotiations with the super-majors, but subsequently negotiated smaller deals with several international companies. In other countries, the market position of national companies has expanded. In Russia, the bulk of reserves and producing assets are once again in the hands of state-owned firms – principally Gazprom (the world's largest gas company) and Rosneft (an integrated oil company) – as the government has sought to reassert strategic control over the sector. Most Russian oil and gas companies had been privatised in the 1990s. Foreign company upstream assets have been partially or wholly transferred to the national company in Venezuela, Bolivia and Ecuador.

National companies are extremely diverse. The most advanced, such as Norway's StatoilHydro, Brazil's Petrobras and Malaysia's Petronas, are comparable in size, efficiency, technological sophistication and management practices to the larger international companies. Saudi Aramco, which has invested heavily in training and research, is widely recognised as the most technically advanced of the Middle East national companies. Others, particularly in some Middle East countries, lack high-quality human resources and advanced technical capabilities, and focus mainly on operating existing facilities rather than actively developing new reserves.

A common characteristic of all national oil companies is that their corporate objectives go beyond the maximisation of the return on capital to shareholders (*i.e.* the state and, in some cases, private investors, too). They are typically required to contribute to broader national goals, including promoting industrialisation and economic and social development, ensuring energy security and supporting foreign policy (Marcel, 2006).

3. The three national companies in China are all fully state-owned but have listed subsidiaries, which are partially privately owned.
4. Iran unveiled plans in early 2008 to partially privatise its national company, National Iranian Oil Company, through the sale of a minority stake in a new holding company with assets worth a total of $90 billion.

The majority of national companies are required to supply oil products and/or gas to the domestic market at subsidised prices. This is the case for all of the national oil companies in OPEC countries and for many others in large consuming countries, including China, India, Indonesia, Brazil and Mexico. In many cases, some or all of the resulting financial losses incurred by the national company are covered by payments out of the state budget. Most national companies are expected to provide jobs for local workers, to give preference to local suppliers in procuring goods and services, and to encourage the transfer of technical knowledge and expertise to local firms. These wider, often non-commercial objectives may diminish the national companies' technical and economic efficiency by comparison with private firms (see below). Most national companies have close ties with their government owners, with geopolitical and strategic goals explicitly or implicitly superimposed on their purely commercial objectives.

Table 14.1 ● **Key indicators of leading oil and gas companies, 2007**
(ranked by total oil and gas production)

Name	Country	State ownership (%)	Proven reserves (end-2007)		Production		Financial indicators ($ billion)	
			Oil (billion barrels)	Gas (tcm)	Oil (mb/d)	Gas (bcm)	Gross revenue	Net income after tax
Saudi Aramco	Saudi Arabia	100	264.3	7.1	10.9	68.4	168.0	n.a.
Gazprom	Russia	51	10.0	29.8*	0.9	548.5	92.2	23.0
NIOC	Iran	100	138.4	26.8	4.4	106.7	51.0	n.a.
Pemex	Mexico	100	12.2	0.4	3.5	56.0	103.9	4.3
ExxonMobil	US	-	11.1	1.9	2.6	97.0	390.3	40.6
BP	UK	-	10.1	1.3	2.4	84.2	291.4	21.2
CNPC	China	100	22.4	2.3	2.8	57.8	131.9	17.7
Shell	UK	-	4.9	1.2	1.9	84.9	355.8	31.9
Sonatrach	Algeria	100	12.2	4.5	1.6	90.0	57.0	7.6
Adnoc	UAE-Abu Dhabi	100	92.2	5.6	2.7	22.5	17.1	n.a.
PDVSA	Venezuela	100	87.0	4.7	2.6	25.0	96.2	n.a.
Chevron	US	-	7.1	0.6	1.8	51.9	214.1	18.7
KPC	Kuwait	100	101.5	1.6	2.2	12.0	83.4	n.a.
INOC	Iraq	100	115.0	3.2	2.3	4.3	n.a.	n.a.
Total	France	-	5.8	0.7	1.5	50.0	187.6	18.6
Petrobras	Brazil	56	9.6	0.4	1.9	23.7	112.6	12.2
Rosneft	Russia	80	13.4	0.2	2.0	15.7	29.9	12.9
Lukoil	Russia	-	15.7	0.8	2.0	14.0	82.2	9.5
LNOC	Libya	100	32.4	0.9	1.9	10.9	n.a.	n.a.
ConocoPhillips	US	-	6.3	0.7	1.1	52.6	194.5	11.9
Eni	Italy	-	3.3	0.6	1.0	42.3	124.7	14.8
Qatar Petroleum	Qatar	100	10.9	18.3	1.0	42.9	192.4	n.a.

Table 14.1 ● **Key indicators of leading oil and gas companies, 2007**
(ranked by total oil and gas production) (continued)

Name	Country	State ownership (%)	Proven reserves (end 2007)		Production		Financial indicators ($ billion)	
			Oil (billion barrels)	Gas (tcm)	Oil (mb/d)	Gas (bcm)	Gross revenue	Net income after tax
Petronas	Malaysia	100	7.9	3.0	0.8	57.3	53.6	14.4
NNPC	Nigeria	100	22.0	3.2	1.4	18.3	n.a.	n.a.
StatoilHydro	Norway	63	2.4	0.6	1.1	34.7	68.1	7.6
TNK-BP	Russia	-	7.9	0.1	1.4	8.5	38.7	5.3
Surgutneftegas	Russia	-	7.4	0.4	1.3	14.1	23.3	3.4
Repsol YPF	Spain	-	1.0	0.2	0.5	32.3	77.5	5.5
Sinopec	China	100	3.0	0.2	0.8	8.0	154.7	7.7
ONGC	India	100	4.1	0.5	0.5	22.3	24.0	4.9
Turkmengas	Turkmenistan	100	-	2.9	-	52.8	n.a.	n.a.
EnCana	United States	-	1.3	0.4	0.1	37.7	21.4	0.9
EGPC	Egypt	100	1.9	1.0	0.3	22.4	n.a.	n.a.
PDO	Oman	100	3.4	0.6	0.4	15.0	11.4	n.a.
Sonangol	Angola	100	4.0	0.3	0.7	0.8	n.a.	n.a.
Devon	US	-	1.0	0.1	0.2	24.5	11.5	3.6
BG	UK	-	0.5	0.3	0.2	26.6	16.7	3.6
Anadarko	US	-	1.0	0.2	0.3	19.7	15.9	3.8
Apache	US	-	1.1	0.2	0.3	18.6	10.0	2.8
Occidental	US	-	2.2	0.1	0.4	7.3	20.1	5.4
CNR	Canada	-	1.4	0.1	0.3	14.0	11.7	2.4
Tatneft	Russia	-	6.1	<0.1	0.5	0.7	13.9	1.7
Novatek	Russia	-	0.4	0.7	0.1	28.5	2.4	0.7
CNOOC	China	100	1.6	0.2	0.4	5.8	12.0	3.5
Inpex	Japan	-	1.1	0.1	0.2	10.9	8.0	1.1
Kazmunaigas	Kazakhstan	100	3.0	0.1	0.4	3.0	4.0	1.3
Talisman	Canada	-	0.6	0.1	0.2	10.5	8.8	1.9
Marathon	US	-	0.7	0.1	0.2	9.6	64.6	4.0
Ecopetrol	Ecuador	100	1.0	0.1	0.3	0.1	11.1	2.6
SPC	Syria	100	2.5	0.2	0.2	5.5	n.a.	n.a.

* Explored natural gas reserves (categories A+B+C1 in Gazprom's accounts) which are considered to be comparable to proven reserves.
Note: National companies are shaded.
Sources: Company annual reports; IEA analysis.

14

The growing maturity of some national companies is reflected in their expanding technical capabilities and international expansion. Some have invested heavily in developing in-house expertise, with the aim of reducing their reliance on partnerships with international companies, extracting more of the value added from oil-sector activities and contributing to broader economic and social development. National companies have generally suffered less than the international companies from manpower shortages, as they were largely sheltered from the boom-bust cycle of the 1980s and 1990s in the international upstream sector. The national companies' growing experience and capabilities have enabled them to contract directly with oilfield-services companies, in some cases by-passing the international companies completely. The growing importance of services companies as developers and owners of technology, which can be licensed to operators, has helped to facilitate this development (Box 14.1). Some national companies, notably Petrobras and StatoilHydro, have emerged as world leaders in deepwater drilling.

The national companies, especially in net oil-importing (consuming) countries such as China and India, are also expanding internationally, mainly in competition with international companies. National companies accounted for a record one-third of global upstream mergers and acquisition (M&A) spending in 2006, the bulk of which was cross-border (Herold and Harrison Lovegrove, 2007). They were the buyers in the largest transaction in every region outside North America, accounting for four of the ten largest transactions worldwide. National companies' share of global M&A fell slightly to around 29% in 2007, though the value of deals outside their base countries remained level at around $13 billion (Herold and Harrison Lovegrove, 2008). Several national companies now have significant upstream producing assets overseas (Figure 14.3). Others, including Saudi Aramco, have invested in downstream operations. Recent exploration bidding rounds in non-OECD countries, including Algeria, Libya and Egypt, have attracted increasing numbers of national companies. National companies are generally more willing to accept involvement in non-oil related infrastructure projects, such as roads, schools and hospitals, in order to gain access to upstream assets.

For producing countries, internationalisation is motivated by strategic and economic considerations. These include securing access to markets, capturing additional value from their oil and gas production, reducing their exposure to volatile crude oil prices, gaining access to skills and technology, and expanding the business in the long term (Fryklund, 2008). Although security of supply is often cited as the principal objective of overseas investment by national companies in consuming countries, a desire to seek out profitable business opportunities and to leverage the company's technical and financial resources is also often a major driver. This would appear to be the case with the Chinese national companies, CNPC, Sinopec and CNOOC, which have been recently among the most active national companies in building up portfolios of overseas assets (IEA, 2007).

Box 14.1 ● The rise of the oilfield-services companies

Oilfield-services companies provide a range of services related to oil and gas exploration and production, but do not typically produce petroleum themselves. These services include seismic data acquisition, processing and analysis, well drilling, completion, evaluation and stimulation, and production-related services (well monitoring, production maintenance, flow assurance and enhanced recovery technologies). In addition, oil companies increasingly sub-contract their information technology and systems integration. The customers of oilfield-services companies include national, international and private domestic oil companies. The services companies have grown rapidly in recent years with the surge in upstream investment and the growing reliance of national companies for the technical expertise to help them develop their reserves. In some cases, they are used in preference to their own domestic service companies. In a variant of the customary relationship, Chinese oil companies often make use of domestic contractors who use technologies and equipment purchased from international service companies.

In areas where national oil companies are looking for arrangements other than exploration concessions, production sharing or joint ventures, oilfield-services companies offer an alternative form of partnership and, in so doing, compete with the international companies. In addition to providing a growing range of advanced technologies and services, oilfield-services companies are now able to offer integrated project-management services and even turnkey operations.

The revenue growth rates of the top three service companies – Schlumberger, Halliburton and Baker Hughes – over the period 2005-2007 averaged 25% per annum, mainly through organic growth (but with the scale of the figure explained largely by the big cost increases described in Chapter 13). Oilfield-services companies have increasingly focused on their core upstream business, at the expense of more peripheral activities. Some of them are moving away from their North American bases and establishing an increasingly international presence, thereby reducing their dependency on US natural gas cycles and riding the wave of the expansion of international activity. They have also generally left the drilling activity to major drilling contractors; the offshore market has seen the merger of some of the largest drilling companies, as a result of the high level of investment required for the latest generation of offshore drilling units.

Some of the largest service companies nonetheless offer a nearly complete portfolio of services, including the provision of integrated services, whereby they co-ordinate the activities of several contractors, ranging from well drilling and completion to field development, but without holding equity in the field. Investment in personnel recruiting, training and development has been stepped up. The three largest companies have hired over 15 000 technical staff per year over the last three years, while their R&D expenditures have increased by 15% to 20% per year and now exceed those of most of the international and national oil companies.

14

Internationalisation strategies and priorities vary markedly among the national companies. Strategies include stand-alone investments, strategic partnerships and joint ventures, equity stakes in listed companies, asset swaps and government-to-government deals. Some governments provide diplomatic support to their national companies to gain access to acreage and assets, with mixed success. Nonetheless, most national companies have a long-term ambition to expand internationally, vertically along the supply chain and, in some cases, horizontally across oil, gas and related sectors. Consequently, national companies increasingly compete with each other in the hunt for assets. But partnerships between national companies are also becoming more common. Asian companies have been particularly active in partnering with other national companies in recent years. All three Chinese national companies have joint-venture investments with other national companies, mainly in Africa. In April 2008, India's ONGC agreed to form a joint venture with Venezuela's PDVSA to develop the latter's extra-heavy oil reserves in the Orinoco Belt.

Figure 14.3 ● **Share of national oil and gas companies' upstream production from overseas assets, 2007**

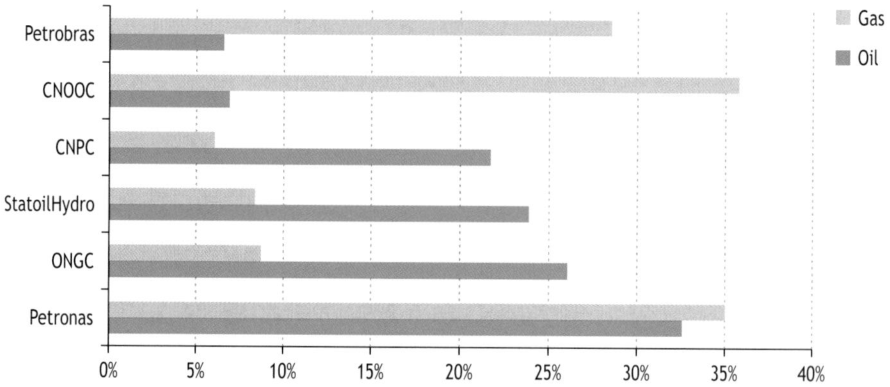

Sources: Company reports; IEA estimates and analysis.

The recent surge in oil prices has unquestionably contributed to the growing confidence and expanding reach of the national companies in producing countries. Higher revenues have reduced or eliminated financial constraints on their funding of capital-spending programmes or mergers and acquisitions. Their upstream investment has risen sharply (see Chapter 13). In addition, many national companies, both producers and consumers, have improved their corporate governance, establishing management structures that are more arms-length from government. Several – including the three Chinese national companies and Gazprom – have become partially privately owned, with their shares listed on major stock exchanges. As a result, they become subject to the same financial and accounting controls as international companies. Stock-market listings have also allowed them to raise capital from private sources to supplement direct government funding.

International oil companies in profitable retreat

The international oil companies, which have traditionally dominated the global oil and gas industry, are increasingly being squeezed by the growing power of the national companies and by dwindling reserves and production in mature basins outside OPEC countries. Their recent record profits and robust balance sheets mask increasing difficulties in acquiring new upstream assets and expanding production in the long term. Indeed, the five "super-majors" — ExxonMobil, Shell, BP, Total and Chevron — have seen a drop in their collective oil production in the last three years, while that of other private companies (mainly smaller international companies) has been flat (Figure 14.4). Part of the decline in the super-majors' output is an automatic consequence of the provision in production-sharing agreements that cuts their share of production as prices rise. Production by the national companies has grown strongly since 2003. Nonetheless, the international companies still rank among the largest oil and gas producers worldwide. The super-majors alone accounted for 12% of world oil production in 2007.

Figure 14.4 ● **Year-on-year increase in oil production of surveyed companies by type of company**

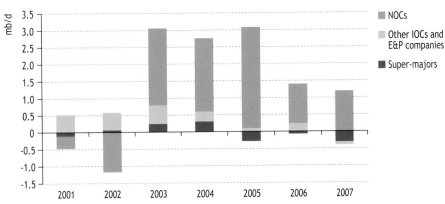

Note: For 50 surveyed companies.
Sources: Company reports; IEA estimates.

Higher oil and gas prices have underpinned a sharp rise in the gross revenues of the international oil companies and in their profits — despite higher operating costs and host-government taxes and royalties. The net income (after tax) of the five super-majors totalled $131 billion in 2007 — a four-fold increase over 2002 (in nominal terms). For most companies, the bulk of the increase in income has come from upstream activities, which have traditionally generated much higher investment returns than refining, marketing and chemicals (even though margins in those sectors have also improved in recent years). For the super-majors, net income rose broadly in line with crude oil prices between 2002 and 2005, but has since grown less rapidly in response to higher government takes and rising costs (Figure 14.5).

Figure 14.5 ● Net income of the super-majors versus the average IEA crude oil import price, 2000-2007

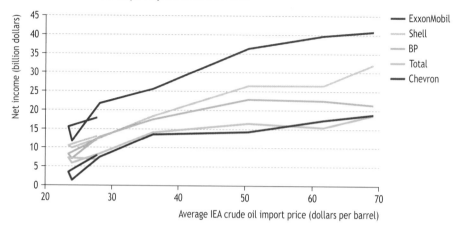

How the international companies have disposed of their revenues reveals much about their corporate strategies. The combined operating cash-flow[5] — a better indicator of the availability of discretionary financial resources than net income — of 20 of the largest companies almost tripled from $118 billion in 2000 to $323 billion in 2006, before falling back slightly to $284 billion in 2007 (Figure 14.6). Half of the increase over the seven years to 2007 was returned to shareholders in the form of equity buybacks (or share repurchases) and dividends. Over that period, almost 36% of operating cash-flow was used in these ways. Buybacks have become more important than dividends, accounting for about one-fifth of total outlays in 2007, compared with less than one-tenth in 2000. The current rate of share buybacks cannot be sustained indefinitely. For example, if ExxonMobil was to maintain its current rate of buybacks, it would cease to be a public company in around 15 years.

Capital spending by the international companies on both exploring for and developing oil and gas reserves has risen significantly, though most of this increase is explained by rising unit costs rather than increased physical activity (see Chapter 13). As a share of operating cash-flow, total spending on exploration and development by the 20 companies surveyed here jumped from 37% in 2000 to a high of 57% in 2003, but has since fluctuated between 40% and 50%. The share devoted to reserve acquisitions from other firms has also fallen in recent years, reflecting both a renewed strategic focus on organic growth and increasing competition from national companies. These trends are explained largely by the spending patterns of the five super-majors, which account for 59% of the total available cash of the 20 largest companies surveyed.

Despite increased spending on exploration, the super-majors have been struggling to replace their proven reserves. Since 2000, their oil and gas reserves-replacement ratio (reserves addition related to production) has averaged 107%, but plunged to 54% in 2007

---

5. Operating cash-flow is a net figure: the amount of cash a company generates from operating activities, less the cost of sales.

Figure 14.6 ● International oil company outlays from operating cash-flow

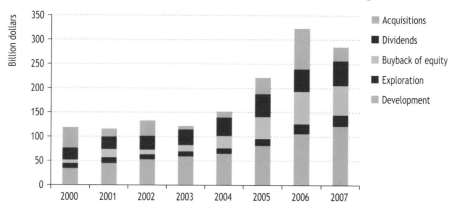

Note: Based on data for 20 companies, including the five super-majors plus Anadarko, Apache, BG, ConocoPhillips, CNR, Eni, Hess, Lukoil, Marathon, Nexen, Occidental, Petro-Canada, Repsol YPF, Talisman and Woodside.

Sources: Company reports.

(Figure 14.7). Smaller international companies have been much more successful. Some 21 other leading companies (including pure exploration and production companies) replaced almost 200% of their production on average between 2000 and 2007. The differences are explained, at least in part, by relatively higher spending by the smaller companies on both acquisitions and exploration.

A lack of opportunities to invest upstream is one of the principal reasons for the apparent under-investment in exploration since the 1990s and the resulting low reserves replacement rates by international oil companies, as most reserves are controlled by national companies. Because of their financial strength and technical and project management skills, the super-majors have a competitive advantage over smaller private and national companies in pursuing complex and "lumpy" projects; but such projects are becoming fewer and farther between outside the OPEC countries and, in any case, carry higher risks. Smaller firms are often better placed to take on the development of smaller new fields and old fields well into decline, both of which account for a growing proportion of capital spending in mature basins, such as the North Sea and onshore North America. Large amounts of prospective North American acreage remain off limits to exploration for environmental reasons. Allied to these problems is a general shortage in recent years of skilled personnel and drilling equipment, which have pushed up rig-rates and the cost of oilfield-services and, in some cases, prompted companies to postpone project approval or to slow completion.

Notwithstanding the limited availability of upstream investment opportunities and bottlenecks in skilled labour and equipment, the relatively low ratio of upstream investment to operating cash-flow among the international companies appears to reflect a deliberate policy of maximising short-term accounting profits. In essence, the management and shareholders (represented by large institutional investors) have

14

Figure 14.7 ● International oil company oil and gas reserves replacement ratio

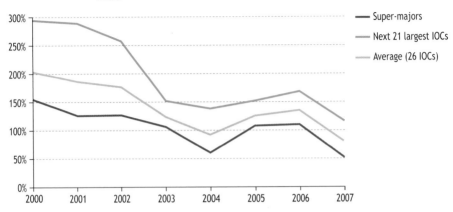

Note: The ratio is calculated as reserve additions divided by production in each year, expressed as a percentage. All series are production-weighted averages. The reserve replacement ratios shown here are based on the US Securities and Exchange Commission (SEC) reporting rules. The vagaries of those rules can result in large year-on-year adjustments to reserves. For example, Shell's ratio was only 17% in 2007, reflecting the effects of deconsolidation of reserves at the Sakhalin-2 project, in which its stake was reduced from 55% to 27.5%. The associated reserves, however, were reduced by much more, as it was previously permitted to book all of them. The sharp fall in 2004 for the super-majors partly reflects a downward restatement of reserves by Shell.

Sources: Company reports; IEA estimates.

judged that it is better to maximise short-run returns by limiting capital spending, so as to return a larger share of cash-flow to shareholders. In recent years, financial markets have focused increasingly on the rate of return to average capital employed (RoACE) - a financial indicator used by markets to benchmark and value oil companies. RoACE automatically falls in the short-term as investment rises, as a smaller proportion of total capital employed is depreciated. Thus, companies with a larger proportion of mature, or legacy, assets tend to achieve a higher RoACE. Since the end of the 1990s, investors appear to have given greater weight to RoACE than to other, more long-term measures of corporate value and performance, such as reserves and production capacity (Osmundsen *et al.*, 2005; Jaffe and Soligo, 2007). In addition, RoACE is usually one of several indicators used to remunerate senior managers. RoACE rose for all of the five super-majors from 2002 to 2005, but has been flat or has fallen for some of them since then (Figure 14.8).

The increased focus on maximising short-run profits is reflected in the highly conservative price assumptions and high hurdle rates of return oil companies use to determine whether or not to invest in specific projects. Most oil companies continue to assume a crude oil price well below actual market levels. For example, BP raised the assumed price of Brent crude oil which it uses to calculate the net present value of projects under evaluation from $40 to $60 per barrel for five years ahead in February 2008, when the market price was close to $100. In a survey of almost 250 oil companies made by Citigroup in December 2007, the gap between the planning price and the price

Figure 14.8 ● Return on average capital employed of the super-majors

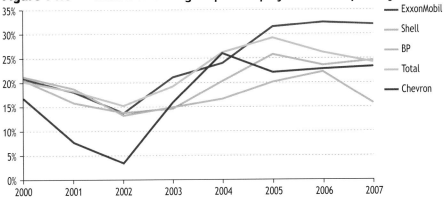

Sources: Company reports.

implied by the futures market had increased to a record level of more than $20 a barrel.[6] Volatile oil prices and the long lead-times associated with major upstream projects increase the risk that prices may fall below assumed planning levels by the time the project comes on stream, though futures and derivatives markets increasingly allow companies to hedge part of their exposure to new investments by taking short positions to match future production flows.

How the strategic direction of the international companies may change in the medium to long term is uncertain. As the super-majors and other international companies face intense competitive pressure from national and oilfield-services companies, as well as from specialist upstream companies, refiners and marketers, some analysts have even questioned whether the fundamental business model of international companies is still viable. In recent years, their response to the changing business environment has been to focus on their core business activities – oil and gas production, refining and processing, chemicals production, transportation, distribution and marketing – and they have, for the most part, resisted the temptation to diversify on a large scale into other energy-supply businesses (with the exception, in some cases, of power generation). There has been a shift towards natural gas and, specifically, liquefied natural gas (LNG) – an area in which the super-majors and some other international companies can play to their technological, financial and management strengths (IEA, 2008). All the super-majors plan to increase their spending on LNG as a share of their total capital spending.

Questions are being raised about whether the international companies should or will retain the traditional vertically integrated business model. One option is to divest or spin off into joint ventures much of their downstream portfolios, including refining, chemicals and retailing. Another is to pursue horizontal integration by investing in alternative energy technologies, including renewables and nuclear power. For

---

6. Reported in *The Financial Times*, 5 February 2008. The latest Lehman Brothers global exploration and production spending survey, published in December 2007, found that the average price at which companies would reduce their investment was $50.65 per barrel of WTI crude oil and $5.23 per thousand cubic feet of natural gas (Lehman Brothers, 2007).

example, Total, which already holds a stake in Areva, the world's leading provider of nuclear power services, announced in 2007 its intention to expand its investments in the nuclear sector and has since joined forces with GDF Suez to develop a nuclear power plant in the United Arab Emirates. BP continues to build up its alternative energy business, having invested $1.5 billion in the three years to 2007 and with a further $1.5 billion planned for 2008. But even with expenditure on this scale, alternative energy represents for these companies only a small part of the overall business. Other companies, including ExxonMobil, have been reluctant so far to commit capital on a large scale to non-hydrocarbons-related activities, on the grounds that they lie outside their area of competence and the profitability of such ventures is uncertain. History indeed suggests that large firms in maturing industries struggle to adapt to new, substitute technologies, as evidenced by the oil companies' unsuccessful foray into renewables and synthetic fuels in the 1970s and 1980s.

Whatever the chosen path, if the international companies are to survive in the long term as major players in the upstream sector, in the face of threats to their market share from the national companies and the oilfield-services companies, they will need to maintain their competitive advantage in managing large-scale, complex upstream projects, notably in frontier regions and in gas. Research and development of cutting-edge technology will remain critical to achieving this goal. All the super-majors and most of the other large international companies have recently sharply increased their research budgets to meet the increasing technical challenges they will face in developing new reserves and to remain competitive with oilfield-services companies. For example, Shell spent $1.2 billion on research in 2007 — almost double what it had spent the year before, while the 2008 research budgets have been increased by BP by 15% to $1.3 billion, and by Total by 20% to $1 billion. But services companies are also increasing their research budgets, on the back of strong cash-flow and higher profits. Schlumberger increased its spending by close to one-fifth in 2007 and by a similar amount in 2008, to a level of almost $900 million. A growing proportion of this spending is devoted to deepwater and gas-related technologies, notably LNG. Shell is building the first-ever floating liquefaction platform, which is set to be deployed in northwest Australia. Carbon capture and management is expected to account for a growing share of research budgets in the future.

Implications for future investment and supply

How the structure of the global oil and gas industry evolves in the coming decades will have important implications for investment, production capacity and prices. The national oil companies' share of global oil and gas production is expected to rise in the medium to long term, by virtue of their control over most of the world's remaining oil resources. In the Reference Scenario, their share of oil production rises from 57% in 2007 to 62% in 2030 — not allowing for the fluctuations in ownership under production-sharing agreements as the crude oil price changes (Figure 14.9).[7] Their share of natural

---

7. In practice, the ownership of some reserves will inevitably change between the host-country national companies and private companies under production-sharing deals as crude oil prices fluctuate.

gas output also rises, from 44% to 55%. These projections assume sufficient investment is made in exploration, development and production to meet demand at the assumed price. This assumption is already in question as a result of the risk that major resource-rich countries may favour slower depletion of their hydrocarbon resources. A further question arises as to the ability and readiness of the national companies, financially and technically, to bring new upstream capacity on stream on a sufficient scale in a timely and efficient way, particularly in the light of their lower efficiency, taken as a group, and their wider remit. For example, the large subsidies to domestic oil product and gas sales that characterise most national companies undercut their profitability and cash-flow and, therefore, limit funds for capital spending, as does the cost of the social and economic programmes that they are often tasked with running. One recent study (Eller *et al.*, 2007) found wholly state-owned firms that sell oil products at subsidised prices to be only 35% as technically efficient as large privately owned international companies which are under no obligation to subsidise. One result of these factors is that national companies are generally less well placed than the international companies to raise capital on favourable terms on international financial markets.

Figure 14.9 ● World oil and gas production by type of company in the Reference Scenario

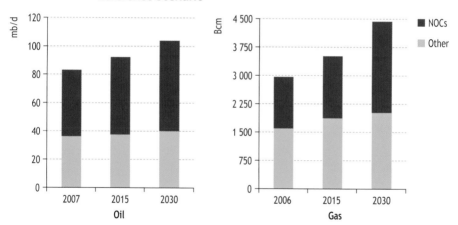

Note: The projections assume no change in the ownership of reserves. Oil production does not include processing gains.

Though this indicator needs to be hedged with many qualifications, revenue per employee provides one indication of both the technical efficiency of a company's operations and the degree to which its sales are made at prices below full market value. Output in volume terms per employee provides another indication of technical efficiency, but again with many qualifications relating to geological conditions and the degree of vertical integration (the larger a company's downstream business, the lower the upstream production per employee). There is a clear correlation between the two indicators, as higher productivity unsurprisingly contributes to higher revenue per employee. Both indicators are generally higher for the super-majors than for the national oil companies (Figure 14.10). Saudi Aramco has the highest volume productivity of any of the companies surveyed here, reflecting not only good business practice, but the relatively large share of upstream output in its overall business and its low reserve-development costs, thanks to favourable geology. ExxonMobil — the most profitable of all the international companies in absolute terms — has the highest revenue per employee.

Figure 14.10 ● **Revenue and hydrocarbon production per employee by type of company, 2007**

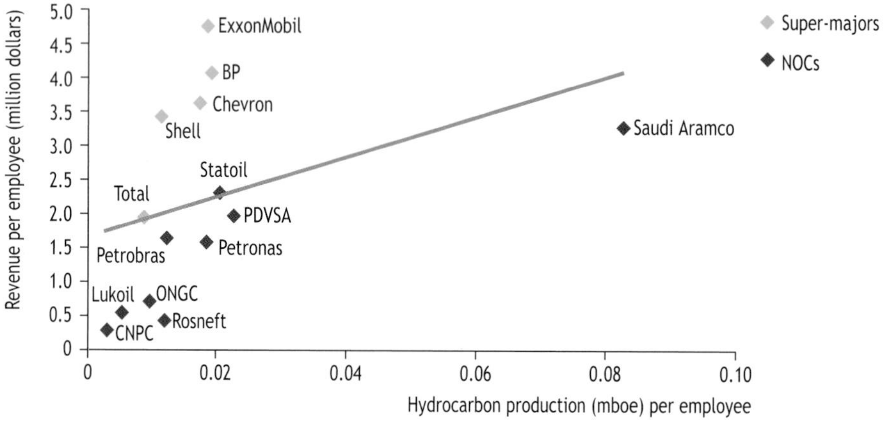

Sources: Company reports; IEA analysis.

Towards a more efficient industry

Some government owners are already introducing reforms to improve the performance of the national oil companies. Important elements include the following:

- Reduction of subsidies on domestic sales through price reform, to increase oil company revenues, to eliminate waste and to bolster their self-financing capacity.

- Promotion of competition in the domestic upstream and/or downstream sectors.

- Stricter accounting and financial standards, reporting and monitoring.

- Establishment of an arms-length management structure, including an autonomous board of directors, to protect management from *ad hoc* political interference.

- Improved access to international credit markets, through public share offerings and commercial bonds.

- Focus on core activities and the transfer of social and peripheral industrial activities to separate bodies.

Progress has been patchy so far. In most countries with national oil companies, subsidies remain large and competition limited. In Iran and Saudi Arabia alone, oil product subsidies, mostly carried by national oil company distributors, reached a staggering $53 billion in 2007 – up by $6 billion on the previous year – and they are thought to have risen further in 2008. But a growing number of countries, especially in Asia, are reducing, or are planning to reduce, retail subsidies on oil products in response to soaring costs (see Chapter 3). Russia is planning gradually to phase out subsidies on domestic sales of gas, which amounted to an estimated $30 billion in 2007 (see Chapter 1).

Though financial accounting and reporting remain opaque in some countries, notably in Africa (see Chapter 15), important improvements have been made in some countries and the majority of national companies have become more commercially driven and have established more transparent and formal decision-making processes and frameworks. For example, Algeria liberalised its upstream industry in 2005, involving the removal of the obligation on foreign companies to partner with the national company, Sonatrach, and the transfer of regulatory functions from Sonatrach to new government agencies. The three Chinese national companies have divested many of their non-core activities and, between 2000 and 2002, opened their equity to foreign investors through initial public offerings, in order to raise capital for international expansion. The growing reliance of national companies on international capital markets and the sale of minority equity stakes have led to improved compliance with international accounting standards, greater transparency and better corporate governance.

Strengthening strategic partnerships

Partnerships between the national and international companies provide one important means of securing the financial, technical and management resources required to develop national company reserves. The mutual benefits that could accrue are compelling: the national companies control most of the world's remaining reserves, but some lack the technology and skilled personnel to do much more than simply maintain existing producing assets; the international companies are opportunity-constrained, but have the management skills and technology to help national companies develop their reserves.

The super-majors, with their project-management experience and technical expertise, are particularly well placed to help national companies develop liquefied natural gas projects and complex gas fields, as well as deploy enhanced oil recovery techniques. For example, Chevron won a production-sharing contract with PetroChina in 2007 to develop the onshore Chuandongbei gas field in the Sichuan Basin, which is high in sulphur and carbon dioxide, is relatively wet and suffers from low rock permeability. In 2007, under a similar agreement, Shell started producing gas from the remote Changbei field, which has tight gas reservoirs requiring advanced technology to boost recovery rates. Although national companies can buy many new technologies off the shelf and hire oilfield-services companies to deploy them, the international companies still lead

14

the way in applying cutting-edge technologies and in managing large and technically complex projects. The super-majors and other international companies also have the financial strength to underwrite mega-projects — a major attraction where budgetary and borrowing restrictions limit the financial capacity of national oil companies. The National Iranian Oil Company and the Kuwait Petroleum Corporation, for example, are required to hand over the bulk of their revenues to their government owners, putting at risk their ability to meet their long-term official capacity targets.

The strategic match between what the international companies have to offer and the national companies need is likely to become closer in the long term. Worldwide, new developments are set to become more technically challenging, as the easiest reserves are depleted and drilling shifts to deepwater and less accessible locations and reservoirs. The associated financial challenge could be heightened by a drop in oil prices, which would put project finance at risk, especially in those countries accustomed to diverting a large share of the companies' cash-flow to the national treasury to finance social spending or energy-consumption subsidies.

Such strategic partnerships are already being formed. They have operated successfully in several countries, including Abu Dhabi, Oman and Qatar. Yet such successes have been limited. There have been difficulties in finding common ground, amidst frustrations on both sides about the results of previous joint ventures. Rising confidence of the part of the national companies in their ability to "go it alone" has met reluctance on the part of international companies to accept a role as contractors. They have preferred to hold out for production-sharing and concession agreements that allow them to book reserves and which promise higher returns. This stand-off has opened the way for service companies to establish themselves in countries that refuse to give foreign companies access on these terms.

For international-national company partnerships to develop successfully, innovative approaches will need to be adopted that better align the needs and expectations of both sides. The international companies seem likely to have to accept a role closer to that of the service providers, but perhaps offering a more comprehensive package of services than the service companies are currently able to provide. They will need to maintain their technical edge: technical hitches and delays that have plagued a number of recent mega-projects have tarnished the reputation of the international companies in these areas.

International companies could also, on suitable terms, assist the host-country in meeting its social and economic development goals. This would involve maximising the use of local staff and contractors promoting the transfer of skills to the local workforce — an attractive proposition to the national companies. An expanded pool of skilled labour would help relieve the acute shortages that have contributed to upstream cost inflation worldwide in recent years, benefiting both the national and international companies (see Chapter 13). The obstacles should not be under-estimated. Transferring skills and technology in practice can be very difficult, however, because of weak management and an ill-adapted corporate culture within the national company (Marcel, 2006). Contractual arrangements have to be appropriate.

National companies, for their part, will need to offer contract terms that provide adequate financial incentives for the international companies. The Saudi government failed to attract the participation of the super-majors in large-scale integrated gas exploration and development projects in the early 2000s because the companies considered the returns on offer inadequate in view of the risks and opportunities involved. Mexico has had little success in persuading international companies to sign service agreements as the fixed returns on offer are judged too small and the reserves cannot, by law, be booked by the international companies. Iran has also had limited success in attracting upstream investment by the super-majors under buyback deals, under which the National Iranian Oil Company retains ownership of the reserves. The ability to book reserves is an increasingly important consideration for the international companies, as financial markets focus increasingly on reserve-replacement ratios.

International strategic alliances can be one way of consolidating new relationships. In the absence of satisfactory partnership arrangements, national companies are likely to acquire foreign-owned assets outright as they expand in size, ambition and financial and technical strength. Such a development could raise concerns about the impact on supply security, but inter-regional integration can also be seen as a means of building mutual dependence.

Traditionally, upstream joint ventures and partnerships between national and international companies have involved the latter providing technical input to projects in the former's home country. But such partnerships are likely increasingly to involve investments in third-party countries, as national companies seek to expand internationally. Total recently sold a 20% stake to each of Qatar Petroleum and Algeria's Sonatrach in the Taoudenni Ta7 and Ta8 permits in a project in Mauritania. This type of deal is seen as a means of building a foundation for future collaboration. Upstream-downstream asset swaps are one way forward, providing the national companies with an opportunity to integrate their businesses more fully downstream while leaving the international companies to exploit their core strengths.

Governments of both producing and consuming countries have a role to play. The government owners of the national companies can encourage foreign participation by pursuing institutional, regulatory and fiscal reforms. The consuming countries need to show that they recognise the sovereign right of resource-rich countries to manage their resources in the way they judge best serves their national interest, offering support through high-level dialogue and multi-lateral trade and development agencies.

14

Chapter 15

PROSPECTS IN OIL- AND GAS-EXPORTING SUB-SAHARAN AFRICAN COUNTRIES

Could their resources alleviate energy poverty?

H I G H L I G H T S

- Conventional oil production in the ten largest hydrocarbon-producing countries in sub-Saharan Africa reached 5.6 mb/d in 2007, of which 5.1 mb/d was exported. In the Reference Scenario, output grows to 6.9 mb/d in 2015 and then rises more gradually to 7.4 mb/d in 2030. Oil exports climb to 6.4 mb/d in 2030. Gas production in these countries increases from 36 bcm in 2006 to 163 bcm in 2030. Most of the increase is exported. These projections hinge on a reduction in gas flaring, adequate investment and avoidance of disruption to supplies through civil unrest.

- The cumulative government take from oil and gas revenues in the ten countries analysed here is projected, in aggregate, at $4.1 trillion over 2006-2030. Nigeria and Angola remain the largest exporters, with combined cumulative revenues of about $3.5 trillion. Oil accounts for the bulk of these revenues. Taxes on oil and gas production account for more than 50% of total government revenues in most of the oil- and gas-rich sub-Saharan African countries.

- Despite the vast hydrocarbon wealth of these countries, most of their citizens remain poor. As a result, household access to modern energy services is very limited. Two-thirds of households do not have access to electricity and three-quarters do not have access to clean fuels for cooking, relying instead on fuelwood and charcoal. Unless there are major government initiatives to address this problem, the number of electricity-deprived people is projected to increase over the projection period. More than half of the total population of these countries still relies on fuelwood and charcoal for cooking in 2030.

- Tackling energy poverty is well within these countries' means. We estimate the capital cost of providing minimal energy services (electricity and liquefied petroleum gas stoves and cylinders) to these households over the *Outlook* period to be about $18 billion. This is roughly equivalent to only 0.4% of the governments' take from oil and gas exports over the *Outlook* period.

- An improvement in the efficiency of revenue allocation and the accountability of governments in the use of public funds would improve the likelihood of oil and gas revenues actually being used to alleviate poverty generally and energy poverty specifically. Energy is key to sustainable development, bringing major benefits to public health, social welfare and economic productivity. Since affordability is the main barrier to access, efforts to tackle energy poverty need to go hand in hand with broader policies aimed at raising incomes and promoting economic development.

Overview[1]

This chapter provides an outlook for oil and gas production, government take and household energy access in the ten largest hydrocarbon-producing sub-Saharan African countries (Table 15.1).[2] These countries account for 99% of the region's proven[3] oil reserves and 97% of its gas reserves. They also produce 99% of the region's oil and 93% of its gas. Worldwide, these countries contribute 7% to global output of oil and 12% of oil trade. Gas exports from these countries represent about 5% of global gas trade. Exports of both oil and gas (in the form of liquefied natural gas, LNG) are set to grow rapidly.

Table 15.1 ● **Production and reserves in assessed sub-Saharan African countries** (ranked by oil reserves)

	Oil			Gas		
	Reserves (billion barrels)	Production (mb/d)	Exports (mb/d)	Reserves (bcm)	Production (bcm/yr)	Exports (bcm/yr)
Nigeria	36.2	2.35	2.03	5 207	29.3	18.9
Angola	9.0	1.70	1.64	270	0.8	-
Sudan	5.0	0.47	0.39	85	-	-
Gabon	2.0	0.23	0.22	28	0.1	-
Congo*	1.6	0.21	0.21	91	-	-
Chad	1.5	0.14	0.14	-	-	-
Equatorial Guinea	1.1	0.36	0.36	37	1.3	-**
Cameroon	0.2	0.09	0.06	135	-	-
Côte d'Ivoire	0.1	0.06	0.03	28	1.7	-
Mozambique	-	-	-	127	2.7	2.7
Total	56.8	5.61	5.09	6 008	35.9	21.6
% in world	4.3%	7.0%	12.1%	3.4%	1.2%	5.2%

* Also referred to as Congo-Brazzaville or the Republic of Congo.
** LNG exports commenced in 2007 from Equatorial Guinea.
Sources: Production and exports – IEA analysis; reserves – O&GJ (2007). For production, oil data is for 2007 and gas data is for 2006. All reserves data are for end-2007.

The economies of these countries are heavily reliant on the oil and gas sector (OECD, 2008). Oil and gas contributed 87% to GDP in Equatorial Guinea in 2006, while oil contributed 57% to Angolan GDP in the same year. Oil accounted for over 70% of GDP in Congo in 2006. Taxes on oil and gas production constitute a very large portion of total government tax revenues in these sub-Saharan African countries. Except in Cameroon, Côte d'Ivoire and Mozambique, oil and gas sector revenues account for more than half

---

1. The analysis in this chapter benefited from a joint IEA/Norwegian Ministry of Foreign Affairs high-level workshop in Maputo, Mozambique on 12 May 2008. Details can be found at www.worldenergyoutlook.org/workshops.asp.

2. There are 49 countries in total in sub-Saharan Africa. See Annex B for a full list.

3. Unless otherwise stated, all the reserves figures cited in this chapter are proven (1P) at end-2007, from the *Oil and Gas Journal* (*O&GJ*, 2007).

of total government revenues (Figure 15.1). In Congo, the figure is over 80%. The share of the value of oil and gas exports in total exports is also very high. Oil exports alone constitute over 90% of total exports in Angola, Equatorial Guinea and Sudan.

Figure 15.1 ● **Share of oil and gas in total exports and of oil and gas revenues in government revenues in assessed sub-Saharan African countries, 2006**

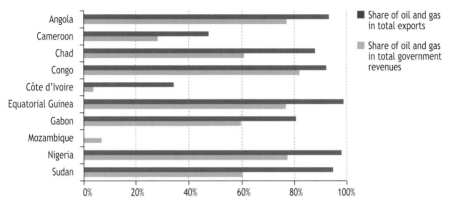

Note: No information is available for share of total exports in Mozambique.
Source: Information provided to the IEA by the African Development Bank.

Despite the wealth these resources represent, household energy access in the countries assessed here is very limited. Less than a third of households in Angola, Cameroon, Chad, Congo, Equatorial Guinea, Gabon, Sudan and Mozambique have access to electricity (Table 15.2). Electricity access in *rural* areas is even lower in all countries: it is estimated to be only 16% in Côte d'Ivoire and 26% in Nigeria. Other modern forms of energy are also scarce. Fewer than 25% of households in Angola, Cameroon, Chad, Côte d'Ivoire, Congo and Sudan have access to clean fuels for cooking, like liquefied petroleum gas (LPG), kerosene, biogas and ethanol gelfuel. The majority of households cook with fuelwood and charcoal over open fires or in inefficient stoves. Over 95% of *rural* households in Angola, Cameroon, Chad, Congo and Sudan rely on fuelwood and charcoal for cooking, a share comparable to that applying in Benin, Ghana and Zambia.

Oil- and gas-rich countries could use the proceeds from taxes and royalties on production to pay for wider energy access and to meet other basic needs of their poorest households. Sharply higher revenues from the high oil and gas prices which have prevailed recently are making this more affordable. In addition, these countries could make direct use of their gas resources, for example, by using currently flared gas for power generation or distributing it in cities. The LPG extracted from natural gas or produced in refineries can provide a low-cost source of supply for distribution networks. Yet the use of oil and gas resources for domestic consumption is rarely a government priority in these countries, while companies usually have little interest in getting involved in small-scale energy-distribution projects in immature local markets because of the cost.

15

Table 15.2 ● Number of people without access to electricity and relying on fuelwood and charcoal for cooking in assessed sub-Saharan African countries

	Total population, 2006 (million)	Number of people without electricity access* (million)	(%)	Number of people relying on fuelwood and charcoal for cooking* (million)	(%)
Angola	16.6	14.6	88	15.7	95
Cameroon	18.2	14.2	78	14.2	78
Chad	10.5	10.1	97	10.2	97
Congo	3.7	2.9	78	2.9	80
Côte d'Ivoire	18.9	11.6	61	14.7	78
Equatorial Guinea	0.5	0.4	73	0.3	59
Gabon	1.3	0.9	70	0.4	33
Mozambique	21	18.6	89	16.9	80
Nigeria	144.7	76.6	53	93.8	65
Sudan	37.7	26.9	71	35.2	93
Total	**273.1**	**176.9**	**65**	**204**	**75**

* Most recent estimates.
Sources: Population statistics are from UNPD (2007). The number of people without electricity access and relying on fuelwood and charcoal is from IEA analysis, based on national surveys and information provided from the World Bank, United Nations Development Programme and World Health Organisation.

In brief, energy poverty is stark in the ten countries analysed here, as stark as in other countries in sub-Saharan Africa. In the absence of new policy initiatives, the number of people living without electricity and exposed to the health risks associated with the burning of fuelwood and charcoal for cooking will actually rise over the *Outlook* period, as the population grows. Tackling this problem will require comprehensive and co-ordinated economic and social development plans and policies, with a much greater focus on effective management of the wealth generated by hydrocarbon resources. A first requirement is to make oil and gas revenues transparent to the public. They will ultimately hold governments accountable for the allocation of these revenues.

Outlook for oil and gas production, exports and government revenues

Resources and reserves

Proven oil reserves in the ten sub-Saharan African countries assessed here are estimated at 57 billion barrels, some 4% of world reserves. At a current production level of 5.6 million barrels per day (mb/d), these reserves would sustain production for another 28 years. Significant offshore undiscovered oil resources lie in water between 2 000 metres and 4 000 metres deep in some areas, especially offshore Angola (USGS, 2000). Proven gas reserves amount to 6 trillion cubic metres (tcm) or about 3% of world reserves. Undiscovered resources are particularly abundant in the Niger and Congo deltas.

Nigeria has the largest proven hydrocarbon reserves of any African country, which stood at 68 billion barrels oil equivalent at end-2007. They amount to 73% of all the oil and gas reserves of the ten sub-Saharan African countries assessed here (Figure 15.2). The Nigerian government plans to expand its proven oil reserves, which currently amount to 36 billion barrels, to 40 billion barrels by 2010. Most of the reserves are found along the country's Niger River Delta, in southern Nigeria and offshore in the Bight of Benin, Gulf of Guinea and Bight of Bonny. Virtually all of the large discoveries in recent years on the west coast of Africa have been made in deepwater offshore fields.

Figure 15.2 ● Proven oil and gas reserves in assessed sub-Saharan African countries, end-2007

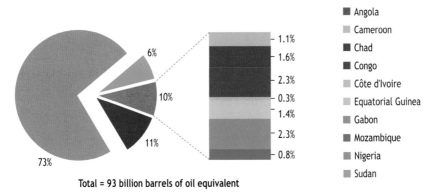

Total = 93 billion barrels of oil equivalent

Sources: *O&GJ* (2007); IEA analysis.

Oil and gas production and exports

There is considerable difference in production maturity among the oil-rich sub-Saharan African countries. In Table 15.3, we classify the countries into three categories, according to the percentage of initial 2P reserves already produced: new producers; steady and rising producers; and declining producers. The largest oil producers – Nigeria, Angola and Sudan – are expected to increase their production capacity significantly, while Chad is only now beginning its production cycle.

Aggregate oil production in these sub-Saharan Africa countries was 5.6 mb/d in 2007. Conventional oil production is projected to increase to 6.9 mb/d in 2015 and to 7.4 mb/d in 2030 (Figure 15.3). Production in Nigeria and Angola combined represents 84% of total production in 2030, compared with about three-quarters today. All of the sanctioned and planned projects in these two countries – 15 projects in Angola in fields holding some 5.4 billion barrels and 11 projects in Nigeria with 5.1 billion barrels — are offshore. All of the identified reserves with no firm projects planned are offshore in Angola, while over 65% of the identified reserves in Nigeria are in onshore fields.

Table 15.3 ● Oil production maturity of assessed sub-Saharan African countries, 2007

		Share of cumulative production in total initial 2P reserves
New producers	Chad	21%
Steady and rising producers	Sudan	23%
	Angola	25%
	Côte d'Ivoire	30%
	Equatorial Guinea	32%
	Nigeria	34%
	Congo	41%
Declining producers	Gabon	51%
	Cameroon	67%

Sources: O&GJ (2007); IEA databases and analysis.

Figure 15.3 ● Oil and gas production in assessed sub-Saharan African countries

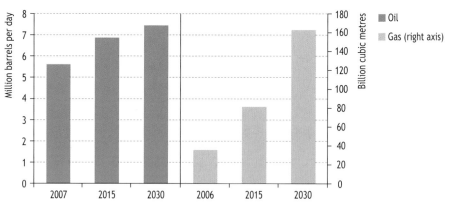

Sub-Saharan African countries exported 5.1 mb/d of oil in 2007, or about 91% of total production. Most of these exports were crude oil. Despite rising local demand for oil, driven in large part by the economic boost provided by rising oil-related earnings, exports are projected to rise to 6.4 mb/d in 2030. Oil exports from Angola, Sudan and Nigeria are expected to continue to grow steadily over the *Outlook* period. Cameroon becomes a net oil importer after 2020.

Gas production and exports, largely as LNG, are also expected to grow strongly. In the Reference Scenario, the marketable gas production of the complete group of countries increases from 36 bcm in 2006 to 82 bcm in 2015 and 163 bcm in 2030. The largest gas producers in 2030 are Nigeria, Angola, Equatorial Guinea and Mozambique. Most of the increase in gas output is exported. Exports rise from 21.6 bcm in 2006 to 63 bcm in 2015 and 130 bcm in 2030. Nigeria's gas exports are expected to reach 101 bcm by 2030, while Angola's reach 7 bcm in 2012. A reduction in gas flaring is expected to make a major contribution to marketable gas supply (Box 15.1). Primary oil and gas demand in these countries is projected to grow on average by 3.5% per year over the *Outlook* period.

Box 15.1 ● Gas flaring: what are the costs?

Worldwide, 150 bcm of associated gas was flared in 2005, emitting 400 million tonnes of carbon dioxide into the atmosphere (World Bank, 2007). The sub-Saharan African countries assessed here flared 40 bcm – a level unchanged since 2000 (Figure 15.4). This is almost three times the region's gas consumption. Nigeria is among the world's biggest flarers, with some 25 bcm flared in 2005, nearly half of its total gas production.[4] Nigeria's ratio of gas flared to oil produced is 18 times higher than that in the North Sea. So much gas is flared because there is no infrastructure to bring the gas to market, a consequence of the poor potential returns and high risks associated with building such infrastructure.

Gas flaring wastes a valuable resource. Capturing and using the gas could bring large economic, social and environmental benefits. In the case of Nigeria, the monetary value of the gas lost in 2005, at a price of $5 per MBtu, was about $5 billion. Nigeria is committed to reducing flaring. It signed the Kyoto Protocol in December 2004 and its gas-flaring reduction projects qualify under the Clean Development Mechanism (CDM), under which the flared gas has a potential value of $800 million, based on current Certified Emission Reduction prices, as an addition to its market value. Options for reducing flaring include gas reinjection in oil and gas fields, distribution to local markets by pipeline, and gas processing into LNG, LPG or GTL. But several gas-export projects have been delayed and Nigeria's domestic market has been very slow to develop due to domestic gas-pricing policies, which set prices too low to make investments in distribution networks profitable, and poor payment discipline on the part of industrial and power consumers. Consequently, the initial target set by Nigeria to stop flaring in 2008 will not be met.

In practice, reducing gas flaring will require the imposition and enforcement of strict environmental standards, penalties on flaring and financial incentives to accelerate the development of domestic infrastructure and markets for associated gas. Emerging-country producers need fully to consider the long-term economic value of associated gas when negotiating and executing contracts with operators.

15

---

4. Flaring is believed to have been reduced to 22 bcm in 2006 (IEA, 2008).

Figure 15.4 ● Gas flaring in assessed sub-Saharan African countries

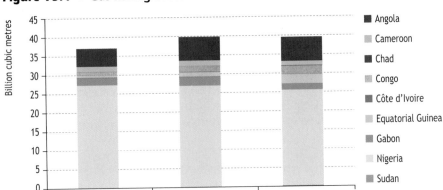

Source: World Bank (2007).

A significant portion of Nigeria's natural gas is already processed into LNG. Nigeria completed the first phase of the Nigeria LNG Limited (NLNG) facility on Bonny Island in 1999. In 2006, NLNG completed its fifth train, increasing annual production capacity to 24 bcm per year. A sixth train was completed in late 2007, raising production capacity to 31 bcm per year, but this has not yet been brought into operation, for lack of feedstock. Three other projects are under development – Brass LNG, Olokola LNG and a seventh train at NLNG – but a final investment decision has not been taken on any of them, making it unlikely that any will be commissioned before 2012. In Angola, Chevron and Sonangol, together with other shareholders including Total, BP and Eni, are planning to build a 7-bcm LNG plant, which is expected to be operational in 2012.

The West Africa Gas Pipeline project was commissioned in December 2007, with commercial operation expected to begin in 2008. Initial capacity is 2.1 bcm per year and it is expected to ramp up to a full capacity of 4.6 bcm per year within 15 years. The 678-km pipeline carries natural gas from Nigeria to Ghana, Togo and Benin. It is intended to supply gas to power stations in all three countries in order to reduce dependence on diesel. Nigeria and Equatorial Guinea are in discussion about a pipeline connecting the two countries to feed a second train at Equatorial Guinea's LNG plant on Bioko Island.

Nigeria and Algeria are studying the possibility of constructing a trans-Saharan gas pipeline. The 4 023-km pipeline would carry 20 bcm to 30 bcm per year of associated natural gas from oilfields in Nigeria's Delta region to Algeria's Beni Saf LNG export terminal on the Mediterranean. It is estimated that construction of the $7-billion line would take six years. Current and planned oil and gas infrastructure in sub-Saharan Africa is shown in Figure 15.5.

Civil unrest has bedevilled some of these countries at various times in past years, substantially increasing the risk associated with exploiting their reserves and holding back investment. Civil conflicts at the Niger Delta have resulted in serious supply disruptions, as attacks on oil facilities have forced companies to halt or slow production and delay loadings. Around 550 kb/d of Nigeria's oil-production capacity has been unavailable since 2006 as a result. The cost of deepwater exploration could rise further in the wake of general cost inflation (See Chapter 13).

Figure 15.5 ● Oil and gas supply and infrastructure in sub-Saharan Africa

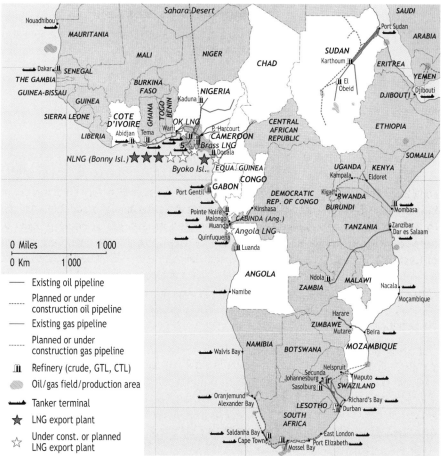

The boundaries and names shown and the designations used on maps included in this publication do not imply official endorsement or acceptance by the IEA.

Sources: IEA analysis based on information provided by PFC Energy and Petroleum Economist.

Oil refining

There are 11 refineries in the assessed countries and another 10 in the rest of sub-Saharan Africa. Total crude distillation capacity at the 11 refineries is just over 800 kb/d. Nigeria has four refineries, but all of them operate well below their official capacity, leaving some 77% of product demand to be met by imports in 2007. In the past, the government has opted to export crude oil and collect taxes on imported refined products rather than invest in improving refining capacity. The Nigerian government has not been able to attract any significant private investment in the refining sector.

The Angolan government is keen to attract investment in a second, greenfield refinery in Lobito. Refineries in Africa face difficulties in competing with producers from the Middle East and Asia. They often do not enjoy the benefit of economies of scale, and their product slate can be unsuited to local demand. India is emerging as a key exporter of refined products to Africa.

The lack of refining capacity is an important political issue in Africa. Most oil-producing countries would like to extract more of the value of their crude oil by refining it locally, rather than exporting it and importing products. Increased local availability should also help to lower the cost of supplying local markets.

Oil and gas export revenues

Based on projected exports and our assumptions for oil prices (see Chapter 1), the government take[5] from oil and gas exports from the assessed countries is estimated to rise from some $80 billion in 2006 to about $250 billion in 2030. Revenues in Nigeria and Angola dwarf those in all the other countries. Nigeria's revenues in 2030 reach nearly $150 billion and Angola's some $80 billion. These two countries account for 86% of the $4.1 trillion cumulative revenues of all ten countries over 2006-2030 (Figure 15.6).

Per-capita oil and gas revenues vary widely among the assessed countries. Revenue per capita over the *Outlook* period averages some $515 in Nigeria but is close to $2 000 in Angola. In Gabon, average annual revenue per capita is some $2 700. It is over $5 000 in Equatorial Guinea.

Figure 15.6 ● Cumulative government oil and gas revenues in assessed sub-Saharan African countries, 2006-2030

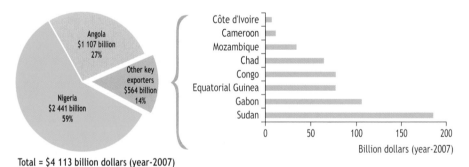

Total = $4 113 billion dollars (year-2007)

Household energy access in sub-Saharan African countries

Sub-Saharan Africa desperately needs sustained and sustainable economic development, and clean cooking fuels and access to electricity are two prerequisites. Yet, the share of households *without* electricity access across all countries in sub-Saharan Africa

---

5. We have assumed the average government take equates to 67%.

is 73% on average, compared with 27% in non-OECD Asia and 10% in Latin America (IEA, 2006b). Moreover, there appears to be virtually no correlation between oil and gas resource endowments and access to modern energy in sub-Saharan Africa. In the countries with limited or no oil and gas reserves, the percentage of the population *without* access to electricity ranges from 6% in Mauritius to 94% in the Democratic Republic of Congo (IEA, 2006b).[6] Six of the ten sub-Saharan African countries assessed here have the same or a higher share of people without electricity access than the average for sub-Saharan Africa as a whole. Likewise, the share of the population relying on fuelwood and charcoal for cooking is similar in these hydrocarbon-rich countries to that in the sub-Saharan African countries not analysed here, where it ranges from about 95% in Ethiopia to some 20% in South Africa.

Cooking practices

The current use of fuelwood and charcoal for cooking in sub-Saharan Africa has serious implications for the environment, for economic development and for health. Charcoal is widely used for cooking and is usually produced from forest resources. Because of the low conversion efficiency of the kilns used to produce charcoal, there has been localised deforestation and land degradation around urban centres. In Angola, the major influx of people to peri-urban areas, or shanty towns, at the end of the civil war has put tremendous pressure on biomass resources. Severe local deforestation has occurred around most large cities. For example, all forest has been cleared within a radius of 200 to 300 kilometres of Luanda, Angola (IEA, 2006a).

In households that rely on fuelwood, women and children are responsible for fuel collection, a time-consuming and exhausting task. Collection time has a significant opportunity cost, limiting time to improve education and engage in income-generating activities. Modern energy services for cooking promote economic development by freeing-up household time for more productive purposes.

Lack of access to clean fuels for cooking can have a serious impact on health. Exposure to indoor air pollution from burning fuelwood, charcoal and other biomass in poorly ventilated areas has been linked to many different diseases, including acute and chronic respiratory diseases, tuberculosis, asthma, cardiovascular disease and negative peri-natal health outcomes. Indoor air pollution disproportionately affects women and children, who spend the most time near the cookstove. An estimated 79 000 people die prematurely in Nigeria alone each year because of the use of fuelwood and charcoal for cooking (Table 15.4). The percentage of the national burden of disease attributable to the use of fuelwood and charcoal for cooking is nearly 7% in Angola and more than 5% in Cameroon and Chad (WHO, 2007). In every country in Table 15.4, more people die prematurely each year from illnesses caused by indoor air pollution than from malaria.

Due to affordability and access barriers to the uptake of LPG and other cleaner-burning fuels for cooking, many households will continue to use fuelwood and charcoal for cooking. Improving the way these resources are used is an important way of reducing their harmful effects. The first requirements are improved stoves and better

15

6. See Annex B in the 2006 edition of the *World Energy Outlook* for estimated electrification rates in Africa, non-OECD Asia, Latin America and the Middle East.

ventilation: adding chimneys to stoves is the most effective improvement to be made from the point of view of health, while kitchen design and ventilation also play a key role in reducing emissions. Particulate levels in houses using wood, but with good ventilation, can be lower than those in houses using liquid fuels in poorly designed stoves. Governments can enhance the sustainability of biomass resources by increasing the area of the country dedicated to plantations, and through monitoring and control of charcoal production.

Table 15.4 ● **Annual premature death and disability associated with indoor air pollution in assessed sub-Saharan African countries**

	Premature deaths attributable to use of fuelwood and charcoal for cooking	Disability-adjusted life years attributable to use of fuelwood and charcoal	Share of total national burden of disease attributable to use of fuelwood and charcoal
Angola	22 000	747 000	6.9%
Cameroon	12 900	417 000	5.5%
Chad	8 700	285 900	5.6%
Congo	700	18 300	1.2%
Côte d'Ivoire	9 300	290 000	3.4%
Gabon	200	4 000	0.9%
Mozambique	9 700	300 200	2.4%
Nigeria	79 000	2 591 500	3.8%
Sudan	4 400	79 900	0.7%
Total	146 900	5 957 400	-

Note: No data available for Equatorial Guinea. The disability-adjusted life year (DALY) is a health gap measure that extends the concept of potential years of life lost due to premature death to include equivalent years of "healthy" life lost by virtue of being in poor health or disabled. The DALY combines, in one measure, the time lived with disability and the time lost due to premature mortality. One DALY can be thought of as one lost year of healthy life. The burden of disease quantifies mortality and morbidity due to a given disease or risk factor.

Source: WHO (2007).

Electricity access

Access to reliable electricity is important for many services, such as lighting and communications, but crucial for refrigeration, which avoids food waste and allows local clinics to keep medicines on hand. Clinics lacking electricity cannot perform such routine functions as sterilising instruments or safely storing vaccines.

Yet, as we have seen (Table 15.2), in eight out of the ten sub-Saharan African countries assessed here, less than a third of the population has access to electricity. Even where access to electricity is available, it does not necessarily mean that electricity is available on demand. Even those Africans who do have access frequently have to cope with unreliable supply. Power disruptions are a fundamental obstacle to economic activity, including at the household level. In war-torn countries, such as Angola, Congo, Côte d'Ivoire, Chad and Sudan, the infrastructure for electricity transmission and distribution has often been destroyed. Service restoration is more costly than the average cost of serving new customers in a stable environment. Inadequacies in the supply infrastructure are one reason why many people make illegal connections, sometimes resulting in injuries, electrocution, fire, explosions and death — often involving children.[7] In addition to the health risks, illegal connections also mean loss of revenue to the electricity distribution companies and, consequently, greater difficulty in financing infrastructure improvements. In order to take advantage of economies of scale as a step towards easing regional power shortages, regional power pools are being developed (Box 15.2).

Box 15.2 ● Regional power pools and the Grand Inga project

Regional power pools have been formed in Central (CAPP), East (EAPP), Southern (SAPP), and West (WAPP) Africa (Figure 15.7). The pools are at very different stages of development, both technically and institutionally. The political process is well advanced in the WAPP, supported by political agreements at the head of state level through the Economic Community of West African States. The SAPP was the first operational power pool in Africa, sponsored under the authority of the Southern African Development Community (SADC). The pools, particularly the WAPP and SAPP, have facilitated significant cross-border exchanges of power.

Regional power pools are able to reduce costs and improve conditions on the supply side. Operational costs are lower, due to investment in least-cost power generation plants on a regional basis. Benefits on the supply side, all contributing to increased reliability, include reduced coincident peak loads on the regional power pool, compared with the sum of the individual peak loads for each national power grid, shared power generation reserves for the interconnected power grids, and increased robustness to deal with local droughts or other unexpected events.

One of the key projects that will support the regional pools is the Grand Inga dam project in the Democratic Republic of Congo (DRC). The project is estimated to cost $80 billion and expected to be able to provide 40 GW of power. Difficulties associated with the project include an absence of political consensus and legal harmonisation. Nigeria is expected to be the largest consumer. It is hoped that the carbon-emission reduction potential will help attract necessary investment.

Most of the power will be used for industry or for export. Inga 1 and Inga 2 were commissioned in 1972 and 1982, as part of an industrial development scheme in the DRC. The two dams currently operate at only 40% capacity because they have never received maintenance. The World Bank is partially financing a project to rehabilitate these dams.[8] When Inga 2 was built, a 1 800-km transmission line was also built to transport the power to state-owned copper mines in the Katanga province, bypassing nearly every city and village underneath. A component of the Grand Inga project could be expanded household electricity access, particularly in the DRC, where access is estimated to be 13% in urban areas and only 3% in rural areas.

15

---

7. To date, there have been no comprehensive studies on the number of deaths and injuries from illegal connections. There is a need to better quantify the number in order to raise awareness of the consequences arising from the inability to obtain legal electricity connections.
8. See www.worldbank.org/drc.

Nigeria is experiencing a severe electricity shortage. Three new gas-fuelled power stations are unable to generate electricity because the country has over-sold gas for export and because the domestic electricity-supply infrastructure is inadequate. Nigeria's power generation capacity plunged to less than 1 000 MW in July 2008.[9] As a step towards improving the situation, in February 2008 Nigeria announced a new gas policy, which will prioritise the domestic use of gas over export. Under the policy, all gas developers are expected to allocate a specified amount of gas from their reserves and annual production to the domestic market. Gas for domestic use will be supplied at the lowest commercially sustainable prices to strategic sectors, such as electricity. The Nigerian government plans to build 15 new gas-fired power plants to increase generating capacity to 10 GW by 2010.

Figure 15.7 ● **Regional power pools in Africa**

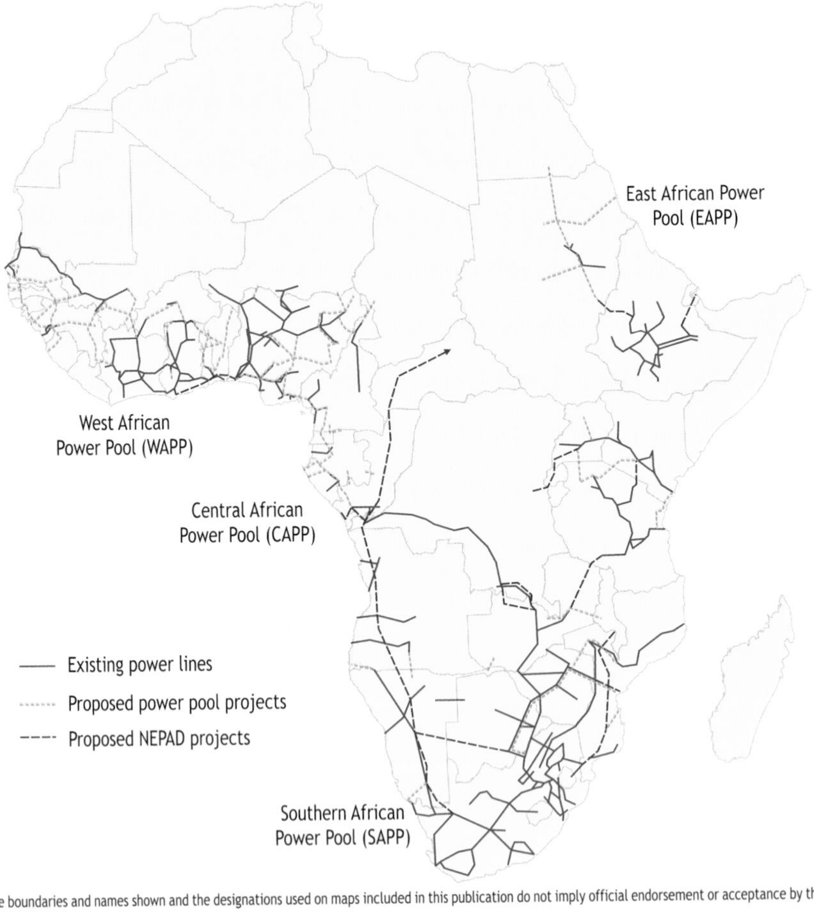

The boundaries and names shown and the designations used on maps included in this publication do not imply official endorsement or acceptance by the IEA.

Note: The Maghreb power pool is not shown.
Source: NEPAD (2008).

9. A committee was set up in June 2008 by the Nigerian government to review the electricity sector. It concluded that $85 billion is needed to meet power demand, estimated to be some 20 GW ("As oil money floods in, most Nigerians wouldn't know it", *Global edition of the New York Times*, 22 July 2008).

Box 15.3 ● Government programmes to promote the use of clean cooking fuels and rural electrification in Africa: success stories

Strong government support is essential to expand energy access, because low incomes prevent a large number of people from accessing even basic services. Gas and electricity are now widely available in Cape Verde and electrification rates are much higher than a decade ago in Botswana, in both cases due to well-chosen government reforms and effective implementation.

The governments of Kenya and Tunisia have also addressed the lack of energy access through innovative policy frameworks and financing mechanisms. In Kenya, the household energy mix is dominated by the use of fuelwood and charcoal for cooking. To reduce high dependence on these fuels, the government introduced a number of measures to improve access to and the affordability of LPG. Households' access to credit was improved, largely through the Kenyan Union of Savings and Credit Co-operatives (KUSCCO), an umbrella organisation for nearly 4 900 agricultural co-operatives in Kenya. Rapid growth of LPG followed the decision to remove the VAT and import duty on LPG, and to set standards for LPG stoves, cylinders and accessories. Lack of standardised LPG cylinders, with inter-changeable valves and regulators, had previously been a major obstacle to the development of efficient and competitive LPG retail markets in Kenya. The acceleration in the penetration of LPG in Kenya demonstrates the facilitating role governments can play, providing a policy and regulatory framework attractive to prospective energy and financial investors, and to users (Kabutha et al., 2007).

The Tunisian government expanded electricity access from 37% in the early 1970s to an impressive 99% in 2006 (IEA, 2006b). The government laid out its targets in five-year plans aimed at overall rural development. Renewable-energy projects were selected at the regional level as part of rural development plans, which covered health, education, water and other infrastructure. Success was attributed to efficient central direction, decentralised implementation, transparent norms and guidelines, and innovative technical decisions, such as the use of single-wire earth systems.[10] Private sector participation in construction and the participation of the local supply industry were also important. But national political commitment is widely regarded as the key factor in the success of the programme.

Projected trends in access to modern energy services

In the Reference Scenario, which assumes the continuation of existing policies, the number of people *without* access to electricity in the ten sub-Saharan African countries assessed here rises from some 177 million today to 191 million in 2030 (Table 15.5), as the population grows. This is despite the fact that 56% of the people in these countries have access to electricity in 2030, up from 35% today. The number of people relying on

---

10. These systems use single-wire transmission lines from the central grid to supply power, at low cost, to remote areas.

fuelwood and charcoal for cooking similarly rises, from 204 million to 244 million, again despite a rise in the share of the population with access to clean fuels for cooking, from 25% to 43%. The disparity between rural and urban areas remains pronounced. The majority of the people who gain access to both electricity and cleaner fuels for cooking over the projection period live in urban areas.

Table 15.5 ● Access to electricity and reliance on fuelwood and charcoal in assessed sub-Saharan African countries

| | Number of people without electricity access | | | | Number of people relying on fuelwood and charcoal for cooking | | | |
| | 2006 | | 2030 | | 2006 | | 2030 | |
	Million	%	Million	%	Million	%	Million	%
Angola	14.6	88	18	59	15.7	95	18	60
Cameroon	14.2	78	17	64	14.2	78	17	65
Chad	10.1	97	18	92	10.2	97	16	79
Congo	2.9	78	4	68	2.9	80	4	69
Côte d'Ivoire	11.6	61	14	50	14.7	78	21	73
Equatorial Guinea	0.4	73	0.4	50	0.3	59	0.4	42
Gabon	0.9	70	1.2	66	0.4	33	0.5	28
Mozambique	18.6	89	22	72	16.9	80	18	58
Nigeria	76.6	53	66	29	93.8	65	109	48
Sudan	26.9	71	30	51	35.2	93	40	69
Total	176.9	65	191	44	204	75	244	57

Note: Assumptions for GDP growth rates are based on information provided to the IEA from the World Bank, the African Development Bank and the OECD. Population growth rates from the UN Population Division.
Source: IEA databases and analysis.

Economic growth is the main factor driving the improvements in energy access. In part because of higher oil prices, economic growth in the countries assessed here is expected to be faster than in the rest of sub-Saharan Africa. Urbanisation rates are also an important factor driving energy demand, as households in cities are more likely to be connected to the grid and to have access to cleaner cooking fuels. Nigeria is making progress in reducing the number of people who lack access to electricity, a trend that is projected to continue through the *Outlook* period. But the very large number of people who lack access to clean cooking fuels is projected to rise considerably. Mozambique and Angola are expected to make progress in expanding the supply of cleaner cooking fuels.

Quantifying the costs involved in expanding access

Expanding access to electricity and modern cooking stoves will require substantial additional investment in power generation and networks and appliances beyond that projected in our Reference Scenario. In order to illustrate the challenge, we have estimated the cost over the *Outlook* period to achieve universal access to modern energy services (electricity and LPG[11]) by 2030 in the ten countries assessed here. The figure comes to some $18 billion, almost half of this arising in Nigeria (Figure 15.8).

We assume that a constant percentage of people gain access to electricity each year. A minimum consumption rate of 73 kWh per person per year is assumed.[12] The costs have been calculated separately for central grid, mini-grid and off-grid technologies. Central grid power is the least expensive option but will not be available to most rural households. Off-grid diesel generators have the lowest investment cost per kW, followed by mini-grid hydro-based electrification. However, generators entail an additional annual expense for diesel of about $24 per person. Solar photovoltaics technology is very expensive, and its role is assumed to be limited (Box 15.4).

Figure 15.8 ● **Total additional cost* of universal access to electricity and clean cooking stoves in assessed sub-Saharan African countries**

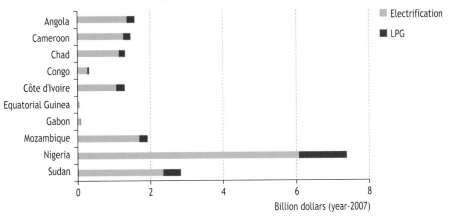

* From 2006 to 2030, over and above the Reference Scenario.
Source: IEA analysis.

The average cost of providing electricity in urban areas is $370 per household. The cost of electrifying peri-urban areas, where most of the people without access live, is higher. Peri-urban areas are challenging to serve because they are poorly built and are not laid out uniformly. In rural areas, the average cost is estimated to be $425 per household. To provide electricity by 2030 to the 191 million people who would otherwise have no access will require investment of some $15 billion, covering generation, transmission and distribution.

---

11. LPG is used as a proxy for all clean cooking fuels.
12. Minimum electricity consumption is set at 1 kWh per household per day or 73 KWh per person per year (assuming an average household size of five).

The costs of switching to LPG for households that rely predominately on fuelwood and charcoal for cooking include capital expenditure for the stove and cylinder, and recurring expenditure for the fuel itself. In this analysis, we look only at the capital expenditure for the LPG stove and cylinder, which is assumed to be $65 per household. This upfront capital cost is a very significant barrier to change. The total cost of providing stoves and cylinders to all households otherwise relying on fuelwood and charcoal for cooking is some $2.9 billion.

Box 15.4 ● The prospects for renewables to meet rural household energy needs

Renewable energy supply — mostly hydropower — is expected to grow rapidly in the coming decades in Africa. Yet, introduction of these technologies will require strong government support. *Hydropower* potential in sub-Saharan Africa is estimated to amount to more than 1 800 TWh of technically exploitable resources (Karekezi and Kithyoma, 2008). *Small hydropower* is an important source of energy in rural areas. The Hidraluapasso mini-hydro project in northern Angola, for example, will provide 26 MW at a cost of $120 million (UNEP, 2008).

Solar energy is perhaps the most widespread renewable energy resource. A very large number of African countries have daily solar radiation ranging between 4 and 6 kWh per square metre. Nonetheless, the cost of an off-grid installation can be prohibitive, ranging from $550 to $1 200 per household (Moner-Girona *et al.*, 2006). *Wind energy* is gaining popularity, but many sub-Saharan African countries have low wind speeds, particularly those near the equator. Chad, however, has good wind potential in some parts of the country.

The use of renewable energy in sub-Saharan Africa could help mitigate the impact of high oil prices, especially if renewable energy systems replace diesel generators. But the institutional frameworks and infrastructure needed vigorously to expand renewable energy systems has been lacking. Government policies and programmes to promote renewable energy are needed.

Of course, owning stoves and cylinders does not ensure that people will use them if they cannot afford the fuel. Fuel costs are very expensive for African households, many of whom live on less than $1 per day.[13] LPG prices have soared over the past few years and, assuming an average cost of LPG of $1.50 per kilogram — based on 2008 consumer prices in a sample of African countries — the total fuel bill for a household of five would be over $200 per year. Bulk transport costs are higher in landlocked countries and poor transport can increase the cost of fuel delivery. In Chad, LPG

---

13. The World Bank estimates that, on average, some 47% of households in sub-Saharan Africa live on less than $1 per day.

costs about $2.30 per kilogram. Price subsidies on LPG have had a poor record of success in many countries, because they often fail to benefit the poorest households (Box 15.5).[14]

Box 15.5 ● Subsidies: how best to safeguard energy-poor households?

As in all developing countries, there is pressure on African governments to shield their consumers, through universal subsidies, from sharply rising oil and gas prices. But the downside of such energy subsidies is widely acknowledged: unintended inequitable distribution, inefficiencies, over-consumption, smuggling and a drain on government resources that could be more efficiently used. The result is, often, increased social inequality and, usually, economic inefficiency. Wealthy households are much more likely to benefit from subsidies than the poorest ones.

Financial assistance is most effective when it is successfully *targeted* at the poorest households and offered as income support rather than universal fuel subsidies. After eliminating LPG price subsidies in 2002, Brazil introduced a gas assistance programme that provides bi-monthly subsidy payments for the poorest households. The new approach provides an annual per-capita subsidy to qualifying households that amounts to more than 60% of the retail LPG price — more than 20 times the previous general price subsidy — even though the net government subsidy expenditures are only about half as large (Goldemberg *et al.*, 2004). Another alternative to universal fuel subsidies is to provide pre-paid cards that could be used only for LPG purchases by qualifying households.

When it is specifically energy-related, financial assistance should be linked to high up-front charges, such as connection charges, which impede access and be carefully directed to the households that need it most. To be coherent with demand-side management programmes, financial assistance should not, generally, be related to consumption.

The total cost of some $18 billion needed to achieve access to electricity and to clean cooking stoves and cylinders in the ten countries analysed here is a mere 0.4% of the projected government take from oil and gas export revenues in 2006-2030. Table 15.6 shows the variation by country. For example, Nigeria has a large number of people without access to modern energy services, but also has very large prospective oil and gas revenues. Cameroon will see its oil revenues decline over the projection period so that the share needed to expand access would be 13%, compared with 0.3% for Nigeria. Angola, with its small population and massive oil and gas revenues, would need to spend only 0.1% of oil and gas revenues to 2030 to see all of its citizens enjoy a minimal electricity service and cleaner cooking stoves. The cost as a share of government take is only 0.1% in Equatorial Guinea.

15

---

14. See Chapter 20 in *WEO-2007* for a discussion of the implications of LPG subsidies in India (IEA, 2007).

Table 15.6 ● Cumulative cost of providing universal access to modern energy in assessed sub-Saharan African countries, 2006-2030

	Investment requirements for universal electricity access ($ billion)	Investment requirements for stoves and cylinders ($ billion)	Costs of universal access to electricity and clean cooking stoves and cylinders as a share of government take (%)
Angola	1.36	0.22	0.1
Cameroon	1.26	0.20	13.0
Chad	1.14	0.17	2.0
Côte d'Ivoire	1.06	0.23	18.0
Congo	0.27	0.04	0.4
Equatorial Guinea	0.03	0.01	0.1
Gabon	0.08	0.01	0.1
Mozambique	1.70	0.23	5.6
Nigeria	6.09	1.32	0.3
Sudan	2.35	0.49	1.5
Total	15.35	2.91	0.4

Managing revenues from oil and gas

Investments in expanding energy access can reap long-term benefits to sustainable development.[15] But as long as affordability is a barrier to the uptake of modern energy services, the private sector will not have sufficient incentive to invest on the scale required. Expanding energy access, accordingly, needs to be a policy priority for governments. In most of the countries assessed here, this will entail fundamental political, institutional and legislative reform, as well as efforts to strengthen the capability of regional and local authorities to implement programmes and to expand access to credit. Successful strategies to improve domestic energy access require good information on all the relevant topics, including plans for the development of domestic resources and infrastructure, and for hydrocarbon exports. High priority needs to be given to energy alongside health, education and other development objectives.

The overall cost of expanding energy access, while large in absolute terms, is small compared with these countries' potential earnings from oil and gas exports. Hydrocarbon revenues provide the means by which energy poverty can be overcome. Moreover, the era of high energy prices brings greater opportunity. Only a small proportion of the available revenues, after debt servicing, needs to be dedicated to energy-poverty alleviation, rather than dissipated in subsidies, military spending or corruption.

Sound capture and management of hydrocarbon revenues requires efficient design of auctions and contracts, and transparent reporting by producers and governments (Humphreys *et al.*, 2008). It is important that international standards be applied for negotiating and finalising contracts. Equally important are well-functioning systems

---

15. The link between energy and economic development is laid out in Chapter 10 in *WEO-2004*.

for ensuring ethical conduct in the public service. Only one African country, South Africa, features among the 37 countries that have ratified the OECD Anti-Bribery Convention – a major benchmark in the international battle against bribery and corruption. These countries have introduced legislative amendments to strengthen their anti-bribery laws.[16]

Several hydrocarbon-rich countries across the world have created sovereign wealth funds (SWFs) – state-owned investment funds composed of financial assets such as stocks, bonds, property or other financial instruments – as a means of improving the standard of living of every household in the longer term. The funding often comes from revenue generated from the export of natural resources. SWFs, however, may not be the right solution for low-income countries, especially those with rigidities in labour and capital markets. In countries without strong institutions, they may present undesirable opportunities for corruption and mismanagement. Given the scale of the challenge of poverty and development, countries could be better off investing their oil wealth in infrastructure, education and health. After initial mistakes in revenue management following the discovery of natural gas in the Netherlands (termed the "Dutch Disease"), the government there spent gas revenues on physical infrastructure projects, such as bridges, roads and communication, paving the way for higher economic growth (termed the "Dutch Cure"). An abundance of resource wealth offers an opportunity for economic development if governments manage effectively the wealth and the economic impacts of its application (Box 15.6).

Box 15.6 ● Revenue management in Botswana: a success story

One of the world's poorest countries at independence in 1966, Botswana has done remarkably well in using its mineral wealth, mainly from diamond resources, to transform the economy. Recognising that the revenues from diamonds represented sales of a declining asset, the government of Botswana saw clearly the need for reinvestment of these revenues in order to sustain development.

Botswana adopted a policy which requires that all mineral revenues be re-invested and devised its own rule-of-thumb for tracking this re-investment, the Sustainable Budget Index (SBI) (Lange and Wright, 2002). The amount of rent generated by mining and the share recovered by the government are reported, and the way government has used mineral rents is assessed in terms of the SBI.

Botswana has used these revenues to effect remarkable improvements in infrastructure, human capital and the basic services supplied to its population. GDP per capita in Botswana rose by 5.9% per year on average from 1996 to 2006, compared with an average decline of 7% per year for sub-Saharan African countries. Some 95% of the population in Botswana has access to an improved water source. Electricity access is estimated to be around 40%. Reliance on charcoal and fuelwood for cooking is some 65%, less than the share in seven of the countries assessed here.

16. See the *OECD Working Group on Bribery: Annual Report 2007* for more information.

The share of the population relying on fuelwood and charcoal for cooking in urban areas is less than 20%. Botswana joined the World Bank's category of upper-middle-income countries in the 1990s.

Botswana is widely considered to be an excellent example of effective resource management with future generations in mind. As a result of prudent management, not only has the domestic economy been developed but the country has also accumulated a substantial portfolio of international financial assets.

Much valuable experience is available in the management of income-generated natural resources. Norway's experience is being used to help advance its Oil for Development programme. Another relevant initiative is the Extractive Industry Transparency Initiative (EITI), supporting improved governance in resource-rich countries through the verification and publication of company payments and government revenues from oil, gas and mining. Among the countries analysed here, Cameroon, Congo, Côte d'Ivoire, Equatorial Guinea, Gabon and Nigeria have met the conditions to become candidate countries in the EITI. Public access to reliable, verified information is a basic condition of improved accountability by governments for funds derived from resource exploitation; permitting public verification that revenues from this source are actually used for the purposes of the fight against poverty and the implementation of the Millennium Development Goals.

PREFACE

In an attempt to inform the global negotiations on a climate-change agreement, which are due to culminate in Copenhagen at the end of next year, this part of the *Outlook* analyses the interaction of energy and the climate.

Chapter 16 sets out the implications for greenhouse-gas emissions of the Reference Scenario examined in Part A. It shows the evolution of energy-related greenhouse-gas emissions through to 2030 and puts it in the broader context of emissions from all sources. It explains the relationship between the level of annual emissions and the long-term concentration of greenhouse gases in the atmosphere, which will determine the increase in the future global average temperature. The prospective temperature rise goes well beyond what the international community now regards as acceptable.

Change in the energy sector is an essential component of an acceptable, alternative outcome – but it is only one component. Chapter 17 looks at what overall emissions-limitation level the international community might decide upon, how that would translate back into an atmospheric concentration of CO_2-equivalent gases and what means might be used to achieve stabilisation of that concentration. It also sets out the analytical framework for our modelling of energy and emissions in two scenarios: the 550 Policy Scenario, in which greenhouse-gas concentration is stabilised at 550 parts per million of CO_2-eq, and a 450 Policy Scenario, in which concentration is limited to 450 ppm CO_2-eq.

Chapter 18 sets out in detail the projections of energy demand and supply and emissions in the two climate-policy scenarios, by sector and by major regional group. They provide a picture of the policy responses and technological transformation that would be required, in each case, to meet the climate goal, through a plausible combination of cap-and-trade, sectoral agreements and national policies and measures.

Finally, Chapter 19 assesses the implications of those scenarios for investment in the energy sector and how an efficient global carbon market could help minimise costs and so contribute to the realisation of the international community's agreed objectives.

CHAPTER 16

IMPLICATIONS OF THE REFERENCE SCENARIO FOR THE GLOBAL CLIMATE

Where would policy inaction leave us?

- The Reference Scenario describes a future based on established trends and policies, without new initiatives by governments on energy security or climate change. In this baseline scenario, rising global fossil-fuel use continues to drive up energy-related CO_2 emissions, from 28 Gt in 2006 to 41 Gt in 2030 — an increase of 45%.

- Some 97% of the global increase in energy-related CO_2 emissions to 2030 arises in non-OECD countries. China (6.1 Gt), India (2 Gt), and the Middle East (1.3 Gt) together account for three-quarters of the increase. Cities in non-OECD countries account for half of the world's energy-related CO_2 emissions in 2030, up from 38% today. Emissions in the OECD group of countries peak after 2020 and then decline. Only in Europe and Japan are emissions in 2030 lower than today.

- In the 1980s, global energy-related CO_2 emissions rose more slowly than primary energy demand but this decarbonisation of the energy sector started to slow and reverse in the 1990s, as the share of nuclear power fell back while that of coal rose. The Reference Scenario projects the continuation of this recarbonisation until after 2020, before energy demand growth once again outpaces emissions growth.

- The power-generation and transport sectors contribute over 70% of the projected increase in world energy-related CO_2 emissions to 2030. The projected increase in power sector emissions for the OECD — 0.4 Gt between 2006 and 2030 — is less than the increase in emissions from China's power plants in the past two years alone.

- Per-capita energy-related CO_2 emissions in OECD countries are 6% lower on average in 2030 than today. In non-OECD countries, they increase markedly. China's emissions reach those of Europe by around 2025, at more than 7 tonnes per capita, and the Middle East surpasses Japan by 2030, at over 9 tonnes. Despite a 15% decline, per-capita emissions in the United States, at 16 tonnes, are the highest of any country bar Russia in 2030.

- World greenhouse-gas emissions, including non-energy CO_2 and all other gases, are projected to grow from 44 Gt CO_2-equivalent in 2005 to 60 Gt CO_2-eq in 2030, an increase of 35% over 2005. The share of energy-related CO_2 emissions in total greenhouse-gas emissions increases from 61% in 2005 to 68% in 2030.

- As emissions of greenhouse gases build up in the atmosphere faster than natural processes can remove them, their concentrations rise. The Reference Scenario puts us on a path to doubling the aggregate concentration in CO_2 equivalent terms by the end of this century, entailing an eventual global average temperature increase up to 6°C.

- Air pollution is projected to decline slightly over the *Outlook* period, though not in all regions. Reduced emissions of pollutant aerosols bring considerable benefits to human health, but also a reduction in their associated cooling effect on the climate.

Projected trends in energy-related CO_2 emissions

Overview

In the Reference Scenario, rising global use of fossil energy is set to continue to drive up energy-related carbon-dioxide (CO_2) emissions over at least the next two decades (Figure 16.1). A range of government policies, including those intended to address climate change, air pollution and energy security, has helped to slow the rate of growth in emissions in some countries in recent years. In most countries, however, emissions are still rising fast. World energy-related CO_2 emissions grew by 2.5 Gigatonnes (billion tonnes, Gt) from 1990 to 2000; by 2006 they had shot up a further 4.5 Gt to reach 28 Gt. In the Reference Scenario, which takes account only of government policies adopted before mid-2008,[1] emissions jump by 45% to 41 Gt in 2030, an average rate of growth of 1.6% per year. By comparison, emissions grew by 1.8% per year between 1990 and 2006. Non-OECD countries account for almost all of the projected growth in world emissions to 2030. Projected world emissions in 2030 are nonetheless 1.4 Gt (3.2%) lower than in last year's *Outlook*, mainly because fossil-energy demand grows less quickly (Box 16.1).

Figure 16.1 • Energy-related CO_2 emissions in the Reference Scenario by fuel and region

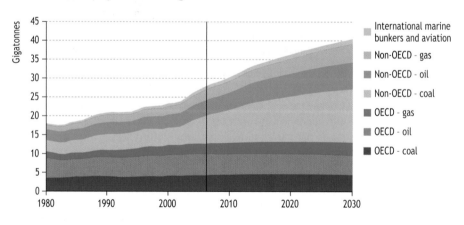

1. See Chapter 1 for a detailed description of the Reference Scenario assumptions.

Box 16.1 ● Projected energy-related CO_2 emissions compared
with *WEO-2007*

Energy-related CO_2 emissions are 3.2% lower in 2030 than projected in last year's *WEO*, due to significantly lower consumption of fossil fuels, mainly oil. Our higher price assumptions for fossil fuels, again notably oil, stimulate more energy conservation and faster uptake of more efficient end-use technologies. They also promote faster deployment of low-carbon supply-side technologies, such as renewables and nuclear power. In addition, a number of new government policies and measures have been implemented since mid-2007 and are taken into account in this year's Reference Scenario, tempering the growth in fossil-fuel consumption.

Lower CO_2 emissions growth in OECD countries (0.1% per year 2006-2030, compared with 0.6% 2005-2030 in *WEO-2007*) results from a combination of higher energy prices, lower GDP assumptions and new policies introduced since last year and now included in the Reference Scenario. Oil demand is most affected, cutting total CO_2 emissions in 2030 by 1.4 Gt compared with *WEO-2007*. In *WEO-2008*, OECD emissions peak after 2020 and decline thereafter.

Emissions grow more slowly in all three OECD regions. In non-OECD countries, the changes vary more by region. This year's *Outlook* assumes faster economic growth in the major energy-exporting countries, leading to faster emissions growth, particularly in the Middle East. Emissions in most other non-OECD regions, however, grow at a slightly slower rate than was projected last year. They nonetheless still account for around two-thirds of emissions in 2030. Emissions in non-OECD countries in aggregate have been rising fast in recent years, despite rapidly rising prices (Table 16.1).

Table 16.1 ● Impact of retail-price increases on primary energy demand and
energy-related CO_2 emissions by region, 2004-2006

| | % increase in retail energy prices 2004-2006 | | | | Implied increase in shadow carbon price $ per tonne of CO_2* | % change | |
	Coal	Oil	Gas	Weighted average		Energy demand	CO_2 emissions
China	24	36	15	28	21	+18	+24
India	-7	21	20	12	22	+12	+11
Other Asia	1	22	47	21	40	+3	+3
Brazil	27	60	16	53	141	+3	+2
Latin America	7	17	34	21	29	+9	+9
Africa	-4	27	36	25	65	+7	+6
Middle East	25	36	19	31	64	+10	+9

* The implied price increase per unit of carbon, based on the average carbon content for each fuel in that region. In theory, the imposition of an explicit carbon price at the levels shown would have been equivalent to the actual changes in energy prices.

16

In the 1980s, global energy-related CO_2 emissions rose more slowly than primary energy demand, mainly because the shares of natural gas, nuclear power and renewables in the power mix expanded. On average, emissions grew by 1.7% per year between 1980 and 2006, while energy use rose by 1.9%. However, this "decarbonisation" of the energy sector started to slow and reverse in the 1990s, as the share of nuclear power fell back while that of coal rose. In the Reference Scenario, "recarbonisation" of the energy sector is projected to continue until after 2020, when a changing supply pattern enables the rate of growth in emissions (Figure 16.2) once again to fall below the rate of growth of primary energy demand. Global carbon intensity — measured by tonnes of energy-related CO_2 emitted per thousand dollars of GDP at constant purchasing power parity — is projected to decline from 0.45 tonnes in 2006 to 0.35 tonnes in 2020 and to 0.30 tonnes in 2030, with intensity falling in all regions. But energy-related CO_2 emissions continue to rise, in absolute terms, as the world becomes wealthier.

Figure 16.2 ● Average annual growth in world primary energy demand and energy-related CO_2 emissions in the Reference Scenario

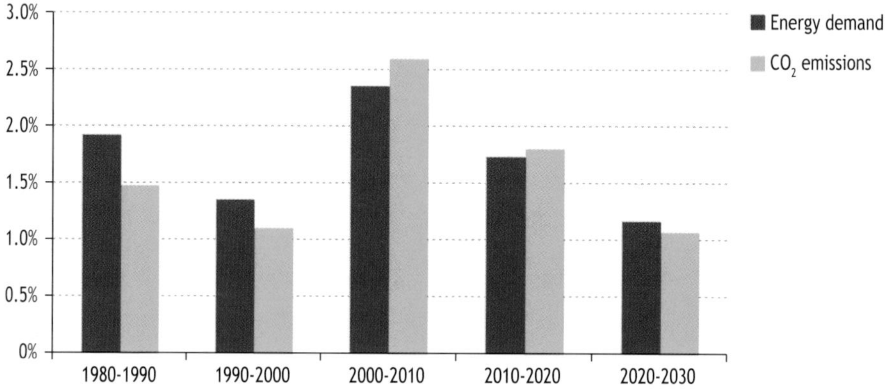

Regional trends

Historical patterns of energy-related CO_2 emissions vary widely across the globe (Figure 16.3). Emissions in 13 OECD countries increased by more than 20% between 1990 and 2006, while the Czech Republic, Germany, Hungary, Poland, the Slovak Republic, Sweden and the United Kingdom reduced their emissions over the same period. OECD emissions overall increased by 16% between 1990 and 2006, while those of non-OECD countries in aggregate shot up by 52%, in line with their faster economic growth, causing emissions from non-OECD countries as a whole to overtake those of OECD countries in 2005. Emissions in some countries, mostly in the former Soviet Union, actually fell during the same period, as their economies underwent massive restructuring (Table 16.2). In contrast, China overtook the United States in 2007 as the world's largest emitter of energy-related CO_2. One reason for China's high emissions is the CO_2 "embedded" in its exports, which far outweighs the CO_2 embedded in its imports (see *Spotlight*). For non-OECD countries in general, urbanisation is a major driver of CO_2 emissions growth (Box 16.2).

Figure 16.3 ● Average annual increase in energy-related CO_2 emissions by region in the Reference Scenario

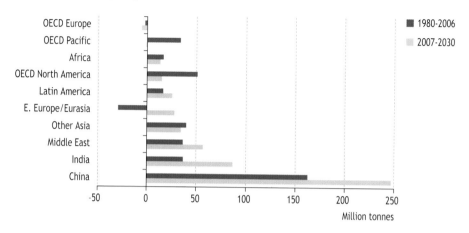

Table 16.2 ● Energy-related CO_2 emissions by region in the Reference Scenario (Gigatonnes)

Region	1980	1990	2000	2006	2020	2030
OECD	10.65	11.04	12.43	12.79	13.31	13.17
North America	5.30	5.57	6.54	6.62	6.95	7.06
United States	*4.66*	*4.85*	*5.66*	*5.67*	*5.77*	*5.80*
Europe	4.12	3.89	3.90	4.06	4.16	3.99
Pacific	1.23	1.58	1.99	2.11	2.21	2.11
Japan	*0.88*	*1.07*	*1.19*	*1.21*	*1.15*	*1.06*
Non-OECD	6.85	9.29	10.17	14.12	21.89	26.02
E. Europe/Eurasia	3.41	4.03	2.45	2.65	3.18	3.34
Russia	*n.a.*	*2.18*	*1.50*	*1.57*	*1.92*	*2.00*
Asia	2.14	3.52	5.20	8.36	14.17	17.30
China	*1.42*	*2.24*	*3.08*	*5.65*	*10.00*	*11.71*
India	*0.29*	*0.59*	*0.98*	*1.25*	*2.19*	*3.29*
Middle East	0.34	0.59	0.97	1.29	2.09	2.61
Africa	0.41	0.55	0.69	0.85	1.08	1.17
Latin America	0.55	0.60	0.86	0.97	1.38	1.60
Brazil	*0.18*	*0.19*	*0.30*	*0.33*	*0.50*	*0.58*
World*	18.05	20.95	23.41	27.89	36.40	40.55
European Union	*n.a.*	*4.04*	*3.80*	*3.94*	*3.95*	*3.76*

*Includes emissions from international marine bunkers and international aviation.

Non-OECD countries account for 97% of the rise in world emissions (excluding international marine bunkers and international aviation) through to 2030 in the Reference Scenario, taking their share of global emissions from 52% in 2006 to 66% in 2030. This is a faster rate of increase than that of their share in energy demand

16

because of an increase in the carbon-intensity of their fuel mix. China alone accounts for 49% of the global increase in emissions and India for 17%, reflecting the rapid economic development of these countries and their dependence on coal. The Middle East emerges as another major emitting region, as its emissions double over the *Outlook* period. Its incremental emissions from 2006 to 2030 are more than three times those of all OECD regions combined (Figure 16.4).

Figure 16.4 ● Incremental energy-related CO_2 emissions by country and region, 2006-2030

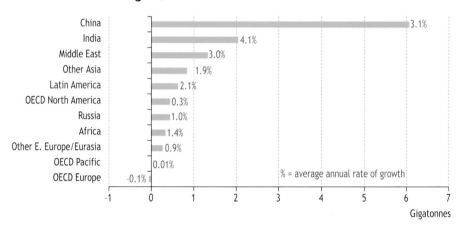

$$\ldots\ldots\ldots\ldots\ldots\ldots\ldots S\ P\ O\ T\ L\ I\ G\ H\ T\ldots\ldots\ldots\ldots\ldots\ldots\ldots\ldots$$

How much of the world's energy-related CO_2 emissions are "embedded" in internationally traded goods and services?

In the *World Energy Outlook*, CO_2 emissions are attributed to the country or region in which the fossil fuel from which the emissions arise is consumed, in accordance with United Nations Framework Convention on Climate Change (UNFCCC) inventory reporting guidelines (for the same reason, emissions from international aviation and shipping are also excluded). Yet the consumption benefits from goods and services produced are often realised in a country other than that in which the emissions arose. This is an issue of concern to some emerging economies, which tend to be more export-orientated and whose exports tend to consist of more energy-intensive manufactured goods. The concept should not be confused with carbon leakage as defined by the Intergovernmental Panel on Climate Change (IPCC), which refers only to changes in emissions resulting directly from climate policy (Box 17.3). A consumption-based accounting system would be extremely difficult, if not impossible, to design, while the current system based on emissions within national borders has the important advantage of simplicity. Nevertheless, a brief examination of the issue can be informative.

There are a number of ways of calculating the emissions embedded in international trade, none of them perfectly accurate due to the lack of complete, reliable and up-to-date data. Energy and energy-related CO_2 emissions are embedded in imports as well as exports, and some goods and services are more emissions-intensive than others. A detailed input-output analysis of China was published in WEO-2007, tracking the distribution of fuels, raw materials and intermediate goods to and from industries throughout the economy. The analysis took carbon intensities and trade data into account and estimated energy-related CO_2 emissions embedded in domestic production for export to be 34% of total 2004 emissions (IEA, 2007). Input-output analysis is highly complex because it involves the calculation of carbon intensity all along the production chain and across the economy, including outsourcing (Houser et al., 2008). Moreover, even such a detailed analysis might not accurately reflect the situation in a country such as China, where production facilities are expanding at a rapid pace.

At the global level, a much simpler methodology is necessary. The percentage of exports in GDP can be used as a simple proxy for the share of energy-related CO_2 emissions that are embedded in domestic production for export. The countries for which up-to-date trade data is available represent 83% of total world energy CO_2 emissions. Grouping those countries into eight regions (Figure 16.5), our estimate of the share of emissions embedded in exports in 2006 ranges from 15% for North America to 48% for the Middle East. The difference reflects variations in the amount and type of exports and the carbon intensity of energy use. The shares for China (44%) and Asian countries other than China and India (41%) are next highest after the Middle East, though for different reasons. Of the 23 Gt of energy-related CO_2 emissions in our sample, one-third was embedded in production for export. China alone accounted for 2.3 Gt (31%) of this, with Europe and Russia combined responsible for another 1.7 Gt (23%). Africa and Latin America each accounted for just 2% of the total embedded emissions.

For China at least, the proxy seems to be a reasonable one, i.e. the carbon content of China's exports is similar to that of its domestic consumption and investment (Weber et al., 2008). Weber et al. find that in 2005, 33% of China's CO_2 emissions were embedded in exports. Although that is a smaller percentage than in our analysis, they find that the share has been steadily increasing, from 12% in 1987. The share of total energy use and carbon emissions embedded in international trade is likely to fall over the projection period if emerging economies, such as China, become more orientated towards their domestic markets.

16

Figure 16.5 ● Ten largest inter-regional flows of energy-related CO$_2$ emissions embedded in exports of goods and services, 2006
(Million tonnes)

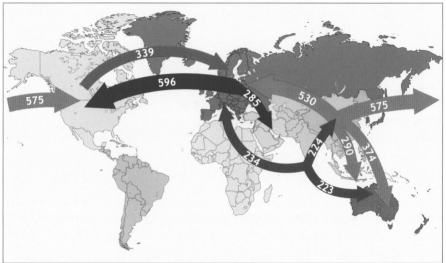

The boundaries and names shown and the designations used on maps included in this publication do not imply official endorsement or acceptance by the IEA.

Sources: UNCTAD (2008); IEA databases and analysis.

Trends per capita and per unit of GDP

World CO$_2$ emissions per capita had been declining until around 2000 but have risen rapidly since. This upward trend is set to continue through to 2030 (Table 16.3). The OECD currently has higher average per-capita emissions than non-OECD regions (though the range is wide between non-OECD countries). In 2006, per-capita emissions in the United States amounted to 18.6 tonnes, followed by Russia with 11 tonnes, Japan with 9.5 tonnes and the European Union with 8 tonnes. China's per-capita emissions were 4.3 tonnes (close to the global average, but 40% of the level of the OECD), while in India they were 1.1 tonnes and a mere 0.9 tonnes in Africa. United States, Japanese and EU per-capita emissions are expected to fall, though not dramatically, over the Reference Scenario projection period. In 2030, Russia's per-capita emissions are projected to have overtaken those of the United States, while China's are likely to exceed those of Europe. Africa's per-capita emissions, on the other hand, are only one-sixth of the world average in 2030.

OECD countries today have lower CO$_2$ emissions per unit of GDP (in year-2007 dollars at market exchange rates) than non-OECD countries. Emissions per unit of GDP decline in both groups of countries over the *Outlook* period, but the decline is faster in non-OECD countries than in OECD countries (Figure 16.6). Nevertheless, by 2030, CO$_2$ emissions per unit of GDP in OECD countries are three times lower than in non-OECD countries.

Table 16.3 ● Per-capita energy-related CO_2 emissions by region in the Reference Scenario (tonnes)

Region	1980	1990	2000	2006	2020	2030
OECD	11.0	10.5	11.0	10.8	10.5	10.1
North America	16.5	15.3	15.7	15.0	13.9	13.2
United States	*20.2*	*19.1*	*19.7*	*18.6*	*16.8*	*15.8*
Europe	8.7	7.8	7.5	7.5	7.4	7.0
Pacific	7.1	8.4	10.1	10.5	10.9	10.7
Japan	*7.5*	*8.7*	*9.4*	*9.5*	*9.3*	*9.0*
Non-OECD	2.0	2.2	2.1	2.6	3.5	3.8
E. Europe/Eurasia	10.6	11.6	7.1	7.8	9.6	10.4
Russia	*n.a*	*14.7*	*10.3*	*11.0*	*14.6*	*16.3*
Asia	0.9	1.3	1.6	2.4	3.6	4.1
China	*1.4*	*2.0*	*2.4*	*4.3*	*7.0*	*8.0*
India	*0.4*	*0.7*	*1.0*	*1.1*	*1.6*	*2.3*
Middle East	3.7	4.5	5.9	6.8	8.5	9.3
Africa	0.9	0.9	0.9	0.9	0.9	0.8
Latin America	1.9	1.7	2.1	2.1	2.6	2.8
Brazil	*1.5*	*1.3*	*1.7*	*1.8*	*2.3*	*2.5*
World*	4.1	4.0	3.9	4.3	4.8	4.9
European Union	*n.a*	*8.6*	*7.9*	*8.0*	*7.9*	*7.5*

*Includes emissions from international marine bunkers and international aviation.

Figure 16.6 ● Average annual rate of change in energy-related CO_2 emissions per unit of GDP* by region, 2006-2030

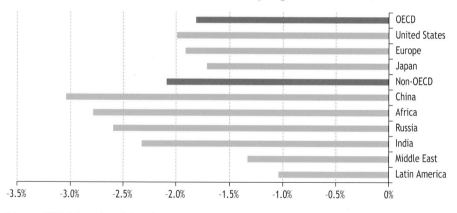

* In year-2007 dollars at market exchange rates.

These projections hinge critically on GDP growth assumptions. In the recent past, many energy projections — including our own — failed to anticipate the full magnitude of the surge in economic growth in China. If growth worldwide were to turn out to be a lot faster than we assume, per-capita emissions would rise even faster than projected.

16

Addressing this uncertainty, the *WEO-2007* included a High Growth Scenario in which world energy-related CO_2 emissions were 2.9 Gt (7%) higher in 2030 than in the *WEO-2007* Reference Scenario (IEA, 2007).

Box 16.2 ● Global city energy-related CO_2 emissions in the Reference Scenario

In 2006, cities accounted for 67% of the world's energy consumption (see Chapter 8 for information on our methodology). This energy use translates into 19.8 Gt of CO_2 emissions – roughly 71% of global energy-related CO_2 emissions (Figure 16.7). The share of global CO_2 emissions in cities is higher than that for energy use because as developing countries urbanise, they tend to shift from biomass and waste (assumed to be CO_2 neutral) to more CO_2-intensive energy sources. Since city residents also tend to consume more energy than rural residents, they therefore emit more CO_2 per capita. This, coupled with the projected increase in global urbanisation, produces a Reference Scenario trend towards an increasing proportion of global CO_2 emissions from cities. The implementation of new climate-change policies in cities is therefore especially important (see Chapter 17).

In the Reference Scenario, CO_2 emissions from cities increase at 1.8% per annum, faster than global CO_2 emissions at 1.6%. By 2030, it is projected that almost 30.8 Gt will be emitted in the world's cities, a 55% increase over 2006 levels by 2030, the equivalent of adding twice the entire emissions of the United States. The share of cities in global CO_2-emissions by 2030 is 76%. As is the case for energy use, the vast majority (89%) of CO_2-emissions growth in cities through the *Outlook* period comes from non-OECD countries. Cities in non-OECD countries account for two-thirds of the global CO_2 emissions in 2030, up from 53% today.

On a regional basis, CO_2 emissions closely follow energy use in OECD countries. In cities in the United States, CO_2 emissions in 2006 were 4.5 Gt and reach 5 Gt by 2030, maintaining roughly the same share as city energy consumption throughout the projection period. Cities in the EU are projected to increase their CO_2 emissions from 2.7 Gt in 2006 to 2.9 Gt by 2030, growing at 0.2% per annum, while CO_2 emissions for the EU as a whole actually decrease by 0.2% per annum. This sees cities' share of total EU CO_2 emissions increase from 69% today to 77% by the end of the projection period. Australasian cities are projected to increase from 0.34 Mt in 2006 to 0.38 Mt of CO_2 emissions by 2030, maintaining roughly the same share as city energy consumption through the projection period.

However, the trend is very different in non-OECD countries, typified by China. The share of energy-related CO_2 emissions in Chinese cities, at 86% in 2006, is higher than that of energy consumption. This is due to increased consumption of fossil fuels and lower consumption of traditional biomass. Emissions of 4.8 Gt in 2006 are projected to increase to 10.3 Gt by 2030, growing faster than national CO_2 emissions, at 3.2% per annum.

Figure 16.7 ● Energy-related CO_2 emissions in cities by region in the Reference Scenario

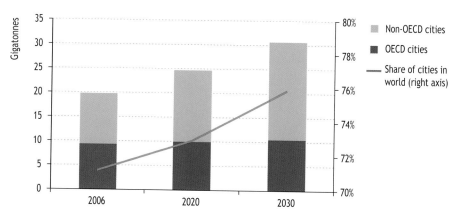

Sectoral trends

Power generation

Fossil-fuel power plants emitted 11.4 Gt of CO_2 in 2006, 41% of the world total. This share has been rising steadily, from 36% in 1990 and 39% in 2000, and continues to grow in the Reference Scenario, to 44% in 2020 and 45% in 2030. Power-sector CO_2 emissions reach 16 Gt in 2020 and 18 Gt in 2030. Cumulatively, power generation contributes over half the increase in energy-related CO_2 emissions to 2030 in the Reference Scenario. This growth is driven by the relatively rapid growth in demand for electricity and in the use of fossil fuels, especially coal, in power generation (see Chapter 6). Emissions from coal-fired power plants reached 8.3 Gt in 2006 and are projected to rise further to 12.1 Gt by 2020 and 13.5 Gt by 2030 – nearly three-quarters of total power sector emissions.

Nearly all of the increase in power-sector CO_2 emissions is expected to come from non-OECD countries, where rising electricity demand and increased reliance on coal are particularly pronounced (Figure 16.8). Having emitted 6.5 Gt of CO_2 in 2006, non-OECD power sector emissions are projected to double by 2030. In the OECD, CO_2 emissions rise by only a small percentage over the projection period because electricity demand growth is more restrained than in non-OECD countries and because more gas and renewable energy enters the fuel mix at the expense of oil and coal. The projected total increase for the OECD between 2006 and 2030 – 0.4 Gt – is less than the increase in emissions from China's power plants in the past two years.

World average emissions per MWh of electricity generated fall slightly as a result of continuing gains in the thermal efficiency of power plants and greater use of renewables (Figure 16.9). However, these savings are not nearly large enough to outweigh the increase in electricity demand.

16

Figure 16.8 ● Energy-related CO_2 emissions from power plants by fuel and region in the Reference Scenario

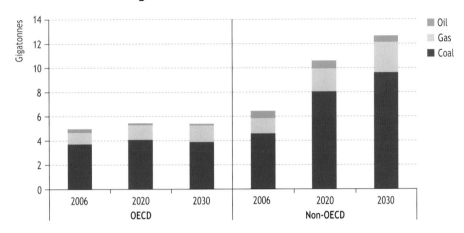

Figure 16.9 ● CO_2 intensity of power generation by region in the Reference Scenario

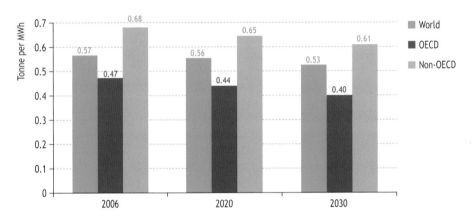

Transport

Transport contributed 23% of world energy-related CO_2 emissions in 2006. It remains the second-biggest emitting sector over the *Outlook* period, though its share of total emissions falls slightly. Transport contributes one-fifth of the increase in global emissions to 2030, growing from 6.4 Gt in 2006 to 8.9 Gt in 2030 (Table 16.4). The two main drivers of growth are increasing vehicle ownership and use in non-OECD countries and increasing international travel, in the form of passenger aviation and navigation (marine freight) (Figure 16.10). Almost 0.4 Gt of the increase is from international marine bunkers and international aviation, whose emissions together grow to 1.4 Gt by 2030. These emissions are not included in UNFCCC inventories.

Table 16.4 ● Transport sector energy-related CO_2 emissions by region in the Reference Scenario (Million tonnes)

Region	1980	1990	2000	2006	2020	2030
OECD	2 254	2 713	3 295	3 513	3 664	3 526
North America	1 423	1 622	1 951	2 108	2 244	2 219
United States	*1 229*	*1 412*	*1 701*	*1 809*	*1 880*	*1 840*
Europe	605	770	915	983	996	923
Pacific	226	321	429	422	424	384
Japan	*156*	*208*	*255*	*244*	*205*	*167*
Non-OECD	855	1 239	1 527	1 952	3 153	4 029
E. Europe/Eurasia	301	445	286	353	454	447
Russia	*n.a.*	*296*	*188*	*227*	*277*	*270*
Asia	210	339	578	773	1 500	2 206
China	*83*	*121*	*229*	*371*	*851*	*1 278*
India	*56*	*82*	*92*	*101*	*246*	*455*
Middle East	79	150	217	303	499	594
Africa	83	105	149	185	229	262
Latin America	181	201	298	338	471	520
Brazil	*72*	*81*	*126*	*141*	*199*	*218*
World*	3 652	4 565	5 630	6 444	8 013	8 921
European Union	*n.a.*	*749*	*879*	*948*	*957*	*883*

*Includes emissions from international marine bunkers and international aviation.

In OECD countries, road-transport related CO_2 emissions are expected to be broadly flat through to 2030. This contrasts sharply with the increase seen over the past 25 years. The vehicle stock[2] in OECD countries is projected to rise by 30% (almost 200 million vehicles) by 2030, much less than the three-fold increase (almost 770 million vehicles) projected for non-OECD countries (see Chapter 3). Average LDV fleet CO_2 emissions in OECD countries are projected to fall from 176 g per kilometre in 2006 to 133 g/km in 2030. This results from incremental improvements in the efficiency of internal combustion engines, increased penetration of biofuels and the continued uptake of hybrid vehicles. These efficiency improvements are already starting to be realised, as high oil prices begin to change consumer preferences in OECD countries. In the United States, light truck sales took a sharp downturn in early 2008, being replaced by smaller passenger cars, and the share of hybrids in total vehicle sales passed 3% for the first time (Green Car Congress, 2008). Sports utility vehicles (SUVs) have seen a sharp decline in sales — especially in the United States. Globally, however, improvements in vehicle fuel efficiency are not enough to compensate for the increase in traffic volume over the *Outlook* period.

Aviation accounted for 11% of world transport emissions in 2006, almost equally split between domestic and international travel. Its share increases to around 13% in 2030 in the Reference Scenario. Recent increases in fuel prices are encouraging

16

2. Total vehicles excluding two- and three-wheelers.

companies to streamline airline operations and to replace old, inefficient aircraft more quickly than previously. However, despite higher fuel prices and a corresponding increase in ticket prices, air passenger volumes increased by around one-third from 2004 to 2007 (Airbus, 2007). The number of commercial aircraft is projected to rise from 18 000 in 2006 to around 44 000 in 2030. Over three-quarters of the current fleet is expected to be retired by 2030 and the new generation of large aircraft that is introduced between now and 2030 is expected to be around 50% more efficient per passenger-kilometre than the current fleet. Alternatives to oil-based fuels in the airline sector are less advanced than for road transport, although some in-flight testing of biofuel blends has been undertaken. We therefore assume that the aircraft fleet remains entirely dependent on oil over the *Outlook* period.

Figure 16.10 • Change in transport sector CO_2 emissions by mode and region in the Reference Scenario, 2006-2030

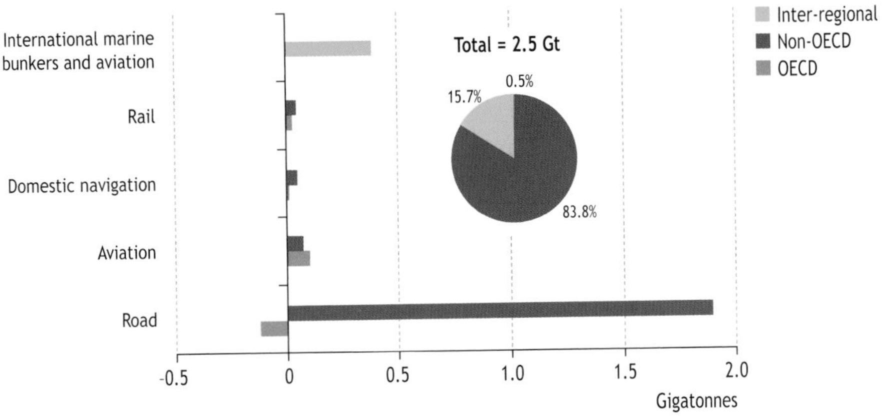

Industry

In the industry sector in 2006, CO_2 emissions from fossil-fuel combustion reached 4.6 Gt, or 16% of total CO_2 emissions. On average, emissions grew by 0.9% per year from 1990 to 2006, but between 2002 and 2006 they grew more rapidly, at 5% per year. This was mainly due to a surge in heat demand for iron and steel, cement and other energy-intensive industries in China. In the Reference Scenario, global industry-sector CO_2 emissions grow by 1.4% per year to 6.4 Gt in 2030 (Figure 16.11). While emissions from OECD countries decline over the projection period, those from non-OECD countries continue to grow. Globally, the share of coal in emissions from the industrial sector increases slightly, from 56% in 2006 to 60% in 2030, driven entirely by non-OECD countries. Iron and steel production contributes most — around one-third — to the increase in industrial emissions, followed by non-metallic minerals, chemicals and petrochemicals production.

Figure 16.11 ● Industry sector energy-related CO_2 emissions by region in the Reference Scenario

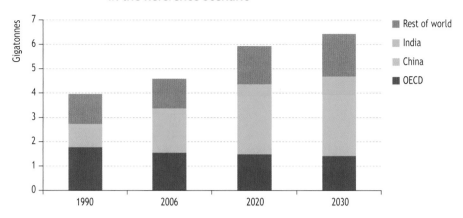

In OECD countries, industry CO_2 emissions declined by 0.9% per year between 1990 and 2006. Although value added in the industrial sector is projected to grow by 1% per year between 2006 and 2030, industrial energy demand grows by only 0.3% per year and direct emissions actually decline, by 0.4% per year, due to switching to less carbon-intensive fuels and electricity. Rising fuel prices are expected to promote the use of more energy-efficient manufacturing technologies. In non-OECD countries, where value added in industry is assumed to grow by 4.3% per year, industry CO_2 emissions rise by 2.1% per year over the *Outlook* period. Nearly half of the additional CO_2 emissions in industry come from China and a further one-quarter from India. In China, the bulk of this growth comes from the iron and steel industry, though the increase in emissions from this sector decelerates progressively. In India, industry emissions grow at 4.9% per year, faster than in any other region, with coal's share rising from 66% in 2006 to 81% in 2030.

The iron and steel, chemical and petrochemical, non-metallic minerals, and paper, pulp and print industries accounted for 65% of global emissions from industry in 2006. The share declines over the projection period to 61% in 2030 as production in less energy-intensive sectors grows faster.

Residential, services and agricultural sectors

At the world level, the agriculture sector was directly responsible for 2% of energy-related CO_2 emissions in 2006, the services sector for 3% and the residential sector for 7%. Together, these "buildings" sectors contribute 5% of the total increase in global emissions to 2030, with growth coming mainly from increased floor space in buildings of various types, especially in non-OECD countries. In China, for example, average floor space per capita is projected to increase from 24 m² in 2006 to 37 m² in 2030. The increase in ownership of energy-consuming home appliances, both in OECD countries and in large emerging countries, is also a contributing factor.

Final (direct) energy consumption in these sectors grows by 1.5% per year between 2006 and 2030 in non-OECD countries, compared with a negligible increase in OECD countries. The very low retirement rate of the building stock in the OECD, with typical

16

lifetimes of more than 40 years (IEA, 2008), keeps CO_2 emissions per square metre at relatively high levels, because the Reference Scenario assumes that heating demand in old, poorly insulated buildings is met mainly through the use of fossil fuels.

When power sector CO_2 emissions associated with the electricity consumed in buildings are taken into account, the residential sector accounted for 17% of the 2006 world total. This sum of direct and indirect emissions increases by 40% between 2006 and 2030, accounting for 15% of the total increase in global emissions to 2030. The most rapid growth in household demand between 2006 and 2030 comes from appliances, with electricity demand growing at 1.1% per year in OECD countries and 3.7% per year in non-OECD countries. In the OECD, appliances account for 73% of the increase in energy-related CO_2 emissions in the residential sector, space heating for 21%, lighting for 5% and water heating for 1%.

Most new buildings will be constructed in non-OECD countries during the coming decades and non-OECD buildings therefore account for 88% of the total increase in building emissions worldwide, though the introduction of building codes (standards for new building efficiency) slows the rate of growth. Non-OECD CO_2 emissions from buildings (including indirect emissions) grow in total from 3.9 Gt to 7.0 Gt in 2030, a rate of 2.4% per annum, while emissions in OECD countries grow at just 0.4% per year between 2006 and 2030. These figures reflect lower direct use of coal and oil for domestic heating and cooking in OECD countries and strong growth in gas consumption in non-OECD countries – driven partly by switching from traditional biomass (Figure 16.12).

In the services sector, world CO_2 emissions (direct and indirect) grow by 1.7% per year between 2006 and 2030. Total residential emissions grow by 1.4% per year over this period, reflecting slower growth in energy demand for residential buildings compared to commercial ones.

Figure 16.12 ● **Increase in direct and indirect energy-related CO_2 emissions by region in the residential, services and agriculture sectors, 2006-2030**

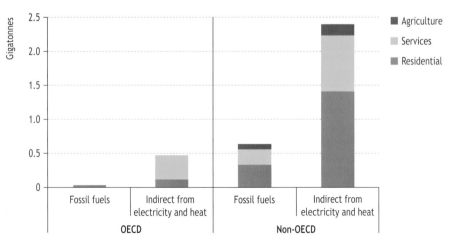

Projected trends in overall greenhouse-gas emissions

The *World Energy Outlook* has for several years presented projections of energy-related CO_2 emissions, based on our fossil-energy demand projections. The burning of coal, oil and gas is expected to be the main source of growth in CO_2 emissions in the coming decades (Box 16.3). Nonetheless, non-energy related emissions of CO_2 (notably from land-use changes such as deforestation and the chemical process of cement manufacture) and emissions of other greenhouse gases[3] from all sectors will remain important. Together, these sources currently account for 39% of total greenhouse-gas emissions. The significance of our energy projections for the concentration in the atmosphere of greenhouse gases in total, and so for climate change, can be understood only if these non-energy emissions are taken into account. This year's *Outlook* includes an assessment of the total emissions picture for the first time.

Box 16.3 ● Greenhouse-gas emissions data and projections

Historical energy-related CO_2 emission estimates are derived from energy consumption data, taken from the proprietary databases of the IEA. Projections of energy demand and associated CO_2 emissions are then made using the World Energy Model (see www.worldenergyoutlook.org for more details). Land-use emissions data are taken from the latest *OECD Environmental Outlook* (OECD, 2008). Emissions data for 2005 with projections out to 2020 for non-energy-related CO_2 and for all non-CO_2 gases covered by the Kyoto Protocol have been provided to the IEA by the United States Environmental Protection Agency (EPA).[4] A range of original sources was used by the EPA to prepare this database, using the latest information available. The data was categorised into the 16 countries and regions used in this *Outlook*. Most other gases, including ozone precursors (nitrogen oxides [NO_x], carbon monoxide [CO], non-methane volatile organic compounds, sulphur dioxide [SO_2]), CFCs and aerosols, were not considered.

All greenhouse gases are converted to tonnes of carbon dioxide equivalent (CO_2-eq), using their 100-year global warming potentials as evaluated by the IPCC (2007). The climate-carbon cycle model MAGICC (Version 5.3) was used to give longer-term projections of all greenhouse-gas emissions out to 2100 and beyond, and to calculate the atmospheric stocks and eventual concentration levels that would result. Other models, including IMAGE 2.4 from the Netherlands Environmental Assessment Agency, were used to verify the emissions assumptions, particularly for land-use CO_2.

16

---

3. The main long-lived gases covered by the Kyoto Protocol, other than CO_2, are methane (CH_4), nitrogen dioxide (N_2O), perfluorocarbons (PFCs), hydrofluorocarbons (HFCs), sulphur hexafluride (SF_6), chlorofluorocarbons (CFCs) and hydrochlorofluorocarbons (HCFCs). The latter two are dealt with under the international Montreal Protocol relating to ozone-depleting substances.

4. EPA projections of emissions go out only as far as 2020, so linear extrapolations were made out to 2030. The data reported in this section were used in the Reference Scenario multi-gas analysis.

Estimating non-energy emissions is difficult and so projections of them are subject to wide ranges of uncertainty (IPCC, 2007). There is also considerable uncertainty about the degree of radiative forcing of many of the non-CO_2 greenhouse gases, as well as the offsetting cooling effects of other gases, such as anthropogenic aerosols (very small particulates).[5] Data on the additional effects of non-sulphur aerosols, tropospheric ozone and stratospheric nitrogen oxide emissions from aircraft are even weaker.

In 2005, global greenhouse-gas emissions amounted to 44.2 Gt of CO_2-eq.[6] The main gases are CO_2, CH_4 and N_2O. In terms of CO_2-equivalent, together they account for almost 99% of anthropogenic greenhouse-gas emissions (Figure 16.13). CO_2 is the dominant gas, accounting for around 81% of CO_2-equivalent global greenhouse-gas emissions. Energy-related CO_2 accounts for 61% of all greenhouse gases in CO_2-equivalent terms and for 76% of total CO_2 emissions.

Figure 16.13 ● World anthropogenic greenhouse-gas emissions by source, 2005

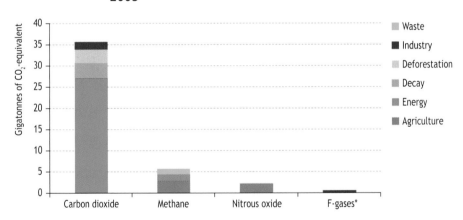

* F-gases include HFCs, PFCs and SF6 from several sectors, mainly industry.
Note: Industry CO_2 includes non-energy uses of fossil fuels, gas flaring, and process emissions. Energy methane includes coal mines, gas leakages, and fugitive emissions. Nitrous oxide from industry and waste amounts to 0.12 Gt CO_2-eq.
Sources: EPA data provided to the IEA; IEA databases; IPCC (2007); OECD (2008).

---

5. Air pollutants, sulphurous oxides and aerosols provide negative radiative forcing, *i.e.* a cooling effect. Their total negative forcing could be roughly equivalent to the current total positive forcing of all the non CO_2 greenhouse gases combined but their impact is very uncertain. They are not considered further in this section. See the section "Local and regional air pollution" below for projections of aerosol emissions to 2030.
6. Emissions of different greenhouse gases can be compared in terms of their CO_2-equivalent, which is based on their global warming potential over a 100-year time horizon as standardised by the IPCC (2007).

CO_2 from industry and land-use change accounts for the largest share of non-energy related greenhouse-gas emissions. Land use, land use change and forests (LULUCF) is a broad category that includes a range of emitting activities such as deforestation, unsustainable use of traditional biomass, burning of scrubland, decay of biomass after logging, peat fires, decay of drained peat soils and loss of organic matter from soils after cultivation. It represents the largest non-energy source, being 19% of total CO_2 emissions or 15% of total greenhouse-gas emissions. Other leading sources of non-energy emissions are cement production and natural gas flaring that together account for around 4% of total greenhouse-gas emissions.

Methane is the second-largest contributor to greenhouse gases, with most of the emissions coming from leakages during natural gas extraction and distribution, and from farming. Methane from the energy and waste sectors accounts for about 6% of total greenhouse-gas emissions, with a similar percentage coming from the agriculture sector. The share of ozone-depleting fluorinated "F-gases" in total greenhouse-gas emission is only about 1%.[7] Nitrous oxide, mainly from agriculture but also from industry and waste, with small amounts from energy use, accounts for most of the remaining non-energy related greenhouse-gas emissions.

By sector, agriculture accounts for half of all methane emissions, 95% of total nitrous oxide, and around 60% of all non-CO_2 gases. These agricultural emissions are influenced by population growth, increased calorific intake per capita, dietary changes to more meat and milk products, crop yields and the intensity of agricultural production and farm management methods.

In the Reference Scenario, total greenhouse-gas emissions are projected to increase by about 35%, from 44.2 Gt CO_2-eq in 2005 to 59.6 Gt CO_2-eq in 2030 (Figure 16.14). Non-CO_2 emissions, which arise mainly in the agricultural sector, are projected to increase, but at a slightly lower rate than the 50% increase in energy CO_2 emissions. Industry CO_2 emissions increase at a similar rate whereas land-use CO_2 emissions, mainly from deforestation, are projected to decline.

Excluding energy-related CO_2, emissions are projected to increase by 11% between 2005 and 2030. By volume, methane emissions increase the most — from 5.7 Gt CO_2-eq in 2005 to 8.2 Gt CO_2-eq. Most of the increase comes from wastewater, ruminant digestion, coal mines and leakages from pipelines due to rising global gas demand. Gas leakages have been reduced in OECD countries (where higher gas prices have increased the incentive to do so) and there are moves to reduce flaring and venting in several producing countries. N_2O emissions grow by around 41%, especially those from nitrogenous fertilizer use. F-gases more than double during the period, mainly due to continuing replacement of ozone-depleting substances by HFCs, causing a three-fold increase of the latter by 2030.

16

---

7. Emissions of ozone-depleting substances controlled under the Montreal Protocol reached a peak of about 7.5 Gt CO_2-eq (20% of total GHG emissions) in 1990 but then decreased significantly as they were replaced by the F-gases. Some of these F-gases cause warming directly; others are produced with methods that yield strong warming by-products. This decrease is expected to continue as CFCs are phased out in developing countries.

Figure 16.14 ● World anthropogenic greenhouse-gas emissions by source in the Reference Scenario, 2005-2030

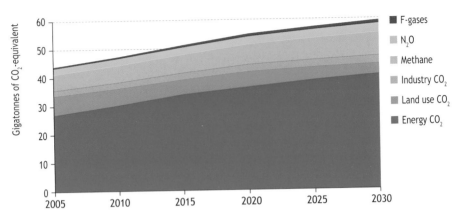

There are large differences in projected emissions of greenhouse gases other than energy-related CO_2 across regions (Figure 16.15). In OECD countries, methane emissions from landfills decline by 2030 due to greater capture and use of the gas, while in non-OECD countries this technology is taken up more slowly and emissions continue to rise. Agricultural emissions increase proportionately more in Africa, China, Eastern Europe/Eurasia and Latin America, where there is greater scope for more intensive farming through better farm management and additional fertilizer use. In OECD countries, these emissions begin to decline due to advanced, precision application of fertilizer, use of soil nitrogen inhibitors and reduction of ruminant methane. SF_6 emissions increase in regions where the power generation sector is expanding. PFC emissions tend to fall by 2030 except in Latin America, Africa and the Middle East, whereas HFC emissions increase virtually everywhere.

Figure 16.15 ● Total greenhouse-gas emissions other than energy-related CO_2 by region in the Reference Scenario

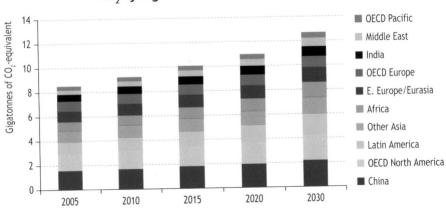

Long-term greenhouse-gas concentrations and average global temperature

The concentration of CO_2 in the atmosphere has risen from around 280 ppm in pre-industrial times to 385 ppm and continues to rise today. This level exceeds by far the natural range over the last 650 000 years (180 to 300 ppm) as determined from ice cores, seabed sediment cores and tree ring records. Methane concentrations have increased from 715 to 1 774 parts per billion over the same period. The total CO_2-equivalent concentration[8] of all long-lived greenhouse gases, taking into account land-use change, is currently around 455 ppm. This is around 60% higher than the level in pre-industrial times.

As a general rule, higher greenhouse-gas emissions lead to higher greenhouse-gas concentrations.[9] These in turn lead to rising global temperatures and more severe climatic consequences. However, the links between emissions of greenhouse gases and climate change are extremely complex and factors such as carbon sinks, albedo (solar heat reflection) effects, cloud cover, land-use change and aerosols can possibly partially neutralise these effects (IPCC, 2007). Nonetheless, it is clear that the rapid growth of greenhouse-gas emissions, as projected in the Reference Scenario, would lead to a substantial long-term increase in global temperatures.

The present average global temperature is estimated to be 0.76°C higher than the pre-industrial level. The rate of temperature change has accelerated, rising to about 0.19°C over the past two decades. The temperature increase per decade is more than twice as fast as that observed over the preceding hundred years.

Our projected increase in energy-related CO_2 emissions to 2030 lies in the middle of the range of CO_2-equivalent emissions scenarios that have been modelled, assuming an absence of new climate policies (IPCC, 2007), with respect to both emissions and concentrations (Figure 16.16). Most of these scenarios project emissions to continue to rise during this century. The projected CO_2 emissions are also consistent with model outputs of concentrations from MAGICC (Version 5.3). Atmospheric CO_2 concentrations by around the end of the next century are in line with the 660 to 790 ppm CO_2 (855 to 1 130 ppm CO_2-eq) ranges assessed from the five scenarios considered (IPCC, 2007). This leads to a temperature rise above pre-industrial levels of about 6°C.

---

8. The concentrations of greenhouse gases other than CO_2 in the atmosphere can be measured in terms of the equivalent CO_2 concentration that would result in the same level of radiative forcing. Today, their additional warming effect is largely offset by the cooling effects of anthropogenic aerosols and tropospheric ozone. The current overall warming effect is therefore considered to be similar to that of CO_2 alone (385 ppm), though this result is very uncertain.

9. 1 ppm of atmospheric CO_2 today mathematically equates to around 7.7 Gt CO_2. In the past 50 years, around 58% of all the CO_2 emitted has stayed in the atmosphere — the rest has been removed over different timescales by various processes, including absorption by oceans and the biosphere, or has been broken down (Hansen, 2005). Consequently, at the present levels of atmospheric concentration, each additional 13.3 Gt of CO_2-equivalent gases released corresponds to an approximate increase in concentration of around 1 ppm. This may change in the future as some of the removal processes reach saturation.

16

Figure 16.16 ● Energy-related CO_2 emissions in the Reference Scenario to 2030 compared with other published scenarios to 2100

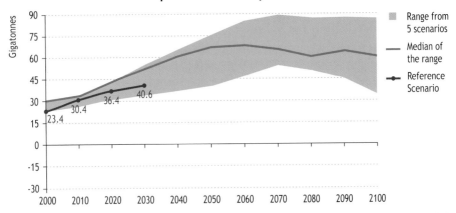

Note: Shaded area gives the ranges taken from five scenarios published since 2001. Some of these included emissions of non-energy CO_2 and other greenhouse gases.

Sources: IPCC (2007); Nakicenovic (2007) and IEA analysis.

The world is already experiencing the ill-effects of rising average global temperature on physical and biological systems, and the situation is worsening (see, for example, IPCC, 2007 and Rosenzweig *et al.*, 2008). There is a risk of breaching unpredictable tipping points, such as a rise in arctic temperatures precipitating a massive release of methane from permafrost zones. Melting permafrost could also threaten oil and gas extraction infrastructure and pipeline stability. Developing countries are particularly vulnerable to global warming, as they are more dependent on resource sectors such as agriculture and with poor infrastructure, often lack the financial resources and capacity to readily adapt to a changing climate. These potentially dramatic impacts have been described in detail by the IPCC and others, and are discussed further in Chapter 17.

The impact of global warming on the energy sector

As well as playing a leading role in causing global warming, the energy sector could itself be substantially affected by a change in the global climate. Worryingly, some sources of renewable energy — one of the main climate-change mitigation options — could be adversely affected.[10]

Hydropower

Hydropower is the world's largest renewable source of electricity, generating 3 035 TWh in 2006, around 16% of total electricity. The unexploited potential is large, particularly in non-OECD countries. However, although hydropower is a key mitigation option, climate change may have an overall net negative impact on water resources and therefore affect its future generation potential (Kundzewicz *et al.*, 2007).

---

10. In contrast, receding sea ice might enable more gas and oil to be extracted from beneath the Arctic Ocean, raising the consumption of fossil fuels and accelerating the melting of the ice and rise in sea levels.

Growing concerns about competition for water supply, as well as other environmental and social concerns, may constrain some project developments. Where climate-change impacts result in water scarcity, the need for adaptation may result in improved water-use efficiency through metering and incremental pricing, increased withdrawal of water for irrigation and the trading of water rights. There could be some adverse effects on local hydropower plant operation and costs. Climate change is also likely to alter river discharge rates and hence water availability for in-stream uses, including hydropower, navigation, fisheries and recreation, as well as for out-of-stream demands, such as irrigation, municipal use, industrial use and cooling (Kundzewicz *et al.*, 2007).

The overall effect on hydropower production potential would be mixed: there could be an increase in some regions, for example, in Scandinavia and Russia, but a fall elsewhere, for example, in Portugal, Spain and Australia. In alpine areas, run-off may decrease in summer and increase in winter, exacerbating sedimentation problems but perhaps also making the management of water storage easier. There may be less storage as snow and ice in winter, thereby adversely affecting river flows in summer and autumn. In Nepal, China and elsewhere, storage of water as ice in glaciers may decrease and seasonal discharge rates change. Hydrological regimes driven more by precipitation than by snow and glacier-melt processes could experience increased year-to-year variability of mean annual discharges, thus adversely affecting the hydropower generation potential (Horton *et al.*, 2005).

Sudden discharge outbursts from lakes formed by rapidly melting glaciers have already created surges of water and debris sufficient to damage hydropower facilities and threaten local communities. Some hydropower generators have already adjusted their production forecasts downwards to reflect changing precipitation projections, thus affecting the economics over the lifetime of a plant.

Other renewable energy systems

In all the scenarios considered in this *Outlook*, increased deployment of other forms of renewable electricity, heating, cooling and transport fuels is projected. However, the prospect of climate change introduces uncertainties which could affect virtually all forms of renewable energy.

- Wind resource intensity and duration can affect turbine capacity factors and extreme gales may damage turbines and shorten their working life.

- Solar radiation levels are subject to reductions of up to 20% in some regions (Bull *et al.*, 2007), due to increased cloud cover, and there is a risk of damage to solar collection facilities from extreme weather conditions, such as hail. In addition, higher ambient temperatures can reduce the output and life of photovoltaic cells.

- Biomass may experience lower crop yields due to water shortages and increased warming, though higher atmospheric CO_2 levels will increase crop and forest growth rates. There could be effects on biomass use for traditional cooking and heating purposes as well on biofuel production for transport fuels. Longer frost-free periods and fewer freezes can benefit some crops more than others, and there will be regional differences, with Africa and southern Asia more likely to be adversely affected than Russia (Lobell *et al.*, 2008).

16

■ Geothermal power generation will be less efficient if warmer water or air is used for cooling. This will also apply to thermal power plants.

Thermal and nuclear power

For coal, gas, oil and nuclear power plants, the lower the temperature of the cooling system, the higher the plant efficiency. Higher average temperature of the cooling water taken from waterways, together with possibly reduced supply in dry periods, could result in lower power output: plant shutdowns are already being experienced under hot ambient air conditions. Greater investment in closed-cycle cooling systems is likely in some areas. Higher temperatures will also reduce the effectiveness of closed-cycle cooling systems. Such power generation constraints could coincide with peak demand for air-conditioning, putting stress on the entire power-supply system.

Concerns about the future availability of cooling water, when in competition with drinking water and irrigation, may restrict power project developments. Other risks include surface erosion affecting open-cast mining of coal, disruptions to offshore oil and gas extraction platforms and refineries due to hurricanes, impacts on LNG and oil transport systems, and greater cost for gas and oil pipelines designed to pass through unstable regions with melting permafrost. Existing infrastructure may need replacing.

Local and regional air pollution

Rising energy consumption, increasing mobility and continuing reliance on fossil fuels are damaging ambient air quality in many developing countries. Emissions of SO_2, NO_x, CO and particulate matter (PM) are harmful to human health as well as being the cause of environmental problems, such as acid rain, reduced visibility and ground-level ozone formation, though they can also reduce the overall warming impact of greenhouse-gas emissions (see footnotes 5 and 8).

Air pollution remains a major public health issue in cities across the developing world, notably in China and India, where ambient air quality continues to deteriorate (IEA, 2007). In addition to the local consequences of unabated emissions, the effects of air pollution are felt beyond national borders. For example, when monsoon winds are prevalent, the citizens of Bangladesh and Pakistan suffer from pollutants generated in India. Likewise, the air quality in Pakistan and Bangladesh affects the citizens of India and other border countries.

Projected trends in local and regional air pollution[11]

World SO_2 emissions in the Reference Scenario are projected to decline only very slightly from 88.8 Mt in 2005 to 88.4 Mt in 2030 (Table 16.5). Emissions of NO_x follow a similar path, decreasing from 80 Mt in 2005 to 72 Mt in 2020 before returning almost to today's level by 2030 at 78 Mt. SO_2 and NO_x emissions decline over the years to 2020, due primarily to stricter controls in OECD countries, but by the end of the *Outlook*

---

11. Projections in this section are based on the Greenhouse Gas and Air Pollution Interactions and Synergies (GAINS) model developed by the International Institute for Applied Systems Analysis (IIASA), available at http://gains.iiasa.ac.at.

period, as OECD emissions stabilise, emissions in Asia, especially India and the Middle East, are still rising. Emissions of particulate matter, on the other hand, exhibit a steady decline at the world level over the *Outlook* period. At 28 Mt in 2030, emissions will be about one-quarter lower than in 2005.

Table 16.5 ● **Emissions of major air pollutants by region in the Reference Scenario** (Million tonnes)

	2005	2015	2020	2030	2005-2030*
Sulphur dioxide (SO₂)					
OECD	27.8	13.3	11.6	11.6	-3.4
Non-OECD	61.0	71.6	72.1	76.8	0.9
E. Europe/Eurasia	4.9	4.0	3.7	3.5	-1.4
Asia	38.3	47.1	47.3	53.3	1.3
China	*25.9*	*30.8*	*29.2*	*30.1*	*0.6*
India	*6.8*	*9.6*	*11.3*	*16.0*	*3.5*
Middle East	6.4	8.7	9.2	9.1	1.4
Africa	6.0	7.2	7.3	6.7	0.5
Latin America	5.4	4.6	4.5	4.2	-1.0
World	88.8	84.9	83.6	88.4	0.0
Nitrous oxides (NOₓ)					
OECD	37.0	23.9	18.5	17.2	-3.0
Non-OECD	43.3	51.0	53.2	61.2	1.4
E. Europe/Eurasia	5.4	4.9	4.9	5.1	-0.2
Asia	23.8	30.9	32.2	37.3	1.8
China	*13.8*	*19.2*	*19.4*	*21.0*	*1.7*
India	*3.7*	*4.8*	*5.4*	*8.0*	*3.1*
Middle East	4.9	5.5	5.8	7.1	1.5
Africa	4.3	4.7	4.9	5.5	1.0
Latin America	4.9	5.0	5.4	6.2	1.0
World	80.3	74.8	71.7	78.4	-0.1
Particulate matter (PM2.5)					
OECD	4.4	3.2	3.0	3.1	-1.3
Non-OECD	32.7	29.7	27.5	25.1	-1.1
E. Europe/Eurasia	0.7	0.7	0.7	0.7	-0.4
Asia	24.1	21.2	19.3	17.4	-1.3
China	*14.0*	*12.0*	*10.6*	*9.2*	*-1.6*
India	*4.6*	*4.4*	*4.2*	*4.0*	*-0.6*
Middle East	0.4	0.4	0.4	0.5	0.6
Africa	5.6	5.6	5.4	4.9	-0.5
Latin America	1.9	1.8	1.7	1.7	-0.5
World	37.1	32.9	30.5	28.2	-1.1

* Average annual growth rate

SO_2 emissions in OECD countries are projected to decline sharply, from 28 Mt in 2005 to about 12 Mt in 2020, and remain flat from then until 2030. Many policies and measures play a role in the decline of emissions in OECD countries, mainly policies that aim to reduce acidification, ground-level ozone and particles by controlling emissions of SO_2,

NO_x and particulate matter from large combustion plants in power stations, petroleum refineries, steelworks and other industrial processes. Emissions caps have been set by the Large Combustion Plant Directive in the European Union and by the Clean Air Interstate Rule (CAIR) in the eastern United States. Non-OECD countries, on the other hand, see their SO_2 emissions increase at a rate of around 1% per year, from 61 Mt in 2005 to 77 Mt in 2030. NO_x emissions also increase steadily in non-OECD countries over the projection period.

In China, SO_2 emissions in the power-generation sector stabilise around 2020, due to stricter regulation, but they continue to rise in the transport sector. Despite rapidly growing transport demand to 2030, the enforcement of vehicle-emission controls in China limits NO_x emissions growth in this sector. Less-rigorous controls in the power-generation and industry sectors, however, result in overall NO_x emissions growing by 1.7% per year on average over the *Outlook* period, to 21 Mt in 2030. Particulate emissions, mainly from burning biomass in the residential and agriculture sectors, decline in China by 1.6% per year over the *Outlook* period because of faster penetration of improved cooking stoves and stricter controls on industry, power plants and vehicles.

India currently lacks a comprehensive strategy to control SO_2 emissions, which more than double over the *Outlook* period. As in China, the gradual introduction of vehicle-emission standards tempers the overall increase in NO_x emissions in India, but they still more than double, rising from 4 Mt in 2005 to 8 Mt in 2030, due to weaker regulation on industry and power plants. India's NO_x emissions alone account for 5% of the world's total in 2005, rising to 10% in 2030. Together, India and China account for over one-third of global NO_x emissions in 2030. The decline in particulate-matter emissions is much slower in India, 0.6% per year in 2005-2030, than in China, 1.6% per year, because the use of biomass resources for cooking and heating and for agricultural production still accounts for about half of energy demand in these sectors in India in 2030.

The Middle East is also expected to see worsening local and regional air pollution due to rapidly rising oil and gas use in the power sector and limited emission-control requirements. SO_2 emissions are projected to increase by more than 40% from 2005 to 2030, reaching 9 Mt in 2030. SO_2-emission controls are not expected to be imposed on power plants in the Middle East until after 2020. NO_x emissions are also projected to rise rapidly, by 1.5% per year on average over the *Outlook* period.

Regulatory programmes, international treaties and emissions-control technologies already exist to tackle many local and regional air pollutants. Furthermore, actions in pursuit of air pollution, climate change and other goals are often mutually supportive: improving energy efficiency, for example, reduces fossil-fuel consumption, reduces air pollution and greenhouse-gas emissions and benefits human health. Such policy integration, producing what are termed "co-benefits", has been recognised by the IPCC and others as a promising approach in both developing and developed countries.

Industrialised countries provide numerous examples of how air quality can be improved despite growing energy consumption. The health benefits associated with more stringent environmental regulation and standards have often been found to outweigh the costs. For example, EPA claims that CAIR offers health benefits more than 25 times greater than the costs of the policy by 2015 (EPA, 2007).

THE POST-2012 CLIMATE POLICY FRAMEWORK
What role for energy in Copenhagen?

H I G H L I G H T S

- Strong, urgent action is needed to curb the growth in greenhouse-gas emissions projected in the Reference Scenario and the resulting rise in global temperatures. A new post-2012 global climate-change policy regime — to be agreed in Copenhagen in late 2009 — aims to set a clear, quantified global goal for the stabilisation of greenhouse gases in the atmosphere, ensuring broad participation and putting in place robust policy mechanisms to ensure the stated objective is achieved.

- With energy-related CO_2 accounting for 61% of global greenhouse-gas emissions, the energy sector will be at the heart of discussions on a target for stabilising the concentration of greenhouse gases — and how to meet it. This *Outlook* considers two climate-policy scenarios: a 550 Policy Scenario, in which the concentration of greenhouse gases is stabilised at 550 parts per million of CO_2 equivalent, resulting in a temperature rise of around 3°C; and a 450 Policy Scenario, in which the concentration is stabilised at 450 ppm CO_2-eq, with a temperature rise of around 2°C.

- Slow rates of capital-stock turnover, particularly in the power sector, mean that, in the absence of disproportionate expenditure, plants that have already been built or are under construction — and their associated emissions — are effectively "locked-in". This power-generation capacity accounts for over 75% of Reference Scenario CO_2 emissions in 2020. This limits the scope for the sector to reduce emissions promptly without large-scale and very costly early retirement. Given this constraint and the time required to arrive at and implement a global agreement, we assume that, in the 450 Policy Scenario, the greenhouse-gas concentration initially overshoots the target level and then declines.

- Five key regions — China, the United States, the European Union, India and Russia — account for 65% of global energy-related CO_2 emissions. Achieving a 450 or 550 ppm CO_2-eq trajectory requires that all major emitters cut their emissions substantially. This must include non-OECD countries, whose emissions in the Reference Scenario in 2030 exceed the *global* emissions level of the 450 Policy Scenario.

- There is a wide range of international policy mechanisms that could be adopted to meet an agreed climate objective. Given countries' varied circumstances and negotiating positions, they are likely to be used in combination. This *Outlook* analyses the implications for the energy sector of a hybrid policy framework of cap-and-trade, sectoral agreements, and national policies and measures.

- In both climate scenarios, "OECD+" countries — a group that includes the OECD and non-OECD EU countries — are assumed to take on national emissions-reduction targets and to participate in an international cap-and-trade system covering the power-generation and industry sectors. Other Major Economies are assumed to implement national policies and measures in these sectors. These two groups are assumed to adopt sectoral agreements in the industry and transport sectors and national policies in the buildings sector. Other Countries are assumed to implement only national policies, across all sectors, but can generate and sell emissions credits.

Co-ordinated global action to address climate change

The Reference Scenario trends in world energy use put the world on course for the concentration of carbon dioxide (CO_2) in the atmosphere to double from 380 parts per million in 2005 to around 700 ppm in the next century. Taking into account all greenhouse gases in all sectors, this would lead to a CO_2-equivalent (CO_2-eq) concentration of around 1 000 ppm, corresponding to a rise in global average temperature of up to 6°C, relative to pre-industrial levels. Co-ordinated action is needed urgently to put the world on a different emissions trajectory. Following the publication of the IPCC's *Fourth Assessment Report* in 2007, a new global consensus on the need for action has emerged. There is now widespread recognition that "warming of the climate system is unequivocal" and that "most of the global average warming over the past 50 years is very likely due to anthropogenic greenhouse gases increases" (IPCC, 2007). Governments and industry alike are now incorporating climate-change considerations more seriously into their policies and business plans.

Progress has been made towards a global agreement and on implementing measures at the national and regional levels. The leaders of the G8 countries agreed in June 2007 at Heiligendamm, to "consider seriously" the goal of halving global emissions by 2050.[1] In Hokkaido in 2008, the G8 went a step further, pledging to "consider and adopt" this goal in the forthcoming global climate-change negotiations. In late 2007, a meeting of nearly every world government, at the 13th Conference of the Parties (COP) of the United Nations Framework Convention on Climate Change (UNFCCC), reached agreement on the "Bali Road Map", a two-year process to improve implementation of the Convention through long-term, co-operative action, including commitments to mitigate climate change and actions to be taken beyond 2012 (the last year covered by commitments under the 1997 Kyoto Protocol). Negotiations will continue in December 2008, at the 14th COP in Poznan, Poland. The road map is expected to be completed by

---

1. Based on IPCC analysis, a reduction of this magnitude would be broadly consistent with stabilising the concentration of greenhouse gases at between 450 ppm and 500 ppm CO_2-eq in the long term.

December 2009, at the 15th COP in Copenhagen, when key decisions will be taken on how the world will respond to the challenge of climate change. The UNFCCC process is supplemented by other high-profile international efforts, including the US-led Major Economies Energy Security and Climate Change Initiative and the Asia-Pacific Partnership.

The energy sector will have to be at the heart of discussions on what level of concentration to aim for and how to achieve it. Energy-related emissions of CO_2 currently account for 61% of total greenhouse-gas emissions, a share that is projected to rise to 68% in 2030 in the Reference Scenario (see Chapter 16). For several years the *World Energy Outlook* has provided analysis of the implications of trends in the energy sector and the associated government policies for energy-related CO_2 emissions. This year's *Outlook* builds on this analysis and breaks new ground by modelling the implications and results of a plausible post-2012 international climate-policy framework under two scenarios, one in which agreement is reached to stabilise the concentration of greenhouse gases at 550 ppm CO_2-eq and another where the agreed stabilisation level is 450 ppm CO_2-eq. We do not focus on a first-best, theoretical world. Instead, we take account of the policy mechanisms currently under discussion, as well as of differences in countries' circumstances and negotiating positions, to consider the implications of an indicative, but plausible, combination of international emissions caps, sectoral agreements and national policies and measures. The intention is not to forecast the political decision that will be taken in Copenhagen, but rather to inform the negotiations there by providing policy makers and the energy industry with a robust, quantified analysis of how the energy sector could respond to the need for deep emissions cuts.[2]

Agreeing on a global, post-2012 climate-policy regime is an enormous challenge. The defining issues to be resolved are:

- What is the appropriate scale of ambition?

- What are the most efficient mechanisms for achieving the agreed objective?

- Which country-by-country commitments and actions would represent a fair and equitable outcome?

There is a host of complications and subordinate issues. Setting the objective entails arriving at an agreement on the acceptable level at which the concentration of greenhouse gases in the atmosphere is to be stabilised, the timescale over which that is to be achieved, and the associated path of emissions abatement. This means taking into account all the available evidence on the environmental, economic and social costs and benefits of action — and inaction. The timescales set must take account of the need for action over a long term, which depends on continuity and reasonable

17

---

2. The analysis in this *Outlook* benefited from a high-level climate-change workshop in Copenhagen on 17 April 2008. Details of this can be found at www.worldenergyoutlook.org/workshops.asp. Delegates expressed a wish that our analysis present a small number of realistic scenarios, focusing on the levels of stabilisation that are most relevant to international negotiations.

certainty, while yet allowing flexibility to adapt the framework according to lessons learned and changing circumstances and scientific knowledge. The equitable sharing of responsibilities will mean either wide acceptance of quantified emissions limitations or, at least, agreement on the range of actions to be undertaken by the respective groups of parties. What should the balance be between the available abatement measures, including international cap-and-trade systems, sectoral agreements and discreet policies and measures, whether applied internationally or nationally? One option is a graduated approach, whereby countries assume responsibilities progressively and at different times. There will need to be credible enforcement mechanisms and appropriate institutional arrangements.

There is no correct blueprint for the outcome. Judgements will inevitably differ, according to broad environmental, financial, distributional and political considerations. With so many variables and so many countries involved, compromises must be reached and trade-offs negotiated.

Defining the long-term global climate objective

An international agreement on climate change needs to have at its core a clear long-term goal of stabilising greenhouse-gas concentrations at an appropriate level and an emissions trajectory to achieve that goal in the most efficient and realistic way. Both elements will be decided collectively by negotiation. These decisions will be based on an appraisal of the costs and benefits of different stabilisation levels and how they might be achieved, taking full account of the practicalities.

Environmental and societal effects of different stabilisation levels

There is no international consensus as yet on a long-term stabilisation or emissions objective, or on the emissions trajectory to its attainment. Nonetheless, international discussions are increasingly centred on a stabilisation level that ranges between 450 and 550 ppm CO_2-eq. According to the IPCC's *Fourth Assessment Report*, stabilisation at 450 ppm CO_2-eq corresponds to a 50% chance of restricting the increase in global average temperature to around 2°C, while stabilisation at 550 ppm yields a rise of around 3°C (compared with 1 000 ppm and up to 6°C in the Reference Scenario).[3] This *Outlook* analyses the implications for the energy sector of international and national policy action to achieve these stabilisation levels in a 450 Policy Scenario and a 550 Policy Scenario (Box 17.1).

---

3. Stabilisation levels of between 445 and 490 ppm CO_2-eq (between 350 and 400 ppm CO_2) correspond to temperature rises of between 2.0° and 2.4°C. At 550 ppm CO_2-eq, there would be a 24% probability of exceeding a 4°C temperature rise. The wide range reflects the uncertainty associated with different emission pathways and the sensitivity of climate to those emissions (IPCC, 2007).

Box 17.1 ● Discerning a stabilisation limit from the IPCC findings

The IPCC's *Fourth Assessment Report* presents findings of analysis of the impact on the environment and society of different stabilisation levels and temperature increases (Figure 17.1). A 450 ppm CO_2-eq stabilisation target would be extremely demanding, requiring emissions of greenhouse gases to peak within the next few years followed by annual reductions of 6% or more.[4] Average annual per-capita CO_2-eq emissions would need to fall to around 2 tonnes by 2050, a significant drop from the current average of 7 tonnes (IPCC, 2007). Currently, emissions range from 26 tonnes per capita in the United States and Canada to 2 tonnes in South Asia. A 450 ppm target would require energy-related CO_2 emissions to fall by 50% to 85% below 2000 levels by 2050 to be consistent with the IPCC's 450 to 490 ppm CO_2-eq range. According to the IPCC, even with stabilisation at 450 ppm CO_2-eq (which is far below that implied by our Reference Scenario projections), the resulting change in global climate would lead to a significant rise in sea-level, species loss and increased frequency of extreme weather events.

A 550 ppm CO_2-eq target would also require very early actions, substantially greater than in the Reference Scenario, in order to quickly decelerate the growth in annual emissions. To meet this target, CO_2 emissions would have to peak — and decline — during the *Outlook*'s projection period. The next few years are, therefore, crucially important. Any delay will result in an increased risk of a still higher temperature increase, which could give rise to irreversible change or demand even more costly and rapid emission-reduction rates later on.

Practical considerations in reducing emissions

When choosing an appropriate global emissions trajectory, policy makers will need to take into consideration the practical implications in terms of technological requirements and costs, particularly in the energy sector. A stabilisation objective of 450 or 550 ppm CO_2-eq would pose a major transformational challenge for the sector, involving substantial additional investment over and above that needed in the Reference Scenario.

The normal cycle of capital replacement is a key constraint on the speed with which low-carbon technologies can enter into use without incurring disproportionate cost. The rate of capital replacement differs substantially by industry and by region, depending on the path of technological progress, costs, the policy environment and capital lifetimes.[5] The energy sector has a relatively slow rate of capital replacement in general, due to the long lifetime of much of its capital (see Chapter 1). As a result,

17

---

4. Some studies, such as Hansen *et al.* (2008), have even suggested that a 1°C temperature rise limit should be set if dangerous interference with the climate system is to be avoided. This would require an overall CO_2-eq stabilisation level of 400 ppm, which would be substantially more challenging than even the most ambitious category of scenarios in the IPCC's *Fourth Assessment Report* (IPCC, 2007).
5. See Lempert *et al.* (2002) for a discussion of the drivers of rates of capital replacement.

Figure 17.1 ● Potential effects of stabilisation of atmospheric concentrations of greenhouse gases at different levels

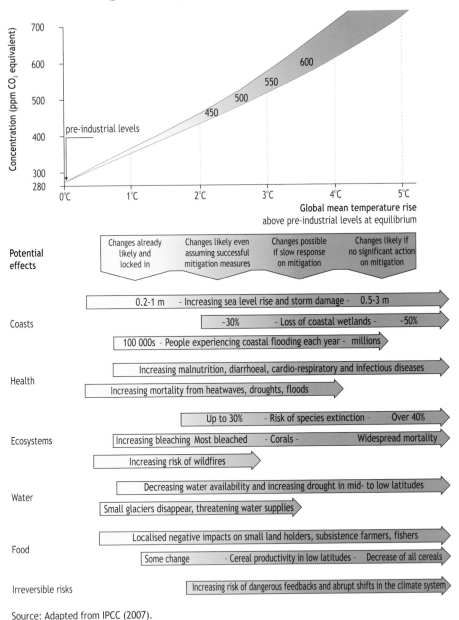

Source: Adapted from IPCC (2007).

more efficient technologies normally take many years to spread through the energy sector. It will be necessary to face up to the reality of the cost of early capital retirement if radical measures are to be taken to speed up this process so as to deliver deep cuts in emissions.

The rate of capital-stock turnover is particularly slow in the power sector, where large up-front costs and long operating lifetimes mean that plants that have already been built — and their associated emissions — are effectively "locked-in". This limits the scope for the sector to reduce emissions without large-scale and very costly early retirement. In the Reference Scenario, three-quarters of the emissions from electricity generation worldwide in 2020 (and more than half in 2030) comes from power stations that are already operating today (Figure 17.2). As a result, even if all power plants built from now onwards were carbon-free, CO_2 emissions from the power sector would still be only 25%, or 4 Gt, lower in 2020 relative to the Reference Scenario.[6]

Figure 17.2 • **Energy-related CO_2 emissions from existing and future power plants in the Reference Scenario**

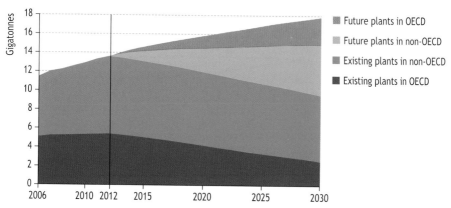

Note: Due to the timescales associated with planning and building new plants, all emissions up to 2012 are assumed to be locked-in.

Source: IEA analysis.

Technology lock-in is also a barrier to reducing emissions in the industrial sector. In the steel sector, where capital plant typically has a lifetime in excess of 25 years, around 60% of all the plants in the world will be less than ten years old in 2010, leaving little scope for replacing them over the following decade with more efficient ones. The picture is similar in the cement industry (see Chapter 18). In industry as a whole, the potential for emissions cuts without early retirement is in line with what is required in the 550 Policy Scenario, but falls far short of what is needed in the 450 Policy Scenario.

Climate scenarios modelled in *WEO-2008*

Our choice of climate scenarios for this year's *Outlook* — corresponding to stabilisation of greenhouse-gas concentration at 450 and 550 ppm CO_2-eq — reflects both the current state of knowledge and understanding of the environmental and societal

---

6. OECD countries would account for just a third of this reduction.

impacts of climate change, as well as the costs and practicalities of reducing emissions in the energy sector. For each scenario, we have calculated both a trajectory for the concentration of greenhouse gases in total (Figure 17.3) and an energy-related CO_2 emissions trajectory to 2030 that is consistent with these stabilisation levels (Figure 17.4).

Figure 17.3 ● **Greenhouse-gas concentration trajectories by scenario**

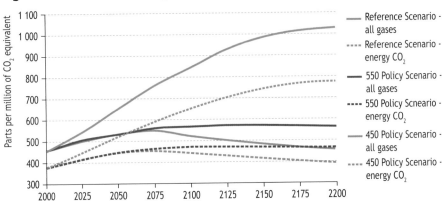

Note: We used MAGICC (Version 5.3)[7] to confirm that the projected emissions for all greenhouse gases to 2030 would result in concentration trajectories consistent with achieving stabilisation at around 700 ppm CO_2 (equivalent to around 1 000 ppm CO_2-eq) in the Reference Scenario, at 450 ppm CO_2 (550 CO_2-eq) in the 550 Policy Scenario and 380 ppm CO_2 (450 ppm CO_2-eq) in the 450 Policy Scenario.

Because of technology lock-in and in view of the time needed to agree and implement a global post-2012 framework and of the scale of effort that would be required in OECD and non-OECD countries alike, the 450 Policy Scenario follows a trajectory to 2020 that overshoots the ultimate objective,[8] with greenhouse-gas concentration initially rising above 450 ppm CO_2-eq, but then declining. A 450 stabilisation trajectory without overshoot would need to achieve substantially lower emissions in the period up to 2020 and, realistically, this could be done only by scrapping very substantial amounts of existing capital across all energy-related industries.[9] In any case, given the scale of new investment required, it is unlikely that the necessary new equipment and infrastructure could be built and deployed quickly enough to meet demand.

---

7. MAGICC is a Model for the Assessment of Greenhouse-gas Induced Climate Change, created by Professor Tom Wigley (www.cgd.ucar.edu/cas/wigley/magicc/).
8. In an overshoot trajectory, concentrations of greenhouse gases peak above the stabilisation target, but subsequently decline. A substantial overshoot, or the overshoot of a high stabilisation level, would entail major risks and could influence transient temperature, whereas a limited overshoot of a lower stabilisation level should not, given the inertia of the climate system.
9. To achieve a CO_2-eq stabilisation level of 450 ppm without overshooting, the energy sector would need to deliver CO_2 reduction of more than 9 Gt in 2020, relative to the Reference Scenario. Taking into account lock-in in the power and industry sectors, this would require 60% emission reduction from the transport and buildings sectors, on top of fully exploiting the scope for action in both power and industry.

Figure 17.4 ● Energy-related CO_2 emissions in the 550 Policy Scenario and 450 Policy Scenario

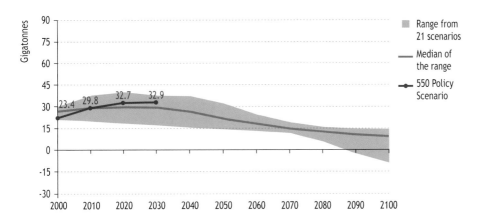

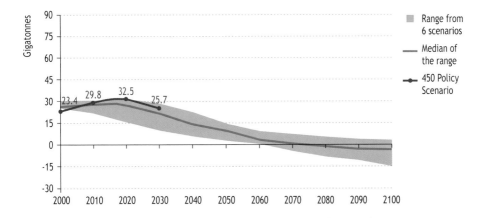

Sources: IPCC (2007); IEA analysis.

Note: The ranges are taken from published scenarios, some of which include industry CO_2 emissions whereas others only include energy-related CO_2 (Nakicenovic, 2007). The 550 Policy Scenario is compared to the IPCC's Class III of scenarios (440-485 ppm CO_2; 535-590 ppm CO_2-eq; ~3°C temperature rise); the 450 Policy Scenario is compared to the IPCC's Class I of scenarios (350-400 ppm CO_2; 445-490 ppm CO_2-eq; ~2°C temperature rise). The *WEO*'s CO_2 pathways are also consistent with the analysis of non-energy CO_2 and other greenhouse gases discussed in Chapter 18.

CO_2 emissions in the 550 Policy Scenario level out around 2020, before falling sharply from 2030. Emissions in the 450 Policy Scenario follow the 550 Policy Scenario trajectory until around 2020 and then begin a sharp, sustained decline. To achieve this much more stringent abatement after 2020, the 450 Policy Scenario requires substantial additional policy effort and technological progress before that date. For both the 450 and 550 Policy Scenarios, the trajectory lies within the range of the various scenarios developed by other bodies and evaluated by the IPCC for the *Fourth Assessment Report*. The 450 Policy Scenario is near the upper limit of the corresponding range of IPCC scenarios, reflecting our overshooting assumption. Nonetheless, due to differences in the underlying assumptions, comparisons of our CO_2-emission trajectories with those of other studies, using different models, can be only indicative.

Although our analysis focuses on the impact of policy actions in the energy sector between today and 2030, emission reductions, in both scenarios, need to continue after 2030 on an even larger scale. The IEA's *Energy Technology Perspectives: Scenarios and Strategies to 2050* report provides a longer term perspective on technological solutions and the roadmaps for delivering them (IEA, 2008a). Substantial emissions reductions are also needed in non-energy sectors. Both the 550 and 450 Policy Scenarios imply that net greenhouse-gas emissions turn negative — *i.e.* carbon absorption exceeds gross emissions — towards the end of this century.[10]

Whatever the overall objective that is adopted, the challenge is huge: both of our scenarios imply very substantial greenhouse-gas emissions reductions compared with the Reference Scenario and require that energy-related CO_2 emissions peak around 2020. In both cases, a major transformation of the energy system takes place, requiring large-scale investment in low-carbon technology development and deployment (see Chapter 19).

Participation

The scale of action needed in both the 450 and 550 Policy Scenarios means that a post-2012 climate-policy framework needs to promote abatement in *all* countries. Yet it is clear that any agreement will need to take into account the importance of a handful of major emitters. The five largest emitters of energy-related CO_2 (China, the United States, the European Union, India and Russia) together account for almost two-thirds of global CO_2 emissions; in the Reference Scenario, this proportion is expected to remain similar in 2020 (Table 17.1). The contributions to emissions reduction made by China and the United States will be critical to reaching the stabilisation goal in both scenarios. While the United States has historically been the highest emitter of energy-related CO_2, China overtook it in 2007 and per-capita emissions in China are now above the world average. Neither country has a quantified national emissions commitment under the Kyoto Protocol. The participation in appropriate ways of non-OECD countries will be indispensable: by 2020, they account for 62% of global CO_2 emissions in the Reference Scenario.

---

10. In theory, this could be achieved by carbon sequestration, either through afforestation and reforestation, by the production of bio-char as part of the biomass energy conversion process which can then be integrated into the soil or by carbon capture and storage technologies applied to the combustion of biomass for heat and power generation or hydrogen production.

Table 17.1 ● The world's five biggest emitters of energy-related CO_2

Country/region	% of global emissions in 2007	% of global emissions in 2020 in the Reference Scenario
China	21	27
United States	20	16
European Union	14	11
India	4	6
Russia	6	5
Total	65	65

The scale of the reduction in energy-related emissions by country grouping varies markedly with different levels of international participation (Figure 17.5). Were the OECD alone to take on all the burden of reducing emissions, the OECD countries would need to achieve reductions of almost 27% by 2020, *vis-à-vis* the Reference Scenario. In fact, achieving the 450 ppm emissions trajectory thereafter without the participation of non-OECD countries would not be possible (see *Spotlight* below). In both the 450 and 550 Policy Scenarios, even after allowing for international emissions trading and the active engagement of non-OECD countries, OECD countries would have to make very substantial emissions reductions *domestically*, such is the scale of the global challenge.

Figure 17.5 ● Regional shares of world energy-related CO_2 emissions in the Reference Scenario for different levels of participation, 2020

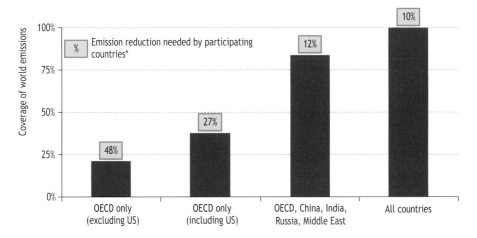

* Relative to the 450 and 550 Policy Scenarios.

Why is it an absolute "must" for non-OECD countries to play their part in a global climate-change regime?

Over half of today's global energy-related CO_2 emissions are from non-OECD countries, a share that is rising rapidly. In the Reference Scenario, 97% of the increase in emissions between 2006 and 2030 occurs in non-OECD countries. In China alone, in *every year* between 2007 and 2030, energy-related CO_2 emissions rise on average by more than the total increase, *over the whole period*, of all OECD countries.

Achieving the global emissions reductions required to limit greenhouse-gas concentration to 550 ppm CO_2-eq without the participation of non-OECD countries would be extremely challenging, to say the least. The global abatement needed in 2030 in the 550 Policy Scenario equates to 58% of OECD Reference Scenario emissions (Figure 17.6). For the OECD alone to take on all of this burden would pose huge practical difficulties, entail substantial scrapping of capital and be highly inefficient since abatement costs would be much lower in non-OECD countries.

The message from the 450 Policy Scenario is clear: it is simply not possible to lower concentration to 450 ppm CO_2-eq without the participation of non-OECD countries. In 2030, non-OECD emissions in the Reference Scenario exceed *global* emissions in the 450 Policy Scenario. In other words, if non-OECD countries do not reduce their emissions relative to the Reference Scenario, a 450 ppm trajectory could not be achieved, even if OECD countries reduce their emissions to zero.

Figure 17.6 ● Reduction in world energy-related CO_2 emissions in the 450 and 550 Policy Scenarios compared with total OECD emissions in the Reference Scenario in 2030

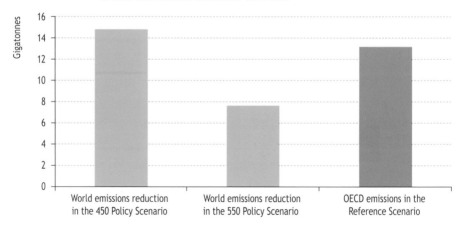

Principles for allocating responsibilities

The allocation of national responsibilities for emissions reduction is a fundamental issue in negotiations on a global climate agreement. Although it is often discussed in the context of cap-and-trade arrangements, it is equally relevant to sectoral approaches and to a formalised system of national policies and measures. Reaching a global agreement on allocations is particularly challenging, as there are many different views on how the appropriate allocation of responsibilities can be gauged and what would represent a "fair" outcome (Box 17.2). We make no suggestion here as to which allocation or method of allocation is most appropriate — this is entirely a matter for negotiation.

Box 17.2 ● Principles for differentiating responsibilities*

Some of the most discussed principles for the possible allocation of responsibilities between countries or groups of countries are the following:

- *Current or historic emissions level:* Requiring that current or recent emissions be the benchmark from which all countries achieve reductions.

- *Cumulative emissions:* Holding countries responsible for their total contribution to climate change, including those emissions made in the past. This model rose to prominence with the Brazilian proposal (BMST, 2000) during the original Kyoto Protocol negotiations.

- *Population:* Aiming to equalise global per-capita emissions allowances by a given date.

- *GDP per capita:* Recognising ability to pay for climate-change mitigation. In Kyoto, binding targets were only applied to the world's richer nations.

- *Emissions per unit of GDP:* Recognising the "necessary" pollution that comes with a high level of output.

- *Reduction potential:* Reflecting differing scope for reducing emissions (this will typically involve sectoral bottom-up analyses, taking into account factors such as economic structure and fuel mix).

- *Costs or benefits of reduction:* Reflecting different national endowments, mitigation costs and potential to benefit from abatement.

- *Building on existing national groupings:* Basing responsibilities on, for example, OECD/non-OECD or UNFCCC groupings.

* For a more detailed discussion, see Höhne *et al.* (2003) and Bodansky (2004).

Discussion of the relative merits of the different mechanisms for reducing emissions — including cap-and-trade, sectoral agreements and national policies — can become clouded by the misconception that the choice of mechanism will determine the scale of the abatement each country faces. However, this choice does not affect allocation, nor who pays for the abatement; a wide range of allocations is possible, regardless of the mechanisms adopted. Rather, it is the different principles for determining a "fair" allocation of responsibilities that yield very different national outcomes. Table 17.2 demonstrates, for illustrative purposes, the outcomes of applying four different principles under a global system of national emissions allowances, in order to achieve in 2020 a 10% reduction relative to the Reference Scenario in world energy-related CO_2 emissions. If national emissions reductions were determined on the basis of endowments allocated equally per head of population, the total allocation for many non-OECD countries would be substantially higher than their current and projected emissions under the Reference Scenario.[11] This would give them scope for generating income through trading their surplus, and scope to profit from any further reductions they achieve relative to the Reference Scenario. On the other hand, allocations based on GDP or current (or recent) emissions result in a lower figure for the required emissions reductions in OECD countries. Irrespective of the principles applied, additional financial transfers, which may form part of a post-2012 agreement, could potentially be made to adjust for any residual "unfairness" in the initial emissions allocation.

Table 17.2 ● Change in 2020 of regional energy-related CO_2 emissions, under different allocation mechanisms, to achieve a 10% reduction in global emissions relative to the Reference Scenario

Country/region	Allocation mechanism			
	Based on 2020 Reference Scenario shares	Equal per-capita emissions	Based on current emissions	Relative to current GDP
United States	-10%	-75%	+15%	+19%
European Union	-10%	-47%	+17%	+77%
Japan	-10%	-55%	+23%	+85%
Other OECD	-10%	-49%	-5%	+23%
China	-10%	-41%	-34%	-67%
India	-10%	+153%	-33%	-36%
Africa	-10%	+378%	-8%	+9%
Russia	-10%	-71%	-4%	-49%
Middle East	-10%	-51%	-27%	-50%
Latin America	-10%	+76%	-10%	+0%
World	**-10%**	**-10%**	**-10%**	**-10%**

Notes: Red indicates an increase compared with the Reference Scenario. A 10% reduction in global emissions in 2020 is consistent with the emissions trajectories in both the 450 and 550 Policy Scenarios.

Source: IEA analysis.

---

11. China, which already exceeds the global average for per-capita emissions, is an important exception to this.

Policy mechanisms

Sharp reductions in global emissions will not be achieved without a structured agreement on the adoption and implementation of a framework of effective international policy mechanisms. Options for such a framework abound in the economic, political and environmental literature. In international discussions, many OECD countries are currently considering a system of national emissions caps with trading of emissions credits among countries — including some non-OECD countries. Theory suggests that an approach such as this, or a global carbon tax, both of which place an international price on carbon, potentially offer the lowest-cost solution in economic terms.[12] However, it is politically and practically very difficult to determine a fair and equitable initial allocation of emission quotas.

Non-OECD countries have generally avoided overt consideration of emissions caps for fear that such caps would restrict their economic development. However, many of them would be prepared to consider a more formalised system of national policies and measures aimed at specified emission reductions, if accompanied by support from developed countries through technology transfer, financial support or other measures. There is also growing interest in international sectoral approaches (involving agreements on national commitments to deploy common processes or adopt common standards such as intensity targets to reduce emissions in specific sectors). These could operate on a stand-alone basis for some groups of countries or sectors, or as a complement to a system of national emissions caps.

In principle, any one of these elements could alone be the basis of a post-2012 regime. However, as current political debate shows, and given practical issues in the energy sector, the reality is that nations adopt the approach or approaches that best reflect their varied interests and capabilities. Thus, an effective future regime is likely to involve a combination of policy mechanisms, tailored to particular needs but also, hopefully, interlinked, in order to achieve maximum economic efficiency.[13] Our analysis focuses on the three main approaches set out above, namely international *cap-and-trade* systems, *sectoral agreements* and enhanced *national policies and measures*. Alongside these approaches, technology transfer and financial assistance can be used to contribute to efficiency and fairness.

In the 450 and 550 Policy Scenarios, all three approaches are assumed to be adopted in a hybrid way, with their combination tailored according to the circumstances and political realities in different countries/regions and sectors (Figure 17.7). The mix is more or less the same in both scenarios and takes into account current national

17

---

12. For example, IMF (2008) notes that "market-based policies have an important advantage over performance standards".
13. These elements should not be considered as static choices. An international regime can and should evolve over time in order to build on lessons learned and to reflect changing environmental and national circumstances. They can also form part of a graduated approach, whereby countries assume greater responsibilities over time.

positions as negotiations develop towards an international agreement on climate change. The results of the two scenarios, reported in the next chapter, are offered as a direct input into those negotiations.

Figure 17.7 ● **Hybrid policy framework assumed in the 450 and 550 Policy Scenarios**

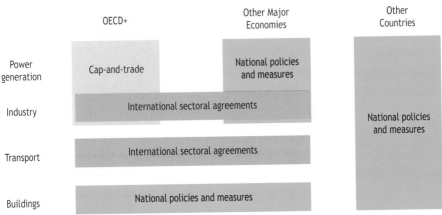

Notes: OECD+ includes all OECD countries, as well as those EU countries that are not members of the OECD. The Other Major Economies group contains the largest emitters outside OECD+ (based on their total emissions of energy-related CO_2 in 2006): China, Russia, India, Iran, Saudi Arabia, Indonesia, Brazil and South Africa. For modelling purposes, we include the entire Middle East region and exclude South Africa. In the 450 Policy Scenario, Other Major Economies are assumed to participate in the cap-and-trade system in power generation and industry from 2020 onwards.

OECD countries and countries that are members of the European Union but not the OECD — "OECD+" — are assumed to introduce binding economy-wide emissions targets, with a cap-and-trade system covering the power-generation and industry sectors. "Other Major Economies" — other major non-OECD+ economies — and "Other Countries" would have the opportunity to generate and trade emissions credits, but they are not assumed to face binding emissions caps. Rather, they undertake to adopt national policies and measures in the power-generation and industry sectors. To reflect concerns about carbon leakage and competitiveness in the industry sector, we have assumed that international sectoral agreements covering the OECD+ and Other Major Economies groups are adopted with respect to iron and steel and cement,[14] as a complement to cap-and-trade and national policies in those industries. In the transport sector, we have assumed that sectoral agreements are applied across the OECD+ and Other Major Economies, while national policies and measures apply in Other Countries. In the buildings sector, all countries are assumed to adopt only national

---

14. The power sector is not covered by a formal sectoral approach in the scenarios, though countries may, in reality, decide to pursue other forms of collaboration in this sector in order to facilitate technology transfer.

policies and measures. Other Countries are assumed to undertake across all sectors only national policies and measures and to do so only where this is compatible with their development objectives.[15] The same mix of approaches in each country/region is assumed in the 450 and 550 Policy Scenarios with one exception: the Other Major Economies group is assumed to participate in the cap-and-trade regime from 2020 in the 450 Policy Scenario.

Cap-and-trade systems

The majority of proposed post-2012 regimes for emissions abatement are underpinned by caps on the quantity of emissions in participating countries. A major advantage of such caps is that they offer a high degree of certainty of meeting an emissions goal — a crucial factor given the climate risks associated with exceeding a global target trajectory. The drawback is that they impose uncertain costs on the economy.

The most straightforward form of a quantity-based approach is a series of absolute, fixed country emissions limits. This is the principal feature of the Kyoto Protocol: industrialised nations agreed to binding targets for greenhouse-gas emissions over the period 2008-2012, involving on average a 5.2% reduction relative to 1990 levels. The Bali Action Plan states explicitly that the UNFCCC process of negotiating an international agreement on climate change for the period beyond 2012 should consider "quantified emission limitation and reduction objectives" by all developed country Parties (UNFCCC, 2007).

With a set of emissions caps, markets can be established to allow trading of emissions credits to take place, which, in principle, can enhance the overall economic efficiency and lower the global cost of reducing emissions. These transactions set a price on emissions, expressed in terms of or limited to CO_2, allowing the market to select areas for emissions reduction along the energy chain and in other parts of the economy. Depending on the regime, trading may take place between countries or companies, or both. To achieve the most efficient outcome, emissions caps must apply to each source of emissions, in order to allow full trading. For practical reasons, this normally means at the level of companies above a certain size. The EU Emissions Trading Scheme provides for trading between all the companies covered (the largest emitters in industry and the power sector) across all EU countries. Under the Kyoto Protocol, industrialised countries are allowed to trade credits, while the Clean Development Mechanism (CDM) allows these countries to obtain credits from non-OECD countries in return for undertaking low-carbon investments.

17

---

15. While the scenarios assume that Other Countries are not required to play a part in cap-and-trade or sectoral approaches, they could still be given financial and technological incentives to achieve quantified emissions reduction or sectoral standards. One way this could be achieved is through a crediting mechanism for a number of sectors to enable these countries to receive funds from OECD+ countries in return for undertaking abatement activities — an enhanced version of the existing Clean Development Mechanism.

Emissions-trading systems in OECD countries

Cap-and-trade systems are already becoming widespread across OECD countries. In addition to the EU scheme, several countries have established their own emissions-trading systems or have announced such schemes for the future (Table 17.3). A global post-2012 framework could seek to expand the international carbon market in order to allow trading between these different systems.

Although national emissions caps can encompass all sectors, emissions trading at the company level is more viable in some sectors than others. With the exception of New Zealand, which intends to adopt a comprehensive, economy-wide approach, most planned and existing systems focus on a small number of major emitting sectors. Typically, these include the power-generation sector and heavy industry, which account for a large share of total greenhouse-gas emissions and whose emissions can be relatively easily attributed to individual companies. Moreover, emitting companies in these sectors tend to be large, greatly reducing the cost per unit of emissions of compliance, monitoring and trading.[16] It is, however, possible for more diffuse sources of energy-related CO_2 emissions, such as road transport, also to be covered by upstream cap-and-trade systems: in this case, fuel producers, rather than end users, participate in emissions trading.

In areas such as agriculture, land use and buildings, emissions are very difficult to monitor and attribute, so these sectors do not lend themselves readily to emissions trading at the company level. Consequently, any post-2012 cap-and-trade system would be unlikely to cover emissions from all sectors.[17] However, as such a system evolved and if monitoring improved, additional sectors could subsequently be added.[18]

Emissions-trading systems in non-OECD countries

Most non-OECD countries do not have any formal quantified commitment under the Kyoto Protocol to limit their greenhouse-gas emissions. Cap-and-trade systems require substantial administrative capacity to monitor, verify and enforce emissions objectives – usually not available in these countries. Were non-OECD countries to seek to advance down this route, they would first need to build national and sector-based emissions inventories and then create credible trading rules and means of enforcing them. Subsidies are another obstacle to the effectiveness of emissions-trading systems in non-OECD countries, as they dampen price signals.

In the longer term, there would be undoubted benefits from including the largest non-OECD emitters, such as China and India, in an international cap-and-trade system. Their inclusion would offer greater global certainty about the long-term global

---

16. Most existing schemes include a minimum threshold for participation, such as the thermal capacity of installations.

17. They could, however, be included in a country's emissions cap.

18. This evolutionary expansion of emissions-trading schemes is the approach being taken by the European Union, which is considering the addition of aviation, and New Zealand, which aims to eventually include all its emissions, including the majority that arise from agriculture.

Table 17.3 ● Existing, announced and proposed emissions-trading systems

Region	Scheme name and start date	Participation	Timetable/ambition	Features
Existing systems				
European Union	Emissions Trading Scheme (2005)	Power generation and energy-intensive industry (e.g. iron and steel, cement and lime, paper, refineries, glass, ceramics and vehicles); aviation planned	Phase II: 6.5% reduction relative to 2005 for 2008-2012 Phase III under discussion (2012-2020)	Mandatory with cross-border trading; increased use of auctioning in Phase II
New South Wales (Australia)	Greenhouse Gas Abatement Scheme (2003)	Power sector and (voluntarily) consumers >100GW	Set to 2012, with commitment to extend scheme to 2020 - would be replaced by Federal scheme	Mandatory; participants allocated annual benchmark, fixed penalty/price cap
Norway	Emissions Trading Scheme (2005)	Energy production, refining, iron and steel, cement, lime, glass, ceramics	Phase II: 2008-2012	Mandatory; other gases from 2008; Phase II auctioning; €100/t(CO_2) penalty
Alberta (Canada)	Climate Change & Emissions Management Act (2007)	Electricity, energy, chemicals (for emitters >100t CO_2-eq per year)	Annual targets	Mandatory (with buy-out options)
New Zealand	Emissions Trading Scheme (2008)	Forestry (incl. deforestation), waste, liquid fossil fuels, stationary energy, industrial processes, agriculture	Sectors phased in, starting with forestry (2008-2010)	Mandatory; internationally tradable; range of penalties
Switzerland	2008	Heating process fuels. Ceramics, glass, paper, chemicals, aluminium, lime, food, printing	2008-2012	Voluntary but legally-binding once committed; tax for non-compliance
Announced systems				
South Korea	2008	Large emitting companies	2008-2011	Voluntary
US (regional)	Regional Greenhouse Gas Initiative (2009)	Power generation (coal, oil and gas-fired with capacity over 25MW)	3-year periods from 2009-2018	Mandatory; North-East states participation
Canada	2010	Power generation, iron and steel, cement, lime, chemicals	2% intensity improvement per year	Mandatory (but with range of compliance mechanisms); all gases
Japan	Trial of Voluntary ETS (2008)	All industry, plus others; project-based domestic CDM for small- and medium-sized enterprises	2008 start	Voluntary ETS: history-based allocation New Voluntary ETS: intensity or volume

17

Table 17.3 ● Existing, announced and proposed emissions-trading systems *(Continued)*

Region	Scheme name and start date	Participation	Timetable/ambition	Features
Australia	2010	Facilities exceeding an emissions threshold, plus upstream fuel. Considering agriculture, forestry		Mandatory; all gases
Proposed systems				
US	Lieberman-Warner Bill (2012) Act S. 2191	Power, transport, manufacturing, facilities producing or importing petrol- or coal-based transportation fuel	Reduces emissions by 71% from 2005 levels by 2050	Mandatory; Carbon Market Efficiency Board; all gases
US	Bingaman-Specter Bill (2012) Act S.1766	Oil and gas upstream; coal downstream	Emissions at 2006 levels by 2020	Mandatory; price cap

Source: IEA based on Reinaud *et al.* (2007).

emissions trajectory and meeting the ultimate stabilisation goal, reducing the risk of industrialised countries "exporting" emissions by relocating their industries outside the cap-and-trade zone.

If non-OECD countries were included in a cap-and-trade system, it would be important to ensure that their participation was on terms consistent with their meeting development objectives. There are a number of ways this could be achieved, including through generous emissions allocation, a comprehensive package of financial and technological support, or a graduated approach that sets caps only for countries above a threshold level of development. Another option is to set non-binding targets for non-OECD countries (Box 17.3).

Box 17.3 ● Non-binding targets for non-OECD countries?

A possible barrier to the adoption of binding emission targets by non-OECD countries is the uncertainty over the total cost that would be incurred to meet them. This uncertainty reflects the difficulty of predicting the pace and extent of their future economic growth, and the associated emissions and the cost of efforts to curb them. So-called non-binding targets offer a possible solution: a country with emissions below its target could sell the difference on the international carbon market. It would not, however, be obliged to buy emissions if they were above the target (Philibert, 2000). With appropriate domestic policies, such non-binding targets could only be beneficial to the country concerned. Hence, they are sometimes called "no-lose" targets. They could be applied nation- or sector-wide.

A country adopting a non-binding target could undertake specific mitigation measures towards the goal and, after verification, sell excess allowances to generate revenue. Frequent compliance checks would deliver these financial benefits more quickly. If selling were to be allowed before compliance were established, a country having sold more allowances than the difference between the target and its actual emissions would be required to buy allowances to cover the excess sales. Investors in mitigation would need some such guarantee that their emissions reductions could be sold, even if other developments took the country's total emissions above the specified limit.

17

Sectoral agreements

Arrangements to curb emissions from a particular sector of the economy can potentially make an important contribution to the global emissions-reduction objective. In this *Outlook*, the term "sectoral agreement" is defined as *an international agreement that commits participating countries to adopting common processes or objectives in order to reduce greenhouse-gas emissions from a specific sector*. One example is an agreement to reduce energy intensity in the steel sector by a specified amount over a set period. Action at the sectoral level is sometimes referred to under the broader term of "sectoral approaches".[19]

Some countries may implement sectoral agreements as a stand-alone means of achieving abatement. For certain sectors or countries, sectoral agreements may offer lower transaction costs or be easier to negotiate than emissions caps. In the European Union, sectoral policy approaches (such as vehicle-emission standards) are increasingly being deployed to stimulate sectors not yet fully covered by emissions targets. Since sectoral agreements are seen by some as less onerous than cap-and-trade systems, they may pave the way for non-OECD countries to participate in a global framework in a manner consistent with their economic development priorities (Baron *et al.*, 2007). They could provide a stepping stone towards later participation in a global cap-and-trade system. Sectoral agreements could also operate as a complement to cap-and-trade,[20] during the time it takes for that mechanism to bed down, or in order to address concerns over carbon leakage and competitiveness (Box 17.4).

Sectoral agreements could take various forms, the most prominent being intensity or efficiency targets. Depending on the sector, there could be a unit efficiency target for specific items of equipment or appliances (which could be met, for example, through standards) or an average efficiency target for the energy inputs to that sector (for example, a country's power sector could be required to meet a goal in terms of tonnes of CO_2 per megawatt hour generated). In the European Union, average carbon efficiency targets have been proposed for vehicle manufacturers, in order to reduce the CO_2 emissions of the average new car sold to 130 grammes per kilometre by 2012, from an average of 158 g in 2007. Another option is to mandate the use of certain technologies, as in the case of the European Union's biofuels mandate and renewable fuels obligation. Future possible mandates could specify, for example, that coal power stations must have carbon capture and storage, or that solar panels must be installed. Another option would be to prohibit technologies or practices that are heavily polluting, such as gas flaring or urban use of sports utility vehicles.

There are many ways of setting targets. They could be developed by reference to existing best practice, by assuming a given rate of technological progress and capital-stock turnover, or by reference to a country's existing level of energy efficiency or carbon per unit of output in given sectors. Japan has suggested identifying the leading existing technologies in key sectors, analysing sectoral emissions-reduction potential, and encouraging countries to set sectoral targets and use sectoral indicators, taking into account their national circumstances. Other approaches are focused on making

---

19. In addition to sectoral agreements, there are many opportunities for using sector-level insights and initiatives in building a post-2012 climate framework. These include bottom-up approaches to calculating national emissions caps, sharing of knowledge or technology on a sector-by-sector basis, and sector-level accreditation of countries' policies and emissions reductions.
20. For example, the European Union's Renewables Directive, a form of sectoral approach, operates as a complement to the EU Emission Trading Scheme.

Box 17.4 ● Carbon leakage and loss of competitiveness

The impact of climate policies on a country's economic competitiveness and the potential for carbon leakage — the relocation of emissions to regions made more competitive as a result of others adopting policies to reduce CO_2 emissions — are potential barriers to reaching a new agreement on climate change.[21] These issues normally relate to participation under cap-and-trade, but may also arise in connection with other approaches. Penalties on carbon emissions within the constrained region create incentives for affected industries, especially the most energy intensive, either to source carbon-intensive inputs from an unconstrained, region or to relocate completely. As a result, constrained countries risk losing market share to unconstrained, competing countries. Furthermore, while one country may be seen to be reducing emissions, these may just be relocated elsewhere. Global emissions may even increase if the relocated production facility uses more carbon-intensive technology. Thus, carbon leakage undermines the effectiveness of climate measures and penalises those countries that take the lead in combatting climate change. These concerns argue in favour of working towards a global cap-and-trade regime that is as inclusive as possible: the more countries that participate under the same constraints, the less the scope for carbon leakage and loss of competitiveness.

International sectoral agreements provide a way of addressing these concerns, as they commit countries outside the cap-and-trade area to meeting similar standards of energy or CO_2 performance per unit of output. Other possible solutions include the free allocation of emissions allowances to affected industries and border-price adjustment mechanisms, under which importers pay a tax equivalent to the carbon price within the constrained area.

Nonetheless, even in the absence of such policies, analysis suggests that any negative impact on competitiveness and emissions abatement may be small.[22] There are many barriers to industrial relocation, at least in the short term, including the risk and cost associated with physically moving productive assets. Transportation costs, existing import restrictions and capacity constraints are also limiting factors.[23] Moreover, a relatively small proportion of industrialised countries' GDP comes from commodities with significant implied carbon costs (either from direct emissions or from electricity inputs). In the European Union, only 1% of GDP is derived from traded commodities where the implied carbon cost amounts to over 4% of that commodity's value added (Hourcade et al., 2007). There is still relatively little analysis of carbon leakage, although this situation should improve as new data becomes available from current and future trading regimes.

---

21. See Reinaud (2008) for a detailed discussion of competitiveness and leakage issues.

22. For example, CICERO (2007) modelling estimates that carbon leakage would be under 3% for the Kyoto regime as a whole and concludes that, if these figures were accurate, "the problem is not critical with respect to environmental effectiveness – or competitiveness effects."

23. The significance of these factors is highlighted by large price differences across regions. Analysis by BNP Paribas shows that cement prices vary greatly from one region to the next (from as low as $20 per tonne in some countries to over $110 per tonne in others).

17

incremental improvements from each country's starting point.[24] A key challenge will be to ensure that sectoral approaches eventually move towards a full reflection of the carbon price that is faced by other sectors.[25]

Sectoral agreements of the type modelled in this *Outlook* are not appropriate for all sectors. They are best suited to sectors that account for a significant share of emissions, that have a high concentration of participants (thus limiting transaction costs) and that are exposed to global competition. Processes and products must also be reasonably uniform, if common standards are to be set. Sectoral agreements can only be used where it is feasible to measure energy efficiency or emissions. Figure 17.8 shows how different sectors compare against some of these criteria. Those circled in the top right corner are likely to be the most appropriate for sectoral agreements as the number of participants is limited and the products are internationally traded and are relatively uniform. For example, the manufacture of large commercial aeroplanes is dominated by two companies — Boeing and Airbus — and their products are sold around the world. Aluminium, steel and motor-vehicle manufacturing are other good candidates. In contrast, sectors such as chemicals and buildings encompass a diverse range of products and processes, while agriculture is characterised by small-scale, diverse emitters.

Figure 17.8 • **Suitability of sectors to sectoral agreements**

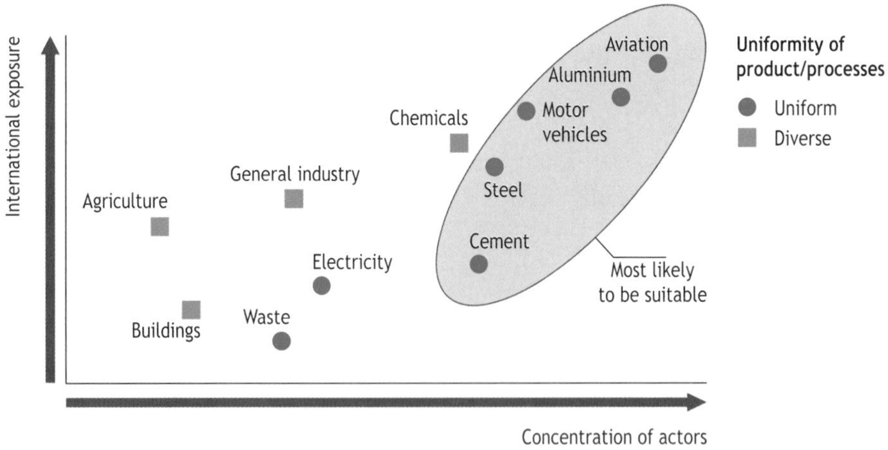

Note: Not to scale; positions are indicative.
Source: IEA analysis.

24. A combination of these two principles is possible. Modelling of a "differentiated convergence triptych" (den Elzen *et al.*, 2007) shows the world converging towards the efficiency levels of the current best country in each sector.
25. When adopting a sector-by-sector approach, there is a risk of making fragmented decisions that do not reflect the relative costs of abatement across the global economy and, therefore, result in inefficiency. In the end, all sources should face the same cost of carbon to reach a least-cost allocation of reduction efforts.

Sectoral approaches already exist in a number of sectors. The Asia-Pacific Partnership on Clean Development and Climate is an intergovernmental public-private initiative to share information and best practice in eight sectors[26] among its partners — Australia, Canada, China, India, Japan, Korea and the United States — which together account for over 50% of both the world population and world energy use. Industry-led sectoral initiatives, such as the Cement Sustainability Initiative, and the initiatives of the International Aluminium Institute and the International Iron and Steel Institute, have all made important progress on emissions measurement, one of the major challenges associated with the implementation of sectoral agreements within a post-2012 framework.

The 450 and 550 Policy Scenarios incorporate sectoral agreements in the transport sector across OECD+ and Other Major Economies. In response to some countries' concerns about carbon leakage and international competitiveness, we have also assumed that sectoral agreements for iron and steel and cement are adopted in these same regional groups (overlapping with cap-and-trade in OECD+). Although a good candidate for a sectoral agreement, the aluminium sector is not covered for lack of good data. A sectoral agreement has not been modelled for the power-generation sector (Box 17.5).

Box 17.5 ● Sectoral approaches and the power-generation sector

The power sector is more fragmented and less engaged in international trade than sectors such as cement and steel. It is accordingly less amenable to a quantified sectoral agreement of the kind assumed in our climate scenarios. Nonetheless, there is significant potential for other forms of sectoral approach in the power-generation sector. These could include:

● Initiatives to share knowledge.

● Joint research, development and demonstration programmes.

● Technology-transfer agreements.

While national circumstances and energy-security concerns will continue to play a key role in determining the evolution of the power sector, such forms of collaboration could be important in ensuring that all countries have access to the most efficient technologies, which in turn could lead to significant fuel and CO_2 savings. A recent IEA study estimates a technical CO_2-reduction potential of around 2.5 Gt per year from improving the efficiency of fossil-fuelled power generation (IEA, 2008b).

17

---

26. Aluminium; buildings and appliances; cement; cleaner fossil energy; coal mining; power generation and transmission; renewable energy and distributed generation; and steel.

National policies and measures

Cap-and-trade and sectoral agreements are unlikely to cover all sectors in all regions. However, regardless of the long-term climate goal that is set, it is important that emissions of greenhouse gases from all potential sources are abated. National policies and measures, tailored to local circumstances and markets, can cover all aspects of energy and carbon efficiency. In both the 450 and 550 Policy Scenarios, we assume that only national policies are adopted in the buildings sector in all three regional groupings. This is because the sector is characterised by a large number of small emitters, heterogenous products and processes, and large regional differences. The Other Major Economies are assumed to adopt national policies and measures in power generation and industry, as well as in the buildings sector. In the Other Countries grouping, *only* national policies are assumed to be adopted, covering *all* sectors.

National initiatives have been the driving force behind much of the global abatement to date and will continue to play a role across all sectors, even those covered by other mechanisms, to ensure that practical measures for achieving sectoral standards or meeting emissions targets are put in place. These national initiatives are likely to include fiscal policy (such as carbon taxes and incentives for households and businesses to curb emissions), regulation, information provision, national procurement and public funding. As well as policies at the national level, local government policies, particularly in cities, have a major role to play in helping countries meet their national climate-change obligations (Box 17.6).

Box 17.6 ● CO_2 savings potential of cities

There is a very large potential to reduce energy use and CO_2 emissions in cities, which currently account for over 70% of energy-related CO_2 emissions (see Chapter 16). Local governments can influence energy use in cities, both directly and indirectly, and often have policy instruments at their disposal which differ from those of national governments. There are three key areas where local governments have significant policy influence which can be used to achieve energy and CO_2 savings:

- Cities can encourage the use of integrated energy-production technology, such as combined cooling, heat and power (CCHP). The density of demand for energy services in cities provides economies of scale (less infrastructure unit cost per capita) as well as greater energy efficiency due to low transmission and distribution losses.

- Cities have considerable influence over passenger transport modes, particularly for short trips. The provision of safe pedestrian and bicycle routes can encourage residents to use these transport modes in preference to passenger vehicles. Land-use and planning powers can be used to create low-emission zones, impose congestion charges and improve public transport.

- Local governments can also influence the efficiency of energy use in buildings. In particular, local governments are instrumental in enforcing the energy components of buildings codes. Electricity production and heat generation in buildings can also be regulated through planning laws: Barcelona introduced a "Solar Thermal Ordinance", a law requiring 60% of hot water to be supplied through solar thermal collectors. This approach was later adopted in a less-stringent form in the national building codes of Spain.

The importance of cities in addressing the challenges posed by climate change is gaining increased recognition, with several having already set climate targets (Table 17.4). In the 1990s, three major city networks working on climate change emerged: The Climate Alliance; ICLEI Local Governments for Sustainability – Cities for Climate Protection Campaign; and Energie-Cités. In 2005, the C40 Cities – Large Cities Climate Leadership Group – was founded. In addition to the international city networks, a number of national networks have been formed or have re-orientated their work towards climate change. These include the Nottingham Declaration Partnership in the United Kingdom; the US Conference of Mayors; Canada's Partners for Climate Protection; the Spanish Network of Cities for Climate; the Kyoto Club in Italy; and the Colgei (Coalition of Local Governments for Environment Initiative) Group in Japan. The activity of these networks can explain in large part the readiness of some cities to adopt specific greenhouse-gas abatement targets.

Despite the many initiatives that some cities have undertaken, only a few are actively pursuing CO_2-mitigation policies. Significant obstacles include competing demands for resources, the tension between short re-election periods and long-term infrastructure challenges, and lack of co-operation beyond city borders. National governments have a role to play in putting in place incentives to encourage cities to undertake CO_2-abatement activities.

Table 17.4 ● Examples of city climate-change policy targets

City	Name	Date	Greenhouse-gas reduction target	Reference year
Toronto, Canada	Climate change, clean air and sustainable energy action plan	2007	6% by 2012, 30% by 2020, 80% by 2050	1990
Tokyo, Japan	Climate Change Strategy	2007	25% by 2020	2000
Berkeley, US	Draft of Climate Action Plan	2008	33% by 2020	2000
Bristol, UK	Climate Change Plan	2005	60% by 2050	2000
Mexico City, Mexico	2002-2010 Valley of Mexico Metropolitan Area Air Quality Improvement Programme (Proaire III)	2000	3% CO_2 reduction by 2010	2000
Cape Town, South Africa	Integrated Metropolitan Environmental Policy	2001	10% CO_2 reduction by 2010	2005
London, UK	The Mayor's Climate Change Action Plan	2007	60% by 2025	1990
Paris, France	Plan Climat	2007	25% by 2020	2004

17

Without such national and local government policies, other mechanisms may not deliver sufficient emissions abatement quickly enough. Price effects, for example, can take some time to feed through the system. In the European Union, emissions were flat between 2004 and 2006 in spite of energy-price increases equivalent to an increase of $30 per tonne of CO_2.

National policies and measures in non-OECD countries

National policies and measures in non-OECD countries, which may not initially have quantified, country-wide obligations under a post-2012 climate framework, will be a necessary component of effective international abatement action. The 450 and 550 Policy Scenarios both assume that a comprehensive set of national policies and measures, across all sectors, is adopted in the Other Countries group. In relation to the group of Other Major Economies, national policies and measures have been modelled for power generation, industry and buildings.

It is important that countries' emissions-reduction strategies take full account of their development needs, thereby fitting the Bali Action Plan description of "nationally appropriate mitigation actions ... in the context of sustainable development". One of the most prominent proposals is the Sustainable Development Policies and Measures (SD-PAMs) model, which offers an opportunity for non-OECD countries to reduce emissions through tailored, development-focused policies, guided by domestic priorities (Ellis *et al.*, 2007). In the energy sector, policies that countries would be likely to pursue as SD-PAMs include measures to promote energy efficiency, the broader use of renewable energy sources, and steps to reduce energy subsidies without damaging the welfare of poorer sections of society.

Formalising the place of such national policies and measures in a global post-2012 framework would help to ensure progress towards a global emissions goal. Such an approach would give full recognition to countries' domestic actions and could help to direct technology financing and capacity-building. It could be an interim step towards country-wide, quantified emission-limitation commitments, based on the sound integration of climate-policy objectives into domestic policy.

CHAPTER 18

CLIMATE POLICY SCENARIOS
The road from Copenhagen?

H I G H L I G H T S

- In the 550 Policy Scenario, total greenhouse gas emissions plateau by 2020 and reach 48 Gt CO_2-eq in 2030. Global energy-related CO_2 emissions peak in 2025 and then decline slightly to 33 Gt in 2030. Both total greenhouse-gas and energy-related CO_2 emissions are 19% lower in 2030 than in the Reference Scenario. Energy-related CO_2 emissions from OECD+ countries are one-fifth lower in 2030 than in 2006. Other Major Economies see an increase of around 60% from 2006 to 2030, instead of a doubling in the Reference Scenario.

- The carbon price in OECD+ reaches $90/tonne of CO_2 in 2030 in the 550 Policy Scenario. This, together with sectoral agreements and national policies in Other Major Economies and Other Countries, lead to substantial changes in the global energy mix: total energy demand in 2030 is 9% lower than in the Reference Scenario, mainly as a result of efficiency gains. The role of renewable energy, mainly wind, rises, while demand for coal falls 27% and that of both gas and oil declines by 8%. Lower fossil-fuel demand results in substantial co-benefits in the form of reduced energy imports and local air pollution.

- Oil demand in the 550 Policy Scenario rises to 95 mb/d in 2020 (4 mb/d less than in the Reference Scenario) and to 98 mb/d (almost 9 mb/d less) in 2030. More than half of the savings in world oil demand occur in the transport sector in OECD+ and Other Major Economies, as a result of the introduction of international sectoral agreements on reducing emissions from light-duty vehicles and aviation. Oil prices reach $100 per barrel in 2030, 18% lower than in the Reference Scenario, due to the lower demand. OPEC production still increases, to 49 mb/d in 2030, almost 13 mb/d higher than today.

- In the 450 Policy Scenario, emissions fall sharply after 2020, in contrast to their stabilisation in the 550 Policy Scenario, as a result of much stronger and broader policy action. Other Major Economies, in addition to OECD+ countries, are assumed to participate in a cap-and-trade system, which results in a carbon price of $180/tonne of CO_2. Hydropower, biomass and other renewables see faster deployment in power generation, accounting for 40% of total electricity generation worldwide in 2030. Global energy-related CO_2 emissions peak in 2020 at 32.5 Gt and then decline to 25.7 Gt in 2030. This scenario would require energy-related CO_2 emissions in OECD+ countries to be reduced by almost 40% in 2030 compared to 2006 levels and Other Major Economies to limit their growth to around 20% compared with 2006.

- Both climate-policy scenarios involve substantial reductions in greenhouse-gas emissions before 2020, resulting from appropriate policies and technology deployment. This would require a credible regulatory framework, the gradual development of a global carbon market and sustained investment in research and development.

Methodology and assumptions

Modelling approach

This chapter presents the results of *WEO-2008*'s two climate policy scenarios: the 450 Policy Scenario, which leads to the stabilisation of greenhouse gases at 450 ppm CO_2-eq, and the 550 Policy Scenario, leading to stabilisation at 550 ppm. Each scenario combines the three climate policy mechanisms discussed in Chapter 17 – cap-and-trade, sectoral agreements, and national policies and measures. The portfolio of policy mechanisms is tailored, on a sector-by-sector basis, to the economic and policy circumstances of three country groupings, namely OECD+, Other Major Economies and Other Countries (see Annex B for definitions). We apply these mechanisms as follows:

- In the power-generation and industry sectors, in both scenarios, OECD+ countries participate in a cap-and-trade system. In the 450 Policy Scenario only, given the need for much more substantial emissions reduction post-2020, Other Major Economies also conform to emissions caps in these sectors from 2020.

- In both OECD+ and Other Major Economies, we assume that sectoral agreements are adopted in both scenarios in the iron and steel, cement, and vehicle- and aircraft-manufacturing sectors, drawing on the potential of the best available technologies.

- In both scenarios, national policies and measures are assumed to be adopted in the buildings sector in OECD+, in buildings, power generation and industry sectors in Other Major Economies, and across all sectors in Other Countries.

The 450 and 550 Policy Scenarios use the World Energy Model (WEM) to assess the implications of these policies – at global, regional and sectoral levels – on energy demand, the energy mix, energy-related CO_2 emissions and investment. CO_2 prices under the cap-and-trade regime have also been calculated.

In the 550 Policy Scenario, the total energy-related CO_2 emissions arising from the above policies amounts to 32.9 Gt in 2030. Of this, the cap on power generation and industry in OECD+ is some 4.7 Gt in 2030. This corresponds to a reduction of 32% relative to these sectors' emissions in OECD+ in the Reference Scenario. Across all sectors, OECD+ emissions in 2030 in the 550 Policy Scenario are around 20% below 2006 levels.

The 450 Policy Scenario follows a similar CO_2 emissions trajectory to the 550 Policy Scenario until 2020, but then diverges sharply downwards to an emissions level of 25.7 Gt in 2030. From 2020, the cap on the power-generation and industry sectors in OECD+ countries is more stringent and these sectors' emissions are also capped in Other Major Economies from this date. Across all sectors, energy-related CO_2 emissions in OECD+ in 2030 are reduced by around 40% in the 450 Policy Scenario, compared to 2006 levels. In Other Major Economies, the level in 2030 is still around 20% higher than in 2006.

Economic growth

There is abundant literature estimating the impact of policy action to reduce emissions on economic growth. Most studies have focused on the long-term impact of stabilisation at 550 ppm CO_2-equivalent (CO_2-eq) or more, though increasing attention has also been given recently to 450 ppm CO_2-eq stabilisation. Recent estimates of the losses of global GDP in 2030 which are attributable to action to cut the atmospheric concentration of emissions to 550 ppm are in the range of 0.2% to 2.5% of world output. The few estimates that exist for 450 ppm are in the range of 0.5% to around 3% (Table 18.1).

Table 18.1 ● Macroeconomic cost of mitigation

Source	Stabilisation level	Loss of world GDP relative to the baseline in 2030	Loss of world GDP relative to the baseline in 2050
	(ppm CO_2-eq)	(%)	(%)
Environmental Outlook 2008 (OECD, 2008)	450	0.5	2.5
	550	0.8	0.9
World Economic Outlook 2008 (IMF, 2008)	550	-	2.6-2.8*
IPCC 4th Assessment Report (IPCC, 2007)	445-535	<3	<5.5
	535-590	0.2-2.5	<4

* In 2040 (world GNP).

Some model simulations in the literature assume implementation pathways for each mitigation policy which are perfectly cost-effective: this certainly underestimates the actual implementation costs. Global GDP losses are highly dependent upon the type of policy implemented, how revenues from emissions trading are redistributed, the effectiveness of financing mechanisms and the trajectory of the decarbonisation path during the transition. Given the uncertainties, we have not tried to quantify the impact of our Policy Scenarios on GDP. However, we have calculated the additional energy-related investment costs of the 450 and 550 Policy Scenarios as a proportion of GDP (based on the GDP level in the Reference Scenario).

Energy prices

In both climate-policy scenarios, energy prices differ significantly from those in the Reference Scenario. They are, however, assumed to be the same in both climate-policy scenarios. Demand reduction in the 450 Policy Scenario goes well beyond that in the 550 Policy Scenario, which would normally put additional downward pressure on prices. However, in the 450 Policy Scenario, we expect production costs for oil (and other fossil fuels) to increase relative to the 550 Policy Scenario, mainly as a result of higher carbon

18

prices, which in this scenario also cover key producing regions, such as the Middle East and Russia. Overall, we assume that these two factors will broadly offset each other, leaving energy prices at the same level in both scenarios.

On this basis, it is assumed that fossil-fuel prices in both scenarios fall relative to the Reference Scenario in response to lower oil, gas and coal demand, the decline in demand stemming from the introduction of new and additional policies aimed at improving energy efficiency and increasing the shares of nuclear and renewable energies. Lower oil demand means there is less need to produce oil from costly fields higher up the supply curve in non-OPEC countries. As a result, oil prices are lower than in the Reference Scenario after 2015, when most of the fields already under construction will have been completed and the impact of reduced demand is felt by producers. Oil prices remain at $100 per barrel in 2030 — a fall of $22, or 18%, compared with the Reference Scenario.

As in the Reference Scenario, natural gas prices are assumed broadly to follow the trend in oil prices, because of the continuing widespread use of oil-price indexation in long-term gas supply contracts. Natural gas prices in Pacific, North American and European hubs are between 18% and 19% lower in 2030 than in the Reference Scenario. Coal import prices are also affected by the different supply-demand equilibrium. The contraction of the coal market is assumed to drive down coal prices relative to the Reference Scenario, especially towards the end of the *Outlook* period when coal demand falls most heavily. Coal prices increase from $65 per tonne in 2006 to $120 in 2015, then fall to $85 in 2030, compared with $110 in 2030 in the Reference Scenario — a reduction of 23%.

Electricity prices increase, reflecting carbon penalties and the higher costs of lower-carbon power-generation technologies. The biggest increases, unsurprisingly, occur in countries where cap-and-trade is applied (Figure 18.1).

Figure 18.1 ● Change in electricity prices in OECD+ countries in the 550 Policy Scenario compared with the Reference Scenario

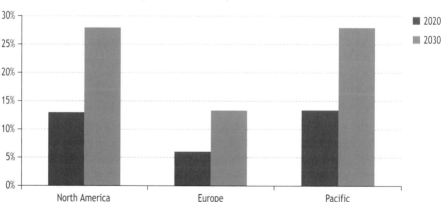

Note: The electricity price is a weighted average of end-use prices in the industry and buildings sectors. The European Union is the only region with a carbon price of $30/tonne of CO_2 included in the Reference Scenario.

Carbon prices

In the 550 Policy Scenario, the carbon price that results from the cap-and-trade mechanism reaches $40 per tonne of CO_2 in 2020 and $90 in 2030 in OECD+ countries. The price increases over time, as the least-expensive mitigation options are exploited first. A lot of unexploited cheap options could exist in Other Countries. A more effective Clean Development Mechanism (CDM) than the current one could help tap part of that potential. In the 550 Policy Scenario, another interesting unexploited option lies in the power sector in Other Major Economies. There could be a significant flow of capital and technology from OECD+ to Other Major Economies if the latter were to set "no-lose" targets to carry them beyond the emission reductions achieved through national policies and measures in the period 2020-2030 (see Box 17.3 in Chapter 17). There would be mutual benefits: OECD+ countries would have access to a large CO_2 market, generating a lower price than that in OECD+ alone; Other Major Economies would gain from the flow of capital and technology from OECD+ countries (see Chapter 19).

In the 450 Policy Scenario, carbon prices in OECD+ countries in 2030 reach $180, twice as high as in the 550 Policy Scenario, because the stringency of the cap is greater. The price emerging in Other Major Economies is initially lower than that in OECD+ countries, because we assume most of the CO_2 reductions occur domestically, with limited linkage between the two markets. The prices in Other Major Economies converge to that in OECD+ countries towards 2030.

Overview of the results of the climate scenarios

Primary energy demand

550 Policy Scenario

In the 550 Policy Scenario, world primary energy demand expands by about 32% between 2006 and 2030, to reach nearly 15 500 Mtoe, an average annual increase of 1.2%, compared with the faster rate of 1.6% in the Reference Scenario (Table 18.2).

Table 18.2 ● **World primary energy demand in the 550 Policy Scenario** (Mtoe)

	2006	2020	2030	Average annual growth rate 2006-2030 (%)	% difference from the Reference Scenario in 2030
Coal	3 053	3 694	3 575	0.7	-27
Oil	4 029	4 553	4 689	0.6	-8
Gas	2 407	3 010	3 383	1.4	-8
Nuclear	728	976	1 086	1.7	20
Hydro	261	389	456	2.4	9
Biomass	1 186	1 499	1 826	1.8	10
Other renewables	66	237	468	8.6	34
Total	11 730	14 358	15 483	1.2	-9

18

The rate of demand growth falls to 0.8% per year from 2020-2030, after running at 1.5% per year in the period 2006-2020. This is a more pronounced drop-off in growth than that seen in the Reference Scenario, with energy intensity falling faster in the 550 Policy Scenario than in the Reference Scenario, particularly towards the end of the *Outlook* period. By 2030, primary energy intensity is 9% lower than in the Reference Scenario.

Total primary energy demand in 2030 in the 550 Policy Scenario is some 1 500 Mtoe lower than in the Reference Scenario. Other Major Economies account for 58% of this, OECD+ for 28% and Other Countries for 14%. OECD+ countries limit their increase in energy demand from 2006 to 2030 to 4%, while energy demand in Other Major Economies rises by 70% over the same period. Energy demand in Other Countries follows a middle path, being 35% higher in 2030 than in 2006.

Coal demand in 2030 drops most, in both absolute and percentage terms, compared to the Reference Scenario (Figure 18.2). Over the projection period, it grows by 0.7% per year on average in the 550 Policy Scenario, compared with 2% per year in the Reference Scenario. It increases by 21% from 2006 to 2020, and declines thereafter. The introduction of national policies and measures in Other Major Economies — in particular policies to promote energy efficiency, nuclear, renewables and more efficient coal-fired power plants — accounts for the bulk of the difference in coal demand between the Reference Scenario and the 550 Policy Scenario. In 2030, coal demand is still 17% higher than today.

Figure 18.2 ● Change in primary energy demand in the 550 Policy Scenario relative to the Reference Scenario by fuel and region, 2030

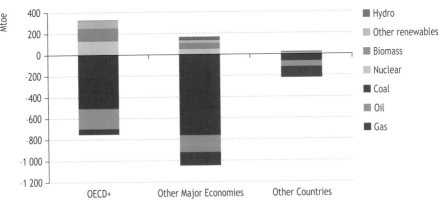

Oil demand rises to 94.7 mb/d in 2020 (4 mb/d less than in the Reference Scenario) and in 2030 to 97.6 mb/d (almost 9 mb/d less). More than half of the savings in world oil demand occur in the transport sector of OECD+ and Other Major Economies. Mainly due to the introduction of international sectoral agreements for light-duty vehicles and aviation, oil demand in OECD+ in 2030 is 15% lower than today. More efficient vehicles and the expansion of biofuels are not sufficient to offset the impact of rising vehicle ownership in Other Major Economies and Other Countries where, together, oil demand expands by around 60%. Natural gas demand is projected to grow by 1.4% per year, compared with 1.8% in the Reference Scenario, with the reduction occurring mostly in Other Major Economies.

The share in the world primary energy mix of low-carbon energy, such as hydropower, nuclear, biomass and renewables, increases from 19% in 2006 to 25% in 2030. Hydropower demand increases in the 550 Policy Scenario to reach 456 Mtoe in 2030, compared with 414 Mtoe in the Reference Scenario. Other renewables, such as wind and solar, receive a much bigger boost, rising seven-fold from just 66 Mtoe in 2006 to the same level as hydro in 2030. Modern biomass use also increases — both in power generation and in decentralised heat production for residential, commercial and industry needs — to around 1 200 Mtoe in 2030. Nuclear grows twice as fast as in the Reference Scenario to reach nearly 1 100 Mtoe in 2030.

450 Policy Scenario

In the 450 Policy Scenario, primary energy demand grows at an average 0.8% per year to 2030, half the rate of growth in the Reference Scenario. Demand approaches 14 400 Mtoe in 2030 — a reduction of about 7% relative to the 550 Policy Scenario and 16% relative to the Reference Scenario (Table 18.3). The annual saving compared with the Reference Scenario is comparable to the current energy demand of OECD North America. The reduction in the use of fossil fuels (over 4 000 Mtoe in 2030 relative to the Reference Scenario) is partially offset by an increase in low-carbon

Table 18.3 ● World primary energy demand in the 450 Policy Scenario
(Mtoe)

	2006	2020	2030	Average annual growth rate 2006-2030 (%)	Difference from the Reference Scenario 2030 (%)
Coal	3 053	3 639	2 381	-1.0	-51
Oil	4 029	4 549	4 308	0.3	-16
Gas	2 407	2 987	2 950	0.9	-20
Nuclear	728	987	1 364	2.7	51
Hydro	261	391	555	3.2	34
Biomass	1 186	1 494	2 119	2.4	28
Other renewables	66	235	683	10.2	95
Total	11 730	14 282	14 361	0.8	-16

18

fuels (nearly 1 400 Mtoe). Despite the sharp decline in fossil-fuel use, relative to the Reference Scenario, fossil fuels still account for 67% of primary energy demand in 2030, 14 percentage points less than today.

Coal demand in the 450 Policy Scenario peaks around 2020 and declines thereafter: the level in 2030 is close to that of 2002. Coal accounts for more than 60% of the reduction in fossil-fuel use, relative to the Reference Scenario. Two-thirds of the reduction in coal use occurs in Other Major Economies, mainly in the power sectors of China and India, due to the introduction of a carbon price in Other Major Economies after 2020. OECD+ countries account for 30% of the global decrease in coal consumption. Their domestic coal use — facing a carbon price of around $180 per tonne of CO_2 in 2030 — is cut sharply, by two-thirds in 2030 compared with the Reference Scenario.

Oil demand in this scenario increases through to 2020 reaching 94.6 mb/d, but then its use declines to just under 90 mb/d in 2030. Oil demand expands on average at 0.3% per year over the *Outlook* period. More-stringent sectoral agreements for light-duty vehicles (LDVs) are responsible for the bulk of the savings. Oil use is reduced by around 17% in 2030, relative to the Reference Scenario, in both OECD+ and Other Major Economies, and by 11% in Other Countries. In OECD+ countries, oil demand declines steadily to less than 80% of today's levels in 2030. Demand continues to expand elsewhere, by around 60% in Other Major Economies and by around 20% in Other Countries.

Gas demand expands throughout the period to 2030, growing at 0.9% per year — half the growth rate of the Reference Scenario. Savings in gas demand are evenly distributed between OECD+ and Other Major Economies, each region accounting for close to 40% of global savings. The carbon price in the power sector makes low-carbon generation more attractive than gas. Higher electricity prices in the residential sector encourage energy efficiency and renewable investment, which reduce the use of fossil fuels.

Nuclear (increasing by 51% from the Reference Scenario in 2030), hydropower (+33%), modern biomass (+60%) and other renewables, such as wind and solar (+95%), all experience sharp growth relative to the Reference Scenario. The carbon price in OECD+ and Other Major Economies makes renewables more competitive than fossil fuels and encourages faster deployment for heat and power than in the Reference Scenario in all countries.

Energy-related CO_2 emissions

A plausible trajectory towards stabilisation of the atmospheric concentration of greenhouse gases at 550 ppm CO_2-eq would see energy-related CO_2 emissions levelling out by 2025 (Figure 18.3). In 2030, world energy CO_2 emissions reach 32.9 Gt — 19% less than in the Reference Scenario. That is an increase of 18% over the 2006 level, compared with an increase of 45% from 2006 to 2030 in the Reference Scenario. In the 450 Policy Scenario, global energy-related CO_2 emissions peak in 2020 and then decline to 25.7 Gt in 2030.

Figure 18.3 ● Energy-related CO_2 emissions reduction by region in the 550 and 450 Policy Scenarios relative to the Reference Scenario

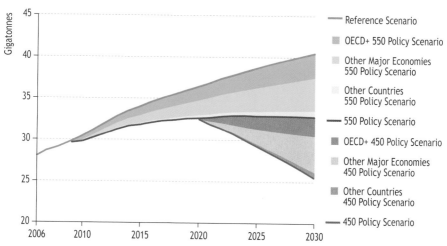

550 Policy Scenario

In the 550 Policy Scenario, energy-related CO_2 emissions in 2030 are 10.4 Gt in the OECD+ countries, as opposed to 13.4 Gt in the Reference Scenario – one-fifth lower than in 2006, instead of 3% higher, as in the Reference Scenario (Table 18.4). The Other Major Economies group, on the other hand, still generates a large increase in emissions in the 550 Policy Scenario, but to a lesser degree than in the Reference Scenario: a 61% increase from 2006 to 2030, instead of the doubling seen in the Reference Scenario. Emissions from Other Major Economies overtake those of OECD+ by 2012, to reach 16.8 Gt in 2030. In Other Countries, the percentage reduction, compared with the Reference Scenario, is not as large as for the other two groups, but is still substantial – 13% in 2030. CO_2 emissions from Other Countries increase by 26% to 4.4 Gt in 2030, as opposed to the 45% increase to 5 Gt seen in the Reference Scenario.

In the 550 Policy Scenario, world CO_2 emissions per capita increase from 4.3 tonnes in 2006 to 4.4 tonnes in 2015, before falling back to 4.0 tonnes in 2030. This is in contrast to the Reference Scenario, where global per-capita emissions rise steeply to 4.7 tonnes in 2015 and continue to rise thereafter, to 4.9 tonnes in 2030. OECD+ countries are largely responsible for the eventual decline in per-capita emissions in the 550 Policy Scenario. Per-capita CO_2 emissions in those countries decline steeply, from 10.6 tonnes in 2006 to 9.2 tonnes in 2020 and 7.8 tonnes in 2030. Per-capita emissions in Other Major Economies increase, from 3.3 tonnes in 2006 to 4.4 tonnes in 2030. The difference is made all the more striking by the fact that population grows at just 0.4% per year in OECD+ over the *Outlook* period, compared with 0.8% in Other Major Economies.

18

Table 18.4 ● Energy-related CO_2 emissions by sector and fuel in the 550 and 450 Policy Scenarios (Gt)

	OECD+				Other Major Economies				Other Countries			
	550			450		550		450		550		450
	2006	2020	2030	2030	2006	2020	2030	2030	2006	2020	2030	2030
Power generation	5.1	4.3	3.3	2.1	5.0	7.5	7.9	5.0	1.3	1.6	1.6	1.2
Other energy sector	0.7	0.6	0.7	0.6	0.5	0.8	1.0	0.7	0.2	0.2	0.2	0.2
Industry	1.6	1.5	1.4	1.0	2.3	3.2	3.4	2.5	0.7	0.8	0.8	0.8
Transport	3.6	3.6	3.2	2.9	1.2	2.1	2.7	2.6	0.7	0.9	1.0	1.0
Buildings	1.7	1.6	1.5	1.2	1.0	1.2	1.3	1.1	0.5	0.5	0.6	0.6
Non-energy use	0.4	0.3	0.3	0.3	0.4	0.6	0.6	0.5	0.1	0.2	0.2	0.2
Total	13.0	11.9	10.4	8.2	10.4	15.4	16.8	12.4	3.5	4.3	4.4	3.9
Oil	5.7	5.2	4.7	4.3	2.7	4.1	4.7	4.3	1.4	1.7	1.8	1.7
Gas	2.9	3.2	3.4	2.7	1.6	2.2	2.7	2.3	1.0	1.3	1.4	1.3
Coal	4.5	3.5	2.3	1.2	6.1	9.1	9.4	5.7	1.1	1.3	1.2	0.9

CO_2 emissions from coal use in the 550 Policy Scenario increase by 10% between 2006 and 2030, but that is dramatically lower than the 60% increase seen in the Reference Scenario over the same period. Coal emissions are 1.2 Gt higher in 2030 than in 2006. In this same scenario, emissions from oil equal those from coal in 2030, while in the Reference Scenario coal emissions are 36% greater than those from oil. This reflects the paucity of alternatives to oil in the transport sector, highlighting the fact that finding a substitute for oil in transport is a key issue not only for security of supply but also for climate-change mitigation. Gas-related emissions increase most over the *Outlook* period — 2.1 Gt (38%) — mainly due to fuel switching in the power sector. However, this is less than the 2.8 Gt (52%) increase in the Reference Scenario.

The 550 Policy Scenario sees a decline in CO_2 intensity (tonnes of CO_2 emissions from energy use per unit of GDP, at fixed purchasing power parities) at a rate of 2.6% per year over the *Outlook* period. In the Reference Scenario, the rate of decline at world level is just 1.7% per year. The average quantity of CO_2 emitted per tonne of oil equivalent of fossil energy used worldwide is projected to decrease from 2.94 tonnes in 2006 to 2.83 tonnes in 2030, reflecting the decline in coal consumption.

A significant proportion of the reduction in emissions is derived from the implementation of national policies and measures, particularly in Other Major Economies. The primary motivation behind the adoption of national policies and measures is often not climate change but a quest for greater security of supply, greater efficiency or lower local pollution. Therefore, related greenhouse-gas emission reductions can be considered a co-benefit. As these benefits in terms of greenhouse-gas abatement may not be subject to any verification or enforcement, however, there is no certainty that they will be achieved. The policies listed in Table 18.5 have particularly significant impacts.

Table 18.5 ● Major initiatives to reduce energy-related CO_2 emissions in Other Major Economies

Country/region	Policy
China	300 GW hydro installed capacity by 2020
	Nuclear power contributing more than 5% of national energy requirements by 2020
	Plans to shut down coal-fired units of less than 50 MW and later 100 MW
	Implementation of the second phase of fuel-economy standards in cars
India	Integrated Energy Policy recommendation to increase coal plant efficiency from 30.5% to 39%
	Vehicle Emission Standard that follows the European Vehicle Emission Standards
Russia	Policies to increase the share of nuclear power
Brazil	Incentives for renewable energy (PROINFA)

In order to reduce CO_2 emissions by 7.6 Gt, the 550 Policy Scenario requires development — on a significant scale — of less CO_2-intensive technologies (Figure 18.4). In 2030, 4.8 Gt of avoided CO_2 emissions — 63% of total CO_2 emissions reductions compared to the Reference Scenario — stem from efficiency improvements in the end-use sector and in power generation. A further 0.6 Gt of CO_2 savings come from

18

the operation of an additional 86 GW of nuclear capacity, beyond that built in the Reference Scenario. The large-scale deployment of renewable and carbon capture and storage (CCS) technologies in the power sector gives rise to 1.2 and 0.8 Gt of CO_2 savings, respectively. The decarbonisation of the power sector alone involves notably the construction every year to 2030 of an additional 7 coal-fired plants and 3 gas-fired plants with CCS, 11 new nuclear plants and almost 12 000 wind turbines, while hydropower is expanded every two years by 64 GW — the equivalent of three dams of the capacity of China's Three Gorges Dam.[1]

Figure 18.4 ● **Energy-related CO_2 emissions by source in the 550 and 450 Policy Scenarios relative to the Reference Scenario**

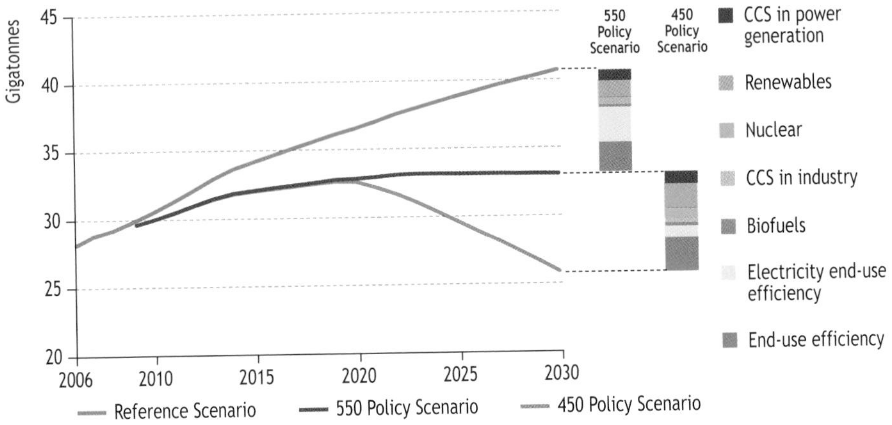

450 Policy Scenario

In the 450 Policy Scenario, energy-efficiency improvements result in reduced demand across all sectors and energy supply shows a significant increase in all low-carbon technologies, compared with the 550 Policy Scenario. Global energy-related CO_2 emissions in 2030 increase by 23% relative to those in 1990 but fall 8% relative to 2006. The rate of decarbonisation of the energy sector required after 2020 is unprecedented, responding to a need to achieve an average annual emissions reduction of 0.67 Gt. This compares with an annual average increase of 0.75 Gt in the period 2000-2006. Fossil-fuel demand and energy-related CO_2 emissions decline in all sectors in OECD+ between 2006 and 2030, but increase in all sectors in Other Major Economies. There is a slight increase in fossil-fuel demand and energy-related CO_2 emissions in Other Countries.

Energy-related CO_2 emissions in Other Major Economies peak in 2020 at around 15 Gt (2 Gt less than in the Reference Scenario). After the assumed introduction of a carbon price at this time, they decline steeply to 12 Gt in 2030. Emissions in OECD+ are in steep decline, being 3 Gt, or 30%, lower in 2030 than in 1990. Emissions in Other Countries

---

1. This assumes an average plant size of 800 MW for coal-fired plants with CCS, 500 MW for gas-fired plants with CCS, 1 000 MW for nuclear power plants and 3 MW for wind turbines.

also peak in 2020, as they benefit from technological spillovers from OECD+ and Other Major Economies. In absolute terms, Other Major Economies account for the largest savings in 2030, compared to the Reference Scenario (8.3 Gt, or 56% of global savings). OECD+ countries reduce their emissions relative to the Reference Scenario by 5.2 Gt, or 36% of global emissions savings, while Other Countries reduce theirs by 1.2 Gt or 8%. The reduction in CO_2 in end-use sectors in Other Countries, compared with the 550 Policy Scenario, is very small because we do not assume major changes in the national policies of these countries, given their relatively low income and emission levels.

In the more-stringent 450 Policy Scenario, a deeper transformation of energy supply and an even wider adoption of CO_2-mitigation options occurs (Figure 18.4). In order to achieve the necessary additional reduction between the 550 and 450 Policy Scenarios, further end-use efficiency improvements are assumed. Renewable energy is developed considerably further, to realise a further 25% CO_2-emissions reduction compared to the 550 Policy Scenario. CCS technologies are applied more widely in power generation, but are also introduced in the industry sector. Thirteen additional nuclear power plants have to be built yearly, compared to the 550 Policy Scenario. Biofuels penetrate the transportation sector more deeply.

Box 18.1 ● Outlook for energy-related CO_2 emissions to 2050

In the 450 Policy Scenario, global CO_2 emissions increase from 27.9 Gt in 2006 to 32.5 Gt in 2020, then fall to 25.7 Gt in 2030. This trend is in line with the BLUE Map Scenario presented in the IEA's *Energy Technology Perspectives 2008*, which leads to global CO_2 emissions of 14 Gt in 2050. The BLUE Map scenario shows the technology revolution that will be needed in the next four decades if such deep emission cuts are to be achieved. This long-term view is important as guidance for planning because options that are still costly will need government-supported deployment in the years 2020-2030 so as to become competitive after 2030. Important insights are that the power sector needs to be virtually decarbonised, carbon capture and storage must be widely deployed, light-duty vehicles will become electric or hybrid, and biofuels will be needed for aviation, marine and heavy-duty vehicles. Such a scenario would result in a 27% reduction of oil demand in 2050 compared to 2005, reducing the need for oil capacity additions.

Emissions of gases other than energy-related CO_2

As much as a third of the required reduction in greenhouse gases may have to come from gases other than energy-related CO_2. These gases currently make up nearly 40% of total emissions (see Chapter 16). To achieve either 550 ppm or 450 ppm CO_2-eq stabilisation in the long term will require not only significant emissions reductions of CO_2 in the energy sector by 2030, but also aggressive reductions of CO_2 emissions from

18

industry and land use, and reduction of all the other greenhouse gases as well. Neither the 550 nor 450 ppm CO_2-eq stabilisation targets can be achieved by action in the energy sector alone.

Cap-and-trade policies for CO_2 in the OECD+ will tend by 2030 to set the international carbon price that will also be applied to all the other greenhouse gases across all sectors (although it is not yet clear exactly how this extension of a carbon-equivalent price would be implemented in practice). For both the 550 and 450 Policy Scenarios, analysis carried out by the United States Environmental Protection Agency (US EPA) has provided a range of reduction potentials for each of the non-energy related CO_2 gases[2] and their various sources, compared with the Reference Scenario. The marginal abatement costs vary across sectors and over time. For the purpose of our scenarios, the extent of the potential reduction of each gas in 2030 was calculated from the abatement costs after the future price of carbon had been determined. Emissions of CO_2 from land-use change were based on OECD projections (OECD, 2008).[3] They are projected to decline in all scenarios by 2030, to a level around half that of current emissions. For Other Major Economies and Other Countries, it is assumed that the CDM remains in place and includes all gases. The potential emission reductions in these regions can be considered a component of any carbon off-setting mechanism, although if a limit is set to off-setting in the OECD+, this would limit the flow of CDM credits.

550 Policy Scenario

In the 550 Policy Scenario, the inclusion of the power generation and industry sectors in a cap-and-trade scheme for OECD+ resulted in a carbon price of $90 per tonne of CO_2 in 2030. Significant reduction of most of the non-energy-related CO_2 and other gases can be achieved in all regions at this 2030 marginal abatement cost or less. The exceptions include landfill methane and nitrous oxide from adipic acid production in the Other Countries, where only half of the potential out to 2030 is thought to be realisable at this carbon price.

From 2005[4] to 2030, emissions of all types of greenhouse gases rise only 9% in the 550 Policy Scenario, from 44.2 Gt CO_2-eq in 2005 to 48.2 Gt CO_2-eq in 2030 (Figure 18.5). This is around 20% less than in the Reference Scenario, where total emissions rise to 59.6 Gt CO_2-eq in 2030. For each of the greenhouse gases, these reductions in emissions occur progressively as a result of improved process efficiencies, better agricultural management, reduced leakages and less gas flaring. The share of non-energy-related gases decreases from around 39% of total emissions in 2005 to 32% in 2030.

---

2. Although analysed individually, SF_6, PFCs and HFCs are presented here collectively as the group of fluorine containing gases (F-gases).

3. There are considerable uncertainties in projections of all greenhouse-gas emissions, but none more so than from land use (IPCC, 2007).

4. For some non-energy CO_2 gases, no source data was available for 2006; the base year used here is 2005.

Non-energy CO_2 emissions from land use and industry decline by 35% in 2030, while they decline by 26% in the Reference Scenario. Non-CO_2 gas emissions (CH_4, N_2O and F-gases) in 2030 are reduced by 29% in OECD+, 24% in Other Major Economies and 20% in Other Countries, compared with the Reference Scenario. Their shares in 2030 are 21% of all greenhouse gases in OECD+ countries, 38% in Other Major Economies and 41% in Other Countries. The largest growth, in both percentage and absolute terms, in emissions from these non-energy sources over the *Outlook* period occurs in Other Countries.

Figure 18.5 ● *Global emissions of all greenhouse gases in the Reference, 550 and 450 Policy Scenarios*

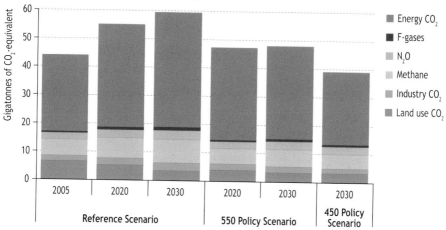

Sources: IEA and US EPA analyses; OECD (2008).

450 Policy Scenario

Since most potential reductions of non-energy-related gases are achieved at a 2030 marginal abatement cost of $90 per tonne of CO_2 or less, the higher carbon price of the 450 Policy Scenario creates little further reduction potential. The share of non-energy-related gases in 2030 increases to 35%, being 3 percentage points greater than in the 550 Policy Scenario, since energy-related CO_2 emissions decline faster (Figure 18.5).

In the 450 Policy Scenario, total emissions peak in 2020 then drop to 34% below the level of the Reference Scenario in 2030. In absolute terms, total greenhouse-gas emissions decline to 39.3 Gt CO_2-eq in 2030, 8.9 Gt CO_2-eq lower than in the 550 Policy Scenario and 4.9 Gt CO_2-eq lower than in 2005. OECD+ countries experience a 31% reduction in non-CO_2 gases in 2030, compared with the Reference Scenario, whereas both Other Major Economies and Other Countries show a 25% reduction. There is little change between the 550 and 450 Policy Scenarios in the regional shares of non-CO_2 emissions in 2030. As for the effects on the different gases, industry-related CO_2 emissions in the 450 Policy Scenario are 25% lower in 2030, than in the 550 Policy Scenario, methane emissions 16% lower, nitrous oxide 4% and F-gases 14%.

18

The 550 Policy Scenario: results by sector

Power generation

In the 550 Policy Scenario, OECD+ countries are assumed to implement policies to encourage the deployment of low-carbon technologies in the power-generation sector, in addition to a cap-and-trade system. Cap-and-trade arrangements are already in place or are being considered in most OECD+ countries. Such explicit pricing of carbon makes renewables, nuclear and CCS technologies more competitive against fossil-fuel based electricity generation. But in OECD+ countries, successful deployment of low-carbon power generation technologies requires more than carbon pricing alone. For example, the successful deployment of renewable energy requires political effort in various ways, including:

- Research and development programmes to reduce the cost of advanced technologies.

- Targeted support mechanisms to speed up the deployment of technologies close to market competitiveness.

- Development of grids to integrate renewables.

- Public acceptance and support.

OECD+ countries in both climate scenarios are therefore assumed to put in place specific policies to speed up the deployment of low-carbon technologies, to supplement emissions-trading schemes. Many governments already favour the use of renewable energy, as a means both of reducing greenhouse-gas emissions and of increasing reliance on domestic energy sources. Typical measures include guaranteed feed-in tariffs and portfolio standards requiring a stated proportion of generation to come from renewables. The Policy Scenarios assume that measures are also adopted to extend the lifetime of existing nuclear power plants and to accelerate the construction of new ones. Along with market incentives stemming from the implementation of a carbon price, the deployment of CCS technology is assumed to be accelerated through support for a number of pilot demonstration projects, leading to commercialisation around 2020. The Policy Scenarios assume that significant research and development programmes are put in place, as well as support for the deployment of CCS in OECD+ countries.

The power sector in Other Major Economies and Other Countries is assumed not to face binding emissions caps in the 550 Policy Scenario. However, it is considered that the Other Major Economies group would participate by implementing national policies and measures, such as green certificates schemes aimed at enhancing the use of renewable energy sources. The most important policies for Other Major Economies considered in the Policy Scenarios include:

- Policies to improve the efficiency of fossil-fuel plants, leading to a greater number of high-efficiency ultrasupercritical and integrated gasification combined-cycle coal plants, rather than conventional subcritical units.

- Policies to encourage the reduction of electricity transmission and distribution losses by accelerating the upgrading of existing systems.

- Incentives and regulations to boost the deployment of renewables. For example, China adopted a renewable energy law in 2005 and India has taken steps to provide more incentives for renewables and already has a thriving wind-power industry. In Brazil, the federal Programme of Incentives for Alternative Electricity Sources (PROINFA) is another example.

- Policies to accelerate the construction of nuclear power plants. A number of countries, including Russia, China and India, have ambitious plans to expand the use of nuclear power, with specific development targets.

Impact on electricity generation and CO_2 intensity

In the 550 Policy Scenario, new policies cut power-sector CO_2 emissions to 12.8 Gt in 2030, a reduction of 29% compared with the Reference Scenario, bringing an energy security co-benefit through reduced fuel import dependence. World electricity generation reaches a little over 30 000 TWh in 2030, 9% lower than in the Reference Scenario, mainly as a result of end-use efficiency improvements (Table 18.6).

Table 18.6 ● Electricity generation and related CO_2 emissions in the 550 Policy Scenario compared with the Reference Scenario

	Electricity Generation (TWh)		Percentage change relative to the Reference Scenario (%)	CO_2 emissions (Gt)		Percentage change relative to the Reference Scenario (%)
	2020	2030	2030	2020	2030	2030
OECD+	12 098	12 898	-5%	4.28	3.32	-39%
Coal	3 424	2 539	-45%	2.86	1.74	-56%
Oil	151	119	-27%	0.12	0.09	-23%
Gas	2 664	3 286	14%	1.30	1.49	6%
Nuclear	2 896	2 956	20%	n.a.	n.a.	n.a.
Renewables	2 963	3 999	13%	n.a.	n.a.	n.a.
Other Major Economies	10 801	13 190	-13%	7.53	7.86	-25%
Coal	5 784	6 438	-28%	6.01	6.14	-29%
Oil	476	410	-9%	0.42	0.36	-8%
Gas	1 480	1 957	-14%	1.11	1.36	-13%
Nuclear	585	933	27%	n.a.	n.a.	n.a.
Renewables	2 476	3452	29%	n.a.	n.a.	n.a.
Other Countries	3 413	4 098	-9%	1.64	1.60	-21%
Coal	858	780	-24%	0.83	0.76	-23%
Oil	238	145	-18%	0.19	0.12	-18%
Gas	972	1 186	-24%	0.61	0.73	-21%
Nuclear	265	277	3%	n.a.	n.a.	n.a.
Renewables	1 079	1 710	15%	n.a.	n.a.	n.a.

18

Over half of the savings occur in Other Major Economies and Other Countries, where the potential to improve end-use efficiency is greatest.

Emissions per unit of electricity produced drop substantially in the 550 Policy Scenario, mainly because of the larger shares in the electricity mix of nuclear power and renewables, and because of switching from coal to gas (Figure 18.6). Overall, the electricity mix decarbonises at a rate of 1.5% per year compared with 0.4% in the Reference Scenario. This is higher than the 0.6% average annual rate of decarbonisation in the period 1970-1990.

The general introduction of a cap-and-trade scheme for power generation in OECD+ countries leads to CO_2 emissions reductions in these countries through short-term switching from coal to gas and through a shift towards low-carbon power-generation technologies for new investment. In the 550 Policy Scenario, OECD+ power-sector emissions are roughly stable through to 2012 and start falling thereafter. In 2020 and 2030 they are, respectively, 16% and 35% lower than in 2006.

In Other Countries, national policies and measures lead to a decrease of 21% in CO_2 emissions from power plants in 2030, compared to the Reference Scenario, although they still increase from 1.3 Gt in 2006 to 1.6 Gt in 2030. Emissions from power plants in China and India in 2030 are, respectively, 4.4 Gt and 1.3 Gt, or 29% and 26% lower than in the Reference Scenario.

Figure 18.6 ● **CO_2 emissions per MWh of electricity generated in the 550 Policy Scenario compared with the Reference Scenario**

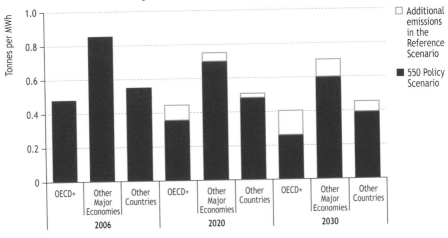

The projected trends in the 550 Policy Scenario involve a more rapid decline in electricity intensity[5] than in the Reference Scenario and a substantial deviation from recent trends. By 2030, electricity intensity relative to 2006 in OECD+ is reduced by 24%, or an additional percentage point reduction by that time compared to the

---

5. Electricity output per unit of GDP.

Reference Scenario, due to lower electricity demand. In 2030, electricity intensity is reduced by three percentage points in Other Major Economies and by two percentage points in Other Countries, compared with the Reference Scenario.

The global power-generation mix

By 2030, the share of fossil fuels in the electricity generation mix falls from 66% in the Reference Scenario to 55% in the 550 Policy Scenario, the current share being 67%. The largest fall is in the share of coal, which drops to 32% in 2030 — 12 percentage points lower than in the Reference Scenario (Figure 18.7).

Figure 18.7 ● **Fuel shares in world electricity generation in the Reference and 550 Policy Scenarios**

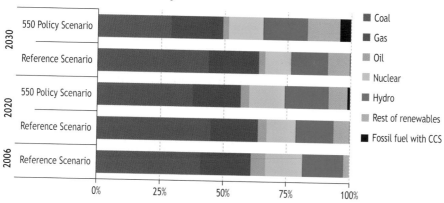

In OECD+ countries, the change in the electricity mix occurs mainly over the next 15 years, while in Other Major Economies and Other Countries it is more pronounced in the second half of the *Outlook* period, reflecting the different rates of capital-stock turnover. Power plants are long-lived assets and the evolution of the power sector in the Policy Scenarios is highly constrained by this fact. The age profiles of existing power plants present a very contrasting picture, creating both a window of opportunity in OECD+ over the next decade and a risk of potentially substantial lock-in of CO_2 emissions for decades to come from fossil-fuel plants to be built in Other Major Economies and Other Countries.

In the 550 Policy Scenario, total coal-fired electricity generation reaches over 9 700 TWh in 2030, 33% less than in the Reference Scenario but still 26% higher than today (Figure 18.8). The total reduction in coal-fired generation is larger than the current level of coal-fired electricity generation in the OECD+. Most of the reduction in coal-fired generation takes place in China, India and the OECD+. Advanced power-generation technologies become available earlier than in the Reference Scenario, particularly cleaner coal technologies, leading to higher efficiency. China, the largest user of coal for power generation, is already promoting the development of advanced coal technologies.

18

Figure 18.8 ● Change in coal- and gas-fired generation by region in the 550 Policy Scenario

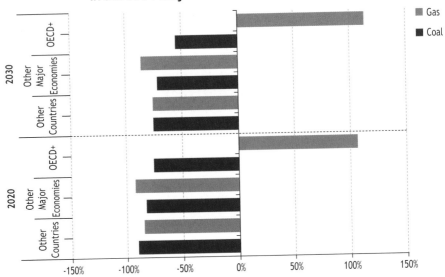

The adoption of CCS occurs mostly in OECD+ countries, where it is already supported by specific research and development programmes. In 2030, the installed capacity of CCS plants amounts to 162 GW worldwide, of which 111 GW (about 70%) is in OECD+ countries. CCS development in Other Major Economies and Other Countries may need to be financed through international co-operation and financial transfers.

The reduction of gas-fired generation in the 550 Policy Scenario is smaller than that of coal. There is less need for base- and mid-load gas-fired capacity, but gas is still the main fuel used in gas turbines to meet peak-load demand. Gas-fired electricity generation is 5% lower in 2030 than in the Reference Scenario, with a total net reduction in 2030 of about 350 TWh. Gas-fired electricity generation still increases by nearly 350 TWh in OECD+, whereas it decreases by over 300 TWh in Other Major Economies and by over 350 TWh in Other Countries. The share of oil-fired plants in the power generation mix shrinks throughout the *Outlook* period; these plants represent only 2% of electricity generation worldwide in 2030.

Distributed generation — production of electricity close to where it is used — plays a greater role in the Policy Scenarios than in the Reference Scenario. It helps save fuel and reduce CO_2 emissions because it reduces network losses. It also reduces the need for investment in transmission networks. It involves greater use of combined heat and power (CHP), mainly in industry, and renewables in buildings, including integrated solar photovoltaic. CHP generation (which improves the economics of gas-fired generation) relies mainly on gas and biomass, and represents 11% of global power generation in the 550 Policy Scenario. Fuel cells using natural gas as a source of hydrogen have a growing market share, but from a very low base, and are used increasingly in CHP. In 2030 the installed capacity of fuel cells reaches 74 GW while their efficiency increases up to 70%.

In the 550 Policy Scenario, renewable energy systems play a major role in the global electricity mix, supplying 30% of total electricity in 2030 (up from 23% in the Reference Scenario). On a regional basis, the share of hydropower, biomass and other renewables increases by 15 percentage points above current levels in the OECD+. The most dramatic increase is projected for Europe, where 39% of electricity is generated from renewable sources in 2030. Renewables account for 20% of total electricity generation in the United States and 18% in Japan in 2030. In Other Major Economies and Other Countries, renewable energy supplies over 5 000 TWh in 2030. The share of renewables in China increases from 16% in the Reference Scenario to 26% in the 550 Policy Scenario, and the share in India from 14% to 24%.

More hydropower plants are built in the 550 Policy Scenario than in the Reference Scenario, mostly in Other Major Economies and Other Countries, where the unexploited potential is still large. In these regions, the share of hydropower reaches 22% in 2030, slightly higher than the current 21% level. Global hydropower capacity reaches around 1 600 GW in 2030, compared with around 900 GW now and 1 400 GW in 2030 in the Reference Scenario.

Electricity from biomass, wind, solar, geothermal and tide and wave power reaches nearly 3 800 TWh in 2030. Their share of electricity generation grows from 2% now to 13% in 2030. Wind power and biomass grow the most (Figure 18.9). In 2030, wind energy supplies 1 360 TWh in OECD+, 443 TWh in Other Major Economies and 144 TWh in Other Countries. Biomass supplies 629 TWh in OECD+, 381 TWh in Other Major Economies and 181 TWh in Other Countries. These increases are delivered through national policies and measures, as well as by projects financed through CDM, but faster deployment of renewables is also due to cost reductions resulting from learning spillover effects from OECD+ countries. In addition, higher electricity prices may encourage people to adopt even more renewables-based technologies, especially solar photovoltaic.

Figure 18.9 ● **World non-hydropower renewable electricity generation by source in the 550 Policy Scenario**

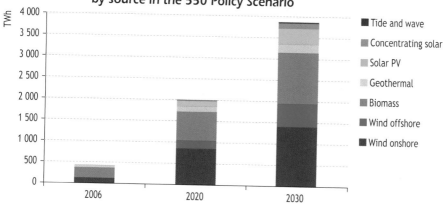

Nuclear power generation reaches over 4 000 TWh in 2030 in the 550 Policy Scenario, about 20% more than in the Reference Scenario, thanks to both licence extension of existing plants over the period 2006-2030 and to the accelerated build-up of new ones.

Globally, the share of nuclear power in electricity generation is 14% in 2030, compared with 15% now. In the OECD+, the 23% share of nuclear power in 2030 is the same as at present. Nuclear power represents 7% of total electricity generation in Other Major Economies and 7% in Other Countries in 2030 (Figure 18.10).

Figure 18.10 ● **Share of nuclear power in electricity generation by region in the 550 Policy Scenario**

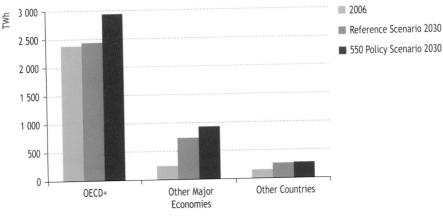

Installed capacities

Global installed capacity in the 550 Policy Scenario is 48 GW lower in 2020 and 134 GW lower in 2030 compared with the Reference Scenario (Table 18.7), due to reduced

Table 18.7 ● **Capacity additions in the 550 Policy Scenario** (GW)

	2007-2020				2021-2030			
	World	OECD+	Other Major Economies	Other Countries	World	OECD+	Other Major Economies	Other Countries
Coal	957	353	543	61	323	84	223	16
of which coal CCS	*22*	*19*	*4*	*0*	*101*	*59*	*42*	*0*
Oil	67	3	22	42	41	12	17	11
Gas	520	258	150	112	498	289	124	85
of which gas CCS	*10*	*10*	*0*	*0*	*28*	*24*	*4*	*0*
Nuclear	124	71	41	12	127	65	55	7
Hydro	490	95	294	101	250	40	119	92
Biomass	103	64	26	14	112	42	46	24
Wind onshore	310	218	82	10	353	225	91	37
Wind offshore	48	39	6	2	93	77	13	3
Solar photovoltaics	79	48	25	6	176	83	67	27
Solar thermal	7	7	0	0	36	23	7	6
Geothermal	9	5	2	2	10	4	2	4
Tidal and wave	2	2	0	0	7	6	0	0
Total	2 717	1 164	1 190	362	2 025	949	765	310

demand as a result of improved energy efficiency. Coal-fired capacity is reduced by 762 GW while gas-fired capacity increases by 107 GW by 2030. There is about 440 GW of additional renewables in the 550 Policy Scenario. Nuclear power-generating capacity is 100 GW higher in 2030 than in the Reference Scenario. Three-quarters of this increase take place in OECD+ countries.

Industry

In the 550 Policy Scenario, energy-related CO_2 emissions from the industry sector in OECD+ are limited by the carbon price that results from the cap-and-trade system. Also, the iron and steel and the cement sectors in OECD+ and Other Major Economies are assumed to be covered by international sectoral agreements, under which these industries in each region need to reduce CO_2 intensity by at least as much as the gap between the intensity of current production and what could be achieved with the deployment of the currently available best technologies. We assume that the CO_2 intensity reduction reaches full potential by 2020 in all OECD+ regions and by 2030 in Other Major Economies. Other Countries are assumed to implement national policies and measures.

In the 550 Policy Scenario, global industry CO_2 emissions reach 5.4 Gt by 2020 and 5.5 Gt in 2030 — 14% lower than in the Reference Scenario (Figure 18.11).[6] Most of the reduction comes from Other Major Economies, reaching 0.7 Gt in 2030 and accounting for 82% of the total reduction relative to the Reference Scenario. This is because the production capacity in these countries, as well as capacity additions over the projection period, is much larger than in OECD+. In addition, there is more potential to reduce energy and CO_2 intensity in Other Major Economies. The CO_2 reduction relative to the Reference Scenario in OECD+ reaches 0.1 Gt, or 11% of the global reduction. Compared with 2006, however, CO_2 emissions from OECD+ decline by 14%, while those from Other Major Economies rise by 43% and those from Other Countries rise by 22%. Emissions from coal combustion for heat generation, which are reduced by 19% in 2030 compared with the Reference Scenario, are more sharply curtailed than those from other fuels because in OECD+ the carbon price raises the coal price most in percentage terms and because other regions also make efforts to shift away from coal use (Table 18.8). Compared with the Reference Scenario, global coal demand declines by 19% in 2030, while total energy demand falls by 9% in industry. The share of coal in global industry CO_2 emissions in 2030 is 56% in the 550 Policy Scenario, compared with 60% in the Reference Scenario. Of all industry sub-sectors, the iron and steel sector curbs emissions most, accounting for around one-third of the reduction in industry emissions in the 550 Policy Scenario, compared with the Reference Scenario. The sub-sectors making the next greatest reductions are the non-metallic minerals and the chemicals and petrochemicals sectors.

18

---

6. Industry sector energy demand and CO_2 emissions are calculated in accordance with IEA energy balances, *i.e.* not including demand/emissions from coke ovens, blast furnaces, petrochemical feedstocks and process emissions.

Figure 18.11 ● Energy-related CO_2 emissions from industry by region in the Reference and 550 Policy Scenarios

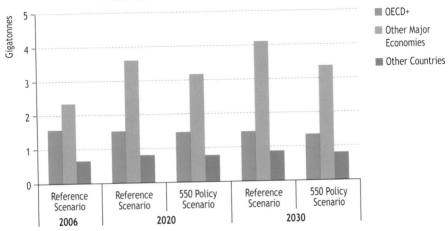

Table 18.8 ● Energy demand and energy-related CO_2 emissions in industry in the 550 Policy Scenario

	Energy demand (Mtoe)*				CO_2 emissions (Gt)			
	2006	2020	2030	Change vs. RS, 2030	2006	2020	2030	Change vs. RS, 2030
World	2 181	2 771	3 019	-9%	4.59	5.42	5.53	-14%
Coal	550	671	676	-19%	2.56	3.10	3.12	-19%
Oil	329	358	356	-8%	1.03	1.12	1.11	-8%
Gas	434	521	566	-6%	1.01	1.20	1.30	-6%
OECD+	882	913	918	-3%	1.58	1.47	1.36	-7%
Coal	117	102	89	-12%	0.53	0.46	0.40	-12%
Oil	146	128	114	-5%	0.46	0.40	0.36	-5%
Gas	254	260	256	-5%	0.59	0.61	0.60	-5%
Other Major Economies	954	1 419	1 609	-14%	2.35	3.17	3.37	-18%
Coal	365	492	510	-22%	1.73	2.30	2.39	-21%
Oil	124	158	166	-10%	0.39	0.49	0.52	-9%
Gas	103	165	205	-8%	0.24	0.38	0.46	-8%
Other Countries	345	439	492	-4%	0.66	0.78	0.81	-7%
Coal	69	77	77	-8%	0.30	0.34	0.33	-8%
Oil	59	72	75	-8%	0.18	0.22	0.23	-8%
Gas	78	96	106	-6%	0.18	0.22	0.24	-6%

* Total in each region includes all energy sources.

Energy-related CO_2 emissions in OECD+ industry fall 7% in the 550 Policy Scenario, relative to the Reference Scenario, reaching 1.4 Gt in 2030. The introduction of the carbon price drives down energy consumption and hence CO_2 emissions, in particular from coal consumption, as end-use industry coal prices more than double, rising at a rate much faster than other energy due to coal's relatively high carbon content. Coal accounts for 55% of total industry sector CO_2 emissions savings in 2030. Emissions from the iron and steel sector decline most, accounting for 27% of the total reduction, followed by the chemicals and petrochemicals sector with 18%.

In the Other Major Economies group of countries, CO_2 emissions in the 550 Policy Scenario reach 3.4 Gt in 2030, 18% lower than in the Reference Scenario. Emissions from coal are expected to be reduced more than emissions from other fuels in both absolute and percentage terms, most of the reduction coming from China's iron and steel and cement sectors. Initiatives have already been taken in China, such as the Top-1000 Enterprises Energy Conservation Programme and the closing of inefficient, small-scale plants in energy-intensive industries (see *WEO-2007*). Such measures in Other Major Economies are assumed to be enhanced in the 550 Policy Scenario. Emissions from the iron and steel sector in 2030 are reduced by 17% and the reduction in the non-metallic minerals sector reaches 22%. Emissions from Other Countries also fall, due to the implementation of national policies and measures and technology transfer from more advanced regions. The reduction in the 550 Policy Scenario amounts to 64 Mt CO_2 by 2030, or 7% of Reference Scenario emissions.

CO_2 emissions from the iron and steel sector worldwide grow from 1.4 Gt in 2006 to 1.7 Gt in 2030 in the 550 Policy Scenario, 16% lower than in the Reference Scenario.[7] Different production processes have very different levels of energy and carbon efficiency. Electric arc furnaces with scrap steel produce less than one-third of the CO_2 emissions per unit of production of typical blast furnaces — though electric arc furnace potential is limited by the availability of scrap steel — and less than 20% of those from the coal-based direct reduced iron process (IEA, 2008a). In the 550 Policy Scenario, wider use of electric arc furnaces is expected, in addition to improvements in blast furnaces. In the cement sector, emissions are almost flat during the projection period.[8] Efficiency improves over time as small-scale vertical shaft kilns are replaced by more efficient large-scale rotary dry kilns. Emissions from the chemicals and petrochemicals sector in the 550 Policy Scenario grow from 0.6 Gt in 2006 to 0.7 Gt in 2030.[9]

Although there is significant variation in production processes between regions, energy indicator work carried out by the IEA allows us to estimate CO_2 reduction potentials by region if best-available technology was applied worldwide (IEA, 2008b).[10] The CO_2 reduction potential in the iron and steel sector is estimated at 0.34 Gt worldwide,

---

7. Iron and steel sector emissions do not include those from coke ovens and blast furnaces.

8. Cement sector emissions in this section are energy-related and do not include process emissions.

9. These figures exclude petrochemical feedstock, which is included in non-energy use in IEA energy balances.

10. The definition of industry energy consumption and CO_2 emissions used in IEA work on energy indicators differs from that in the *World Energy Outlook*, which is based on IEA energy balances. The potentials include opportunites relating to process emissions, as well as coke ovens and blast furnaces for iron and steel.

18

or 300 kg of CO_2 per tonne of steel produced, with the potential varying from 700 kg in Ukraine to 70 kg in Japan, where the process is already efficient. The potential global reduction in the cement sector is estimated at 0.45 Gt, or 180 kg of CO_2 per tonne of cement, ranging from 390 kg in Russia to 60 kg in Japan. In some sectors, the CO_2 intensity of Other Major Economies and Other Countries is lower than that of OECD+ countries. For example, in the cement industry, new and therefore relatively modern plants are usually located in Other Major Economies and Other Countries, where demand has expanded in recent years in accordance with domestic infrastructure development. As a result, the potential for further reductions in those countries is smaller than in some OECD+ countries.

The iron and steel and cement sectors are assumed in the 550 Policy Scenario to reduce their CO_2 intensity by at least as much as the best-available technology permits by 2020 in OECD+ and by 2030 in Other Major Economies. The intensity improvement from 2006 is similar for both regions, but the difference from the Reference Scenario is larger for Other Major Economies. On average, the CO_2 intensity of the iron and steel sector in OECD+ countries is already 25% lower in 2030 in the Reference Scenario and is 32% lower in the 550 Policy Scenario, while that in Other Major Economies declines 18% in the Reference Scenario and 31% in the 550 Policy Scenario (Figure 18.12).

Figure 18.12 ● CO_2 intensity improvement in the iron and steel sector and the cement sector by region in the Reference and 550 Policy Scenarios

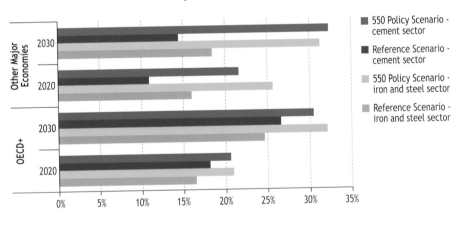

Considering the age profile of capital stock in the iron and steel and cement sectors in Other Major Economies, there is a need in the 550 Policy Scenario to introduce new production capacities that are substantially more efficient than the current average or to retrofit existing capacities (Box 18.2). Technology diffusion from OECD+ and effective financial mechanisms are needed for this to happen (see Chapter 19).

Box 18.2 ● Vintages of capital stock in iron and steel and cement sectors

The vintages of capital stocks in the iron and steel and cement sectors allow us to describe the opportunities for and limits to emissions reduction related to the building of new capacity in these two sectors.[11] In 2010, production capacity less than 10 years old, which will be used until the end of the projection period, accounts for 59% of total capacity in the iron and steel sector and 68% in the cement sector.

In 2030 in the Reference Scenario, 54% of world emissions in the iron and steel and non-metallic minerals (including cement) sectors is emitted from production capacity built before 2010 (Figure 18.13). Most of this capacity exists in Other Major Economies and Other Countries, where the demand for cement is expanding. This underlines the urgent need for action to prevent more capacity being built using inefficient technologies, in particular in Other Major Economies and Other Countries; and it indicates the scope for emissions reduction from retrofitting existing capacity.

Figure 18.13 ● Energy-related CO$_2$ emissions from the iron and steel and non-metallic minerals sectors in the Reference Scenario, 2030

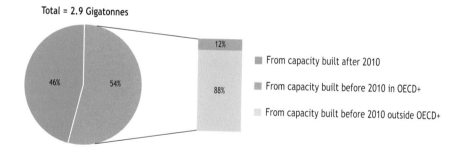

Total = 2.9 Gigatonnes

46%   54%

12%

88%

■ From capacity built after 2010

■ From capacity built before 2010 in OECD+

▨ From capacity built before 2010 outside OECD+

Transport

In the 550 Policy Scenario, CO$_2$ emissions from transport grow 27% from 2006, reaching 8.2 Gt in 2030 (Table 18.9). Transport accounts for one-third of the global increase in emissions from energy-related sources in this scenario. Within the transport sector, road transport accounts for 81% of the CO$_2$ emissions savings relative to the Reference Scenario in 2030 (0.6 Gt). Road transport accounts for 8% of energy-related emissions from all sources. Aviation (domestic and international) amounts to about 13% (0.1 Gt) of the transport emissions reduction in 2030, relative to the Reference Scenario.

18

---

11. Due to a lack of historical data, we only assess new capacity to be built between 2002 and 2010 to meet increasing demand, and not that built to replace ageing plant stock.

Table 18.9 ● Energy demand and energy-related CO_2 emissions in transport in the 550 Policy Scenario

Region	Energy demand (Mtoe)			CO_2 emissions (Gt)			% saving of CO_2 emissions versus Reference Scenario	
	2006	2020	2030	2006	2020	2030	2020	2030
World	2 227	2 758	2 978	6.44	7.72	8.19	4	8
Road	1 625	2 041	2 174	4.71	5.66	5.89	4	9
Aviation	246	303	352	0.73	0.90	1.04	5	8
Other	357	414	452	1.00	1.16	1.26	2	3
OECD+	1 314	1 391	1 309	3.55	3.55	3.18	4	11
Road	1 077	1 118	1 005	3.12	3.05	2.63	5	12
Aviation	166	191	215	0.26	0.30	0.34	4	6
Other	71	83	89	0.17	0.21	0.22	-2	-2
Other Major Economies	463	807	1 058	1.22	2.10	2.73	3	6
Road	333	633	852	0.96	1.77	2.35	3	7
Aviation	48	70	87	0.05	0.08	0.10	7	10
Other	83	104	119	0.20	0.25	0.28	0	1
Other Countries	267	358	394	0.70	0.93	1.01	2	5
Road	215	290	318	0.64	0.84	0.92	2	5
Aviation	32	43	49	0.02	0.02	0.03	4	5
Other	19	25	27	0.05	0.06	0.07	1	4

Note: CO_2 emissions from international aviation have been added to aviation at the World level. Aviation energy demand in all regions includes domestic and international aviation. Energy demand and CO_2 emissions of international marine bunkers are added at World level in the Other category.

The production of motor vehicles and aircrafts is characterised by high concentration, significant international exposure and homogeneity of the technology used. Around 50% of motor vehicle production is dominated by five multinational automakers – Toyota, General Motors, Ford, Volkswagen and DaimlerChrysler (WRI, 2007). As for aircraft, Boeing Corporation and Airbus S.A.S manufacture almost all large commercial jet aircraft, while several manufactures produce the bulk of smaller aircraft. Virtually all manufacturers have assembly and production facilities in several countries. From a technology viewpoint, virtually all motor vehicles use internal combustion engines fuelled by gasoline, diesel, CNG, LPG, biofuels or newer hybrid technologies, while aviation technology is also broadly the same across the industry. The dominance of a few producing companies and the similarity of technologies used suggest that if common standards could be agreed upon, they would likely have global effects.

In both climate-policy scenarios, international sectoral agreements in road transport and aviation are assumed to be adopted. Average fuel economy and CO_2 emissions for new LDVs vary widely across countries at present, depending on the average car size, the performance efficiency and the fuel mix. The 550 Policy Scenario assumes a sectoral agreement on the production of new LDVs that leads to a global average fleet efficiency in 2030 of 120 grammes of CO_2 per kilometre (gCO_2/km), a reduction of 12% from the Reference Scenario, while allowing some flexibility based on regional circumstances. We assume that OECD+ countries with the most efficient fleets today, in Europe and Japan, set the highest standard, reaching an average fleet efficiency of 106 gCO_2/km in 2030 — an improvement of 34% over current fleet efficiency (Figure 18.14). The less efficient OECD+ countries see improvements of almost 40%, but reach a fleet average of only 130 gCO_2/km in 2030, due mainly to the practice in the United States, Canada and Australia of buying larger and more powerful vehicles. In Other Major Economies, average fuel economy is currently close to the average OECD+ level and follows a similar rate of improvement over the projection period. The standard for Other Countries is less stringent, reaching 135 gCO_2/km in 2030.

Figure 18.14 ● CO_2 **intensity standards of light-duty vehicles by region in the 550 Policy Scenario**

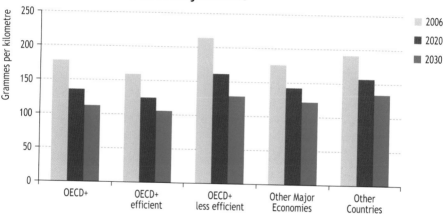

The incremental technology improvements that allow the average efficiency of the LDV fleet to reach these targets are also assumed to be introduced into the heavy-duty vehicle (HDV) fleet as fuel costs are a higher priority in the purchasing decision. This economic motivation is expected to draw more fuel-efficient technologies through to the HDV fleet even in the absence of international sectoral agreements. The fact that many vehicle manufactures produce both LDVs and HDVs will speed up technology diffusion. The global HDV fleet improves from nearly 840 gCO_2/km today to just over 560 gCO_2/km in 2030, a 33% improvement, reflecting significant savings from the level in 2030 in the Reference Scenario of 636 gCO_2/km.

Aviation has been the fastest-growing transport mode in recent years. The increase in oil prices and, to a lesser extent, the recent discussion of inclusion of aviation in emissions trading schemes, notably in Europe, is having a profound effect on airline

18

companies. Some airlines with older, less-efficient planes have become uncompetitive and been forced out of the market. Economic incentives to produce and deploy efficient aircraft are high. In the 550 Policy Scenario, we have assumed that an international agreement is reached between aircraft manufacturers to improve the efficiency of new planes by around 20% by 2020 and around 30% by 2030, compared with 2006 levels. For large planes (above 100 seats) the current fleet efficiency is 4.8 litres/100 revenue passenger kilometres.[12] The figure for the new Airbus 380 is 3 litres/100 rpk. The 550 Policy Scenario would mean that by 2030 around 80% of revenue passenger kilometres will be flown in planes attaining that level of efficiency. As a result, aviation oil consumption falls by 17 Mtoe in 2020 and 32 Mtoe in 2030, compared with the Reference Scenario. CO_2 emissions are reduced by 52 Mt in 2020 and 96 Mt in 2030.[13] In the 550 Policy Scenario, CO_2 emissions from aviation rise to 1 Gt in 2030, 43% higher than current levels. As a result, the share of aviation in energy-related CO_2 emissions in transport grows to 13%, compared with the current level of 11%.

Buildings and other sectors[14]

Worldwide, direct emissions from fossil-fuel consumption (mainly for heating) in the residential, services and agriculture sector (called here "buildings and other sectors") grow at 0.2% per year on average between 2006 and 2030 in the 550 Policy Scenario, compared with a 0.8% growth rate in the Reference Scenario. If we attribute the CO_2 emissions from upstream power generation to this sector as a whole, according to its electricity use, CO_2 emissions at world level grow by 0.4% per year from 2006 to reach 9 Gt in 2030 (compared with 12 Gt in the Reference Scenario), accounting for 17% of the total increase in emissions to 2030. The residential sector accounts for 54% of the cumulative emissions reduction.

The biggest reduction in emissions occurs in OECD+ countries (Figure 18.15), where direct and indirect CO_2 emissions taken together are projected to decline from 4.6 Gt in 2006 to 3.5 Gt in 2030, 1.5 Gt less than in the Reference Scenario. The 550 Policy Scenario sees Other Major Economies emissions growing throughout the *Outlook* period, to reach 4.2 Gt in 2030 — 1.1 Gt less than in the Reference Scenario. Total emissions from Other Countries grow at 0.9% per year between 2006 and 2030, compared with a growth rate in the Reference Scenario of 1.6%. This is 0.26 Gt less in 2030 than in the Reference Scenario.

---

12. Defined as the number of passengers multiplied by the number of kilometres they fly. It is a commonly used measure of air traffic.
13. This analysis focuses exclusively on CO_2 emissions. However, the impact of aviation on climate change is more complicated. The IPCC estimates that the total climate impact of aviation is two to four times greater than the impact of its CO_2 emissions, due to NO_x emissions and contrails.
14. This title is used here, in preference to the usual designation of the "Residential, services and agriculture" sector. This is because, although the figures given relate to the whole of that sector, the discussion of policy instruments is limited to those applying to residential and commercial buildings and the energy-consuming equipment and appliances therein.

The biggest saving comes from electricity. Total indirect CO_2 emissions from electricity consumption in 2030 in the 550 Policy Scenario are 2.4 Gt lower than in the Reference Scenario. Direct emissions from fossil-fuel consumption are 0.47 Gt, or 12%, less than in the Reference Scenario. The reduction in indirect emissions from electricity consumption is due to the slow-down in electricity demand in the 550 Policy Scenario: world electricity demand in this scenario grows at 2.0% per year between 2006 and 2030, 0.4 percentage points less than in the Reference Scenario. This produces savings of over 1 200 TWh of electricity in 2030, equivalent to 315 GW of installed natural gas combined-cycle gas-turbine capacity.

Figure 18.15 ● *Change in energy-related CO_2 emissions in the buildings and other sectors in the Reference and 550 Policy Scenarios, 2006-2030*

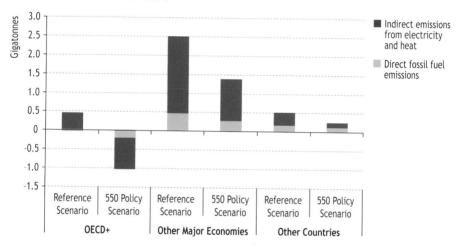

At the world level, the buildings and other sectors account for more than 35% of final energy savings in 2030 in the 550 Policy Scenario. The residential sector accounts for 74% of that. In OECD+, most of the energy savings in the 550 Policy Scenario arise from better-insulated and designed buildings, which create lower heating and cooling energy demand. Among fossil fuels, the biggest savings are from gas, which is partly substituted by solar and biomass for space and water heating. Electricity provides the largest savings in Other Major Economies, based on policies on efficient appliances and air-conditioning standards. In Other Countries, the continuing trend away from the use of traditional biomass for cooking and heating is a major influence.

Both policy scenarios assume the full implementation of the policies now under consideration in all countries. These include policies on lighting, electric appliances, space heating, water heating, cooking and air conditioning, in both the residential and service sectors. In OECD+ countries, equipment standards, building codes, building energy certification and voluntary measures are taken into account in the 550 Policy Scenario. In some cases, mandatory labelling schemes are also assumed.

18

Other Major Economies are assumed to adopt a range of measures to improve the energy efficiency of new equipment and buildings, achieving efficiencies that gradually approach those of the OECD.

The OECD+ group of countries, with a total cumulative saving between 2006 and 2030 of nearly 900 Mtoe, accounts for 24% of world cumulative energy savings in the sector. Better insulation in OECD+ countries can reduce the total amount of energy required for space heating and cooling by a factor of between two and four (IEA, 2008a). Also, the introduction of cap-and-trade in power generation has an impact on electricity prices, which rise 14% in the buildings sector, compared with the Reference Scenario, encouraging savings measures in general, including replacement of old, less efficient, appliances. The higher electricity prices in the two Policy Scenarios create an incentive in several OECD+ countries for greater uptake of solar installations, mainly for water heating.

Demand for fossil fuels in OECD+ buildings in 2030 is 13% lower in the 550 Policy Scenario than in the Reference Scenario and electricity consumption is reduced by 5.7%. The biggest saving is in gas consumption, with consumption down, relative to the Reference Scenario, by 48 Mtoe in the residential sector and 27 Mtoe in the services sector. Part of this gas saving arises from energy substitution — the 550 Policy Scenario contains an additional 22 Mtoe of solar energy for heating in 2030 in the residential sector and 9 Mtoe in services.

The biggest energy saving in the sector will come from Other Major Economies (Table 18.10). It will account for 55% of world energy savings in residential, services and agricultural use in 2030. Electricity accounts for the biggest share of the savings. In Other Major Economies, more efficient household appliances and air conditioning cut residential electricity use by 30 Mtoe in 2030 and services use by 12 Mtoe.

The most important measures in Other Major Economies are those aimed at encouraging energy efficiency in new buildings. The assumed introduction of building codes with specific minimum energy-performance requirements has a significant impact in this region because the total built floor area is projected to double between 2006 and 2030. Building standards in Other Major Economies reach today's OECD levels in 2030, and as a result residential energy consumption is reduced by 135 Mtoe in 2030 in the 550 Policy Scenario compared with the Reference Scenario.

In Other Countries, energy savings in buildings in the 550 Policy Scenario account for 75 Mtoe in 2030, 65% of which comes from reduced consumption of traditional biomass for cooking and heating. Consumption of traditional biomass is 49 Mtoe lower in 2030, compared with the Reference Scenario, declining slightly over the *Outlook* period, whereas in the Reference Scenario it grows at 0.5% per year on average. In both Policy Scenarios, the reduction in the use of biomass as a domestic fuel is more pronounced, thanks to additional policies and measures such as promotion of improved cookstoves in India. These interventions make biomass use more efficient, thus reducing the total volume consumed.

Table 18.10 ● Energy demand and energy-related CO_2 emissions by fuel and region in the buildings and other sectors in the 550 Policy Scenario

	Energy demand (Mtoe)			CO_2 emissions (Gt)		
	2020	2030	Change versus Reference Scenario in 2030	2020	2030	Change versus Reference Scenario in 2030
World	**3 328**	**3 604**	**-8%**	**3.37**	**3.39**	**-12%**
Coal	105	77	-23%	0.42	0.31	-23%
Oil	489	507	-9%	1.43	1.49	-9%
Gas	656	693	-12%	1.51	1.59	-12%
Electricity	1 024	1 215	-8%	n.a.	n.a.	n.a.
Heat	177	186	-8%	n.a.	n.a.	n.a.
Biomass	835	818	-7%	n.a.	n.a.	n.a.
Renewables	41	107	77%	n.a.	n.a.	n.a.
OECD+	**1 406**	**1 525**	**-4%**	**1.63**	**1.54**	**-13%**
Coal	12	7	-25%	0.05	0.03	-22%
Oil	194	181	-7%	0.58	0.54	-7%
Gas	427	416	-15%	1.00	0.97	-15%
Electricity	599	665	-6%	n.a.	n.a.	n.a.
Heat	51	52	-3%	n.a.	n.a.	n.a.
Biomass	98	137	32%	n.a.	n.a.	n.a.
Renewables	25	67	104%	n.a.	n.a.	n.a.
Other Major Economies	**1 213**	**1 313**	**-12%**	**1.21**	**1.27**	**-13%**
Coal	80	56	-25%	0.32	0.23	-25%
Oil	210	232	-12%	0.61	0.68	-12%
Gas	133	169	-7%	0.29	0.36	-7%
Electricity	300	395	-11%	n.a.	n.a.	n.a.
Heat	108	114	-11%	n.a.	n.a.	n.a.
Biomass	370	314	-15%	n.a.	n.a.	n.a.
Renewables	14	31	34%	n.a.	n.a.	n.a.
Other Countries	**708**	**766**	**-9%**	**0.53**	**0.58**	**-8%**
Coal	14	14	-11%	0.05	0.05	-11%
Oil	86	94	-8%	0.25	0.28	-7%
Gas	96	108	-9%	0.22	0.25	-9%
Electricity	124	155	-11%	n.a.	n.a.	n.a.
Heat	19	20	-7%	n.a.	n.a.	n.a.
Biomass	368	367	-10%	n.a.	n.a.	n.a.
Renewables	2	9	112%	n.a.	n.a.	n.a.

Note: Indirect CO_2 emissions are excluded from this Table.

The 450 Policy Scenario: results by sector

Power generation

In the 450 Policy Scenario, the power sector undergoes a dramatic change after 2020. CO_2 emissions in 2030 fall to 8.3 Gt, 35% lower than in the 550 Policy Scenario and 27%

lower than in 2006 (Figure 18.16). The regional breakdown is given in Table 18.11. Energy efficiency and low-carbon power-generation technologies reduce CO_2 emissions from coal, gas and oil plants amounting to 3.9 Gt, 0.5 Gt, and 0.1 Gt respectively, compared with the 550 Policy Scenario in 2030.

Figure 18.16 ● CO_2 **emissions reduction from the power sector in the 550 and 450 Policy Scenarios relative to the Reference Scenario**

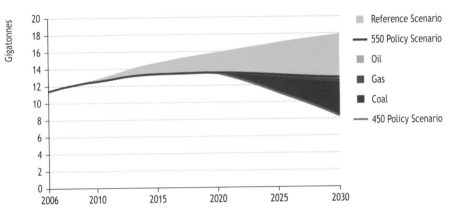

The much higher rate of decarbonisation of the power sector is mostly due to the enlargement of the cap-and-trade regime to include Other Major Economies, resulting in a faster and more efficient deployment of low-carbon technologies. The cap-and-trade regime and the resulting carbon price fosters investment in cleaner power generation technologies and facilitates capital and technology transfers from OECD+ countries to Other Major Economies.

The faster uptake of low-carbon technologies facilitated by the cap-and-trade regime in OECD and Other Major Economies is also beneficial to Other Countries, which benefit from the accelerated learning resulting from faster deployment of renewables and nuclear, and reap benefits from investment by OECD+ in research and development programmes on promising technologies, such as CCS.

Table 18.11 ● Power generation and energy-related CO_2 emissions in the 450 Policy Scenario, 2030

	Electricity generation	Change relative to the 550 Policy Scenario	CO_2 emissions	Change relative to the 550 Policy Scenario
	(TWh)		(Gt)	
OECD+	12 644	-2.0%	2.1	-36.2%
Other Major Economies	12 250	-7.1%	5.0	-36.2%
Other Countries	4 103	0.1%	1.2	-28.0%
World	**28 997**	**-3.9%**	**8.3**	**-35.2%**

World electricity generation in 2030 falls by around 4% relative to the 550 Policy Scenario (Table 18.11), thanks to large energy efficiency gains, partly counterbalanced by the off-take of electric vehicles and plug-in hybrids in the transport sector, which increases transport electricity demand by 50 Mtoe in 2030 compared to the 550 Policy Scenario. At the global level, the power generation mix changes as follows:

- In 2030, electricity production from conventional coal and gas plants decreases by 41% compared to the 550 Policy Scenario.

- This fall is partly replaced by electricity produced by thermal plants with CCS. CCS capacity increases to 363 GW, 9% of fossil fuel-based power capacity worldwide. Thermal plants with CCS produce 8% of total electricity generation in 2030 (Figure 18.17).

- Nuclear power capacity reaches nearly 680 GW in 2030 and supplies over 5 200 TWh, 18% of total electricity generation.

- Hydropower and the rest of renewables achieve faster deployment, resulting in production approaching 12 000 TWh in 2030, representing 40% of the total electricity generation in 2030 and more than half the additional low-carbon electricity, compared with the 550 Policy Scenario.

Figure 18.17 ● **World electricity generation fuel mix in the 450 Policy Scenario relative to the 550 Policy Scenario**

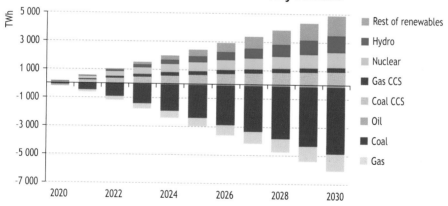

As a result of the assumed tighter emissions cap in OECD+, the carbon price faced by the power sector over 2020-2030 is higher than in the 550 Policy Scenario over the same period. This price, which reaches $180 per tonne of CO_2 by 2030 makes renewables, nuclear and CCS technologies more competitive against basic fossil-fuel electricity generation and favours faster deployment of these technologies. Economic incentives are assumed to be supplemented by tighter regulatory requirements, leading to the progressive phase-out of coal and oil plants in OECD+ countries over the 2020-2030 decade in a process involving a faster rate of capital turnover. Flexibility in the design

18

of these phase-out policies and arrangements to permit the recovery of stranded asset investments are particularly important to the efficiency and cost of these policies. All new fossil-fuel plants built in the OECD+ in the 450 Policy Scenario after 2020 are fitted with CCS (Figure 18.18). The increase of nuclear power generation, relative to the 550 Policy Scenario, is led by OECD+, which accounts for 58% of the increase worldwide to 2030.

Figure 18.18 ● **Electricity generation by fuel and by regional grouping in the 450 Policy Scenario, 2030**

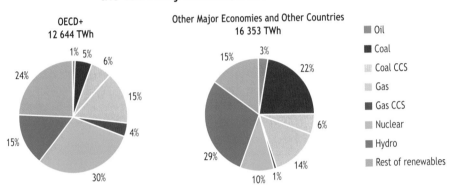

In the Other Major Economies, the introduction of cap-and-trade emissions regimes gives rise to a carbon price which provides a financial incentive to reinforce the national policies and measures favouring low-carbon technologies which are already taken into account in the 550 Policy Scenario. In 2030, about 40% of the renewable electricity generation in the world is in Other Major Economies and about 32% of their new fossil-fuel plants after 2020 are equipped with CCS. In Other Major Economies and in Other Countries, faster technological deployment of cleaner coal technologies leads to an increase in the average efficiency of coal power plants (without CCS) due to the penetration of more efficient ultrasupercritical and integrated gasification combined-cycle plants (Figure 18.19).

In Other Countries, CCS power generation barely kicks in. The share of renewables, however, does increase, thanks to faster cost reductions associated with the learning experience arising from wider deployment in other regions. Hydropower and renewables, including biomass, supply 39% and 20% respectively of electricity in Other Countries.

In the 450 Policy Scenario, CO_2-intensive capacity is replaced by more efficient plants on a wider scale than in the Reference Scenario (Table 18.12). Coal-fired plants in use today are wholly replaced with CCS coal plants, whose capacity is increased by 127 GW, compared to the 550 Policy Scenario. 60 GW of additional capacity in gas-fired plants with CCS is installed by 2030, almost half of newly constructed CCS power plants. The 322 GW increase in hydro capacity, together with additional capacity in onshore wind and solar of 248 GW and 137 GW respectively, accounts for the bulk of low-carbon capacity additions in Other Countries. The sizeable nuclear capacity expansion taking place in OECD+ and Other Major Economies amounts to 140 GW, more than doubling the rate of build-up in the 550 Policy Scenario compared to the Reference Scenario.

Figure 18.19 ● **Shares in world electricity generation by type of coal plant in the Reference, 550 and 450 Policy Scenarios**

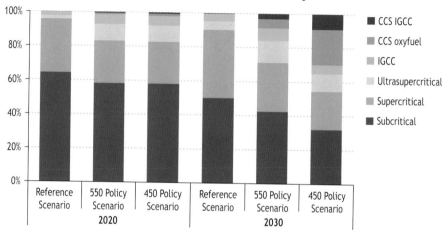

Table 18.12 ● **Capacity additions in the 450 Policy Scenario relative to the 550 Policy Scenario, 2020-2030** (GW)

	World	OECD+	Other Major Economies	Other Countries
Coal without CCS	-117	-25	-80	-12
Coal CCS	127	42	85	0
Oil	41	-3	44	1
Gas without CCS	-115	-183	-4	73
Gas CCS	60	50	11	0
Nuclear	140	81	61	-3
Hydro	322	44	184	94
Biomass	66	12	29	25
Wind onshore	248	94	112	42
Wind offshore	29	17	9	3
Solar PV	75	30	20	25
Solar thermal	62	18	31	12
Geothermal	15	4	4	6
Tidal and wave	3.6	3.0	0.5	0.1
Total	**768**	**92**	**410**	**266**

18

Industry

In the 450 Policy Scenario, the industry sector in OECD+ faces a much higher CO_2 price after 2020 than in the 550 Policy Scenario. Energy-related CO_2 emissions from the industry sector in Other Major Economies are also limited by a carbon price, due to the cap-and-trade system introduced after 2020. Other Countries are assumed to implement the same national policies and measures as in the 550 Policy Scenario, but they benefit from the faster deployment of technology worldwide in the 450 Policy Scenario.

Global fossil fuel demand from the industry sector reaches 1 351 Mtoe in 2030, which is 247 Mtoe or 15% lower than in the 550 Policy Scenario.[15] The difference relative to the Reference Scenario reaches 476 Mtoe. OECD+ demand declines over the projection period, while that of Other Major Economies and Other Countries grows, albeit at a much slower rate than in the Reference Scenario and 550 Policy Scenario.

Global industry CO_2 emissions reach 4.3 Gt in 2030 — 1.3 Gt, or 23%, lower than in the 550 Policy Scenario. The total reduction compared with the Reference Scenario reaches 2.2 Gt by 2030. Most of the reduction comes from OECD+ and Other Major Economies. The reduction compared with the 550 Policy Scenario in Other Major Economies reaches 0.9 Gt and that in OECD+ reaches 0.3 Gt. Efficiency improvements and fuel switching account for the most of the reduction in Other Major Economies, while CCS plays a major role in OECD+. Amongst the fossil fuels, emissions from coal combustion decline most — by 27% compared with the 550 Policy Scenario. The iron and steel sector reduces emissions most in absolute terms, relative to the 550 Policy Scenario, followed by the non-metallic minerals and the chemicals and petrochemicals sectors.

In the 450 Policy Scenario, industry sector CO_2 intensity (CO_2 per unit of GDP) is one-third lower worldwide by 2030 compared with the Reference Scenario, and is cut by around 60% in Other Major Economies, requiring a significant increase in energy efficiency and the deployment of new technologies in the production process. Huge efficiency improvements in existing facilities, through retrofitting or replacement, are required in both OECD+ and Other Major Economies, and could prove very costly.

Major technological breakthroughs, such as CCS, are needed in the 450 Policy Scenario. CCS is assumed to be introduced in the industry sector towards the end of the *Outlook* period, mainly in OECD+ regions. Relatively large potential for CCS implementation exists in blast furnaces in iron and steel production and in cement kilns. By 2030, CCS reduces emissions in the industry sector by 0.3 Gt, accounting for 15% of the total reduction compared with the Reference Scenario. Though CCS is assumed to be one of the key technologies adopted to reduce emissions in the industry sector, the realisation of this expectation depends, among other things, on the development of legal and regulatory frameworks, and further research and development to reduce capture, transport and storage costs and improve system efficiency (IEA, 2008a).

---

15. Industry sector energy demand and CO_2 emissions are calculated in accordance with IEA energy balances, *i.e.* not including energy demand/emissions from coke ovens, blast furnaces and petrochemical feedstocks and process emissions.

Transport

Further CO_2 savings in the transport sector are achieved in OECD+ and Other Major Economies in the 450 Policy Scenario through the strengthening of international transport-sector agreements. Faster deployment of new technology benefits all countries, bringing the sector's CO_2 emissions in 2030 to 7.8 Gt. This represents a saving of 0.4 Gt relative to the 550 Policy Scenario, and total savings of 1.1 Gt over the Reference Scenario. However, the introduction of electric vehicles and plug-in hybrids increases electricity consumption in the transport sector, which means that some of the savings in the transport sector are offset by increased emissions from power generation.

Average global CO_2 emissions per kilometre from the LDV fleet are reduced by a quarter from those of the Reference Scenario in 2030. This is achieved by means of further penetration of hybrids, increased consumption of biofuels and the introduction of electric vehicles and plug-in hybrids. The average fleet efficiency in OECD+ in 2030 is 90 gCO_2/km, a 49% reduction from today's levels or 32% down on the Reference Scenario. In Other Major Economies, the average efficiency will reach 110 gCO_2/km by 2030, an improvement of 18% over the Reference Scenario and 38% below today's levels. Stringent sectoral agreements induce faster technological development and deployment in the global LDV sector. As a result, efficiency in Other Countries also improves, to 122 gCO_2/km in 2030, an improvement of 17% compared to the Reference Scenario in 2030 and 36% below today's levels.

Larger average vehicle size and the long-established consumer preference for power over fuel economy in the United States, Canada, Australia and New Zealand opens up potential for greater savings in these areas. Smaller vehicle sizes on average mean that the current vehicle fleet in Other Major Economies is less carbon-intensive per kilometre than that in the OECD+ today. However, this also means their savings potential is lower.

Plug-in hybrids and electric vehicles make rapid inroads into global new vehicle sales by 2030, increasing their share of the vehicle fleet in 2030, relative to the Reference Scenario. A further increase in biofuels consumption is also required. Biofuels demand increases to over 240 Mtoe in 2030 in the 450 Policy Scenario. This is 40% more than in the 550 Policy Scenario, a doubling compared with the Reference Scenario and an almost 10-fold increase from today's level. The majority of the increase is met by second-generation biofuels, which need to be introduced earlier than envisaged in the Reference Scenario and require a significant increase in global production between 2020 and 2030. The penetration of electric vehicles and biofuels, as well as bigger savings in aviation fuels compared with the Reference Scenario, mean the increase in oil consumption is lower in the 450 Policy Scenario, from around 2 100 Mtoe in 2006 to around 2 500 Mtoe in 2020 and in 2030. Globally, transport oil demand rises slowly through to 2020 and then levels out through to 2030, in contrast to the continuing increase seen in the Reference Scenario. Oil use in transportation in OECD+ drops to around 1995 levels by 2030, while that in Other Major Economies and Other Countries is projected to increase steadily through the projection period, by 3.3% and 1.4% per year respectively.

18

Savings of over 370 Mtoe of oil are achieved in 2030 compared to the Reference Scenario, slightly more than the current use of oil in transportation in the European Union. Savings from LDVs amount to nearly 200 Mtoe, a reduction of 21% compared to the Reference Scenario in 2030. Around a further 130 Mtoe is saved in the HDV fleet by 2030, a reduction of 11%. OECD+ provides 61% of total oil savings, Other Major Economies 27% and the remainder comes from Other Countries.

The ambitious CO_2 reductions in the transport sector in the 450 Policy Scenario can not be achieved without significant global penetration of much more efficient vehicles, full electric vehicles or vehicles powered by hydrogen fuel cells, supported by the associated capital investment in infrastructure (see *Spotlight* in Chapter 3). As in the 550 Policy Scenario, sectoral agreements are not assumed to apply to the HDV fleet in this scenario. Savings in fuel and CO_2 emissions from greater efficiency in the road fleet can be achieved at a lower cost than further improvements in aviation efficiency or the introduction of second-generation biofuels suitable for aviation. Therefore, the aviation sector follows the same emissions trajectory as the 550 Policy Scenario.

Buildings and other sectors

In the 450 Policy Scenario, the introduction of cap-and-trade in Other Major Economies and the more stringent cap for OECD+ will increase the price of electricity in 2030 by 7% in Other Major Economies and by 25% in OECD+, compared with the Reference Scenario. This encourages more significant savings in the residential, services and agriculture sector (called here the "buildings and other sectors") than in the 550 Policy Scenario, with a total reduction in electricity consumption worldwide in excess of 1 850 TWh in 2030 compared to the Reference Scenario. OECD+ and Other Major Economies will each save more than 800 TWh of electricity in 2030.

To achieve these savings a wide range of improvements in the efficiency of appliances and machinery is required, including a worldwide switch from less-efficient incandescent lamps to compact fluorescent lamps for lighting, a massive shift to best-available technologies for appliances, large-scale penetration of solar power for water and space heating, and a substantial share of low-energy or low-carbon buildings in new building in the OECD+.

The higher electricity price in the 450 Policy Scenario creates an incentive in OECD+ and Other Major Economies for greater uptake of renewable heating installations, mainly for water heating. As a result, renewable (excluding biomass) energy consumption in 2030 rises more than 100 Mtoe higher than in the Reference Scenario. In the 450 Policy Scenario, the share of renewables and modern biomass in total energy consumption in the sector is 13% in 2030, seven percentage points more than in the Reference Scenario and nine percentage points more than in 2006.

The reduction in electricity consumption will reduce the *associated* CO_2 emissions in this sector by 4.5 Gt in 2030, compared with the Reference Scenario. Additional fossil-fuel savings compared to the 550 Policy Scenario amount to 14%, yielding savings over and above the Reference Scenario in *direct* CO_2 emissions from fossil fuel consumption of 0.9 Gt in 2030. The biggest savings in CO_2 emissions will occur in OECD+, where direct and indirect CO_2 emissions in the sector, at 2.5 Gt, will be 46% lower in 2030 than in 2006. They are 1 Gt less than in the 550 Policy Scenario and 2.6 Gt less than in the Reference Scenario.

Co-benefits in the 550 and 450 Policy Scenarios

Energy security

The measures taken to contain CO_2 emissions under both policy scenarios have substantial implications for the energy security of consuming regions. OECD+ oil and gas imports in 2030 in the 550 Policy Scenario are some 260 Mtoe, or 15%, lower than the Reference Scenario (Figure 18.20). The oil and gas import savings expand to over 400 Mtoe if China and India are added. OECD+ oil and gas import dependence in 2030 falls from 48% in the Reference Scenario to 44% in the 550 Policy Scenario, which is even lower than in 2006. With lower imports and international fuel prices in 2030, the net oil and gas import bill of OECD+ is reduced by nearly $450 billion, or 31%, compared with the Reference Scenario. The proportion of OECD+ GDP represented by the fuel bill increases from 1.9% in 2006 to 2.3% in 2030 in the Reference Scenario, while it declines to 1.6% in the 550 Policy Scenario, making the economy less vulnerable to international fuel-price fluctuations.

Figure 18.20 • OECD+ net oil and gas imports in the Reference and 550 Policy Scenarios, 2030

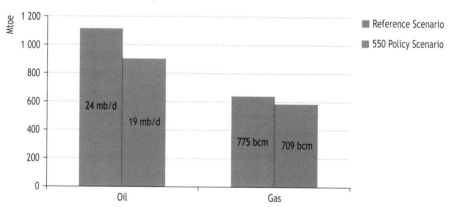

The oil imports of OECD+ decline due to end-use efficiency improvements and switching away from oil, mainly in the transport sector. In 2030, OECD+ oil imports in the 550 Policy Scenario reach around 19 mb/d, 4.5 mb/d or 19% lower than in the Reference Scenario, with import dependence falling from 53% to 47%. The reduction is more than Iran's current oil production. However, despite the decline in global oil demand, there will still be a need for a substantial increase in OPEC production. Total OPEC production in the 550 Policy Scenario reaches just over 49 mb/d in 2030, almost 13 mb/d higher than today. Gas imports in the 550 Policy Scenario decline due to energy efficiency

18

improvements in buildings, but not by as much as oil imports because of fuel switching from coal to gas in power generation. OECD+ gas imports in 2030 decline by 8% to just over 700 bcm from 775 bcm in the Reference Scenario.

In the 550 Policy Scenario, the security of electricity supply is also improved. Global electricity demand in 2030 declines by 223 Mtoe, or 9%, relative to the Reference Scenario, which reduces the urgency of investment to construct or upgrade power-generation plant and distribution networks. Lowered electricity intensity improves the resilience of countries' economies to potential power-supply disruptions. The fuel mix is more diversified. The combined share of the two dominant power-generation fuels, coal and gas, is reduced from 71% to 61% worldwide in 2030. The power sector depends less on imported fossil fuels with the increased uptake of nuclear and renewables.

In the 450 Policy Scenario, energy demand of OECD+ falls below its current level and consuming regions need to import less fuel than in the 550 Policy Scenario. Imports of oil and gas in OECD+ decline by 3% in 2030 from the 550 Policy Scenario and 5% if China and India are included. OPEC oil production is projected to reach 48 mb/d in 2030, some 5 mb/d lower than projected in the Reference Scenario (but still 12 mb/d higher than today's production level). Due to the significant change in the power-generation fuel mix, the reduction in gas imports of OECD+ in 2030 from the 550 Policy Scenario reaches over 60 bcm, or 9%, which would significantly contribute to the gas supply security of the region. Also, OECD+ needs to spend $17 billion less for oil and gas imports in the 450 Policy Scenario compared with the 550 Policy Scenario.

Although the reduction in global electricity demand in 2030 is only 4% compared with the 550 Policy Scenario, the fuel mix changes significantly as a result of the wider use of nuclear and renewables. The share of coal and gas as fuel for power and heat plants in the 450 Policy Scenario in 2030 declines to 47%. This contributes to the security of the electricity sector, making the sector in many countries less import-dependent.

Local and regional air pollution

Lower fossil-fuel demand in the two climate-policy scenarios results in substantial environmental co-benefits in the form of reduced local air pollution. For all pollutants, the biggest reductions occur in the last decade of the projection period, as this is when policies to reduce demand and to enforce stricter regulations on CO_2 emissions have the greatest impact.

In the 550 Policy Scenario, the world's NO_x emissions are projected to decline from 80 million tonnes in 2005 to 70 Mt in 2030, 11% lower than in the Reference Scenario. Fuel substitution and lower fuel use in the power sector accounts for around 60% of the overall global reduction. The transport sector accounts for 20% of the reduction. Emissions of SO_2 also decline, from 89 Mt in 2005 to 73 Mt in 2030, or 18% lower than in the Reference Scenario. The power sector accounts for more than 70% of the overall global reduction in SO_2 emissions in 2030. Particulate matter emissions decline fast over the *Outlook* period – from 37 Mt in 2005 to 26 Mt in 2030, compared with 28 Mt in 2030 in the Reference Scenario.

Non-OECD countries account for most of the reductions in SO_2, NO_x and particulate matter. In China, NO_x emissions still rise in the near term in the 550 Policy Scenario, but they begin to decline after 2015. In 2030, they are 16% lower than in the Reference Scenario (Figure 18.21). SO_2 emissions in China also rise to 2015 then fall, to reach just over 24 Mt in 2030 compared with 30 Mt in the Reference Scenario. China accounts for nearly 40% of the global reduction in NO_x and SO_2 emissions. In India NO_x emissions in the 550 Policy Scenario continue to rise, though at a much slower rate, and are 1.3 Mt lower by 2030 than in the Reference Scenario. SO_2 emissions are 3.6 Mt lower, accounting for 23% of the global decline.

Figure 18.21 ● Percentage reduction in NO_x and SO_2 emissions by region in the 550 Policy Scenario relative to the Reference Scenario

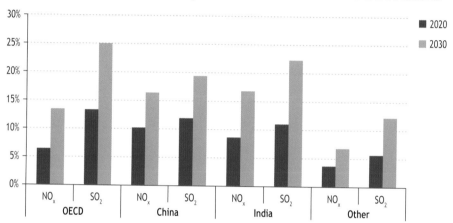

In the 450 Policy Scenario, global NO_x emissions are reduced by 16 Mt, or 20%, from the Reference Scenario in 2030. Two-thirds of the reduction comes from the power sector and 16% from the transport sector. The reduction in global SO_2 in the 450 Policy Scenario is also pronounced, reaching nearly 30 Mt or 34% compared with the Reference Scenario. The power and industry sectors together account for 95% of the total reduction in SO_2 emissions in 2030. Particulate matter emissions are reduced slightly further than in the 550 Policy Scenario.

The reductions in pollution in non-OECD countries are far greater than in OECD countries in the 450 Policy Scenario. NO_x emissions in non-OECD countries are reduced by 13 Mt, accounting for 83% of the global decline compared with the Reference Scenario. SO_2 emissions are reduced by 26 Mt, 88% of the global reduction. Emissions reductions in China and India account for around 60% of the global reduction of both NO_x and SO_2 compared with the Reference Scenario. NO_x emissions in China are reduced by one-third, reaching 14 Mt in 2030 compared with 21 Mt in the Reference Scenario, as a result of reduced use of coal-fired power plants, which also cuts SO_2 emissions. India's NO_x emissions are 2.2 Mt, about 28%, lower than in the Reference Scenario in 2030, and SO_2 emissions are 6.4 Mt, about 40%, lower.

18

CHAPTER 19

IMPLICATIONS FOR ENERGY INVESTMENT
What does transformation entail?

H I G H L I G H T S

- The climate-policy scenarios require a substantial shift in investment patterns and a major transformation of the way investment decisions in the energy sector are taken. In both scenarios, significant additional investment is needed in power plants and in more energy-efficient energy-related capital stock.

- The 550 Policy Scenario requires additional investment of $1.2 trillion in power plants and $3 trillion in energy efficiency relative to the Reference Scenario. Most of this investment goes to deploying existing technologies. In the power-generation sector, investment over the period 2010-2030 rises from $6.1 trillion in the Reference Scenario to $7.3 trillion in the 550 Policy Scenario, bringing forth more renewables, nuclear power and carbon capture and storage. Two-thirds of the additional investment occurs in the OECD+ region. Of the additional $3 trillion of investment in energy efficiency, around half is in transport; buildings need an additional $950 billion and industry close to $530 billion. The total additional global investment (relative to the Reference Scenario) equates to 0.24 % of world GDP per year on average over the period 2010-2030. The savings on energy bills between 2010 and 2030 total over $7 trillion.

- The 450 Policy Scenario requires further power plant investments of $2.4 trillion (in addition to those in the 550 Policy Scenario), over half of which are in the Other Major Economies group. This scenario assumes broad deployment of technologies that have not yet been proven. Research and development now will determine whether these advanced technologies will be available in the future. These investments result from a broad, efficient carbon market and global deployment of the best technologies. Investment in energy efficiency also rises considerably after 2020. During that period, improving energy efficiency in buildings sees the highest investment. Additional investments in total amount to 0.55% of world GDP. Fuel-cost savings are about $5.8 trillion.

- In both scenarios, the policy effort to galvanise energy-efficient purchases by hundreds of millions of households and businesses worldwide is enormous, involving strong price signals, fiscal incentives and well-targeted regulation. In the 550 Policy Scenario, the additional annual expenditure by individuals averages $17 per person. The level is highest in OECD+, at $54 per person per year. In the OECD+ region, this amount is almost $150 over the period 2021-2030 in the 450 Policy Scenario, and is almost 80% higher than that of the 550 Policy Scenario.

- Auctioning of emissions allowances could raise substantial funds, to help fund investments and research, or reduce national economic taxes. In both scenarios, revenues from full auctioning exceed the total additional global investment needed.

The investment challenge of transforming energy

The profound shifts in energy demand and supply in the two climate scenarios call for a transformation of the way investment decisions are taken. They entail significant changes in the pattern of investment across the supply and demand chains, as well as huge additional spending on new capital stock, especially in power plants and in more energy-efficient equipment and appliances — the focus of this chapter.

To achieve the required shifts in the power sector and improvements in energy efficiency, investment and purchasing decisions[1] must change. An important role for governments is to catalyse these investments in a targeted manner. Clear price signals, including carbon pricing and, in many non-OECD countries, the removal of subsidised fuel prices, are an important first step. Current high energy prices, if sustained, will facilitate the transition. However, prices alone are not enough: effective government policies to promote these changes are needed, including information provision, regulation, financing schemes and fiscal incentives.

Investment implications of the 550 Policy Scenario

The 550 Policy Scenario envisages additional investment in power plants, where electricity production must be cleaner, in energy efficiency in industry, buildings and transport, where companies and households alike must invest in more efficient technologies, and in biofuels, where more biorefinery capacity needs to be built (Figure 19.1).[2]

In the power-generation sector, where more low-carbon generating capacity is needed, investment over the period 2010-2030 rises from $6.1 trillion in the Reference Scenario to $7.3 trillion in the 550 Policy Scenario. Over this period, electricity demand is around 5% lower than in the Reference Scenario. However, electricity prices are higher in the 550 Policy Scenario than in the Reference Scenario, in order to provide an appropriate level of return on these investments.

On the demand side (industry, transport and buildings), additional investment of $3 trillion is needed, in order to use energy more efficiently.[3] Half of this investment, $1.5 trillion, is invested in transport; buildings need an additional $0.9 trillion and industry close to $0.5 trillion. Consumers need to purchase more efficient products, ranging from highly efficient electrical appliances to low-carbon passenger vehicles.

---

1. In this chapter, the term "investment" is used to refer to both capital spending by businesses and spending by households and individuals on cars, equipment, appliances and other energy-related expenditures.

2. In the 550 Policy Scenario, the additional investment in biofuels is $54 billion.

3. The total additional investment in energy efficiency in the 550 Policy Scenario, relative to the Reference Scenario, is over 25% higher than additional investment in WEO-2007's Alternative Policy Scenario (which follows a similar emissions trajectory to the 550 Policy Scenario), relative to WEO-2007's Reference Scenario. The unit costs of demand-side efficiency measures have been revised upwards, due to increasing commodity costs and a shortage of skilled labour, particularly in the OECD. This is only partially offset by efficiencies associated with the more widespread deployment of these measures assumed in this Outlook. Cost data come from IEA databases and Argonne National Laboratory in the United States.

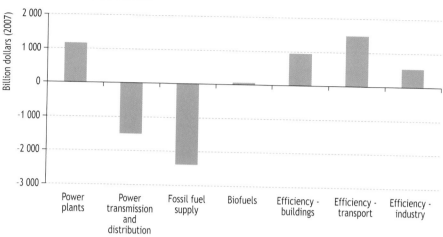

Figure 19.1 ● Change in total world energy-related investments by sector in the 550 Policy Scenario relative to the Reference Scenario, 2010-2030

While challenging, the 550 Policy Scenario can be achieved mainly through the deployment of existing technologies, or incremental improvements to these (such as continued enhancement of the internal combustion engine in passenger vehicles). The challenge is therefore to create the incentives to ensure that the necessary investments are made. Globally, there is enough capital to finance these investment needs. The current financial crisis may take a toll on energy-related investments by making it more difficult to obtain credit or by making them more expensive, but this is unlikely significantly to affect the long-term outlook. Funding will have to come from both public and private sources. Securing funds for energy investment in poor countries will be much more challenging than in OECD countries; additional foreign direct investment is likely to be essential. While availability of capital may not be an issue, the availability of engineering and manufacturing capacity and the supply of materials may create challenges. Such constraints may take a decade or so to extenuate.

Regional implications of the 550 Policy Scenario

There are significant variations in additional investment needs among groups in the 550 Policy Scenario. The OECD+ group incurs by far the highest increases in investment in electricity generation and in efficiency (Figure 19.2). Other Major Economies undertake an additional $170 billion investment in power plants, 8% more than in the Reference Scenario, but face a more substantial increase in investment in energy efficiency. Relative to the other groups of countries, the additional spending on power plants by the Other Major Economies group is small, reflecting large reductions in electricity demand in these countries. Investment in power generation in Other Countries is nearly $140 billion greater than in the Reference Scenario, while investment in energy efficiency increases by $430 billion. The additional average annual investment in power plants and efficiency is equal to 0.24 % of world GDP over the period 2010-2030.

19

Figure 19.2 ● Additional investment in power plants and energy efficiency by region in the 550 Policy Scenario relative to the Reference Scenario, 2010-2030

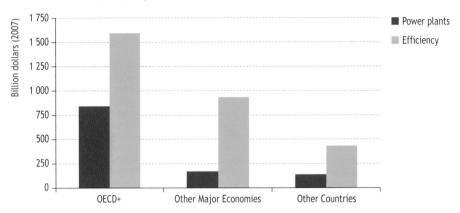

In middle- and low-income countries, the power sector is most often a public utility requiring access to public funds to finance large investments to meet rapidly growing electricity demand. It is, therefore, good news that, compared with the Reference Scenario, total investment in the power sector — including generation, transmission and distribution — is 8% (almost half a trillion dollars) lower in Other Major Economies and 3% lower in Other Countries (Figure 19.3). This is due to lower investment in networks in the 550 Policy Scenario, as a result of lower electricity demand. This is particularly important in alleviating the burden of investment in those countries struggling to raise finance.

Figure 19.3 ● Investment in the power sector in Other Major Economies and Other Countries in the 550 Policy Scenario and Reference Scenario, 2010-2030

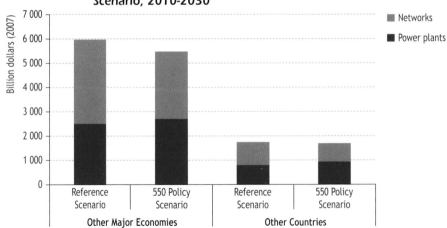

As discussed above, the greatest challenge is to encourage private consumers to invest in energy efficiency by making their homes more energy-efficient — including the purchase of more efficient appliances — and by driving more efficient cars. The additional investment by individuals in the 550 Policy Scenario is estimated at $54 per person per year in the OECD+ region, at $11 per person per year in the Other Major Economies region and at $5 per person per year in Other Countries, corresponding to a global average of $17 per year (Figure 19.4).

Figure 19.4 ● Additional investment* per capita by private consumers in the 550 Policy Scenario relative to the Reference Scenario, 2010-2030

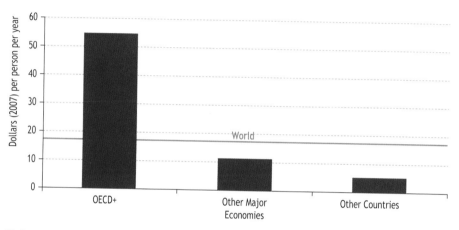

*Refers to additional spending on transport and households (for example, appliances).

Implications of the 550 Policy Scenario for the electricity sector

Globally, additional investment in power plants of nearly $1.2 trillion is needed, in the application of low-carbon technologies. Most of this investment ($0.8 trillion) occurs within the cap-and-trade regime in the OECD+ region, with investment in capital-intensive technologies such as nuclear power, carbon capture and storage (CCS) and renewables. As shown in Chapter 18, the carbon price driving these investments increases over time, rising to $40 per tonne of CO_2 in 2020 and reaching $90 per tonne in 2030.

Figure 19.5 shows projected power-generation costs in Europe and the United States for 2030 under CO_2 prices of $50 and $90 per tonne. Onshore wind and nuclear power become much more competitive relative to conventional fossil-fuel technologies. Coal with CCS becomes commercial by 2030. This assumes that the pilot deployments in the OECD+ region are successful, that sustained learning brings down capital costs, and that efficiency losses are reduced.

19

Figure 19.5 ● Electricity generating costs in Europe and the United States assuming different carbon prices in the 550 Policy Scenario, 2030

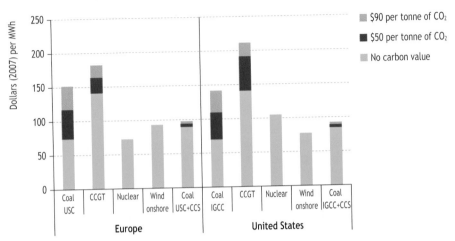

Note: The actual carbon price in the 550 Policy Scenario in 2030 is $90/tonne of CO_2. The generating cost of wind power does not include integration costs. CCS costs do not include CO_2 transport and storage, which add $7 to $20 per MWh of electricity produced. USC = ultrasupercritical; IGCC = integrated gasification combined cycle; CCGT = combined-cycle gas turbine.

The cap-and-trade system cannot eliminate all uncertainties. Investors still have to analyse the fundamental factors determining the cost of abating CO_2 emissions in the future, in order to form CO_2 price expectations upon which they can act. However, the energy sector is used to dealing with such market risks and an efficient carbon market, with an array of financial instruments, will help the sector to function efficiently.

It is uncertainty about climate policy that is one of the greatest risks with which investors in power generation are currently faced. Climate policy will have a significant impact on the absolute and relative costs of different electricity generation options. This is, of course, intended, since the main thrust of climate policy is to alter the technology choices that investors make. However, uncertainty about future climate policy creates great uncertainty about future generating costs and the merits of different investment options. This is likely to lead to delays in investments until greater policy certainty is available. The sooner policy makers can make decisions on climate-change mitigation policies, the less risky investments in new power generation will be. Going forward, it will be important to minimise policy risk by providing a comprehensive, robust post-2012 framework, which instills confidence in the energy sector as to the direction of global policy for the foreseeable future, while yet preserving a modicum of flexibility to permit some modification in the light of experience.

Experiences from the first phase of the European Union's Emissions Trading Scheme (EU ETS) give good indications of how the implementation of a cap-and-trade system affects investments. In the first phase, the CO_2 reductions required by the power sector to fulfill government commitments were mainly delivered through switching fuel from coal to gas within existing installations. Wind power also expanded considerably. At the same time considerable plans for expansion of coal plants emerged, as a response to high gas prices. In that sense, the EU ETS was claimed not to change investment patterns, but only to change the pattern of operating existing plants.

Several reasons for this marginal effect have been highlighted. First, commitments on CO_2 reductions covered only the period to 2012, which was seen as too short to incentivise profound cleaner investments. Second, free allowances for new projects and cancellation of initial allowances following decommissioning proved a counter-incentive to factoring the implied carbon cost into decision-making (Bouttes *et al.*, 2007). With the EU agreement to proceed with the EU ETS beyond 2012 on the basis of full auctioning of emission rights for the power sector, a much stronger signal is sent to investors. There are signs that these signals are having an effect, even before full agreement on the legislation has been reached: several planned coal plants have been cancelled, while other, state-of-the-art coal plants are going ahead; investors are showing great interest in nuclear power in countries where this is not ruled out by government policy and are pushing the debate in countries where nuclear operation or expansion has thus far been excluded.

Implications of the 550 Policy Scenario for the transport sector

While transport is a difficult sector in which to reduce total emissions, due to rapidly growing global demand and a lack of cost-effective alternatives, there is considerable potential for abatement, relative to the Reference Scenario. In the 550 Policy Scenario, the sectoral agreements in road transport and aviation, and national policies lead to additional investment of $1.5 trillion, which delivers substantial reductions in fuel consumption. OECD+ countries make almost 70% of the incremental transport investment. This high share is a function of the higher cost of increasing fuel economy in some parts of the OECD and its larger share of vehicle sales over the projection period.

The sectoral agreements bring forth a variety of technologies to deliver energy and CO_2 savings. While some of the improvements to the internal combustion engine in the 550 Policy Scenario will go to improved performance, most technology improvements benefit fuel efficiency. In addition, energy savings come from more rapid penetration of hybrid cars and light-weight materials. CO_2 savings are also made by increased consumption of biofuels.

The large abatement potential in road transport is in part explained by existing wide differences in the efficiency of vehicles, both across and within regions. For example, the average vehicle in the United States is currently around 40% less efficient than that in Japan (Figure 19.6). The sectoral approach we have modelled works to reduce this differential. Improving vehicle efficiency is cheaper in countries with a larger share of inefficient vehicles, especially heavy ones, in the existing fleet.

19

Figure 19.6 ● Average light-duty vehicle fleet efficiency by region, 2006

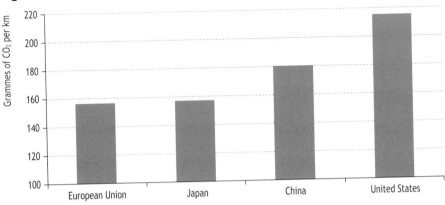

Source: IEA database.

Even with a sectoral agreement in road transport, consumer investment choices will be particularly important in helping to realise the 550 Policy Scenario. Analysis of the sector in the United Kingdom shows that there is a large variance in new car efficiency even within the same class of vehicle, such that if consumers opted for the most CO_2-efficient vehicle in their chosen class, their average overall per-kilometre emissions would fall by around 25% (King, 2008). Downsizing would achieve further abatement. In the Other Major Economies region, where vehicle ownership is growing rapidly, these choices will be particularly important.

However, evidence suggests that consumers tend to discount heavily the claimed value of fuel savings from more efficient vehicles, such that direct government action to encourage low-carbon investments will continue to be important. On the consumer side, this may include improved information provision and fiscal incentives — such as annual or up-front vehicle tax rates that vary according to a vehicle's carbon efficiency.[4] On the producer side, international sectoral agreements may stimulate regulatory approaches, such as the proposed EU legislation on vehicle emissions.

While substantial abatement can be achieved by adopting existing road transport technologies, there is also great potential from new technologies — both through enhancements to the internal combustion engine and, increasingly, hybridisation and electrification of vehicles. There has been a steady increase in the efficiency of new vehicles over recent years, and this can be accelerated by providing the right incentives to manufacturers to undertake research, development and demonstration and to bring more efficient models to market.

---

4. For example, France operates a "bonus-malus" scheme, where government imposes an up-front tax on high-emitting vehicles and a subsidy on low-emitting vehicles. Many countries differentiate vehicle excise duty according to vehicle emissions.

Large financial incentives exist in the aviation industry to use the most efficient aircraft, and the sectoral agreement in the 550 Policy Scenario (see Chapter 18) sees CO_2 savings coming from a combination of improvements in jet engine efficiency, increased load factors, improved aerodynamics, use of light-weight materials and improved air-traffic procedures on top of those in the Reference Scenario.

Implications of the 550 Policy Scenario for buildings and industry

In the 550 Policy Scenario, national policies and measures lead to additional spending of around $950 billion to achieve greater energy efficiency in buildings, about a third of the total additional investment in energy efficiency across all sectors. Most of this additional spending is on electrical equipment such as more efficient refrigerators, much of it by households. Two-thirds of the additional investment in energy efficiency in buildings is projected to be in the OECD+ region. This region achieves the highest savings in CO_2 emissions (see Chapter 18).

Additional investment in energy efficiency in industry is projected to be around $530 billion. As discussed in Chapter 18, this includes the increased use of electric arc furnaces in the iron and steel sector and the wider deployment of large-scale rotary dry kilns in the cement sector. As in buildings, more than half of these industrial investments will be in OECD+, although investment in energy efficiency is generally more cost-effective in Other Major Economies and Other Countries because their equipment is less efficient than OECD+ and the capital costs of various technologies are lower.

Costs and benefits of the 550 Policy Scenario

While the 550 Policy Scenario requires additional spending on energy efficiency and on power plants to address climate change, there are additional benefits to consumers on a global scale. These investments reduce consumption of fossil fuels by 22 billion tonnes of oil equivalent over the period 2010 to 2030. This delivers savings for individuals and business and reduces the burden of energy imports. The lower consumption of fossil fuels, particularly oil and gas, improves supply security.

On a global scale, significant savings in consumer energy bills arise in the 550 Policy Scenario, relative to the Reference Scenario, due to more efficient energy use. Energy bills to pay for electricity, motor fuels and heating fuels are over $7 trillion lower than in the Reference Scenario, as a result of energy savings and lower fossil-fuel prices (Figure 19.7). The net undiscounted savings in the 550 Policy Scenario amount to over $4 trillion.[5] Discounted at a 3% rate, net savings are some $2.7 trillion. With a 10% discount rate, the net savings fall to around $1 trillion dollars.[6] The savings have been

---

5. Net of investment.

6. Discount rates actually vary between sectors and regions; the two uniform rates used here should be seen as indicative only.

19

calculated over the period 2010-2030. For some types of investments, particularly those made after 2020, savings will continue beyond 2030. These extra benefits have not been included in our analysis. Also, in some sectors — notably industry in the OECD+ region — emission reductions come at a cost. This sector participates in a cap-and-trade scheme and pays for the CO_2 it emits.

Figure 19.7 ● Fuel cost savings by region in the 550 Policy Scenario relative to the Reference Scenario, 2010-2030

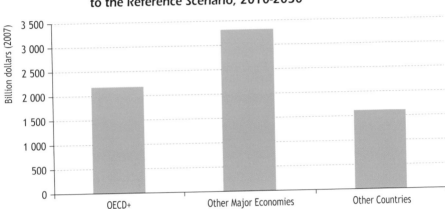

Given the available savings in energy bills in most sectors, consumers and businesses should already be incentivised to undertake these investments. However, energy efficiency is rarely the overriding criterion in the purchase of such goods. These demand-side investments involve substantial up-front costs and experience shows that consumers — ranging from large and small industries, to commercial establishments to transport companies — can be reluctant to depart from the least capital cost solution, even when a higher outlay pays for itself within a few years. They typically focus on the up-front costs of the energy-consuming goods they purchase and tend to heavily discount the full lifecycle costs, including energy usage, particularly when energy prices are low. The challenge may be even more significant in Other Countries, where additional demand-side investments constitute a higher proportion of household income and where there are fewer resources available to achieve fully co-ordinated policies.

Investment implications of the 450 Policy Scenario

The 450 Policy Scenario requires additional investment of $3.6 trillion in power plants and $5.7 trillion in energy efficiency over the period 2010-2030 relative to the Reference Scenario.[7] This additional investment is much higher in the period

---

7. Investment in biofuels in 2010-2030 is $127 billion higher than in the Reference Scenario.

2021-2030 than in the period 2010-2020 (Figure 19.8). In the 450 Policy Scenario, substantially higher investment is needed in power plants. Post-2020, this power sector investment is nearly twice as high as in the Reference Scenario. This is because substantial investments are needed to replace existing fossil-fuel based power plants. Similarly, investment in energy efficiency rises considerably in the 450 Policy Scenario, particularly beyond 2020. During that period, improving energy efficiency in buildings will require the highest investment. The cumulative saving on energy bills over the period 2010-2030 amount to $5.8 trillion — a lower sum than in the 550 Policy Scenario. The energy savings are bigger than in the 550 Policy Scenario, but electricity prices are higher.

Figure 19.8 ● **Change in power plant and energy efficiency investments in the Policy Scenarios relative to the Reference Scenario**

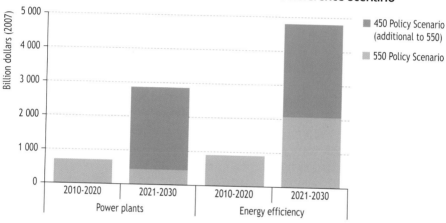

Note: In the 550 Policy Scenario, additional investment in power plants in 2021-2030 is lower than in the period 2010-2020 because electricity demand is much lower in this period and consequently fewer new power plants are built. This changes in the 450 Policy Scenario because there is a greater degree of replacement of existing fossil-fuel based power plants to reduce CO_2 emissions.

The 450 Policy Scenario requires substantial investments and abatement in non-OECD countries (Figure 19.9). Given the level of abatement needed, Other Major Economies are assumed to join the cap-and-trade system in 2020. Investment in power plants in this group is $1.4 trillion higher than in the Reference Scenario, slightly less than the extra $1.6 trillion needed in OECD+. Investment in energy efficiency is also substantially higher. In Other Countries, investment in power plants is over 80% higher than in the Reference Scenario.

Investment by private consumers must rise considerably after 2020. The average annual additional investment per person (to cover residential buildings, appliances and private cars) by region is shown in Figure 19.10. In the OECD+ region, this amount is almost $150 over the period 2021-2030 and is almost 80% higher than that of the 550 Policy Scenario.

19

Figure 19.9 ● Additional energy-related investment by region in the 450
Policy Scenario relative to the Reference Scenario, 2010-2030

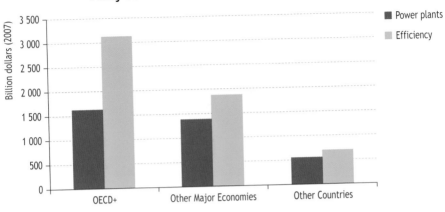

In the 450 Policy Scenario, the additional investment in power plants and demand-side efficiency corresponds to 0.55% of cumulative world GDP over the period 2010-2030, compared with 0.24% in the 550 Policy Scenario. Many of the additional investments in the 450 Policy Scenario are in power-sector technologies that are not currently commercially available. For example, the cap-and-trade system for power generation and industry in the 450 Policy Scenario is assumed to drive $670 billion of CCS, including retro-fitting, while the sectoral agreements in transport lead to the introduction of advanced biofuels and the penetration of electric and fuel-cell vehicles. In order to make this a reality, substantial research and development efforts will be needed (Box 19.1). In any case, there is a real chance that some of these technological breakthroughs will not materialise, which would lead to much higher marginal abatement costs between 2020 and 2030 in order still to meet the 450 emissions trajectory.

Figure 19.10 ● Additional energy-related investment per private consumer
in the 450 Policy Scenario relative to the Reference Scenario,
2021-2030

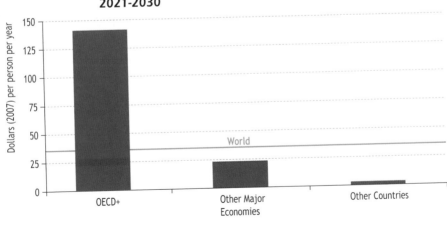

Box 19.1 ● Stepping up research, development and demonstration to promote climate-friendly technologies

While the 550 Policy Scenario could, in theory, be achieved through the widespread deployment of existing carbon-efficient technologies, further technological progress will greatly facilitate, and lower the costs of, meeting it. The 450 Policy Scenario can only be achieved through stepped-up research, development and subsequent demonstration and deployment of technologies. In recognition of this, countries agreed at COP 13 in Bali that energy-sector research and development from both the public and private sectors needs to be scaled-up significantly and quickly.

The private sector currently accounts for around 80-85% of global energy-sector research and development, and will need to continue to provide much of the effort, and in most cases will be best placed to do so. There is evidence that private research in clean technology is increasing. Recent years have seen strong interest from venture capital and private equity firms, where clean energy technology forms over three-quarters of proposals. According to the United Nations Environmental Programme, over $148 billion in new funding entered the sustainable energy sector in 2007, up 60% from 2006 (UNEP, 2008).

By creating demand for low-carbon technologies, carbon markets, sectoral targets and national policies will all play a crucial role in providing the incentives for the private sector to invest and innovate. The development of more competitive energy markets and stable institutions will also encourage private sector innovation. However, by themselves, these measures will be insufficient because of other barriers and market failures that inhibit research and development of low-carbon technologies:

● The requirement for short payback periods may prevent firms from investing in energy technologies that are profitable only in the long term (such as CCS).

● The spin-off benefits of some energy technologies for other sectors or technologies that may be difficult for energy firms to capture.

● Supply-side bottlenecks, such as planning delays and skills shortages, can hinder innovation and may be particularly strong in non-OECD countries.

Moreover, creating long-term, credible demand for low-carbon technologies may be difficult to achieve, especially in the short term, while the time taken for technology development means that innovation needs to start now. Governments and international organisations have a key role to play in reducing these barriers and supporting research and development.

Recognising these benefits, most governments around the world already support research — but there is need for expansion. Despite increasing slightly in recent years, public spending on research and development in the energy sector in real terms is around half the level it was 25 years ago. Moreover, while many

19

Replacement of capital stock in the power sector

As discussed in Chapter 17, the rate of capital replacement in the power sector has an important influence on the speed at which new technologies can be deployed — and therefore on how quickly the energy sector can be transformed to deliver a cleaner energy mix, improvements in energy efficiency and reductions in CO_2 emissions. In OECD+ countries, the capital stock is ageing in the power sector: 40% of the plant stock is now over 30 years old and most importantly, over half of coal-fired capacity is older than 30 years (Figure 19.11).

Figure 19.11 ● Age distribution of power plants in the OECD+ region, 2006

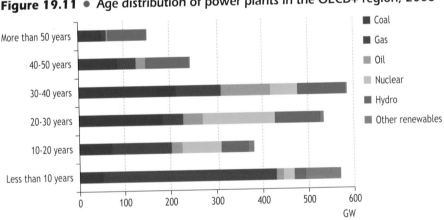

Policies to encourage the retirement of the older and most inefficient fossil-fuel plants in the OECD+ countries can speed up the rate of capital turnover and open up the "window for action" associated with the replacement of plant at the end of its useful life (see Chapter 17). In both Policy Scenarios, the carbon price resulting from the cap-and-trade system provides this incentive. In particular, it influences the lifetime of coal-fired plants, as some of the least-efficient and most polluting coal-fired power plants become uneconomic and are retired earlier. However, seeing this major transformation through will be a test of global resolve in curbing CO_2 emissions. Box 19.2 illustrates how a policy to shut down coal-fired power plants in Ontario, Canada has proven to be a major challenge.

In Other Major Economies and Other Countries, Reference Scenario emissions grow much faster than in OECD+, requiring additional power-generation capacity and therefore presenting greater opportunity for emissions abatement relative to this scenario. However, any delay in implementing emissions-reduction policies will reduce the likelihood of the world achieving its climate-change goal. In the absence of incentives to invest in low-carbon technologies over the 2012-2020 period, the CO_2 mitigation potential in the power sector in non-OECD countries would be reduced significantly, because less efficient solutions become locked in. Although power plants in these regions are relatively new — 73% of capacity is less than 20 years old — government policies can still accelerate capital stock turnover in some cases. In China, for example, the government has a policy to shut down small and inefficient coal-fired power plants. Additional emissions reductions can come from upgrading existing power plants in these two regions. Fitting at least some of coal plants to be constructed between now and 2020 with CCS could yield significant emissions abatement. The possibility of tapping such potential is, however, critically dependent on the success of demonstration and deployment programmes for CCS in OECD+ countries before 2020 and on the improvement of the framework for international collaboration on financing and technology.

In the 450 Policy Scenario, the need for new power plants after 2020 rises considerably, relative to the Reference and 550 Policy Scenarios. Capacity additions in the decade from 2021 to 2030 amount to around 3 000 GW, over 50% higher than in the Reference and 550 Policy Scenarios. Many coal-fired power plants are shut down and replaced with low-carbon technologies: almost 120 GW of additional coal plant capacity will be replaced by coal plants with CCS, relative to the 550 Policy Scenario (see Chapter 18). Two-thirds of these coal capacity additions will take place in Other Major Economies and will then account for almost a tenth of installed coal capacity in this region. This presents a major logistical challenge for manufacturers of power plants. In general, it is more difficult to expand the production of complex technologies, such as nuclear power and CCS, compared with technologies such as wind turbines and photovoltaics.

Box 19.2 ● Shutting down coal-fired power plants in Ontario, Canada

In Canada, provinces oversee, and in many cases own, the electric power systems within their borders. In 2003, the government of Ontario, Canada's largest province, announced a policy to retire all coal-fired generation by 2007 for environmental and health reasons. The 7 560 MW of generating capacity, operated by the provincially owned Ontario Power Generation, accounted for 25% of the province's installed generation capacity and 33 Mt of CO_2 emissions.

19

Implementation of this policy has been beset by technical, cost and environmental challenges. The largest technical challenge arises from the amount of capacity that needed to be replaced and the role of that capacity in balancing electricity supply with demand. While the government processes to procure replacement capacity began within months of the policy announcement, several years will pass before sufficient replacement capacity is in place. Upgrades to the grid have also proven necessary as large, central coal-fired stations are replaced by smaller, more geographically dispersed gas-fired and renewable generation. These technical challenges are the primary reason for a seven-year delay in the original phase out date – from 2007 to 2014.

The main costs arise from the costs of the replacement gas-fired generation, installations to make use of renewable resources (primarily wind), conservation measures and the cost of transmission upgrades. The government has created an agency to procure these supply and conservation resources, and a mechanism to pass the costs through to consumers. While it is difficult to estimate how much of this investment is aimed strictly at coal replacement, the cost of gas-fired generation and transmission expenditures alone amounts to $6.4 billion. The replacement generation capacity is being obtained through long-term contracts with generators, leaving the risks of capacity under-utilisation with electricity consumers. Furthermore, prices in the wholesale market are anticipated to increase as coal-fired generation, which currently sets the market price over 50% of the time, is replaced by gas-fired generation.

The Ontario government is relying on the coal phase-out to contribute 44% of Ontario's greenhouse-gas emissions reductions by 2015 under its Climate Change Action Plan. The ultimate global environmental impact and the ultimate cost to Ontario's electricity consumers of the current policy are difficult to assess because the Ontario electricity market is interconnected with the neighbouring states of New York and Michigan in the United States. Ontario power production is, accordingly, competing with power generators in these states and other nearby states in the United States that rely heavily on coal for power generation, such as Ohio and Indiana. Ontario is currently a significant net exporter of power, of which a significant fraction comes from coal. There are no restrictions on CO_2 emissions in most of these neighbouring jurisdictions.

For these reasons, as coal-fired generation is restricted and eliminated within Ontario, coal-fired generation in the neighbouring jurisdictions can be expected to increase – both to replace exports of Ontario energy and through increased imports to Ontario. The increase in imports would be expected to mitigate price rises within the Ontario market by reducing gas-fired power production within Ontario but also, when these imports are from coal-fired generation, reduce the global environmental benefit from the coal phase out. Substantial global environmental benefits are likely only if neighbouring jurisdictions adopt a carbon-emissions policy of similar stringency.

Technology diffusion and interaction with carbon markets

In both the 550 Policy Scenario and the 450 Policy Scenario, in order to achieve global abatement most efficiently, a substantial emissions reduction takes place in Other Countries. This will almost certainly go beyond the formal responsibilities allocated to these countries in a post-2012 agreement and include abatement paid for by developed countries, to offset their own abatement obligations. Consequently, there must be a mechanism to enable trade on this scale to take place, ensuring allocative efficiency, as well as worldwide availability of the most efficient low-carbon technologies, to ensure productive efficiency.

The Policy Scenarios are therefore underpinned by a flexible global trading environment, which assumes that there is a substantial world carbon market, as well as effective diffusion of technologies and technological expertise across countries. Ensuring that the post-2012 reality reflects these assumptions constitutes a crucial policy challenge.

Carbon markets

A market for trading emissions credits is important for ensuring that abatement occurs at least cost. Where countries' marginal costs of abatement differ, all parties can be made better off by the ability to buy and sell emissions credits. The climate change impact will be the same wherever the greenhouse gases are emitted.

There already exists a rapidly-expanding global carbon market, with trade in 2007 of around 3 Gt CO_2-eq, with a financial value of over $64 billion (Figure 19.12). This trade was derived from existing regimes, most notably the EU ETS (accounting for $50 billion of trade in 2007) and the Clean Development Mechanism ($13 billion). China was by far the biggest seller of CDM credits, with a market share of 73% of transactions. A future global climate regime could build upon and expand the existing carbon market.

In its simplest form, a carbon market would feature just those countries and sectors participating in cap-and-trade arrangements (*i.e.* power generation and industry in OECD+ in our scenarios). This would lead to some trading and cheaper abatement than if participating countries were bound to meet their targets through domestic abatement only. However, abatement costs and potentials are likely to be relatively similar across these countries, so that the amount of trading that takes place would be limited. Many of the most cost-effective abatement options are in Other Major Economies and Other Countries, where carbon intensities are typically higher. Even after taking into account the implementation of national policies and measures, there are likely to be substantial possibilities for abatement that would be cheaper than in developed countries. Consequently, a more comprehensive carbon market, which allows countries outside the cap-and-trade framework to participate, promises greater global cost savings, to the benefit of both OECD+ countries, which could meet their emissions allowances at lower cost, and non-OECD+ countries, which could accumulate and sell emissions credits.

19

In both the 450 and 550 Policy Scenarios, we assume some scope for those countries in the cap-and-trade system to purchase emissions credits from those countries not directly participating in it. However, incorporating countries without emissions caps into a global carbon market creates a fundamental design problem. If countries or businesses receive emissions credits for activities they would have undertaken anyway, this is not new abatement relative to business as usual. Given that countries buying credits are entitled to achieve less abatement themselves, there would be a risk of not meeting the expected global emissions trajectory. The CDM currently attempts to overcome this problem by imposing "additionality" criteria, including allowing CDM accreditation only for projects that would not go ahead without the CDM funding (Box 19.3). In practice, this is an imperfect system and in its current form would be too high-risk and too logistically demanding to be appropriate for the scale of carbon market transactions that would result from a global agreement.

Figure 19.12 ● **Global carbon market trading volumes and values, 2006 and 2007**

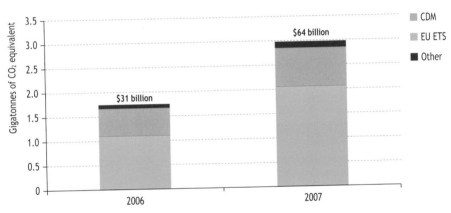

Source: World Bank (2008).

As Other Major Economies and Other Countries assume greater national responsibilities, whether through formalised policies and measures or sectoral agreements, the additionality issue will become even more complex, as emissions credits should be allocated only over and above fulfilment of those responsibilities. Another potential challenge is that CDM credits are currently allocated on a project-by-project basis. If a country's efforts are expressed in terms of national policies and measures, or participation in sectoral agreements, these cannot readily be translated into quantified emissions at project level in order to determine additionality.[8] Nevertheless, the

---

8. For example, it is not enough to justify accreditation for a proposed power plant that betters an average sectoral standard, as a country may need to introduce such plants anyway, in order to compensate for those plants that are worse than the standard.

economic benefits of global carbon trading, as well as the practicalities of meeting ambitious emissions targets, necessitate that a solution be reached to allow all countries to participate in a global carbon market.

Box 19.3 ● What next for the Clean Development Mechanism?

The number of projects registered under the CDM has grown rapidly over recent years. However, the complex project cycle and administrative process dampens its success. The main difficulty lies in proving that a CDM project would not be viable without the expected revenues from Certified Emissions Reductions (CERs). This so-called "additionality" criterion is seen as essential to ensure the environmental contribution of each project.

The requirements to implement a CDM project, the set of rules and regulatory processes administering these rules, and a strong regional and sectoral concentration led Parties to consider improvements. One innovation is so-called programmatic CDM, allowing project activities under a programme to be registered as a single project. Activities that implement a policy or standard can now be submitted as a single CDM project. This evolution is a step forward but difficulties remain, particularly the requirement to measure emission reductions at each project activity.

Recent research shows that CDM risks delivering fewer emission reductions than information on registered projects suggests. Many CDM projects face serious underperformance; by June 2007, only 76% of the initially forecast emissions reductions were actually issued.[9]

The CDM has been successful in revealing cost-effective emission reductions and raising the awareness of climate mitigation in non-OECD countries. Efforts are warranted to make it accessible to countries and sectors where it has not yet penetrated: the CDM's contribution to changing energy production and use in non-OECD countries has, so far, been extremely limited, with CO_2 savings amounting to some 1.9 Gt between 2000 and 2012.

At the same time, some climate policy experts question the urge to expand a system that merely compensates for other countries' excess emissions. Further, as countries grow, and increase their emissions, they will need to contribute more to global abatement, going beyond CDM-funded measures. With the Policy Scenarios implying much greater potential for CDM-style transactions, and with Other Countries already assumed to adopt national policies and measures that count towards the global emissions reduction effort, an improved system will be essential.

Ultimately, the most workable solution would be for more countries to graduate over time to the system of national emissions allowances. As discussed in Chapter 17, given the potential to allocate emissions according to any desired criteria, the solution adopted need not penalise non-OECD countries. In fact, some of these countries could

19

---

9. See Castro and Michaelowa (2008).

even be offered generous allowances, relative to their current emissions, to encourage global adoption of the more efficient system. It is also likely to be advantageous to link other sectors to the global carbon market, in order to realise allocative efficiency gains from a more harmonised global framework.

As with any energy-trading system or financial market, a global carbon market should conform to principles of liquidity, transparency, efficiency and security. A full range of derivative products will be important in order to provide the energy sector with maximum flexibility to achieve its objectives. However emissions allowances are defined, the ability to bank credits (for example, by undertaking additional early abatement) will be important in order to promote the most efficient timing of abatement activities. In theory, an efficient carbon market will equalise spot and future carbon prices, adjusting for interest rates and risk.[10]

Auctioning of emissions allowances

As well as a need for institutions and a market to enable carbon trading, there will need to be a means of allocating emissions allowances that form part of the cap-and-trade system in power generation and industry to emitting companies and other economic agents. This could be left to individual countries to decide according to their individual circumstances but for competitiveness reasons, a consistent approach across countries is desirable. Free allocation based on benchmarking — which reflects efficiency improvement efforts to date — would be an option to promote equity and avoid damaging the international competitiveness of companies. Another option is auctioning, which allows the revenues to accrue to governments, rather than as windfall profits. There are many international precedents to auctioning energy allowances.[11] Based on our scenarios, annual revenue from auctioning in 2030 could exceed $400 billion in the 550 Policy Scenario and $1 800 billion in the 450 Policy Scenario, depending on the proportion of emissions auctioned and assuming they were sold at the carbon prices set out in Chapter 18. To put these numbers into perspective, cumulative revenues from full auctioning between 2013 and 2030 would exceed all the additional investments (relative to the Reference Scenario) in efficiency and power plants, in both the 550 and 450 Policy Scenarios (Figure 19.13).

Governments would have a range of options on how to make efficient use of the substantial revenues raised from auctioning. One option, the most economically efficient from a theoretical perspective,[12] is to use the revenue to cut existing distortive national taxes such as employment taxes. More generally, these revenues could be used to implement a broad reform of the fiscal base, contributing, for example, to the financing of health or pension systems. However, recognising the transformational challenge presented by the Policy Scenarios, all or part of the money could be channelled back into the energy sector, to provide financial incentives for businesses and households to undertake efficient investments, to fund research and development in low-carbon technologies, or for wider climate-change initiatives.

---

10. A major source of risk will be uncertainty over the future of a global climate change regime. If allowances for future trading periods are unknown, or there is a lack of confidence in the continuation of a global regime, this will lead to serious deficiencies in the functioning of the carbon market. An agreement on a post-2012 framework needs to inspire such confidence.

Similar ideas have been proposed in respect of revenues from the auctioning of EU ETS allowances.[13] While different countries will have different political priorities for the use of such extra revenues, in the context of wider tax and consumer debates, these emissions allowance revenues could form a valuable element of climate-policy action in the energy sector, helping to generate public interest in and support for the cap-and-trade system (Hepburn *et al.*, 2006).

Figure 19.13 ● *Revenues from full auctioning of CO_2 allowances compared with additional investment in the 450 and 550 Policy Scenarios relative to the Reference Scenario, 2013-2030*

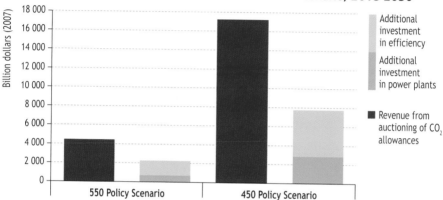

Note: Data are for countries participating in the cap-and-trade system, *i.e.* OECD+ in the 550 Policy Scenario; and OECD+ and (post-2020) Other Major Economies in the 450 Policy Scenario.

Of course, regions may not wish to engage in full auctioning (indeed, the EU ETS has been increasing auctioning only gradually). However, even with partial auctioning, substantial revenues could be raised. With only 10% auctioning, revenues in OECD countries between 2021 and 2030 would outweigh current public energy sector R&D in these countries by a factor of five.

Technology diffusion

The Policy Scenarios show the need for emissions reduction across all regions and across all sectors. Achieving this in an efficient manner will depend on all regions having access to the best available technologies. This is particularly important in the power sector, which in the 550 Policy Scenario accounts for almost two-thirds of the reduction in energy-related CO_2, relative to the Reference Scenario. The Policy Scenarios assume that all countries will have access to the most efficient new power stations and,

---

11. For a discussion, see Ecofys (2006).
12. See Parry (1997) for a theoretical discussion.
13. The European Commission (2008) has proposed that a certain percentage of the proceeds from the auctioning of EU ETS allowances be used "to reduce greenhouse gas emissions, to adapt to the impacts of climate change, to fund research and development for reducing emissions and adapting, to develop renewable energies..., for the capture and geological storage of greenhouse gases, to contribute to the Global Energy Efficiency and Renewable Energy Fund, for measures to avoid deforestation and facilitate adaptation in developing countries, and for addressing social aspects".

19

most notably, carbon capture and storage. While much of the development of this technology is currently being undertaken within the OECD+ countries, much of its early deployment will need to be in Other Major Economies such as China.

There are a number of barriers to address in order to maximise the potential from technologies. These include imperfect information, high transactions costs, risk, financing, complex regulatory frameworks and other trade and market barriers (IEA, 2008). Consequently, there are actions that can be taken to improve the potential for technology transfer. At the most fundamental level, this involves continuing to promote free trade and undistorted, competitive global markets. An important first step in this regard would be the removal of energy-related subsidies in many non-OECD countries (see Chapter 1) and the establishment of a global carbon market.

To overcome information barriers, international knowledge sharing is likely to play a key role. The IEA's Energy Technology Collaboration programme promotes exchanges of expertise across both OECD and non-OECD countries; its Implementing Agreements, covering various aspects of building, transport, fossil fuels, nuclear and renewables, provide a framework to enhance the most efficient use of energy worldwide. Other major initiatives include the Asia-Pacific Partnership's "State-of-the-art Clean Technologies" handbooks, which identify the most efficient technologies within each sector. It is also important that all countries have effective intellectual property laws, to provide countries and companies with the confidence to export high-tech, energy-efficient technologies and expertise to the regions where abatement needs to take place (Box 19.4).

Box 19.4 ● The importance of intellectual property laws for technology diffusion

Effective intellectual property laws are often important to facilitate technology diffusion. While such laws are generally well advanced in OECD countries, they are less well established in some non-OECD countries. The poorest countries, because they lack resources to imitate and reproduce existing technology (UK Commission on Intellectual Property Rights, 2002), tend to give low priority to strong intellectual property laws. However, an effective intellectual property system is important for enabling countries to attract the transfer of new technologies.

Where intellectual property cannot be safeguarded, because laws are weak or are not enforced, foreigners have less incentive to share new technologies, both supply-side and demand-side. This constrains efficient global abatement and energy technology development. An OECD empirical study (Park and Lippoldt, 2008) found that strong intellectual property laws stimulate innovation and diffusion (particularly of technology-intensive goods, as is typical in the energy sector). The study also showed a strong correlation between robust intellectual property laws and foreign direct investment, both for developing and developed countries.

As a consequence, it is essential for the global abatement effort that the international community addresses the issue of more robust intellectual property laws in key non-OECD countries. The WTO's 1995 Agreement in Trade-Related

Aspects of Intellectual Property Rights (TRIPS), requiring WTO members to ensure that intellectual property rights do not become barriers to trade, is clearly a step in the right direction. TRIPS itself says little in relation to technology transfer, requiring only that its member countries provide incentives to industry to promote and encourage technology transfer to the WTO's least-developed member countries.

Given that technologies will need to be deployed worldwide, this must be taken into account during the research and development phase. Technologies need to cater for multiple markets. As most research currently takes place in OECD countries, it will be important to take into account the needs of other regions. This can in part be ensured by promoting an effective global carbon market, which will provide incentives to develop such technologies, but can be further encouraged by international public sector collaboration, including with non-OECD countries, during the technology development phase. A positive example of this is the UK-China Near Zero Emissions Coal initiative, where joint research and development is taking place on CCS technology, with a view to demonstration projects in both countries.

There already exist a number of substantial funds and institutions to support technology diffusion. In 2008, the World Bank created the Climate Investment Funds, to provide interim, scaled-up funding to help developing countries mitigate their greenhouse-gas emissions. Total investment is targeted to reach $5 billion over three years. Current World Bank energy funding amounts to $1.8 billion. Our Policy Scenarios indicate that much more will be needed going forward.

Implications for policy

The sheer scale of the transformation to the energy sector in both the 450 and 550 Policy Scenarios would place a substantial burden on both the private and public sectors. Countries must shift away from traditional, carbon-intensive technologies and embrace new ones. It is for governments to galvanise the transformation.

A necessary first step is ensuring the right business climate, to enable energy-efficient investments to be made when and where they will deliver greatest value. The removal of distortive energy subsidies and development of a global carbon market will be very important. Delivering a low-carbon future requires major breakthroughs in technology development and deployment. Governments have the means to put in place incentives to innovate, to encourage promising research activities and to break down international barriers.

Much of the additional spending in the 450 and 550 Policy Scenarios is by households: a huge step-change in the attitudes to energy efficiency and consumer purchases by hundreds of millions of people worldwide is needed. Governments, through information provision, sound regulation and targeted fiscal incentives, have a key role to play in ensuring that, worldwide, the right decisions are taken to safeguard the future of the energy sector — and of the planet.

19

ANNEXES

TABLES FOR REFERENCE SCENARIO PROJECTIONS

General note to the tables

The tables show projections of energy demand, electricity generation and capacity, and energy-related CO_2 emissions for the following regions/countries: World, OECD, OECD North America, United States, OECD Pacific, Japan, OECD Europe, European Union, non-OECD, Eastern Europe/Eurasia, Russia, non-OECD Asia, China, India, Middle East, Africa and Latin America.

For OECD countries and non-OECD countries, the energy demand, electricity generation and energy-related CO_2 emissions data up to 2006, are based on IEA statistics, published in *Energy Balances of OECD Countries, Energy Balances of Non-OECD Countries,* and *CO_2 Emissions from Fuel Combustion.*

The definitions for regions, fuels and sectors can be found in Annex B.

Both in the text of this book and in the tables, rounding may cause some differences between the total and the sum of the individual components. Growth rates are marked "n.a." when the base year is zero or the value exceeds 200%.

Definitional note to the tables

Total primary energy demand is equivalent to *power generation* plus *other energy sector* excluding electricity and heat, plus *total final consumption* excluding electricity and heat. *Total primary energy demand* does not include ambient heat from heat pumps nor electricity trade. *Power generation* includes electricity and heat production by main activity producers and autoproducers. *Other sectors* includes final consumption in the residential, services, agricultural, and non-specified sectors. Total CO_2 emissions (calculated using the IPCC Tier 1 Sectoral Approach) include emissions from *other energy sector,* as well as from *power generation,* and *total final consumption* (as shown in the tables). CO_2 emissions from international marine bunkers and international aviation are included at the world level. CO_2 emissions do not include emissions from industrial waste and non-renewable municipal waste.

Reference Scenario: World

	Energy demand (Mtoe)						Shares (%)		Growth (% p.a.)
	1990	2006	2015	2020	2025	2030	2006	2030	2006-2030
Total primary energy demand	8 757	11 730	14 121	15 123	16 149	17 014	100	100	1.6
Coal	2 219	3 053	4 023	4 374	4 719	4 908	26	29	2.0
Oil	3 218	4 029	4 525	4 744	4 938	5 109	34	30	1.0
Gas	1 673	2 407	2 903	3 130	3 384	3 670	21	22	1.8
Nuclear	525	728	817	842	886	901	6	5	0.9
Hydro	185	261	321	353	383	414	2	2	1.9
Biomass and waste	902	1 186	1 375	1 465	1 562	1 662	10	10	1.4
Other renewables	36	66	158	215	276	350	1	2	7.2
Power generation	2 985	4 424	5 649	6 143	6 655	7 130	100	100	2.0
Coal	1 228	2 075	2 765	3 013	3 227	3 375	47	47	2.0
Oil	377	277	269	244	225	204	6	3	-1.3
Gas	581	947	1 212	1 336	1 478	1 664	21	23	2.4
Nuclear	525	728	817	842	886	901	16	13	0.9
Hydro	185	261	321	353	383	414	6	6	1.9
Biomass and waste	59	81	132	173	225	286	2	4	5.4
Other renewables	32	55	134	181	230	287	1	4	7.1
Other energy sector	878	1 180	1 435	1 557	1 698	1 743	100	100	1.6
of which electricity	*183*	*280*	*363*	*392*	*419*	*442*	*24*	*25*	*1.9*
Total final consumption	6 285	8 086	9 560	10 192	10 817	11 405	100	100	1.4
Coal	762	698	885	934	976	1 007	9	9	1.5
Oil	2 605	3 481	3 975	4 202	4 405	4 590	43	40	1.2
Gas	952	1 233	1 410	1 495	1 594	1 690	15	15	1.3
Electricity	833	1 347	1 785	1 991	2 205	2 420	17	21	2.5
Heat	333	273	312	322	334	342	3	3	0.9
Biomass and waste	796	1 042	1 169	1 214	1 256	1 294	13	11	0.9
Other renewables	4	11	24	34	46	63	0	1	7.4
Industry	1 810	2 181	2 735	2 937	3 140	3 322	100	100	1.8
Coal	472	550	713	761	804	838	25	25	1.8
Oil	329	329	366	374	381	385	15	12	0.7
Gas	362	434	508	539	574	604	20	18	1.4
Electricity	379	560	789	884	976	1 060	26	32	2.7
Heat	150	118	134	136	138	139	5	4	0.7
Biomass and waste	118	189	224	242	266	294	9	9	1.9
Other renewables	0	0	1	1	2	3	0	0	7.8
Transport	1 575	2 227	2 637	2 830	3 004	3 171	108	107	1.5
Oil	1 482	2 105	2 450	2 620	2 771	2 915	94	92	1.4
of which marine bunkers	*113*	*183*	*199*	*209*	*219*	*230*	*8*	*7*	*1.0*
Biofuels	6	24	74	89	104	118	1	4	6.8
Other fuels	88	98	113	121	129	137	4	4	1.4
Other sectors	2 429	2 937	3 310	3 505	3 711	3 918	100	100	1.2
Coal	253	114	118	114	108	100	4	3	-0.5
Oil	439	472	493	515	538	560	16	14	0.7
Gas	445	592	660	699	744	791	20	20	1.2
Electricity	433	764	967	1 076	1 195	1 322	26	34	2.3
Heat	183	156	178	186	195	203	5	5	1.1
Biomass and waste	672	829	871	883	886	881	28	22	0.3
Other renewables	4	11	23	33	44	60	0	2	7.4
Non-energy use	472	740	878	920	961	994	100	100	1.2

Reference Scenario: World

	Electricity generation (TWh)						Shares (%)		Growth (% p.a.)
	1990	2006	2015	2020	2025	2030	2006	2030	2006-2030
Total generation	11 811	18 921	24 975	27 708	30 512	33 265	100	100	2.4
Coal	4 424	7 756	11 100	12 442	13 661	14 596	41	44	2.7
Oil	1 330	1 096	1 046	941	865	791	6	2	-1.3
Gas	1 727	3 807	4 725	5 243	5 847	6 716	20	20	2.4
Nuclear	2 013	2 793	3 134	3 232	3 399	3 458	15	10	0.9
Hydro	2 146	3 035	3 734	4 101	4 459	4 809	16	14	1.9
Biomass and waste	129	239	418	542	693	863	1	3	5.5
Wind	4	130	664	970	1 234	1 490	1	4	10.7
Geothermal	36	59	98	122	148	177	0	1	4.7
Solar	1	4	53	111	201	352	0	1	20.7
Tide and wave	1	1	2	3	5	14	0	0	14.4

	Capacity (GW)					Shares (%)		Growth (% p.a.)
	2006	2015	2020	2025	2030	2006	2030	2006-2030
Total capacity	4 344	5 697	6 264	6 855	7 484	100	100	2.3
Coal	1 382	1 995	2 232	2 475	2 692	32	36	2.8
Oil	415	397	345	305	267	10	4	-1.8
Gas	1 124	1 373	1 461	1 550	1 695	26	23	1.7
Nuclear	368	397	407	427	433	8	6	0.7
Hydro	919	1 134	1 239	1 340	1 436	21	19	1.9
Biomass and waste	45	80	106	137	172	1	2	5.7
Wind	74	271	383	473	551	2	7	8.7
Geothermal	9	14	18	21	25	0	0	4.3
Solar	7	35	72	126	208	0	3	15.2
Tide and wave	0	1	1	1	4	0	0	11.6

	CO_2 emissions (Mt)						Shares (%)		Growth (% p.a.)
	1990	2006	2015	2020	2025	2030	2006	2030	2006-2030
Total CO_2 emissions	20 945	27 889	34 003	36 399	38 687	40 553	100	100	1.6
Coal	8 309	11 678	15 402	16 702	17 890	18 628	42	46	2.0
Oil	8 824	10 768	12 079	12 663	13 193	13 670	39	34	1.0
Gas	3 812	5 443	6 523	7 033	7 603	8 254	20	20	1.7
Power generation	7 484	11 435	14 803	16 005	17 116	18 050	100	100	1.9
Coal	4 928	8 336	11 113	12 101	12 942	13 507	73	75	2.0
Oil	1 198	882	852	774	713	647	8	4	-1.3
Gas	1 358	2 217	2 839	3 129	3 461	3 895	19	22	2.4
Total final consumption	12 449	15 118	17 635	18 663	19 625	20 475	100	100	1.3
Coal	3 246	3 135	3 996	4 218	4 403	4 527	21	22	1.5
Oil	7 062	9 220	10 501	11 121	11 687	12 210	61	60	1.2
of which transport	4 390	6 263	7 292	7 796	8 249	8 680	41	42	1.4
of which marine bunkers	358	582	634	665	697	731	4	4	1.0
of which international aviation	255	397	485	530	580	635	3	3	2.0
Gas	2 141	2 763	3 139	3 324	3 536	3 739	18	18	1.3

A

Reference Scenario: OECD

	Energy demand (Mtoe)						Shares (%)		Growth (% p.a.)
	1990	2006	2015	2020	2025	2030	2006	2030	2006-2030
Total primary energy demand	4 519	5 536	5 878	5 994	6 122	6 180	100	100	0.5
Coal	1 063	1 139	1 209	1 215	1 228	1 192	21	19	0.2
Oil	1 896	2 209	2 152	2 141	2 110	2 070	40	33	-0.3
Gas	840	1 210	1 360	1 399	1 448	1 511	22	24	0.9
Nuclear	450	614	629	628	638	626	11	10	0.1
Hydro	101	111	121	126	130	133	2	2	0.8
Biomass and waste	141	210	305	349	397	440	4	7	3.1
Other renewables	29	42	101	137	171	209	1	3	6.9
Power generation	1 703	2 249	2 485	2 559	2 634	2 682	100	100	0.7
Coal	750	921	1 004	1 005	997	969	41	36	0.2
Oil	151	95	66	46	39	35	4	1	-4.0
Gas	175	409	484	521	547	590	18	22	1.5
Nuclear	450	614	629	628	638	626	27	23	0.1
Hydro	101	111	121	126	130	133	5	5	0.8
Biomass and waste	52	65	95	115	138	156	3	6	3.7
Other renewables	25	35	87	117	145	173	2	6	6.9
Other energy sector	385	437	442	438	471	472	100	100	0.3
of which electricity	*105*	*124*	*132*	*135*	*137*	*138*	*28*	*29*	*0.5*
Total final consumption	3 130	3 825	4 038	4 137	4 208	4 264	100	100	0.5
Coal	231	135	126	122	116	110	4	3	-0.9
Oil	1 629	1 980	1 981	1 991	1 969	1 934	52	45	-0.1
Gas	590	715	760	775	793	808	19	19	0.5
Electricity	548	777	875	923	971	1 018	20	24	1.1
Heat	40	66	72	73	74	74	2	2	0.5
Biomass and waste	89	146	210	234	259	285	4	7	2.8
Other renewables	4	7	14	19	26	35	0	1	7.1
Industry	823	866	900	914	923	926	100	100	0.3
Coal	159	115	110	107	103	99	13	11	-0.6
Oil	169	144	132	127	122	116	17	13	-0.9
Gas	225	248	255	259	261	260	29	28	0.2
Electricity	220	265	288	297	303	306	31	33	0.6
Heat	14	24	26	26	26	26	3	3	0.4
Biomass and waste	36	69	89	97	106	116	8	13	2.2
Other renewables	0	0	1	1	2	3	0	0	7.9
Transport	982	1 301	1 387	1 415	1 414	1 401	100	100	0.3
Oil	955	1 252	1 302	1 321	1 310	1 289	96	92	0.1
Biofuels	0	17	49	58	66	72	1	5	6.3
Other fuels	27	32	36	37	38	40	2	3	0.9
Other sectors	1 038	1 272	1 364	1 425	1 491	1 560	100	100	0.9
Coal	69	18	15	13	11	9	1	1	-2.7
Oil	255	234	202	199	196	191	18	12	-0.8
Gas	311	410	440	455	470	485	32	31	0.7
Electricity	320	502	576	614	655	698	39	45	1.4
Heat	27	42	47	47	48	48	3	3	0.5
Biomass and waste	53	59	72	79	87	96	5	6	2.0
Other renewables	3	6	13	18	24	32	0	2	7.0
Non-energy use	287	386	386	382	381	376	100	100	-0.1

Reference Scenario: OECD

Electricity generation (TWh)	1990	2006	2015	2020	2025	2030	Shares (%) 2006	Shares (%) 2030	Growth (% p.a.) 2006-2030
Total generation	7 568	10 452	11 690	12 287	12 870	13 418	100	100	1.0
Coal	3 055	3 931	4 342	4 477	4 578	4 587	38	34	0.6
Oil	692	417	291	204	168	161	4	1	-3.9
Gas	771	2 098	2 303	2 463	2 577	2 836	20	21	1.3
Nuclear	1 725	2 356	2 413	2 409	2 446	2 400	23	18	0.1
Hydro	1 170	1 286	1 412	1 467	1 510	1 543	12	11	0.8
Biomass and waste	122	205	312	378	450	505	2	4	3.8
Wind	4	116	512	734	920	1 082	1	8	9.7
Geothermal	29	38	59	71	83	95	0	1	3.9
Solar	1	3	44	80	132	196	0	1	18.7
Tide and wave	1	1	2	3	5	14	0	0	14.3

Capacity (GW)	2006	2015	2020	2025	2030	Shares (%) 2006	Shares (%) 2030	Growth (% p.a.) 2006-2030
Total capacity	2 430	2 702	2 845	2 988	3 136	100	100	1.1
Coal	646	691	717	734	738	27	24	0.6
Oil	221	159	111	86	66	9	2	-4.9
Gas	698	753	784	805	867	29	28	0.9
Nuclear	308	308	307	311	305	13	10	0.0
Hydro	444	483	498	510	518	18	17	0.6
Biomass and waste	38	59	72	87	98	2	3	4.1
Wind	64	209	289	351	399	3	13	7.9
Geothermal	6	9	10	12	13	0	0	3.6
Solar	6	31	55	91	129	0	4	13.5
Tide and wave	0	1	1	1	3	0	0	11.4

CO_2 emissions (Mt)	1990	2006	2015	2020	2025	2030	Shares (%) 2006	Shares (%) 2030	Growth (% p.a.) 2006-2030
Total CO_2 emissions	11 041	12 791	13 274	13 313	13 304	13 166	100	100	0.1
Coal	4 108	4 392	4 692	4 690	4 672	4 515	34	34	0.1
Oil	5 013	5 591	5 434	5 382	5 279	5 152	44	39	-0.3
Gas	1 920	2 808	3 149	3 241	3 354	3 499	22	27	0.9
Power generation	3 912	4 985	5 406	5 435	5 430	5 392	100	100	0.3
Coal	3 027	3 727	4 066	4 070	4 028	3 900	75	72	0.2
Oil	476	302	208	146	123	112	6	2	-4.0
Gas	409	956	1 131	1 219	1 279	1 380	19	26	1.5
Total final consumption	6 531	7 153	7 181	7 206	7 138	7 024	100	100	-0.1
Coal	1 019	596	560	538	513	486	8	7	-0.9
Oil	4 168	4 913	4 877	4 886	4 801	4 680	69	67	-0.2
of which transport	2 668	3 462	3 575	3 608	3 553	3 468	48	49	0.0
Gas	1 344	1 644	1 744	1 782	1 823	1 858	23	26	0.5

Reference Scenario: OECD North America

	Energy demand (Mtoe)						Shares (%)		Growth (% p.a.)
	1990	2006	2015	2020	2025	2030	2006	2030	2006-2030
Total primary energy demand	2 258	2 768	2 938	3 014	3 120	3 180	100	100	0.6
Coal	486	587	626	640	674	671	21	21	0.6
Oil	929	1 133	1 110	1 123	1 119	1 108	41	35	-0.1
Gas	516	629	696	698	718	746	23	23	0.7
Nuclear	179	241	250	261	276	282	9	9	0.7
Hydro	51	58	60	61	62	63	2	2	0.3
Biomass and waste	78	101	153	173	197	221	4	7	3.3
Other renewables	19	18	43	59	74	90	1	3	6.8
Power generation	850	1 101	1 200	1 248	1 301	1 346	100	100	0.8
Coal	419	527	569	574	581	580	48	43	0.4
Oil	47	35	20	15	12	11	3	1	-4.9
Gas	95	197	221	233	241	258	18	19	1.1
Nuclear	179	241	250	261	276	282	22	21	0.7
Hydro	51	58	60	61	62	63	5	5	0.3
Biomass and waste	41	26	42	52	65	76	2	6	4.5
Other renewables	18	16	38	52	64	76	1	6	6.7
Other energy sector	185	228	239	237	272	277	100	100	0.8
of which electricity	57	62	65	67	69	70	27	25	0.5
Total final consumption	1 554	1 887	1 988	2 046	2 091	2 129	100	100	0.5
Coal	59	34	31	30	28	27	2	1	-1.0
Oil	823	1 029	1 040	1 059	1 058	1 049	55	49	0.1
Gas	360	365	379	382	389	395	19	19	0.3
Electricity	271	379	419	444	470	496	20	23	1.1
Heat	3	4	4	4	4	4	0	0	0.0
Biomass and waste	37	74	111	121	132	144	4	7	2.8
Other renewables	0	2	5	7	10	14	0	1	7.8
Industry	357	366	376	383	389	391	100	100	0.3
Coal	49	32	30	29	27	26	9	7	-0.9
Oil	60	49	44	44	43	42	13	11	-0.6
Gas	138	134	135	137	138	137	37	35	0.1
Electricity	94	106	111	114	116	117	29	30	0.4
Heat	1	3	3	3	3	3	1	1	0.5
Biomass and waste	16	42	53	57	61	65	11	17	1.9
Other renewables	0	0	0	0	0	0	0	0	3.4
Transport	576	756	809	834	841	841	100	100	0.4
Oil	557	724	755	775	778	773	96	92	0.3
Biofuels	0	11	33	36	41	47	1	6	6.1
Other fuels	19	20	21	22	22	22	3	3	0.3
Other sectors	477	571	602	633	666	702	100	100	0.9
Coal	10	1	1	1	1	0	0	0	-4.6
Oil	82	81	66	65	64	63	14	9	-1.0
Gas	185	192	198	204	209	215	34	31	0.5
Electricity	177	272	307	328	352	378	48	54	1.4
Heat	2	1	1	0	0	0	0	0	-4.0
Biomass and waste	21	21	26	28	30	32	4	5	1.7
Other renewables	0	2	5	7	10	14	0	2	7.9
Non-energy use	143	194	201	196	196	194	100	100	0.0

Reference Scenario: OECD North America

Electricity generation (TWh)	1990	2006	2015	2020	2025	2030	Shares (%) 2006	Shares (%) 2030	Growth (% p.a.) 2006-2030
Total generation	3 809	5 134	5 625	5 941	6 267	6 588	100	100	1.0
Coal	1 790	2 265	2 489	2 581	2 690	2 785	44	42	0.9
Oil	217	144	81	61	47	43	3	1	-4.9
Gas	406	986	1 049	1 094	1 118	1 186	19	18	0.8
Nuclear	687	925	958	1 003	1 058	1 083	18	16	0.7
Hydro	593	678	696	707	719	729	13	11	0.3
Biomass and waste	90	83	131	165	205	239	2	4	4.5
Wind	3	29	167	256	333	395	1	6	11.5
Geothermal	21	23	38	47	55	62	0	1	4.2
Solar	1	1	15	26	42	64	0	1	21.5
Tide and wave	0	0	0	0	0	2	0	0	18.4

Capacity (GW)	2006	2015	2020	2025	2030	Shares (%) 2006	Shares (%) 2030	Growth (% p.a.) 2006-2030
Total capacity	1 201	1 263	1 329	1 402	1 482	100	100	0.9
Coal	354	371	395	419	440	29	30	0.9
Oil	92	46	32	24	17	8	1	-6.7
Gas	431	447	452	456	476	36	32	0.4
Nuclear	113	115	120	127	130	9	9	0.6
Hydro	181	185	188	190	193	15	13	0.3
Biomass and waste	13	23	30	38	45	1	3	5.4
Wind	13	60	90	115	135	1	9	10.2
Geothermal	4	6	7	8	9	0	1	3.8
Solar	1	9	16	25	36	0	2	16.5
Tide and wave	0	0	0	0	0	0	0	13.9

CO_2 emissions (Mt)	1990	2006	2015	2020	2025	2030	Shares (%) 2006	Shares (%) 2030	Growth (% p.a.) 2006-2030
Total CO_2 emissions	5 570	6 625	6 878	6 948	7 051	7 060	100	100	0.3
Coal	1 905	2 233	2 388	2 416	2 485	2 462	34	35	0.4
Oil	2 478	2 932	2 880	2 916	2 903	2 874	44	41	-0.1
Gas	1 187	1 460	1 610	1 615	1 663	1 724	22	24	0.7
Power generation	2 014	2 652	2 825	2 852	2 886	2 906	100	100	0.4
Coal	1 640	2 075	2 243	2 259	2 284	2 268	78	78	0.4
Oil	151	118	65	49	38	35	4	1	-4.9
Gas	222	460	517	544	564	603	17	21	1.1
Total final consumption	3 203	3 593	3 622	3 676	3 679	3 652	100	100	0.1
Coal	262	145	132	126	120	113	4	3	-1.0
Oil	2 114	2 610	2 624	2 673	2 665	2 633	73	72	0.0
of which transport	*1 579*	*2 063*	*2 144*	*2 196*	*2 195*	*2 171*	57	59	0.2
Gas	827	838	866	877	893	906	23	25	0.3

Reference Scenario: United States

	Energy demand (Mtoe)						Shares (%)		Growth (% p.a.)
	1990	2006	2015	2020	2025	2030	2006	2030	2006-2030
Total primary energy demand	1 926	2 319	2 420	2 460	2 533	2 566	100	100	0.4
Coal	458	551	580	594	631	633	24	25	0.6
Oil	770	937	897	902	893	881	40	34	-0.3
Gas	438	501	536	517	515	518	22	20	0.1
Nuclear	159	213	223	232	244	250	9	10	0.7
Hydro	23	25	25	25	26	26	1	1	0.1
Biomass and waste	62	80	126	144	165	185	3	7	3.6
Other renewables	14	12	33	46	59	71	1	3	7.6
Power generation	750	950	1 020	1 052	1 088	1 119	100	100	0.7
Coal	396	497	530	533	543	547	52	49	0.4
Oil	27	20	7	4	4	5	2	0	-5.7
Gas	90	163	170	170	163	163	17	15	0.0
Nuclear	159	213	223	232	244	250	22	22	0.7
Hydro	23	25	25	25	26	26	3	2	0.1
Biomass and waste	40	23	37	48	59	69	2	6	4.7
Other renewables	14	10	29	40	50	59	1	5	7.6
Other energy sector	149	171	173	165	195	195	100	100	0.5
of which electricity	*49*	*49*	*51*	*52*	*53*	*54*	*29*	*28*	*0.4*
Total final consumption	1 305	1 572	1 631	1 666	1 693	1 715	100	100	0.4
Coal	54	29	26	25	24	22	2	1	-1.1
Oil	696	862	853	862	854	841	55	49	-0.1
Gas	303	299	307	307	312	315	19	18	0.2
Electricity	226	320	348	366	386	406	20	24	1.0
Heat	2	3	3	3	3	2	0	0	-0.5
Biomass and waste	23	57	89	97	106	116	4	7	3.0
Other renewables	0	2	5	6	9	12	0	1	7.5
Industry	283	281	280	281	281	278	100	100	0.0
Coal	45	28	25	24	23	22	10	8	-1.0
Oil	44	35	30	29	28	27	13	10	-1.2
Gas	110	104	102	102	102	100	37	36	-0.2
Electricity	75	79	79	79	78	77	28	28	-0.1
Heat	0	2	2	2	2	2	1	1	0.2
Biomass and waste	9	32	41	44	47	50	11	18	1.9
Other renewables	0	0	0	0	0	0	0	0	3.4
Transport	501	649	684	700	701	700	100	100	0.3
Oil	485	623	637	649	645	638	96	91	0.1
Biofuels	0	11	31	35	40	45	2	6	6.0
Other fuels	16	15	16	16	16	16	2	2	0.3
Other sectors	403	482	502	526	554	584	100	100	0.8
Coal	10	1	1	1	1	0	0	0	-4.6
Oil	62	57	40	39	38	37	12	6	-1.7
Gas	164	167	171	175	180	184	35	32	0.4
Electricity	152	241	268	287	307	329	50	56	1.3
Heat	2	1	0	0	0	0	0	0	-6.5
Biomass and waste	14	13	16	17	19	21	3	4	1.8
Other renewables	0	2	4	6	9	12	0	2	7.6
Non-energy use	119	161	165	159	157	154	100	100	-0.2

Reference Scenario: United States

	Electricity generation (TWh)						Shares (%)		Growth (% p.a.)
	1990	2006	2015	2020	2025	2030	2006	2030	2006-2030
Total generation	3 203	4 272	4 616	4 848	5 090	5 332	100	100	0.9
Coal	1 700	2 128	2 303	2 390	2 507	2 624	50	49	0.9
Oil	131	81	28	16	17	20	2	0	-5.5
Gas	382	839	829	824	781	772	20	14	-0.3
Nuclear	612	816	855	890	935	960	19	18	0.7
Hydro	273	292	294	296	299	301	7	6	0.1
Biomass and waste	86	72	117	149	185	216	2	4	4.7
Wind	3	27	147	221	283	328	1	6	11.0
Geothermal	16	17	29	36	43	49	0	1	4.7
Solar	1	1	14	25	40	59	0	1	21.4
Tide and wave	0	0	0	0	0	1	0	0	n.a.

	Capacity (GW)					Shares (%)		Growth (% p.a.)
	2006	2015	2020	2025	2030	2006	2030	2006-2030
Total capacity	1 022	1 051	1 099	1 156	1 217	100	100	0.7
Coal	333	343	365	391	414	33	34	0.9
Oil	70	26	14	11	8	7	1	-8.6
Gas	395	395	389	380	386	39	32	-0.1
Nuclear	100	102	106	112	115	10	9	0.6
Hydro	99	99	100	101	101	10	8	0.1
Biomass and waste	11	20	27	34	40	1	3	5.6
Wind	12	53	78	98	112	1	9	9.9
Geothermal	3	4	5	6	7	0	1	4.2
Solar	1	8	15	23	34	0	3	16.3
Tide and wave	0	0	0	0	0	0	0	13.9

	CO_2 emissions (Mt)						Shares (%)		Growth (% p.a.)
	1990	2006	2015	2020	2025	2030	2006	2030	2006-2030
Total CO_2 emissions	4 845	5 670	5 769	5 773	5 828	5 804	100	100	0.1
Coal	1 792	2 090	2 206	2 234	2 313	2 312	37	40	0.4
Oil	2 042	2 411	2 318	2 336	2 318	2 291	43	39	-0.2
Gas	1 011	1 169	1 244	1 203	1 196	1 202	21	21	0.1
Power generation	1 848	2 403	2 503	2 508	2 527	2 535	100	100	0.2
Coal	1 550	1 956	2 084	2 098	2 133	2 138	81	84	0.4
Oil	88	66	22	12	13	16	3	1	-5.8
Gas	210	381	397	398	381	381	16	15	0.0
Total final consumption	2 725	2 998	2 967	2 990	2 970	2 936	100	100	-0.1
Coal	239	121	110	105	99	93	4	3	-1.1
Oil	1 788	2 188	2 153	2 178	2 154	2 118	73	72	-0.1
of which transport	1 376	1 776	1 814	1 845	1 830	1 804	59	61	0.1
Gas	697	689	704	707	717	725	23	25	0.2

Reference Scenario: OECD Pacific

	Energy demand (Mtoe)						Shares (%)		Growth (% p.a.)
	1990	2006	2015	2020	2025	2030	2006	2030	2006-2030
Total primary energy demand	639	884	960	985	1 000	995	100	100	0.5
Coal	139	221	239	241	237	229	25	23	0.1
Oil	341	380	369	355	343	328	43	33	-0.6
Gas	66	133	154	171	182	190	15	19	1.5
Nuclear	66	118	151	163	176	177	13	18	1.7
Hydro	11	11	12	12	13	13	1	1	0.6
Biomass and waste	10	16	22	26	30	35	2	3	3.4
Other renewables	5	6	12	16	20	24	1	2	5.9
Power generation	241	394	457	481	498	499	100	100	1.0
Coal	60	153	171	173	169	162	39	32	0.2
Oil	56	30	27	19	15	13	8	3	-3.5
Gas	40	71	80	92	100	104	18	21	1.6
Nuclear	66	118	151	163	176	177	30	36	1.7
Hydro	11	11	12	12	13	13	3	3	0.6
Biomass and waste	3	6	8	10	11	13	2	3	3.3
Other renewables	3	5	9	12	14	17	1	3	5.5
Other energy sector	57	61	60	60	60	59	100	100	-0.2
of which electricity	11	16	17	18	18	18	26	30	0.4
Total final consumption	438	588	624	635	640	641	100	100	0.4
Coal	50	44	44	44	43	42	7	7	-0.2
Oil	267	329	326	322	313	302	56	47	-0.4
Gas	26	62	73	77	80	83	11	13	1.2
Electricity	86	138	158	166	173	180	23	28	1.1
Heat	0	5	6	6	7	7	1	1	1.3
Biomass and waste	7	9	14	16	18	21	2	3	3.4
Other renewables	2	1	3	4	5	6	0	1	7.6
Industry	146	172	182	187	189	191	100	100	0.4
Coal	40	41	41	41	41	40	24	21	-0.1
Oil	52	46	43	41	39	37	27	20	-0.9
Gas	10	21	23	25	25	26	12	14	1.0
Electricity	40	53	60	63	65	66	31	35	0.9
Heat	0	3	3	4	4	4	2	2	1.0
Biomass and waste	5	7	11	13	15	17	4	9	3.5
Other renewables	0	0	0	0	1	1	0	0	7.4
Transport	117	159	166	164	159	152	100	100	-0.2
Oil	115	155	160	158	153	146	98	96	-0.3
Biofuels	0	0	1	1	1	1	0	1	10.3
Other fuels	2	3	4	5	5	5	2	4	2.2
Other sectors	130	182	200	207	214	221	100	100	0.8
Coal	10	2	2	2	2	1	1	1	-1.3
Oil	57	54	49	47	46	44	29	20	-0.8
Gas	15	39	46	49	51	53	22	24	1.2
Electricity	44	82	95	101	106	110	45	50	1.2
Heat	0	2	3	3	3	3	1	1	1.7
Biomass and waste	2	2	2	3	3	3	1	2	2.6
Other renewables	1	1	2	4	5	6	1	3	7.7
Non-energy use	45	75	76	77	77	77	100	100	0.1

Reference Scenario: OECD Pacific

	Electricity generation (TWh)						Shares (%)		Growth (% p.a.)
	1990	2006	2015	2020	2025	2030	2006	2030	2006-2030
Total generation	1 128	1 788	2 037	2 135	2 222	2 293	100	100	1.0
Coal	254	656	749	768	762	740	37	32	0.5
Oil	271	147	131	91	75	64	8	3	-3.4
Gas	199	368	367	408	440	505	21	22	1.3
Nuclear	255	452	579	627	675	681	25	30	1.7
Hydro	133	128	141	144	147	150	7	7	0.6
Biomass and waste	12	25	32	37	42	47	1	2	2.6
Wind	0	4	22	37	52	66	0	3	12.1
Geothermal	4	6	9	11	12	14	0	1	3.3
Solar	0	0	7	11	17	25	0	1	28.0
Tide and wave	0	0	1	1	1	1	0	0	n.a.

	Capacity (GW)					Shares (%)		Growth (% p.a.)
	2006	2015	2020	2025	2030	2006	2030	2006-2030
Total capacity	395	448	470	491	521	100	100	1.2
Coal	95	110	114	113	111	24	21	0.7
Oil	61	56	39	33	28	15	5	-3.2
Gas	96	111	131	143	166	24	32	2.3
Nuclear	65	76	82	89	89	16	17	1.3
Hydro	68	75	76	77	78	17	15	0.6
Biomass and waste	4	6	7	8	9	1	2	2.8
Wind	3	8	12	17	21	1	4	9.2
Geothermal	1	1	2	2	2	0	0	3.0
Solar	2	4	7	11	16	0	3	9.4
Tide and wave	0	0	0	0	0	0	0	n.a.

	CO_2 emissions (Mt)						Shares (%)		Growth (% p.a.)
	1990	2006	2015	2020	2025	2030	2006	2030	2006-2030
Total CO_2 emissions	1 579	2 108	2 206	2 209	2 174	2 112	100	100	0.0
Coal	525	874	954	962	941	905	41	43	0.1
Oil	895	913	885	842	802	760	43	36	-0.8
Gas	159	321	367	405	431	448	15	21	1.4
Power generation	548	911	1 000	1 013	1 002	973	100	100	0.3
Coal	281	651	729	737	719	688	71	71	0.2
Oil	174	92	83	58	47	39	10	4	-3.5
Gas	94	168	188	218	236	245	18	25	1.6
Total final consumption	962	1 114	1 125	1 115	1 091	1 058	100	100	-0.2
Coal	224	200	202	201	198	193	18	18	-0.1
Oil	679	770	755	737	710	675	69	64	-0.5
of which transport	321	420	430	421	403	380	38	36	-0.4
Gas	59	144	168	176	184	190	13	18	1.2

Reference Scenario: Japan

	Energy demand (Mtoe)						Shares (%)		Growth (% p.a.)
	1990	2006	2015	2020	2025	2030	2006	2030	2006-2030
Total primary energy demand	444	528	530	534	534	519	100	100	-0.1
Coal	77	112	115	115	111	107	21	21	-0.2
Oil	254	241	210	194	181	168	46	32	-1.5
Gas	44	78	86	98	104	106	15	20	1.3
Nuclear	53	79	94	99	106	104	15	20	1.1
Hydro	8	7	8	8	8	8	1	2	0.6
Biomass and waste	5	7	10	11	13	14	1	3	2.9
Other renewables	3	4	7	8	10	12	1	2	5.2
Power generation	174	226	249	260	267	261	100	100	0.6
Coal	25	61	63	64	60	56	27	21	-0.4
Oil	51	23	21	14	12	10	10	4	-3.5
Gas	33	49	52	63	68	68	22	26	1.4
Nuclear	53	79	94	99	106	104	35	40	1.1
Hydro	8	7	8	8	8	8	3	3	0.6
Biomass and waste	2	4	5	6	6	7	2	3	1.7
Other renewables	1	3	5	6	8	9	1	3	4.9
Other energy sector	37	44	41	40	39	38	100	100	-0.5
of which electricity	7	9	10	10	10	9	21	24	0.0
Total final consumption	305	352	342	339	335	330	100	100	-0.3
Coal	33	31	31	31	31	30	9	9	-0.1
Oil	188	201	178	169	159	150	57	45	-1.2
Gas	15	31	35	36	37	38	9	12	0.8
Electricity	64	84	91	94	97	100	24	30	0.7
Heat	0	1	1	1	1	1	0	0	2.0
Biomass and waste	3	3	5	6	7	8	1	2	4.5
Other renewables	1	1	2	2	2	3	0	1	6.0
Industry	105	102	102	102	102	101	100	100	0.0
Coal	32	30	30	30	30	29	29	29	-0.1
Oil	38	34	30	29	27	25	34	25	-1.3
Gas	4	7	9	9	10	10	7	10	1.3
Electricity	29	28	29	29	30	30	27	29	0.3
Heat	0	0	0	0	0	0	0	0	n.a.
Biomass and waste	3	3	5	5	6	7	3	7	4.3
Other renewables	0	0	0	0	0	0	0	0	n.a.
Transport	76	91	84	79	73	67	100	100	-1.3
Oil	75	89	81	76	70	64	98	95	-1.4
Biofuels	0	0	0	0	0	0	0	1	n.a.
Other fuels	1	2	2	2	3	3	2	5	2.1
Other sectors	91	120	123	126	129	132	100	100	0.4
Coal	1	1	1	1	1	1	1	1	0.5
Oil	43	40	34	33	33	32	33	24	-0.9
Gas	11	24	26	26	27	27	20	21	0.6
Electricity	34	55	60	63	66	68	46	52	0.9
Heat	0	1	1	1	1	1	0	1	2.0
Biomass and waste	0	0	0	0	0	0	0	0	4.2
Other renewables	1	1	2	2	2	3	1	2	6.0
Non-energy use	33	38	33	32	31	30	100	100	-1.1

Reference Scenario: Japan

	Electricity generation (TWh)						Shares (%)		Growth (% p.a.)
	1990	2006	2015	2020	2025	2030	2006	2030	2006-2030
Total generation	836	1 091	1 173	1 210	1 244	1 271	100	100	0.6
Coal	117	299	310	314	295	275	27	22	-0.3
Oil	248	121	112	76	65	53	11	4	-3.3
Gas	167	254	248	284	307	359	23	28	1.4
Nuclear	202	303	362	380	406	398	28	31	1.1
Hydro	89	86	93	95	97	99	8	8	0.6
Biomass and waste	11	22	27	30	32	34	2	3	1.8
Wind	0	2	12	20	28	34	0	3	13.2
Geothermal	2	3	4	5	5	6	0	0	2.6
Solar	0	0	4	6	9	12	0	1	48.1
Tide and wave	0	0	0	0	0	0	0	0	n.a.

	Capacity (GW)					Shares (%)		Growth (% p.a.)
	2006	2015	2020	2025	2030	2006	2030	2006-2030
Total capacity	262	281	289	299	315	100	100	0.8
Coal	44	47	48	45	43	17	14	0.0
Oil	55	51	35	29	25	21	8	-3.3
Gas	61	67	82	91	108	23	34	2.4
Nuclear	48	50	52	56	55	18	17	0.6
Hydro	47	54	55	55	55	18	18	0.7
Biomass and waste	4	5	5	6	6	1	2	2.0
Wind	1	4	7	9	11	1	4	9.1
Geothermal	1	1	1	1	1	0	0	2.2
Solar	2	3	5	7	10	1	3	7.5
Tide and wave	0	0	0	0	0	0	0	n.a.

	CO_2 emissions (Mt)						Shares (%)		Growth (% p.a.)
	1990	2006	2015	2020	2025	2030	2006	2030	2006-2030
Total CO_2 emissions	1 071	1 208	1 171	1 154	1 115	1 064	100	100	-0.5
Coal	298	431	442	444	425	405	36	38	-0.3
Oil	658	587	522	478	443	408	49	38	-1.5
Gas	115	190	206	233	247	251	16	24	1.2
Power generation	363	456	469	475	462	439	100	100	-0.2
Coal	128	271	281	282	265	247	59	56	-0.4
Oil	156	68	64	43	37	29	15	7	-3.5
Gas	78	116	125	149	161	163	26	37	1.4
Total final consumption	662	711	663	642	616	588	100	100	-0.8
Coal	154	146	146	147	146	143	20	24	-0.1
Oil	473	493	436	412	385	358	69	61	-1.3
of which transport	208	244	221	205	186	167	34	28	-1.6
Gas	35	73	81	83	85	87	10	15	0.8

Reference Scenario: OECD Europe

	Energy demand (Mtoe)						Shares (%)		Growth (% p.a.)
	1990	2006	2015	2020	2025	2030	2006	2030	2006-2030
Total primary energy demand	1 622	1 884	1 980	1 994	2 002	2 005	100	100	0.3
Coal	438	331	344	334	317	292	18	15	-0.5
Oil	626	696	674	663	649	634	37	32	-0.4
Gas	258	448	509	530	547	576	24	29	1.0
Nuclear	204	255	228	203	186	166	14	8	-1.8
Hydro	38	41	49	53	55	57	2	3	1.4
Biomass and waste	53	94	130	150	170	185	5	9	2.8
Other renewables	5	18	46	62	77	95	1	5	7.2
Power generation	611	755	828	830	835	837	100	100	0.4
Coal	270	242	264	259	247	228	32	27	-0.3
Oil	47	29	19	12	12	12	4	1	-3.7
Gas	40	141	183	196	206	228	19	27	2.0
Nuclear	204	255	228	203	186	166	34	20	-1.8
Hydro	38	41	49	53	55	57	5	7	1.4
Biomass and waste	8	32	45	53	62	66	4	8	3.0
Other renewables	3	14	40	54	67	80	2	10	7.4
Other energy sector	143	148	143	141	139	136	100	100	-0.4
of which electricity	38	45	50	51	51	50	31	37	0.4
Total final consumption	1 139	1 350	1 426	1 456	1 476	1 494	100	100	0.4
Coal	122	57	51	48	45	41	4	3	-1.4
Oil	539	623	615	610	597	583	46	39	-0.3
Gas	204	288	308	316	324	331	21	22	0.6
Electricity	190	260	298	313	328	342	19	23	1.2
Heat	37	57	62	63	64	64	4	4	0.5
Biomass and waste	45	62	85	97	108	119	5	8	2.8
Other renewables	2	3	6	8	11	15	0	1	6.4
Industry	320	328	342	344	345	345	100	100	0.2
Coal	70	41	39	37	35	33	13	10	-0.9
Oil	57	49	45	42	40	37	15	11	-1.1
Gas	78	94	97	98	98	97	29	28	0.2
Electricity	86	106	117	120	122	123	32	36	0.6
Heat	13	18	19	19	19	19	5	6	0.3
Biomass and waste	15	20	25	28	31	34	6	10	2.2
Other renewables	0	0	0	0	1	2	0	0	9.7
Transport	289	386	412	418	414	408	100	100	0.2
Oil	283	372	387	387	379	371	96	91	0.0
Biofuels	0	5	16	21	23	25	1	6	6.5
Other fuels	6	8	10	11	11	12	2	3	1.6
Other sectors	431	519	562	585	610	636	100	100	0.8
Coal	50	15	12	10	9	7	3	1	-2.8
Oil	116	99	88	87	86	84	19	13	-0.7
Gas	112	180	196	203	210	218	35	34	0.8
Electricity	99	147	174	186	198	210	28	33	1.5
Heat	24	39	43	44	44	45	8	7	0.5
Biomass and waste	30	36	44	48	54	60	7	9	2.1
Other renewables	2	3	6	7	10	13	1	2	6.1
Non-energy use	99	117	109	109	108	106	100	100	-0.4

Reference Scenario: OECD Europe

	Electricity generation (TWh)						Shares (%)		Growth (% p.a.)
	1990	2006	2015	2020	2025	2030	2006	2030	2006-2030
Total generation	2 632	3 530	4 028	4 211	4 381	4 537	100	100	1.1
Coal	1 011	1 009	1 103	1 128	1 126	1 062	29	23	0.2
Oil	203	126	80	52	46	54	4	1	-3.5
Gas	167	745	887	961	1 019	1 145	21	25	1.8
Nuclear	782	978	876	779	714	636	28	14	-1.8
Hydro	443	480	575	616	645	663	14	15	1.4
Biomass and waste	21	96	148	175	203	219	3	5	3.5
Wind	1	83	323	441	535	621	2	14	8.8
Geothermal	4	8	12	14	16	19	0	0	3.5
Solar	0	3	23	42	73	107	0	2	16.9
Tide and wave	1	1	1	2	5	10	0	0	13.3

	Capacity (GW)					Shares (%)		Growth (% p.a.)
	2006	2015	2020	2025	2030	2006	2030	2006-2030
Total capacity	834	992	1 046	1 095	1 133	100	100	1.3
Coal	197	209	208	202	186	24	16	-0.2
Oil	67	57	40	29	20	8	2	-4.9
Gas	171	194	202	206	225	21	20	1.1
Nuclear	130	117	104	95	85	16	8	-1.7
Hydro	196	223	235	243	248	23	22	1.0
Biomass and waste	20	30	36	41	44	2	4	3.3
Wind	48	141	187	220	243	6	21	7.0
Geothermal	1	2	2	2	3	0	0	3.4
Solar	3	18	32	54	76	0	7	13.9
Tide and wave	0	0	1	1	3	0	0	10.6

	CO_2 emissions (Mt)						Shares (%)		Growth (% p.a.)
	1990	2006	2015	2020	2025	2030	2006	2030	2006-2030
Total CO_2 emissions	3 892	4 058	4 190	4 157	4 080	3 995	100	100	-0.1
Coal	1 678	1 285	1 349	1 312	1 246	1 148	32	29	-0.5
Oil	1 640	1 746	1 669	1 624	1 573	1 519	43	38	-0.6
Gas	574	1 027	1 171	1 220	1 260	1 328	25	33	1.1
Power generation	1 350	1 422	1 581	1 570	1 543	1 513	100	100	0.3
Coal	1 106	1 001	1 094	1 074	1 025	943	70	62	-0.2
Oil	151	92	60	39	38	38	6	2	-3.7
Gas	93	328	427	457	480	532	23	35	2.0
Total final consumption	2 367	2 447	2 434	2 415	2 368	2 314	100	100	-0.2
Coal	534	252	226	211	195	179	10	8	-1.4
Oil	1 375	1 533	1 498	1 476	1 426	1 373	63	59	-0.5
of which transport	768	979	1 001	991	955	917	40	40	-0.3
Gas	458	662	710	729	746	762	27	33	0.6

Reference Scenario: European Union

	Energy demand (Mtoe)						Shares (%)		Growth (% p.a.)
	1990	2006	2015	2020	2025	2030	2006	2030	2006-2030
Total primary energy demand	1 652	1 821	1 897	1 903	1 905	1 903	100	100	0.2
Coal	451	324	322	308	287	260	18	14	-0.9
Oil	625	668	642	630	617	602	37	32	-0.4
Gas	295	438	498	517	532	559	24	29	1.0
Nuclear	207	258	230	206	192	174	14	9	-1.6
Hydro	25	26	33	35	37	38	1	2	1.5
Biomass and waste	46	93	131	153	173	188	5	10	3.0
Other renewables	3	14	40	53	67	82	1	4	7.7
Power generation	644	741	800	797	799	798	100	100	0.3
Coal	286	247	256	247	232	210	33	26	-0.7
Oil	61	31	19	13	12	12	4	2	-3.8
Gas	54	135	179	192	202	224	18	28	2.1
Nuclear	207	258	230	206	192	174	35	22	-1.6
Hydro	25	26	33	35	37	38	4	5	1.5
Biomass and waste	8	32	46	55	63	67	4	8	3.2
Other renewables	3	12	36	49	61	73	2	9	7.7
Other energy sector	145	146	141	139	136	133	100	100	-0.4
of which electricity	39	44	48	49	49	48	30	36	0.4
Total final consumption	1 149	1 288	1 351	1 376	1 392	1 407	100	100	0.4
Coal	120	46	38	34	30	26	4	2	-2.3
Oil	523	593	583	578	565	551	46	39	-0.3
Gas	228	285	303	309	316	321	22	23	0.5
Electricity	185	242	274	286	299	311	19	22	1.0
Heat	54	61	66	67	67	68	5	5	0.5
Biomass and waste	38	61	85	98	109	121	5	9	2.9
Other renewables	1	1	3	4	6	9	0	1	7.9
Industry	342	310	318	319	319	318	100	100	0.1
Coal	68	32	27	25	23	21	10	6	-1.9
Oil	58	46	42	39	37	34	15	11	-1.3
Gas	98	95	98	99	99	99	31	31	0.2
Electricity	85	98	106	109	110	111	32	35	0.5
Heat	19	18	19	19	19	18	6	6	0.2
Biomass and waste	14	20	25	28	31	35	7	11	2.3
Other renewables	0	0	0	0	0	1	0	0	25.4
Transport	281	372	397	402	397	391	100	100	0.2
Oil	275	358	371	370	362	353	96	90	-0.1
Biofuels	0	6	17	22	25	26	1	7	6.7
Other fuels	6	8	10	10	11	12	2	3	1.5
Other sectors	428	494	530	550	571	594	100	100	0.8
Coal	50	12	10	8	7	5	3	1	-3.7
Oil	110	91	80	79	78	77	18	13	-0.7
Gas	115	174	187	193	198	204	35	34	0.7
Electricity	95	137	160	170	180	191	28	32	1.4
Heat	35	43	47	48	49	49	9	8	0.6
Biomass and waste	24	35	43	48	54	60	7	10	2.3
Other renewables	1	1	3	4	6	8	0	1	7.4
Non-energy use	97	112	105	105	104	103	100	100	-0.4

Reference Scenario: European Union

	Electricity generation (TWh)						Shares (%)		Growth (% p.a.)
	1990	2006	2015	2020	2025	2030	2006	2030	2006-2030
Total generation	2 567	3 316	3 734	3 885	4 027	4 158	100	100	0.9
Coal	1 050	1 021	1 052	1 061	1 045	969	31	23	-0.2
Oil	221	131	79	51	46	52	4	1	-3.7
Gas	191	682	833	908	966	1 094	21	26	2.0
Nuclear	795	990	884	791	738	667	30	16	-1.6
Hydro	286	308	385	411	428	436	9	10	1.5
Biomass and waste	20	93	150	179	205	218	3	5	3.6
Wind	1	82	320	430	511	590	2	14	8.6
Geothermal	3	6	8	9	11	14	0	0	3.8
Solar	0	2	23	42	72	106	0	3	16.9
Tide and wave	1	1	1	2	5	11	0	0	13.4

	Capacity (GW)					Shares (%)		Growth (% p.a.)
	2006	2015	2020	2025	2030	2006	2030	2006-2030
Total capacity	795	933	977	1 015	1 045	100	100	1.1
Coal	201	202	198	188	169	25	16	-0.7
Oil	73	59	41	29	20	9	2	-5.2
Gas	164	191	198	203	221	21	21	1.2
Nuclear	131	118	106	99	89	16	9	-1.6
Hydro	153	174	182	187	190	19	18	0.9
Biomass and waste	20	31	36	41	44	3	4	3.3
Wind	48	140	183	211	232	6	22	6.8
Geothermal	1	1	1	2	2	0	0	3.6
Solar	3	18	32	54	76	0	7	13.9
Tide and wave	0	0	1	1	3	0	0	10.6

	CO_2 emissions (Mt)						Shares (%)		Growth (% p.a.)
	1990	2006	2015	2020	2025	2030	2006	2030	2006-2030
Total CO_2 emissions	4 044	3 943	4 006	3 949	3 853	3 755	100	100	-0.2
Coal	1 738	1 263	1 268	1 213	1 130	1 022	32	27	-0.9
Oil	1 648	1 682	1 598	1 551	1 501	1 447	43	39	-0.6
Gas	659	999	1 141	1 185	1 222	1 286	25	34	1.1
Power generation	1 492	1 435	1 539	1 512	1 469	1 429	100	100	0.0
Coal	1 171	1 022	1 059	1 023	958	867	71	61	-0.7
Oil	195	98	62	41	40	38	7	3	-3.8
Gas	127	315	418	447	471	523	22	37	2.1
Total final consumption	2 380	2 326	2 300	2 272	2 220	2 165	100	100	-0.3
Coal	530	209	179	162	144	128	9	6	-2.0
Oil	1 337	1 463	1 425	1 399	1 351	1 299	63	60	-0.5
of which transport	748	944	964	950	913	875	41	40	-0.3
Gas	513	654	696	711	726	738	28	34	0.5

	Energy demand (Mtoe)						Shares (%)		Growth (% p.a.)
	1990	2006	2015	2020	2025	2030	2006	2030	2006-2030
Total primary energy demand	4 125	6 011	8 044	8 920	9 809	10 604	100	100	2.4
Coal	1 156	1 915	2 813	3 159	3 491	3 716	32	35	2.8
Oil	1 209	1 636	2 173	2 394	2 609	2 810	27	26	2.3
Gas	833	1 196	1 543	1 732	1 937	2 159	20	20	2.5
Nuclear	75	114	188	214	248	276	2	3	3.8
Hydro	84	150	200	227	254	281	3	3	2.6
Biomass and waste	761	976	1 070	1 116	1 165	1 221	16	12	0.9
Other renewables	7	24	57	79	105	141	0	1	7.7
Power generation	1 283	2 175	3 164	3 584	4 022	4 448	100	100	3.0
Coal	478	1 154	1 761	2 008	2 230	2 406	53	54	3.1
Oil	227	183	203	198	186	169	8	4	-0.3
Gas	406	538	729	815	931	1 073	25	24	2.9
Nuclear	75	114	188	214	248	276	5	6	3.8
Hydro	84	150	200	227	254	281	7	6	2.6
Biomass and waste	6	16	37	58	87	130	1	3	9.1
Other renewables	7	19	47	64	85	113	1	3	7.6
Other energy sector	493	742	993	1 119	1 228	1 271	100	100	2.3
of which electricity	77	157	231	257	282	304	21	24	2.8
Total final consumption	3 042	4 078	5 323	5 846	6 390	6 911	100	100	2.2
Coal	532	563	758	812	860	897	14	13	2.0
Oil	863	1 318	1 795	2 002	2 217	2 427	32	35	2.6
Gas	362	518	650	720	801	881	13	13	2.2
Electricity	286	570	910	1 068	1 234	1 401	14	20	3.8
Heat	293	207	240	249	260	268	5	4	1.1
Biomass and waste	707	896	959	980	998	1 009	22	15	0.5
Other renewables	0	5	10	15	20	28	0	0	7.9
Industry	986	1 316	1 835	2 023	2 217	2 396	100	100	2.5
Coal	313	435	604	654	701	739	33	31	2.2
Oil	160	186	234	247	259	269	14	11	1.6
Gas	137	186	252	280	313	344	14	14	2.6
Electricity	159	295	501	587	673	753	22	31	4.0
Heat	137	94	108	110	112	113	7	5	0.8
Biomass and waste	82	119	135	145	160	177	9	7	1.7
Other renewables	0	0	0	0	0	0	0	0	6.9
Transport	481	744	1 051	1 206	1 372	1 540	100	100	3.1
Oil	414	670	949	1 090	1 243	1 397	90	91	3.1
Biofuels	6	7	24	31	39	46	1	3	7.9
Other fuels	61	66	78	84	90	98	9	6	1.6
Other sectors	1 390	1 665	1 946	2 080	2 220	2 358	100	100	1.5
Coal	184	96	103	101	97	91	6	4	-0.2
Oil	184	237	291	316	342	369	14	16	1.9
Gas	133	182	219	244	274	306	11	13	2.2
Electricity	113	262	391	461	540	624	16	26	3.7
Heat	156	113	132	139	148	155	7	7	1.3
Biomass and waste	619	769	800	804	799	786	46	33	0.1
Other renewables	0	4	10	15	20	28	0	1	7.9
Non-energy use	185	354	492	538	580	617	100	100	2.3

Reference Scenario: Non-OECD

	Electricity generation (TWh)						Shares (%)		Growth (% p.a.)
	1990	2006	2015	2020	2025	2030	2006	2030	2006-2030
Total generation	4 242	8 469	13 285	15 421	17 642	19 847	100	100	3.6
Coal	1 370	3 826	6 758	7 965	9 083	10 009	45	50	4.1
Oil	638	679	755	737	697	630	8	3	-0.3
Gas	956	1 709	2 422	2 781	3 270	3 880	20	20	3.5
Nuclear	288	437	721	823	952	1 058	5	5	3.8
Hydro	976	1 749	2 322	2 634	2 949	3 266	21	16	2.6
Biomass and waste	7	35	107	165	243	358	0	2	10.2
Wind	0	14	152	235	314	408	0	2	15.1
Geothermal	8	21	40	50	65	82	0	0	5.8
Solar	0	1	9	31	69	156	0	1	25.3
Tide and wave	0	0	0	0	0	0	0	0	n.a.

	Capacity (GW)					Shares (%)		Growth (% p.a.)
	2006	2015	2020	2025	2030	2006	2030	2006-2030
Total capacity	1 913	2 995	3 419	3 867	4 348	100	100	3.5
Coal	736	1 304	1 515	1 741	1 954	38	45	4.2
Oil	194	237	234	219	202	10	5	0.2
Gas	426	620	677	744	828	22	19	2.8
Nuclear	60	89	100	116	128	3	3	3.3
Hydro	475	651	741	830	918	25	21	2.8
Biomass and waste	8	21	34	51	74	0	2	10.0
Wind	10	62	94	121	152	1	4	11.9
Geothermal	3	6	7	9	12	0	0	5.2
Solar	1	5	17	35	79	0	2	21.2
Tide and wave	0	0	0	0	0	0	0	n.a.

	CO$_2$ emissions (Mt)						Shares (%)		Growth (% p.a.)
	1990	2006	2015	2020	2025	2030	2006	2030	2006-2030
Total CO$_2$ emissions	9 291	14 119	19 610	21 890	24 105	26 021	100	100	2.6
Coal	4 201	7 286	10 710	12 012	13 218	14 113	52	54	2.8
Oil	3 198	4 197	5 526	6 086	6 637	7 152	30	27	2.2
Gas	1 892	2 636	3 374	3 792	4 249	4 755	19	18	2.5
Power generation	3 572	6 450	9 398	10 570	11 686	12 658	100	100	2.8
Coal	1 901	4 609	7 047	8 031	8 914	9 607	71	76	3.1
Oil	722	580	644	628	590	535	9	4	-0.3
Gas	949	1 261	1 707	1 910	2 182	2 515	20	20	2.9
Total final consumption	5 305	6 985	9 336	10 262	11 210	12 085	100	100	2.3
Coal	2 227	2 538	3 436	3 680	3 889	4 041	36	33	2.0
Oil	2 281	3 327	4 505	5 040	5 608	6 163	48	51	2.6
of which transport	1 109	1 822	2 599	2 993	3 420	3 846	26	32	3.2
Gas	796	1 119	1 395	1 542	1 712	1 881	16	16	2.2

Reference Scenario: Eastern Europe/Eurasia

	Energy demand (Mtoe)						Shares (%)		Growth (% p.a.)
	1990	2006	2015	2020	2025	2030	2006	2030	2006-2030
Total primary energy demand	1 559	1 118	1 317	1 359	1 416	1 454	100	100	1.1
Coal	365	215	249	253	264	270	19	19	1.0
Oil	489	233	281	289	292	291	21	20	0.9
Gas	604	550	633	646	670	688	49	47	0.9
Nuclear	60	75	94	101	110	111	7	8	1.6
Hydro	23	26	31	33	35	38	2	3	1.6
Biomass and waste	18	19	24	29	34	40	2	3	3.2
Other renewables	0	1	5	8	11	15	0	1	14.9
Power generation	751	564	674	695	727	750	100	100	1.2
Coal	203	151	181	185	193	199	27	27	1.2
Oil	127	26	24	23	19	17	5	2	-1.7
Gas	334	280	333	336	345	352	50	47	1.0
Nuclear	60	75	94	101	110	111	13	15	1.6
Hydro	23	26	31	33	35	38	5	5	1.6
Biomass and waste	4	5	6	10	13	18	1	2	5.2
Other renewables	0	0	5	8	11	14	0	2	15.8
Other energy sector	192	169	186	188	190	191	100	100	0.5
of which electricity	36	40	48	48	49	49	24	25	0.8
Total final consumption	1 094	723	839	867	905	930	100	100	1.1
Coal	115	40	43	43	44	45	6	5	0.5
Oil	297	176	220	227	232	233	24	25	1.2
Gas	262	236	263	272	286	297	33	32	1.0
Electricity	128	100	130	139	150	160	14	17	2.0
Heat	279	158	167	168	172	174	22	19	0.4
Biomass and waste	13	13	16	18	20	21	2	2	2.2
Other renewables	0	0	0	0	0	1	0	0	7.2
Industry	398	221	261	268	280	288	100	100	1.1
Coal	58	28	30	31	32	33	13	11	0.7
Oil	52	22	27	28	29	31	10	11	1.5
Gas	86	59	72	74	78	81	27	28	1.3
Electricity	76	49	68	71	76	80	22	28	2.1
Heat	126	61	62	61	61	60	28	21	-0.1
Biomass and waste	0	2	2	2	3	3	1	1	2.6
Other renewables	0	0	0	0	0	0	0	0	10.8
Transport	183	145	180	186	189	188	100	100	1.1
Oil	137	97	127	131	133	131	67	70	1.3
Biofuels	0	0	1	1	2	2	0	1	16.1
Other fuels	46	48	51	53	54	56	33	30	0.6
Other sectors	449	292	329	343	365	384	100	100	1.1
Coal	57	10	10	10	10	9	3	2	0.0
Oil	69	26	29	31	32	34	9	9	1.0
Gas	117	105	120	126	135	143	36	37	1.3
Electricity	40	42	52	56	62	67	14	17	1.9
Heat	153	97	105	106	111	114	33	30	0.7
Biomass and waste	13	11	13	14	15	17	4	4	1.8
Other renewables	0	0	0	0	0	1	0	0	7.2
Non-energy use	64	66	70	70	71	70	100	100	0.3

Reference Scenario: Eastern Europe/Eurasia

	Electricity generation (TWh)						Shares (%)		Growth (% p.a.)
	1990	2006	2015	2020	2025	2030	2006	2030	2006-2030
Total generation	1 924	1 659	2 089	2 193	2 330	2 444	100	100	1.6
Coal	448	395	510	524	554	585	24	24	1.6
Oil	271	56	47	45	34	28	3	1	-2.8
Gas	706	615	784	800	834	865	37	35	1.4
Nuclear	231	289	361	388	424	427	17	17	1.6
Hydro	269	300	355	384	412	437	18	18	1.6
Biomass and waste	0	3	14	21	28	37	0	2	10.9
Wind	0	0	13	23	34	49	0	2	25.4
Geothermal	0	0	5	7	9	11	0	0	14.2
Solar	0	0	0	1	2	4	0	0	n.a.
Tide and wave	0	0	0	0	0	0	0	0	n.a.

	Capacity (GW)					Shares (%)		Growth (% p.a.)
	2006	2015	2020	2025	2030	2006	2030	2006-2030
Total capacity	413	486	481	479	486	100	100	0.7
Coal	112	134	123	114	110	27	23	-0.1
Oil	28	23	18	10	8	7	2	-5.1
Gas	140	170	165	162	159	34	33	0.5
Nuclear	40	45	48	52	53	10	11	1.2
Hydro	92	106	114	122	129	22	26	1.4
Biomass and waste	1	3	4	5	7	0	2	9.8
Wind	0	5	8	11	16	0	3	16.8
Geothermal	0	1	1	1	2	0	0	11.9
Solar	0	0	1	1	3	0	1	40.3
Tide and wave	0	0	0	0	0	0	0	n.a.

	CO_2 emissions (Mt)						Shares (%)		Growth (% p.a.)
	1990	2006	2015	2020	2025	2030	2006	2030	2006-2030
Total CO_2 emissions	4 032	2 647	3 110	3 175	3 276	3 340	100	100	1.0
Coal	1 364	845	993	1 012	1 057	1 086	32	33	1.1
Oil	1 259	570	689	706	706	697	22	21	0.8
Gas	1 408	1 232	1 428	1 458	1 513	1 557	47	47	1.0
Power generation	2 008	1 377	1 621	1 641	1 686	1 721	100	100	0.9
Coal	823	636	761	777	815	840	46	49	1.2
Oil	405	83	78	75	62	55	6	3	-1.7
Gas	779	657	781	788	809	826	48	48	1.0
Total final consumption	1 911	1 161	1 363	1 401	1 452	1 479	100	100	1.0
Coal	530	200	223	226	233	236	17	16	0.7
Oil	788	433	547	563	574	571	37	39	1.2
of which transport	364	263	348	356	356	345	23	23	1.1
Gas	594	528	593	613	646	672	45	45	1.0

Reference Scenario: Russia

	Energy demand (Mtoe)						Shares (%)		Growth (% p.a.)
	1990	2006	2015	2020	2025	2030	2006	2030	2006-2030
Total primary energy demand	879	668	798	816	843	859	100	100	1.1
Coal	182	107	140	148	158	163	16	19	1.8
Oil	273	139	165	167	168	166	21	19	0.7
Gas	367	359	410	410	417	423	54	49	0.7
Nuclear	31	41	56	59	65	65	6	8	1.9
Hydro	14	15	17	17	18	19	2	2	0.9
Biomass and waste	12	7	7	8	11	14	1	2	2.7
Other renewables	0	0	4	5	7	10	0	1	14.2
Power generation	444	368	451	461	477	488	100	100	1.2
Coal	105	82	113	121	131	137	22	28	2.2
Oil	62	17	16	16	14	12	5	2	-1.4
Gas	228	210	242	238	236	236	57	48	0.5
Nuclear	31	41	56	59	65	65	11	13	1.9
Hydro	14	15	17	17	18	19	4	4	0.9
Biomass and waste	4	4	3	4	6	9	1	2	3.2
Other renewables	0	0	4	5	7	10	0	2	14.2
Other energy sector	118	106	115	115	116	116	100	100	0.4
of which electricity	21	26	31	31	31	30	24	26	0.7
Total final consumption	634	432	499	510	527	538	100	100	0.9
Coal	55	16	17	17	16	16	4	3	-0.1
Oil	154	101	124	127	128	127	23	24	0.9
Gas	143	131	147	152	159	166	30	31	1.0
Electricity	71	59	78	83	88	93	14	17	1.9
Heat	203	123	128	129	131	133	28	25	0.3
Biomass and waste	8	2	3	4	4	4	1	1	2.5
Other renewables	0	0	0	0	0	0	0	0	n.a.
Industry	210	131	158	161	167	170	100	100	1.1
Coal	16	10	11	11	11	11	8	6	0.2
Oil	25	11	14	14	15	15	8	9	1.3
Gas	30	32	41	43	45	47	24	28	1.7
Electricity	41	30	45	47	49	51	23	30	2.2
Heat	98	47	47	46	46	45	36	26	-0.2
Biomass and waste	0	0	1	1	1	1	0	0	3.2
Other renewables	0	0	0	0	0	0	0	0	n.a.
Transport	125	97	116	119	120	120	100	100	0.9
Oil	82	56	72	74	74	72	58	60	1.1
Biofuels	0	0	0	0	0	0	0	0	n.a.
Other fuels	43	41	44	45	46	48	42	40	0.6
Other sectors	259	160	178	184	195	204	100	100	1.0
Coal	39	5	5	5	5	4	3	2	-0.9
Oil	28	12	13	14	14	15	8	7	0.9
Gas	57	44	50	53	58	62	27	30	1.4
Electricity	21	21	25	27	29	32	13	16	1.8
Heat	105	75	81	82	85	88	47	43	0.6
Biomass and waste	8	2	3	3	3	3	1	2	2.2
Other renewables	0	0	0	0	0	0	0	0	n.a.
Non-energy use	40	44	47	46	45	45	100	100	0.0

Reference Scenario: Russia

	Electricity generation (TWh)						Shares (%)		Growth (% p.a.)
	1990	2006	2015	2020	2025	2030	2006	2030	2006-2030
Total generation	1 082	994	1 282	1 329	1 394	1 445	100	100	1.6
Coal	157	179	280	311	349	382	18	26	3.2
Oil	129	24	24	23	19	15	2	1	-2.0
Gas	512	458	557	545	536	537	46	37	0.7
Nuclear	118	156	216	227	248	248	16	17	1.9
Hydro	166	173	193	202	211	217	17	15	0.9
Biomass and waste	0	3	4	6	9	14	0	1	6.9
Wind	0	0	5	10	15	24	0	2	42.3
Geothermal	0	0	4	5	7	9	0	1	13.1
Solar	0	0	0	0	0	1	0	0	n.a.
Tide and wave	0	0	0	0	0	0	0	0	n.a.

	Capacity (GW)					Shares (%)		Growth (% p.a.)
	2006	2015	2020	2025	2030	2006	2030	2006-2030
Total capacity	221	255	257	260	262	100	100	0.7
Coal	52	66	66	68	68	23	26	1.1
Oil	6	6	6	4	3	3	1	-2.7
Gas	95	103	100	96	93	43	35	-0.1
Nuclear	22	26	27	30	30	10	11	1.3
Hydro	46	50	53	55	57	21	22	0.9
Biomass and waste	0	1	1	2	3	0	1	8.0
Wind	0	2	3	4	7	0	3	24.4
Geothermal	0	1	1	1	1	0	0	12.1
Solar	0	0	0	0	0	0	0	n.a.
Tide and wave	0	0	0	0	0	0	0	n.a.

	CO_2 emissions (Mt)						Shares (%)		Growth (% p.a.)
	1990	2006	2015	2020	2025	2030	2006	2030	2006-2030
Total CO_2 emissions	2 180	1 570	1 886	1 924	1 976	2 004	100	100	1.0
Coal	688	445	582	614	655	678	28	34	1.8
Oil	625	321	380	383	378	368	20	18	0.6
Gas	866	804	924	927	943	958	51	48	0.7
Power generation	1 162	899	1 106	1 128	1 160	1 179	100	100	1.1
Coal	432	353	486	520	562	588	39	50	2.1
Oil	198	55	53	51	44	39	6	3	-1.4
Gas	532	491	567	556	553	553	55	47	0.5
Total final consumption	961	607	707	720	737	743	100	100	0.8
Coal	254	88	92	90	89	86	14	12	-0.1
Oil	389	231	287	291	291	285	38	38	0.9
of which transport	*217*	*149*	*191*	*193*	*190*	*182*	*25*	*24*	*0.8*
Gas	318	289	328	339	357	372	48	50	1.1

Reference Scenario: Non-OECD Asia

	Energy demand (Mtoe)						Shares (%)		Growth (% p.a.)
	1990	2006	2015	2020	2025	2030	2006	2030	2006-2030
Total primary energy demand	1 599	3 227	4 598	5 188	5 787	6 325	100	100	2.8
Coal	697	1 567	2 390	2 720	3 029	3 244	49	51	3.1
Oil	321	754	1 059	1 203	1 357	1 521	23	24	3.0
Gas	71	235	342	403	473	552	7	9	3.6
Nuclear	10	30	79	95	114	134	1	2	6.4
Hydro	24	58	91	106	120	134	2	2	3.5
Biomass and waste	470	564	593	603	621	646	17	10	0.6
Other renewables	6	19	44	58	74	94	1	1	6.8
Power generation	331	1 181	1 880	2 191	2 490	2 779	100	100	3.6
Coal	229	927	1 468	1 700	1 902	2 069	78	74	3.4
Oil	46	54	57	54	52	49	5	2	-0.4
Gas	16	92	135	163	200	247	8	9	4.2
Nuclear	10	30	79	95	114	134	3	5	6.4
Hydro	24	58	91	106	120	134	5	5	3.5
Biomass and waste	0	4	15	25	43	72	0	3	12.4
Other renewables	6	16	35	47	59	73	1	3	6.6
Other energy sector	165	356	547	633	724	759	100	100	3.2
of which electricity	24	79	136	157	176	193	22	25	3.8
Total final consumption	1 229	2 144	2 964	3 304	3 654	4 003	100	100	2.6
Coal	390	497	685	737	781	817	23	20	2.1
Oil	249	631	908	1 040	1 191	1 352	29	34	3.2
Gas	33	102	159	188	219	250	5	6	3.8
Electricity	85	315	565	682	797	910	15	23	4.5
Heat	14	49	74	81	88	93	2	2	2.7
Biomass and waste	457	548	564	564	563	559	26	14	0.1
Other renewables	0	4	8	11	15	21	0	1	7.7
Industry	394	793	1 192	1 337	1 478	1 607	100	100	3.0
Coal	235	388	550	599	643	680	49	42	2.4
Oil	52	91	118	124	129	133	11	8	1.6
Gas	10	45	71	83	94	105	6	7	3.6
Electricity	51	186	350	421	487	548	24	34	4.6
Heat	11	33	46	49	51	53	4	3	2.0
Biomass and waste	36	50	55	62	74	88	6	6	2.4
Other renewables	0	0	0	0	0	0	0	0	6.0
Transport	122	290	463	564	686	823	100	100	4.4
Oil	108	280	442	536	651	780	97	95	4.4
Biofuels	0	1	8	11	14	18	0	2	14.0
Other fuels	13	9	14	17	20	25	3	3	4.3
Other sectors	638	873	1 030	1 100	1 163	1 224	100	100	1.4
Coal	124	81	88	86	82	76	9	6	-0.3
Oil	51	125	155	171	187	202	14	17	2.0
Gas	5	24	41	53	66	79	3	6	5.1
Electricity	34	126	209	255	302	352	14	29	4.4
Heat	3	16	27	33	37	41	2	3	3.9
Biomass and waste	421	497	501	492	475	452	57	37	-0.4
Other renewables	0	4	8	11	15	21	0	2	7.7
Non-energy use	75	189	279	304	327	349	100	100	2.6

Reference Scenario: Non-OECD Asia

	Electricity generation (TWh)						Shares (%)		Growth (% p.a.)
	1990	2006	2015	2020	2025	2030	2006	2030	2006-2030
Total generation	1 271	4 582	8 160	9 763	11 318	12 832	100	100	4.4
Coal	731	3 107	5 763	6 904	7 936	8 813	68	69	4.4
Oil	160	214	225	215	204	192	5	1	-0.4
Gas	59	429	609	733	905	1 133	9	9	4.1
Nuclear	39	116	301	365	436	515	3	4	6.4
Hydro	275	677	1 064	1 237	1 399	1 560	15	12	3.5
Biomass and waste	0	11	44	74	127	207	0	2	13.2
Wind	0	12	120	179	230	281	0	2	14.0
Geothermal	7	17	29	35	42	49	0	0	4.4
Solar	0	0	6	19	40	81	0	1	30.9
Tide and wave	0	0	0	0	0	0	0	0	n.a.

	Capacity (GW)					Shares (%)		Growth (% p.a.)
	2006	2015	2020	2025	2030	2006	2030	2006-2030
Total capacity	993	1 759	2 097	2 453	2 827	100	100	4.5
Coal	573	1 090	1 304	1 533	1 749	58	62	4.8
Oil	63	74	72	69	66	6	2	0.2
Gas	113	156	178	208	252	11	9	3.4
Nuclear	15	36	44	52	62	2	2	5.9
Hydro	213	336	392	443	494	21	17	3.6
Biomass and waste	3	9	16	27	43	0	2	11.6
Wind	9	52	76	94	111	1	4	11.0
Geothermal	3	4	5	6	7	0	0	3.9
Solar	1	3	10	21	43	0	2	18.3
Tide and wave	0	0	0	0	0	0	0	n.a.

	CO_2 emissions (Mt)						Shares (%)		Growth (% p.a.)
	1990	2006	2015	2020	2025	2030	2006	2030	2006-2030
Total CO_2 emissions	3 519	8 363	12 439	14 168	15 838	17 299	100	100	3.1
Coal	2 532	6 015	9 115	10 343	11 454	12 303	72	71	3.0
Oil	850	1 858	2 603	2 976	3 384	3 823	22	22	3.1
Gas	136	491	721	850	1 001	1 173	6	7	3.7
Power generation	1 080	4 058	6 332	7 311	8 189	8 951	100	100	3.4
Coal	896	3 671	5 833	6 753	7 553	8 212	90	92	3.4
Oil	146	172	182	174	166	158	4	2	-0.4
Gas	38	216	318	383	470	582	5	6	4.2
Total final consumption	2 284	3 969	5 612	6 251	6 912	7 552	100	100	2.7
Coal	1 579	2 217	3 067	3 302	3 498	3 639	56	48	2.1
Oil	644	1 549	2 230	2 578	2 982	3 419	39	45	3.4
of which transport	290	753	1 204	1 472	1 799	2 165	19	29	4.5
Gas	60	203	315	371	432	494	5	7	3.8

Reference Scenario: China

	Energy demand (Mtoe)						Shares (%)		Growth (% p.a.)
	1990	2006	2015	2020	2025	2030	2006	2030	2006-2030
Total primary energy demand	874	1 898	2 906	3 282	3 629	3 885	100	100	3.0
Coal	534	1 214	1 898	2 139	2 341	2 441	64	63	3.0
Oil	116	352	553	639	725	814	19	21	3.6
Gas	13	49	103	132	161	188	3	5	5.8
Nuclear	0	14	46	55	66	78	1	2	7.3
Hydro	11	37	61	71	80	88	2	2	3.6
Biomass and waste	200	227	230	224	227	237	12	6	0.2
Other renewables	0	4	15	22	30	40	0	1	10.4
Power generation	181	769	1 296	1 499	1 667	1 806	100	100	3.6
Coal	153	692	1 136	1 303	1 428	1 514	90	84	3.3
Oil	16	16	18	18	17	17	2	1	0.2
Gas	1	7	22	30	40	50	1	3	8.3
Nuclear	0	14	46	55	66	78	2	4	7.3
Hydro	11	37	61	71	80	88	5	5	3.6
Biomass and waste	0	1	6	10	21	38	0	2	14.9
Other renewables	0	0	7	12	17	22	0	1	18.9
Other energy sector	94	222	371	436	504	516	100	100	3.6
of which electricity	*12*	*47*	*87*	*98*	*105*	*111*	*21*	*21*	*3.6*
Total final consumption	670	1 215	1 808	2 014	2 209	2 384	100	100	2.8
Coal	315	393	547	579	599	605	32	25	1.8
Oil	88	303	490	567	652	742	25	31	3.8
Gas	10	38	75	94	112	129	3	5	5.2
Electricity	43	203	392	471	539	598	17	25	4.6
Heat	13	48	73	80	87	93	4	4	2.8
Biomass and waste	200	226	223	214	206	198	19	8	-0.5
Other renewables	0	3	8	10	14	18	0	1	7.2
Industry	242	528	831	925	1 007	1 070	100	100	3.0
Coal	177	300	428	456	475	481	57	45	2.0
Oil	21	42	56	57	58	60	8	6	1.5
Gas	3	16	32	38	45	51	3	5	4.9
Electricity	30	137	269	320	366	404	26	38	4.6
Heat	11	32	46	48	50	52	6	5	2.0
Biomass and waste	0	1	2	4	12	22	0	2	14.4
Other renewables	0	0	0	0	0	0	0	0	5.4
Transport	41	133	249	310	384	465	100	100	5.3
Oil	30	127	236	293	363	440	95	95	5.3
Biofuels	0	1	5	7	10	12	0	3	13.1
Other fuels	10	6	8	9	11	12	4	3	3.4
Other sectors	345	454	566	605	633	655	100	100	1.5
Coal	109	66	72	71	68	63	15	10	-0.2
Oil	18	66	94	105	114	123	14	19	2.6
Gas	2	15	30	40	49	60	3	9	6.1
Electricity	13	64	119	145	167	187	14	29	4.6
Heat	2	16	27	32	37	40	4	6	4.0
Biomass and waste	200	224	217	203	184	164	49	25	-1.3
Other renewables	0	3	8	10	14	18	1	3	7.2
Non-energy use	43	100	161	174	185	194	100	100	2.8

Reference Scenario: China

	Electricity generation (TWh)						Shares (%)		Growth (% p.a.)
	1990	2006	2015	2020	2025	2030	2006	2030	2006-2030
Total generation	650	2 903	5 559	6 606	7 495	8 241	100	100	4.4
Coal	471	2 328	4 445	5 246	5 876	6 335	80	77	4.3
Oil	49	52	57	58	55	56	2	1	0.3
Gas	3	26	83	121	165	215	1	3	9.2
Nuclear	0	55	176	211	252	298	2	4	7.3
Hydro	127	436	715	826	927	1 020	15	12	3.6
Biomass and waste	0	3	18	28	61	112	0	1	17.1
Wind	0	4	62	101	130	154	0	2	16.6
Geothermal	0	0	2	3	4	5	0	0	n.a.
Solar	0	0	2	11	25	47	0	1	28.9
Tide and wave	0	0	0	0	0	0	0	0	n.a.

	Capacity (GW)					Shares (%)		Growth (% p.a.)
	2006	2015	2020	2025	2030	2006	2030	2006-2030
Total capacity	622	1 189	1 418	1 650	1 867	100	100	4.7
Coal	449	866	1 022	1 187	1 332	72	71	4.6
Oil	16	20	20	18	18	3	1	0.6
Gas	14	33	42	51	60	2	3	6.4
Nuclear	7	21	25	30	36	1	2	7.3
Hydro	132	217	251	282	310	21	17	3.6
Biomass and waste	2	4	6	12	22	0	1	11.6
Wind	3	28	45	56	64	0	3	14.2
Geothermal	0	0	0	1	1	0	0	12.2
Solar	0	1	6	13	24	0	1	27.2
Tide and wave	0	0	0	0	0	0	0	n.a.

	CO_2 emissions (Mt)						Shares (%)		Growth (% p.a.)
	1990	2006	2015	2020	2025	2030	2006	2030	2006-2030
Total CO_2 emissions	2 244	5 648	8 828	10 004	10 996	11 706	100	100	3.1
Coal	1 914	4 670	7 236	8 123	8 823	9 229	83	79	2.9
Oil	304	872	1 373	1 605	1 839	2 089	15	18	3.7
Gas	26	107	218	277	335	388	2	3	5.5
Power generation	652	2 829	4 654	5 342	5 861	6 232	100	100	3.3
Coal	598	2 758	4 542	5 210	5 709	6 055	97	97	3.3
Oil	52	53	58	59	56	56	2	1	0.2
Gas	2	18	53	74	96	120	1	2	8.3
Total final consumption	1 507	2 615	3 848	4 239	4 597	4 894	100	100	2.6
Coal	1 265	1 789	2 482	2 628	2 714	2 725	68	56	1.8
Oil	225	753	1 225	1 436	1 674	1 930	29	39	4.0
of which transport	83	357	669	836	1 038	1 261	14	26	5.4
Gas	17	73	141	175	208	239	3	5	5.1

Reference Scenario: India

	Energy demand (Mtoe)						Shares (%)		Growth (% p.a.)
	1990	2006	2015	2020	2025	2030	2006	2030	2006-2030
Total primary energy demand	320	566	771	905	1 075	1 280	100	100	3.5
Coal	106	223	315	385	473	579	39	45	4.1
Oil	63	136	202	240	287	346	24	27	4.0
Gas	10	31	48	60	76	96	6	8	4.8
Nuclear	2	5	16	23	30	38	1	3	9.0
Hydro	6	10	13	16	19	22	2	2	3.5
Biomass and waste	133	160	171	176	182	188	28	15	0.7
Other renewables	0	1	5	6	8	10	0	1	11.0
Power generation	73	204	297	364	450	554	100	100	4.2
Coal	58	166	228	275	336	407	81	73	3.8
Oil	4	9	9	9	9	8	4	2	-0.2
Gas	3	13	22	29	40	54	6	10	6.2
Nuclear	2	5	16	23	30	38	2	7	9.0
Hydro	6	10	13	16	19	22	5	4	3.5
Biomass and waste	0	1	3	6	10	17	1	3	12.0
Other renewables	0	1	5	6	7	8	0	1	10.8
Other energy sector	19	47	79	95	113	133	100	100	4.4
of which electricity	*7*	*21*	*34*	*42*	*51*	*61*	*44*	*46*	*4.6*
Total final consumption	253	379	506	589	693	820	100	100	3.3
Coal	42	45	69	88	111	140	12	17	4.9
Oil	54	115	168	203	247	300	30	37	4.1
Gas	6	17	23	27	33	40	4	5	3.7
Electricity	18	43	77	100	130	166	11	20	5.7
Heat	0	0	0	0	0	0	0	0	n.a.
Biomass and waste	133	159	168	171	172	172	42	21	0.3
Other renewables	0	0	0	1	1	2	0	0	12.1
Industry	70	109	162	198	242	294	100	100	4.2
Coal	29	35	59	77	102	133	32	45	5.8
Oil	10	21	29	32	35	38	19	13	2.4
Gas	0	6	8	10	11	12	6	4	2.9
Electricity	9	20	37	49	64	80	18	27	6.1
Heat	0	0	0	0	0	0	0	0	n.a.
Biomass and waste	23	28	29	30	31	32	25	11	0.6
Other renewables	0	0	0	0	0	0	0	0	n.a.
Transport	28	39	69	92	125	168	100	100	6.3
Oil	26	37	65	87	117	156	95	93	6.2
Biofuels	0	0	1	1	1	2	0	1	12.4
Other fuels	3	2	3	5	7	10	5	6	7.2
Other sectors	143	193	223	240	260	282	100	100	1.6
Coal	11	10	11	10	9	8	5	3	-1.2
Oil	12	28	34	37	41	45	14	16	2.0
Gas	0	1	2	3	4	6	0	2	8.5
Electricity	9	23	39	50	65	84	12	30	5.6
Heat	0	0	0	0	0	0	0	0	n.a.
Biomass and waste	111	131	138	139	140	138	68	49	0.2
Other renewables	0	0	0	1	1	2	0	1	12.0
Non-energy use	12	37	52	59	67	75	100	100	3.0

Reference Scenario: India

	Electricity generation (TWh)						Shares (%)		Growth (% p.a.)
	1990	2006	2015	2020	2025	2030	2006	2030	2006-2030
Total generation	289	744	1 286	1 654	2 108	2 645	100	100	5.4
Coal	192	508	867	1 124	1 445	1 817	68	69	5.4
Oil	10	31	33	32	32	31	4	1	0.0
Gas	10	62	110	150	204	277	8	10	6.4
Nuclear	6	19	63	87	114	146	3	6	9.0
Hydro	72	114	156	188	222	257	15	10	3.5
Biomass and waste	0	2	6	10	17	30	0	1	12.0
Wind	0	8	50	61	68	75	1	3	9.8
Geothermal	0	0	0	1	1	1	0	0	n.a.
Solar	0	0	1	2	4	11	0	0	30.2
Tide and wave	0	0	0	0	0	0	0	0	n.a.

	Capacity (GW)					Shares (%)		Growth (% p.a.)
	2006	2015	2020	2025	2030	2006	2030	2006-2030
Total capacity	151	254	327	416	516	100	100	5.3
Coal	78	141	186	243	306	52	59	5.8
Oil	10	10	11	12	13	6	3	1.4
Gas	16	21	29	39	52	11	10	5.0
Nuclear	4	8	10	14	18	2	3	6.9
Hydro	36	52	62	74	85	24	16	3.6
Biomass and waste	0	1	2	4	6	0	1	12.5
Wind	6	21	25	28	30	4	6	6.8
Geothermal	0	0	0	0	0	0	0	11.2
Solar	0	0	1	2	6	0	1	25.7
Tide and wave	0	0	0	0	0	0	0	n.a.

	CO_2 emissions (Mt)						Shares (%)		Growth (% p.a.)
	1990	2006	2015	2020	2025	2030	2006	2030	2006-2030
Total CO_2 emissions	589	1 250	1 798	2 187	2 686	3 293	100	100	4.1
Coal	406	844	1 198	1 463	1 802	2 209	68	67	4.1
Oil	164	339	497	593	716	870	27	26	4.0
Gas	19	67	103	131	167	215	5	7	5.0
Power generation	245	702	962	1 162	1 421	1 729	100	100	3.8
Coal	226	645	883	1 067	1 301	1 578	92	91	3.8
Oil	11	27	28	27	26	26	4	1	-0.2
Gas	8	30	51	69	93	125	4	7	6.2
Total final consumption	328	506	762	941	1 170	1 458	100	100	4.5
Coal	175	196	312	395	499	630	39	43	5.0
Oil	144	277	404	492	605	746	55	51	4.2
of which transport	72	99	177	238	323	437	20	30	6.4
Gas	9	32	45	54	67	82	6	6	4.0

Reference Scenario: Middle East

	Energy demand (Mtoe)						Shares (%)		Growth (% p.a.)
	1990	2006	2015	2020	2025	2030	2006	2030	2006-2030
Total primary energy demand	228	522	736	874	990	1 106	100	100	3.2
Coal	3	9	14	17	22	25	2	2	4.4
Oil	150	280	400	445	480	501	54	45	2.4
Gas	73	229	314	401	474	561	44	51	3.8
Nuclear	0	0	0	1	2	2	0	0	n.a.
Hydro	1	2	3	3	4	4	0	0	2.9
Biomass and waste	1	1	3	4	5	7	0	1	7.4
Other renewables	0	1	2	3	4	6	0	1	8.8
Power generation	63	171	252	298	351	414	100	100	3.7
Coal	2	8	12	16	20	24	5	6	4.6
Oil	29	61	80	83	84	79	35	19	1.1
Gas	32	101	155	192	236	298	59	72	4.6
Nuclear	0	0	0	1	2	2	0	1	n.a.
Hydro	1	2	3	3	4	4	1	1	2.9
Biomass and waste	0	0	1	2	3	4	0	1	n.a.
Other renewables	0	0	0	1	2	4	0	1	39.6
Other energy sector	20	61	78	107	114	117	100	100	2.8
of which electricity	4	12	16	18	21	24	20	20	2.8
Total final consumption	165	349	490	569	644	716	100	100	3.0
Coal	0	1	1	1	1	2	0	0	2.9
Oil	115	205	296	336	369	394	59	55	2.8
Gas	32	95	121	146	171	199	27	28	3.1
Electricity	17	46	68	82	98	116	13	16	3.9
Heat	0	0	0	0	0	0	0	0	n.a.
Biomass and waste	1	1	1	2	2	2	0	0	3.4
Other renewables	0	1	1	2	2	3	0	0	4.9
Industry	45	79	110	129	148	169	100	100	3.2
Coal	0	1	1	1	1	2	1	1	2.9
Oil	22	32	40	44	47	50	41	29	1.9
Gas	20	37	55	66	78	91	47	54	3.8
Electricity	3	9	14	17	21	26	11	15	4.5
Heat	0	0	0	0	0	0	0	0	n.a.
Biomass and waste	0	0	0	0	0	0	0	0	2.0
Other renewables	0	0	0	0	0	0	0	0	n.a.
Transport	60	114	159	183	203	218	100	100	2.7
Oil	60	113	158	182	202	216	100	99	2.7
Biofuels	0	0	0	0	1	1	0	0	n.a.
Other fuels	0	0	1	1	1	1	0	0	1.8
Other sectors	41	104	134	152	174	199	100	100	2.7
Coal	0	0	0	0	0	0	0	0	-100.0
Oil	23	29	41	44	48	51	28	26	2.4
Gas	3	36	37	41	47	53	34	27	1.7
Electricity	14	37	54	64	76	90	36	45	3.7
Heat	0	0	0	0	0	0	0	0	n.a.
Biomass and waste	1	1	1	1	1	1	1	1	1.5
Other renewables	0	1	1	2	2	3	1	1	4.9
Non-energy use	20	52	87	105	119	130	100	100	3.9

Reference Scenario: Middle East

	Electricity generation (TWh)						Shares (%)		Growth (% p.a.)
	1990	2006	2015	2020	2025	2030	2006	2030	2006-2030
Total generation	240	681	979	1 163	1 381	1 628	100	100	3.7
Coal	10	36	57	75	97	116	5	7	5.0
Oil	114	242	320	332	339	316	36	19	1.1
Gas	104	380	558	696	866	1 090	56	67	4.5
Nuclear	0	0	1	3	6	9	0	1	n.a.
Hydro	12	24	34	40	45	46	3	3	2.9
Biomass and waste	0	0	3	5	7	9	0	1	n.a.
Wind	0	0	5	8	12	18	0	1	34.9
Geothermal	0	0	0	0	0	0	0	0	n.a.
Solar	0	0	1	3	9	24	0	1	31.6
Tide and wave	0	0	0	0	0	0	0	0	n.a.

	Capacity (GW)					Shares (%)		Growth (% p.a.)
	2006	2015	2020	2025	2030	2006	2030	2006-2030
Total capacity	170	247	285	319	354	100	100	3.1
Coal	5	9	12	15	17	3	5	5.2
Oil	55	63	66	64	56	32	16	0.0
Gas	100	156	183	211	242	59	68	3.8
Nuclear	0	0	0	1	1	0	0	n.a.
Hydro	10	15	18	20	20	6	6	2.9
Biomass and waste	0	1	1	2	2	0	1	20.3
Wind	0	2	3	4	6	0	2	19.7
Geothermal	0	0	0	0	0	0	0	13.6
Solar	0	0	1	4	10	0	3	32.6
Tide and wave	0	0	0	0	0	0	0	n.a.

	CO_2 emissions (Mt)						Shares (%)		Growth (% p.a.)
	1990	2006	2015	2020	2025	2030	2006	2030	2006-2030
Total CO_2 emissions	588	1 291	1 769	2 086	2 352	2 614	100	100	3.0
Coal	12	36	58	72	85	96	3	4	4.2
Oil	413	745	1 038	1 149	1 238	1 285	58	49	2.3
Gas	163	510	672	866	1 029	1 233	39	47	3.7
Power generation	172	457	660	769	889	1 025	100	100	3.4
Coal	9	31	48	61	73	83	7	8	4.2
Oil	89	191	251	260	264	247	42	24	1.1
Gas	74	235	361	448	552	695	51	68	4.6
Total final consumption	367	725	996	1 148	1 284	1 406	100	100	2.8
Coal	2	5	10	11	12	13	1	1	4.3
Oil	297	514	727	825	907	970	71	69	2.7
of which transport	150	302	428	497	552	592	42	42	2.8
Gas	68	206	259	312	364	423	28	30	3.1

A

Reference Scenario: Africa

	Energy demand (Mtoe)						Shares (%)		Growth (% p.a.)
	1990	2006	2015	2020	2025	2030	2006	2030	2006-2030
Total primary energy demand	393	614	721	767	817	857	100	100	1.4
Coal	74	103	122	125	127	123	17	14	0.8
Oil	90	132	151	158	165	170	21	20	1.1
Gas	31	77	105	116	131	143	12	17	2.6
Nuclear	2	3	4	5	10	15	0	2	7.1
Hydro	5	8	10	13	16	20	1	2	3.8
Biomass and waste	191	291	328	347	363	377	47	44	1.1
Other renewables	0	1	2	4	6	9	0	1	10.1
Power generation	69	126	171	190	213	234	100	100	2.6
Coal	39	60	76	80	81	77	47	33	1.1
Oil	11	17	19	18	15	12	13	5	-1.2
Gas	11	37	54	62	74	83	30	36	3.4
Nuclear	2	3	4	5	10	15	2	6	7.1
Hydro	5	8	10	13	16	20	6	9	3.8
Biomass and waste	0	1	5	9	13	18	0	8	15.6
Other renewables	0	1	2	2	4	7	1	3	8.7
Other energy sector	58	87	101	103	105	105	100	100	0.8
of which electricity	*6*	*9*	*11*	*12*	*13*	*14*	*11*	*14*	*1.8*
Total final consumption	293	450	519	552	587	619	100	100	1.3
Coal	19	17	19	19	20	20	4	3	0.8
Oil	74	114	132	139	149	157	25	25	1.3
Gas	9	24	30	32	36	39	5	6	2.0
Electricity	21	41	57	65	75	86	9	14	3.1
Heat	0	0	0	0	0	0	0	0	n.a.
Biomass and waste	169	255	281	294	306	315	56	51	0.9
Other renewables	0	0	0	1	2	3	0	0	50.3
Industry	60	80	97	102	109	115	100	100	1.5
Coal	13	10	11	11	12	11	12	10	0.6
Oil	13	14	16	17	17	18	18	16	1.0
Gas	5	12	15	16	17	18	15	15	1.7
Electricity	12	19	25	28	31	34	23	30	2.5
Heat	0	0	0	0	0	0	0	0	n.a.
Biomass and waste	16	26	29	30	32	34	32	29	1.1
Other renewables	0	0	0	0	0	0	0	0	n.a.
Transport	40	69	80	86	93	98	100	100	1.5
Oil	39	66	76	82	88	93	97	95	1.4
Biofuels	0	0	1	1	1	1	0	1	n.a.
Other fuels	1	2	3	3	4	4	3	4	2.3
Other sectors	182	288	324	345	366	385	100	100	1.2
Coal	3	5	5	5	5	5	2	1	-0.2
Oil	16	27	30	32	34	36	9	9	1.3
Gas	1	5	7	8	9	10	2	3	2.4
Electricity	9	22	31	36	43	51	8	13	3.6
Heat	0	0	0	0	0	0	0	0	n.a.
Biomass and waste	152	229	251	263	273	280	80	73	0.8
Other renewables	0	0	0	1	2	3	0	1	50.3
Non-energy use	11	14	17	18	20	22	100	100	1.9

Reference Scenario: Africa

	Electricity generation (TWh)						Shares (%)		Growth (% p.a.)
	1990	2006	2015	2020	2025	2030	2006	2030	2006-2030
Total generation	316	588	802	899	1 028	1 163	100	100	2.9
Coal	165	258	331	346	355	342	44	29	1.2
Oil	43	60	68	66	55	45	10	4	-1.2
Gas	43	161	244	278	327	375	27	32	3.6
Nuclear	8	11	15	20	39	58	2	5	7.1
Hydro	56	94	121	148	185	233	16	20	3.8
Biomass and waste	0	1	14	25	35	48	0	4	19.7
Wind	0	1	5	9	14	23	0	2	14.7
Geothermal	0	1	3	4	6	9	0	1	10.2
Solar	0	1	2	5	12	30	0	3	18.2
Tide and wave	0	0	0	0	0	0	0	0	n.a.

	Capacity (GW)					Shares (%)		Growth (% p.a.)
	2006	2015	2020	2025	2030	2006	2030	2006-2030
Total capacity	120	176	193	212	237	100	100	2.9
Coal	39	51	53	53	51	33	21	1.1
Oil	19	21	20	18	15	16	6	-1.0
Gas	35	64	67	70	70	30	30	2.9
Nuclear	2	2	2	5	7	2	3	5.8
Hydro	23	31	39	48	61	19	26	4.1
Biomass and waste	0	3	5	8	11	0	4	20.2
Wind	0	2	3	5	8	0	3	12.8
Geothermal	0	0	1	1	1	0	1	8.9
Solar	0	1	2	5	14	0	6	33.5
Tide and wave	0	0	0	0	0	0	0	n.a.

	CO_2 emissions (Mt)						Shares (%)		Growth (% p.a.)
	1990	2006	2015	2020	2025	2030	2006	2030	2006-2030
Total CO_2 emissions	549	845	1 027	1 083	1 142	1 170	100	100	1.4
Coal	236	306	378	392	398	385	36	33	1.0
Oil	248	376	431	450	468	480	44	41	1.0
Gas	65	164	218	241	275	305	19	26	2.6
Power generation	213	372	484	512	534	533	100	100	1.5
Coal	152	232	297	309	314	299	62	56	1.1
Oil	35	52	60	57	48	39	14	7	-1.2
Gas	26	88	127	146	172	195	24	37	3.4
Total final consumption	303	430	498	525	561	589	100	100	1.3
Coal	83	74	82	83	85	86	17	15	0.6
Oil	201	308	356	377	404	425	72	72	1.3
of which transport	104	180	209	223	241	254	42	43	1.4
Gas	19	48	60	65	72	79	11	13	2.1

Reference Scenario: Latin America

	Energy demand (Mtoe)						Shares (%)		Growth (% p.a.)
	1990	2006	2015	2020	2025	2030	2006	2030	2006-2030
Total primary energy demand	346	530	671	732	798	862	100	100	2.0
Coal	17	22	38	44	50	54	4	6	3.8
Oil	159	237	283	299	314	326	45	38	1.3
Gas	54	106	148	167	190	215	20	25	3.0
Nuclear	2	6	11	12	12	13	1	1	3.5
Hydro	31	56	64	71	78	85	11	10	1.7
Biomass and waste	82	101	123	133	143	152	19	18	1.7
Other renewables	1	2	4	6	10	17	0	2	8.5
Power generation	69	132	187	210	240	272	100	100	3.1
Coal	5	9	23	28	33	36	6	13	6.2
Oil	14	26	23	20	16	12	20	4	-3.2
Gas	14	28	51	62	77	93	21	34	5.2
Nuclear	2	6	11	12	12	13	4	5	3.5
Hydro	31	56	64	71	78	85	43	31	1.7
Biomass and waste	2	6	9	12	14	18	4	6	4.9
Other renewables	1	2	4	6	10	15	2	6	8.1
Other energy sector	58	70	82	88	94	100	100	100	1.5
of which electricity	8	16	19	21	23	24	23	24	1.8
Total final consumption	262	411	511	554	600	643	100	100	1.9
Coal	7	9	11	12	13	14	2	2	1.6
Oil	128	193	239	258	276	290	47	45	1.7
Gas	25	61	76	82	89	97	15	15	1.9
Electricity	35	67	89	100	114	129	16	20	2.8
Heat	0	0	0	0	0	0	0	0	n.a.
Biomass and waste	67	81	96	102	108	112	20	17	1.4
Other renewables	0	0	0	0	1	2	0	0	15.0
Industry	88	142	174	187	202	217	100	100	1.8
Coal	7	9	11	11	12	13	6	6	1.6
Oil	20	27	32	34	36	38	19	17	1.4
Gas	16	33	40	43	46	49	23	23	1.7
Electricity	17	32	44	50	57	65	22	30	3.0
Heat	0	0	0	0	0	0	0	0	n.a.
Biomass and waste	29	42	48	49	51	52	29	24	0.9
Other renewables	0	0	0	0	0	0	0	0	n.a.
Transport	77	127	169	187	202	213	100	100	2.2
Oil	71	114	146	159	169	177	90	83	1.8
Biofuels	6	7	14	18	22	25	5	12	5.6
Other fuels	0	6	10	10	11	12	5	6	2.7
Other sectors	81	109	128	139	152	167	100	100	1.8
Coal	0	0	0	0	0	0	0	0	1.4
Oil	25	30	36	38	42	45	28	27	1.7
Gas	6	11	14	16	18	21	11	12	2.5
Electricity	17	35	45	50	56	64	32	38	2.5
Heat	0	0	0	0	0	0	0	0	n.a.
Biomass and waste	32	32	34	34	35	36	29	21	0.4
Other renewables	0	0	0	0	1	2	0	1	15.0
Non-energy use	16	33	39	41	44	46	100	100	1.4

Reference Scenario: Latin America

	Electricity generation (TWh)						Shares (%)		Growth (% p.a.)
	1990	2006	2015	2020	2025	2030	2006	2030	2006-2030
Total generation	492	959	1 256	1 404	1 585	1 780	100	100	2.6
Coal	15	30	97	116	142	154	3	9	7.0
Oil	51	107	95	80	65	49	11	3	-3.2
Gas	45	123	226	273	337	417	13	23	5.2
Nuclear	10	21	43	47	47	49	2	3	3.5
Hydro	364	654	748	825	909	990	68	56	1.7
Biomass and waste	7	20	33	40	47	56	2	3	4.3
Wind	0	1	9	16	24	36	0	2	18.3
Geothermal	1	3	4	5	8	12	0	1	6.6
Solar	0	0	1	4	7	17	0	1	n.a.
Tide and wave	0	0	0	0	0	0	0	0	n.a.

	Capacity (GW)					Shares (%)		Growth (% p.a.)
	2006	2015	2020	2025	2030	2006	2030	2006-2030
Total capacity	217	328	364	404	443	100	100	3.0
Coal	6	20	23	26	28	3	6	6.5
Oil	29	56	58	59	57	13	13	2.9
Gas	38	74	84	94	104	17	24	4.3
Nuclear	3	5	6	6	6	1	1	3.4
Hydro	137	162	178	197	214	63	48	1.9
Biomass and waste	4	6	8	9	11	2	3	4.9
Wind	0	3	5	7	11	0	3	17.3
Geothermal	0	1	1	1	2	0	0	6.7
Solar	0	0	2	4	9	0	2	n.a.
Tide and wave	0	0	0	0	0	0	0	n.a.

	CO_2 emissions (Mt)						Shares (%)		Growth (% p.a.)
	1990	2006	2015	2020	2025	2030	2006	2030	2006-2030
Total CO_2 emissions	603	972	1 266	1 377	1 497	1 598	100	100	2.1
Coal	57	85	166	193	225	243	9	15	4.5
Oil	427	648	765	806	841	867	67	54	1.2
Gas	119	239	335	378	431	488	25	31	3.0
Power generation	99	186	301	338	388	429	100	100	3.5
Coal	21	39	108	131	159	173	21	40	6.4
Oil	46	82	73	61	50	38	44	9	-3.2
Gas	32	65	119	145	179	218	35	51	5.2
Total final consumption	439	699	867	935	1 001	1 058	100	100	1.7
Coal	32	43	54	58	62	67	6	6	1.9
Oil	350	523	645	696	741	778	75	74	1.7
of which transport	200	324	409	445	472	491	46	46	1.7
Gas	56	134	168	181	197	214	19	20	2.0

ABBREVIATIONS, DEFINITIONS AND CONVERSION FACTORS

This annex provides general information on abbreviations, fuel, process and regional definitions, and country groupings used throughout *WEO-2008*. General conversion factors for energy have also been included. Readers interested in obtaining more detailed information about IEA statistics should consult www.iea.org/statistics.

Unit abbreviations

Area	Ha/yr	hectare per year
	GHa	giga-hectare (1 hectare $\times 10^9$)
Coal	tce	tonne of coal equivalent
Emissions	ppm	parts per million
	Gt CO_2-eq	gigatonnes of carbon-dioxide equivalent
Energy	toe	tonne of oil equivalent
	Mtoe	million tonnes of oil equivalent
	MBtu	million British thermal units
	GJ	gigajoule (1 joule $\times 10^9$)
	EJ	exajoule (1 joule $\times 10^{18}$)
	kWh	kilowatt-hour
	MWh	megawatt-hour
	GWh	gigawatt-hour
	TWh	terawatt-hour
Gas	tcf	thousand cubic feet
	mcm	million cubic metres
	bcm	billion cubic metres
	tcm	trillion cubic metres
Mass	kt	kilotonnes (1 tonne $\times 10^3$)
	Mt	million tonnes (1 tonne $\times 10^6$)
	Gt	gigatonnes (1 tonne $\times 10^9$)
Oil	b/d	barrels per day
	kb/d	thousand barrels per day
	mb/d	million barrels per day
	mpg	miles per gallon

Oil and Gas	boe	barrels of oil equivalent
	mboe	million barrels of oil equivalent
Power	W	Watt (1 joule per second)
	kW	kilowatt (1 Watt $\times 10^3$)
	MW	megawatt (1 Watt $\times 10^6$)
	GW	gigawatt (1 Watt $\times 10^9$)
	TW	terawatt (1 Watt $\times 10^{12}$)

Fuel definitions

Biodiesel

Biodiesel is a diesel-equivalent, processed fuel made from the transesterification (a chemical process which removes the glycerine from the oil) of both vegetable oils and animal fats.

Biofuels

Biofuels includes ethanol and biodiesel.

Biogas

A mixture of methane and carbon dioxide produced by bacterial degradation of organic matter and used as a fuel.

Biomass and waste

Solid biomass, gas and liquids derived from biomass, industrial waste and the renewable part of municipal waste.

Brown coal

Includes lignite and sub-bituminous coal where lignite is defined as non-agglomerating coal with a gross calorific value less than 4 165 kcal/kg and sub-bituminous coal is defined as non-agglomerating coal with a gross calorific value between 4 165 kcal/kg and 5 700 kcal/kg.

Clean coal technologies

Clean coal technologies (CCTs) are designed to enhance the efficiency and the environmental acceptability of coal extraction, preparation and use.

Coal

Coal includes both primary coal (including hard coal and lignite) and derived fuels (including patent fuel, brown-coal briquettes, coke-oven coke, gas coke, coke-oven gas, blast-furnace gas and oxygen steel furnace gas). Peat is also included in this category.

Coalbed methane

Methane found in coal seams. Coalbed methane is a source of non-conventic
gas.

Coal-to-liquids

Coal-to-liquids (CTL) refers to both coal gasification, combined with Fischer- Tropsch
synthesis to produce liquid fuels, and the less-developed direct-coal liquefaction
technologies.

Condensates

Condensates are liquid hydrocarbon mixtures recovered from non-associated gas
reservoirs. They are composed of C4 and higher carbon number hydrocarbons and
normally have an API between 50° and 85°.

Dimethyl ether

Clear, odourless gas currently produced by dehydration of methanol from natural gas,
but which can also be produced from biomass or coal.

Ethanol

Ethanol is an alcohol made by fermenting any biomass high in carbohydrates. Today,
ethanol is made from starches and sugars, but second-generation technologies will
allow it to be made from cellulose and hemicellulose, the fibrous material that makes
up the bulk of most plant matter.

Gas

Gas includes natural gas (both associated and non-associated with petroleum deposits
but excluding natural gas liquids) and gas-works gas.

Gas-to-liquids

Fischer-Tropsch technology is used to convert natural gas into synthesis gas (syngas)
and then, through catalytic reforming or synthesis, into very clean conventional oil
products. The main fuel produced in most GTL plants is diesel.

Hard coal

Coal of gross calorific value greater than 5 700 kcal/kg on an ash-free but moist
basis. Hard coal can be further disaggregated into anthracite, coking coal and other
bituminous coal.

Heavy petroleum products

Heavy petroleum products include heavy fuel oil.

Hydropower

Hydropower refers to the energy content of the electricity produced in hydropower plants, assuming 100% efficiency. It excludes output from pumped storage plants.

Light petroleum products

Light petroleum products include liquefied petroleum gas (LPG), naphtha and gasoline.

Middle distillates

Middle distillates include jet fuel, diesel and heating oil.

Modern renewables

Includes hydropower, biomass (excluding traditional use) and other renewables.

Natural gas liquids

Natural gas liquids (NGLs) are the liquid or liquefied hydrocarbons produced in the manufacture, purification and stabilisation of natural gas. These are those portions of natural gas which are recovered as liquids in separators, field facilities, or gas processing plants. NGLs include, but are not limited to, ethane, propane, butane, pentane, natural gasoline and condensates.

Nuclear

Nuclear refers to the primary heat equivalent of the electricity produced by a nuclear plant with an average thermal efficiency of 33%.

Oil

Oil includes crude oil, condensates, natural gas liquids, refinery feedstocks and additives, other hydrocarbons (including emulsified oils, synthetic crude oil, mineral oils extracted from bituminous minerals such as oil shale, bituminous sand and oils from coal liquefaction), and petroleum products (refinery gas, ethane, LPG, aviation gasoline, motor gasoline, jet fuels, kerosene, gas/diesel oil, heavy fuel oil, naphtha, white spirit, lubricants, bitumen, paraffin waxes and petroleum coke).

Other renewables

Includes geothermal, solar PV, solar thermal, wind, tide and wave energy for electricity generation and heat production.

Rest of renewables

Includes biomass and waste, geothermal, solar PV, solar thermal, wind, tide and wave energy for electricity generation and heat production.

Traditional biomass

Traditional biomass refers to the use of fuelwood, animal dung and agricultural residues in stoves with very low efficiencies.

Process definitions

Electricity generation

Electricity generation is the total amount of electricity generated by power plants. It includes own use and transmission and distribution losses.

Greenfield

The construction of plants or facilities in new areas or where no previous infrastructure exists.

International marine bunkers

International marine bunkers covers those quantities delivered to sea-going ships that are engaged in international navigation. The international navigation may take place at sea, on inland lakes and waterways, and in coastal waters. Consumption by ships engaged in domestic navigation is excluded. The domestic/international split is determined on the basis of port of departure and port of arrival, and not by the flag or nationality of the ship. Consumption by fishing vessels and by military forces is also excluded.

Lower heating value

Lower heating value is the heat liberated by the complete combustion of a unit of fuel when the water produced is assumed to remain as a vapour and the heat is not recovered.

Natural decline rate

The base production decline rate of an oil or gas field without intervention to enhance production.

Observed decline rate

The production decline rate of an oil or gas field after all measures have been taken to maximise production. It is the aggregation of all the production increases and declines of new and mature oil or gas fields in a particular region.

Other energy sector

Other energy sector covers the use of energy by transformation industries and the energy losses in converting primary energy into a form that can be used in the final consuming sectors. It includes losses by gas works, petroleum refineries, and coal and gas transformation and liquefaction. It also includes energy used in coal mines, in oil and gas extraction, and in electricity and heat production. Transfers and statistical differences are also included in this category.

Residential, services and agriculture

This sector also includes energy use in the forestry, fishing and non-specified sectors. It also theoretically includes military fuel use for all mobile and stationary consumption (e.g. ships, aircraft, road and energy used in living quarters) regardless of whether the fuel delivered is for the military of that country or for the military of another country. In practice, many countries find this difficult to report.

Power generation

Power generation refers to fuel use in electricity plants, heat plants and combined heat and power (CHP) plants. Both main activity producer plants and small plants that produce fuel for their own use (autoproducers) are included.

Total final consumption

Total final consumption is the sum of consumption by the different end-use sectors. TFC is broken down into energy demand in the following sectors: industry (including manufacturing and mining), transport, other (including residential, commercial and public services, agriculture/forestry and fishing), non-energy use (including petrochemical feedstocks), and non-specified.

Total primary energy demand

Total primary energy demand represents domestic demand only, including power generation, other energy sector, and total final consumption. It excludes international marine bunkers, except for world primary energy demand, where it is included.

Regional definitions and country groupings

Africa

Algeria, Angola, Benin, Botswana, Burkina Faso, Burundi, Cameroon, Cape Verde, Central African Republic, Chad, Comoros, Congo, Democratic Republic of Congo, Côte d'Ivoire, Djibouti, Egypt, Equatorial Guinea, Eritrea, Ethiopia, Gabon, Gambia, Ghana, Guinea, Guinea-Bissau, Kenya, Lesotho, Liberia, Libya, Madagascar, Malawi, Mali, Mauritania, Mauritius, Morocco, Mozambique, Namibia, Niger, Nigeria, Reunion, Rwanda, Sao Tome and Principe, Senegal, Seychelles, Sierra Leone, Somalia, South Africa, Sudan, Swaziland, United Republic of Tanzania, Togo, Tunisia, Uganda, Zambia and Zimbabwe.

Annex I Parties to the United Nations Framework Convention on Climate Change

Australia, Austria, Belarus, Belgium, Bulgaria, Canada, Croatia, Czech Republic, Denmark, Estonia, European Community, Finland, France, Germany, Greece, Hungary, Iceland, Ireland, Italy, Japan, Latvia, Liechtenstein, Lithuania, Luxembourg, Monaco, Netherlands, New Zealand, Norway, Poland, Portugal, Romania, Russian Federation, Slovakia, Slovenia, Spain, Sweden, Switzerland, Turkey, Ukraine, the United Kingdom and the United States.

China

China refers to the People's Republic of China, including Hong Kong.

European Union

Austria, Belgium, Bulgaria, Cyprus, the Czech Republic, Denmark, Estonia, Finland, France, Germany, Greece, Hungary, Ireland, Italy, Latvia, Lithuania, Luxembourg, Malta, the Netherlands, Poland, Portugal, Romania, the Slovak Republic, Slovenia, Spain, Sweden and the United Kingdom.

Latin America

Antigua and Barbuda, Aruba, Argentina, Bahamas, Barbados, Belize, Bermuda, Bolivia, Brazil, Chile, Colombia, Costa Rica, Cuba, Dominica, the Dominican Republic, Ecuador, El Salvador, French Guyana, Grenada, Guadeloupe, Guatemala, Guyana, Haiti, Honduras, Jamaica, Martinique, Netherlands Antilles, Nicaragua, Panama, Paraguay, Peru, St. Kitts and Nevis, Saint Lucia, St. Vincent and Grenadines, Suriname, Trinidad and Tobago, Uruguay and Venezuela.

Middle East

Bahrain, Iran, Iraq, Israel, Jordan, Kuwait, Lebanon, Oman, Qatar, Saudi Arabia, Syria, the United Arab Emirates and Yemen. It includes the neutral zone between Saudi Arabia and Iraq.

Non-OECD Asia

Afghanistan, Bangladesh, Bhutan, Brunei, Cambodia, China, Chinese Taipei, Fiji, French Polynesia, India, Indonesia, Kiribati, the Democratic People's Republic of Korea, Laos, Macau, Malaysia, Maldives, Mongolia, Myanmar, Nepal, New Caledonia, Pakistan, Papua New Guinea, the Philippines, Samoa, Singapore, Solomon Islands, Sri Lanka, Thailand, Tonga, Vietnam and Vanuatu.

North Africa

Algeria, Egypt, Libya, Morocco and Tunisia.

OECD+

OECD countries and those EU countries that are not members of the OECD.

OECD Asia

Japan and Korea.

OECD Europe

Austria, Belgium, the Czech Republic, Denmark, Finland, France, Germany, Greece, Hungary, Iceland, Ireland, Italy, Luxembourg, the Netherlands, Norway, Poland, Portugal, the Slovak Republic, Spain, Sweden, Switzerland, Turkey and the United Kingdom.

OECD North America

Canada, Mexico and the United States.

OECD Oceania

Australia and New Zealand.

OECD Pacific

Australia, Japan, Korea and New Zealand.

Other Major Economies

China, Russia, India, Iran, Saudi Arabia, Indonesia, Brazil and South Africa. For modelling purposes, we include the entire Middle East region and exclude South Africa.

Organization of the Petroleum Exporting Countries (OPEC)

Algeria, Angola, Ecuador, Indonesia, Iran, Iraq, Kuwait, Libya, Nigeria, Qatar, Saudi Arabia, the United Arab Emirates and Venezuela.

Other Asia

Non-OECD Asia regional grouping excluding China and India.

Sub-Saharan Africa

Africa regional grouping excluding North Africa regional grouping.

Eastern Europe/Eurasia

Albania, Armenia, Azerbaijan, Belarus, Bosnia-Herzegovina, Bulgaria, Croatia, Estonia, Serbia, Montenegro, the former Yugoslav Republic of Macedonia, Georgia, Kazakhstan, Kyrgyzstan, Latvia, Lithuania, Moldova, Romania, Russia, Slovenia, Tajikistan, Turkmenistan, Ukraine and Uzbekistan. For statistical reasons, this region also includes Cyprus, Gibraltar and Malta.

General conversion factors for energy

To:	TJ	Gcal	Mtoe	MBtu	GWh
From:	multiply by:				
TJ	1	238.8	2.388×10^{-5}	947.8	0.2778
Gcal	4.1868×10^{-3}	1	10^{-7}	3.968	1.163×10^{-3}
Mtoe	4.1868×10^{4}	10^{7}	1	3.968×10^{7}	11630
MBtu	1.0551×10^{-3}	0.252	2.52×10^{-8}	1	2.931×10^{-4}
GWh	3.6	860	8.6×10^{-5}	3412	1

API	American Petroleum Institute
CAFE	corporate average fuel economy (standards in the US)
CAIR	Clean Air Interstate Rule
CCGT	combined-cycle gas turbine
CCHP	combined cooling, heat and power
CCS	CO_2 capture and storage
CDM	Clean Development Mechanism (under the Kyoto Protocol)
CDU	crude distillation unit
CFC	chlorofluorocarbon
CFL	compact fluorescent lamp
CH_4	methane
CHP	combined heat and power; when referring to industrial CHP, the term co-generation is sometimes used
CMM	coalmine methane
CNG	compressed natural gas
CO	carbon monoxide
CO_2	carbon dioxide
CO_2-eq	carbon dioxide equivalent
COP	Conference of Parties
CTL	coal-to-liquids
DME	dimethyl ether
E&P	exploration and production
EOR	enhanced oil recovery
EPA	Environmental Protection Agency (US)
EPC	engineering, procurement and construction
EU	European Union
EU ETS	European Union Emissions Trading Scheme

FAO	Food and Agriculture Organization of the United Nations
FDI	foreign direct investment
FFV	flex-fuel vehicle
GAINS	Greenhouse Gas and Air Pollution Interactions and Synergies
GDP	gross domestic product
GHG	greenhouse gas
GTL	gas-to-liquids
HFC	hydrofluorocarbon
HCFC	hydrochlorofluorocarbon
IAEA	International Atomic Energy Agency
ICLEI	International Council for Local Environmental Initiatives
IEA	International Energy Agency
IGCC	integrated gasification combined cycle
IMF	International Monetary Fund
IOC	international oil company
IPCC	Intergovernmental Panel on Climate Change
IPP	independent power producer
LDV	light-duty vehicles
LHV	lower heating value
LNG	liquefied natural gas
LPG	liquefied petroleum gas
LULUCF	land use, land use change and forests
MER	market exchange rate
MDG	millennium development goal
MSC	multiple service contract
N_2O	nitrogen dioxide
NEA	Nuclear Energy Agency

NGL	natural gas liquid
NOC	national oil company
NO$_x$	nitrous oxides
OCGT	open-cycle gas turbine
ODI	outward foreign direct investment
OECD	Organisation for Economic Co-operation and Development
OECD+	OECD countries, plus EU countries not in the OECD
OPEC	Organization of the Petroleum Exporting Countries
PDS	public distribution systems
PFC	perfluorocarbon
PM	particulate matter
ppm	parts per million
PPP	purchasing power parity
PSA	production-sharing agreement
RD&D	research, development and demonstration
SD-PAMs	sustainable development policies and measures
SF$_6$	sulphur hexafluoride
SMEs	small- and medium-sized enterprises
SO$_2$	sulphur dioxide
UCG	underground coal gasification
UNCTAD	United Nations Conference on Trade and Development
UNDESA	United Nations Department of Economic and Social Affairs
UNDP	United Nations Development Programme
UNEP	United Nations Environment Programme
UNFCCC	United Nations Framework Convention on Climate Change
UNPD	United Nations Population Division
USGS	United States Geological Survey

WEM	World Energy Model
WHO	World Health Organization
WTI	West Texas Intermediate
WTO	World Trade Organization

REFERENCES

Part A: Global energy trends to 2030

Chapter 1: Context and principal assumptions

DOE/EIA (Department of Energy/Energy Information Agency) (2008), *Annual Energy Outlook 2008*, DOE, Washington, DC.

IEA (International Energy Agency) (2006), *World Energy Outlook 2006*, OECD/IEA, Paris.

— (2007), *World Energy Outlook 2007: China and India Insights*, OECD/IEA, Paris.

— (2008), *Energy Technology Perspectives*, OECD/IEA, Paris.

IMF (International Monetary Fund) (2008a), *World Economic Outlook: Global Slowdown and Rising Inflation*, July, IMF, Washington, DC.

— (2008b), *World Economic Outlook: Housing and the Business Cycle*, April, IMF, Washington, DC.

OECD (Organisation for Economic Co-operation and Development) (2008), *OECD Economic Outlook No. 83*, June, OECD, Paris.

OPEC (Organization of the Petroleum Exporting Countries) (2008), *World Oil Outlook 2008*, OPEC Secretariat, Vienna.

UNPD (United Nations Population Division) (2007a), *World Population Prospects: The 2006 Revision*, United Nations, New York.

— (2007b), *World Population Ageing 2007*, United Nations, New York.

— (2007c), *World Urbanization Prospects: The 2007 Revision*, United Nations, New York.

World Bank (2008), *2005 International Comparison Program: Tables of Final Results*, February, World Bank, Washington, DC.

Chapter 2: Global energy trends

IEA (International Energy Agency) (2007), *World Energy Outlook 2007: China and India Insights*, OECD/IEA, Paris.

Chapter 3: Oil market outlook

IEA (International Energy Agency) (2006), *World Energy Outlook 2006*, OECD/IEA, Paris.

— (2007), *World Energy Outlook 2007: China and India Insights*, OECD/IEA, Paris.

— (2008), *Energy Technology Perspectives*, OECD/IEA, Paris.

Jesse, J.-H. and C. van der Linde (2008), *Oil Turbulence in the Next Decade: An Essay of High Oil Prices in a Supply-constrained World*, Clingendael International Energy Programme, Den Haag, Netherlands.

Stevens, P. (2008), *The Coming Oil Supply Crunch*, Royal Institute of International Affairs, London.

Chapter 4: Natural gas market outlook

DOE/EIA (Department of Energy/Energy Information Administration) (2002), *Manufacturing Energy Consumption Survey*, DOE/EIA, Washington, DC.

IEA (International Energy Agency) (2007), *Natural Gas Market Review 2007*, OECD/IEA, Paris.

— (2008), *Natural Gas Market Review 2008*, OECD/IEA, Paris.

Chapter 5: Coal market outlook

Creedy, D. and H. Tilley (2003), Coalbed Methane Extraction and Utilisation, *Proceedings of the Institution of Mechanical Engineers, Part A: Journal of Power and Energy*, 217 (A1), pp. 19-25.

EPA (Environmental Protection Agency) (2006), *Global Anthropogenic Non-CO_2 Greenhouse Gas Emissions: 1990-2020*, Washington, DC: EPA, June 2006 (revised).

IEA (International Energy Agency) (2003), *World Energy Investment Outlook: 2003 Insights*, OECD/IEA, Paris.

IPCC (Intergovernmental Panel on Climate Change) (2006), *2006 IPCC Guidelines for National Greenhouse Gas Inventories*, National Greenhouse Gas Inventories Programme, IPCC, Institute for Global Environmental Strategies, Kanagawa, Japan, 2006.

Meister, W.G. (2008), *Cost Trends in Mining*, presented at the McCloskey Coal Conference, Nice, France.

Pan, K. (2005), *The Depth Distribution of Chinese Coal Resources*, paper presented at the School of Social Development and Public Policy, Fudan University, Shanghai, China.

Rogers, P. (2007), *Dry Bulk Freight Outlook*, paper presented at Global Insight 2007 Fuel Price Conference: Challenging the Consensus, London, 11-12 December 2007.

WEC (World Energy Council) (2004), *2004 Survey of Energy Resources*, WEC London.

— (2007), *2007 Survey of Energy Resources*, WEC, London.

Chapter 6: Power sector outlook

The Brattle Group (2007), *Rising Utility Construction Costs: Sources and Impacts*, The Edison Foundation, Washington, DC.

IEA (International Energy Agency) (2008a), *Energy Technology Perspectives - 2008: Scenarios and Strategies to 2050*, OECD/IEA, Paris.

— (2008b), *CO_2 Capture and Storage: A Key Carbon Abatement Option*, OECD/IEA, Paris.

IEA-CSLF (International Energy Agency and Carbon Sequestration Leadership Forum) (2007), paper presented *Near-Term Opportunities for Carbon Capture and Storage, Results from the 3rd Calgary Workshop, 28-29 November 2007*.

Chapter 7: Renewable energy outlook

CEA (Council of Economic Advisors) (2008), Testimony of Edward P. Lazear Chairman, CEA before the US Senate Foreign Relations Committee Hearing on *Responding to the Global Food Crisis*, 14 May 2008.

FAO (Food and Agriculture Organization of the United Nations) (2008), *FAOSTAT*, available at http://faostat.fao.org/site/377/default.aspx.

IEA (International Energy Agency) (2004), *Biofuels for Transport: An International Perspective*, OECD/IEA, Paris.

— (2006), *World Energy Outlook 2006*, OECD/IEA, Paris.

— (2007), *Renewables for Heating and Cooling Untapped Potential*, OECD/IEA, Paris.

— (2008a), *Empowering Variable Renewables: Options for Flexible Electricity Systems*. IEA/OECD, Paris.

— (2008b), *Medium-Term Oil Market Report*, OECD/IEA, Paris.

— (2008c), *Energy Technology Perspectives*, OECD/IEA, Paris.

IEA-OES (International Energy Agency - Implementing Agreement Ocean Energy Systems) (2007), *Annual Report*, IEA-OES Executive Committee, Paris.

F.O. Licht (2008), "Ethanol Trade Stabilises at High Level", *World Ethanol and Biofuels Report*, Vol. 6, No. 20, F.O. Licht GmbH, London.

MME (Ministério de Minas e Energia, *Minstry of Mines and Energy*) (2007), *Plano Nacional de Energia 2030, National Energy Plan 2030*, Rio de Janeiro.

Mitchell, D. (2008), *A Note on Rising Food Prices*, Policy Research Working Paper 4682, The World Bank Development Prospects Group, July 2008, World Bank, Washington, DC.

OECD (Organisation for Economic Co-operation and Development) (2008), *Report on Economic Assessment of Biofuel Support Policies*, Trade and Agriculture Directorate Committee for Agriculture, OECD, Paris.

Worldwatch Institute, (WWI) (2008), *Biofuels for transport: global potential and implications for sustainable agriculture and energy in the 21st century*, Worldwatch Institute, Washington, DC.

Chapter 8: Energy use in cities

ABS (Australian Bureau of Statistics) (2007), *5204.0 - Australian System of National Accounts, 2006-07*, Australian Bureau of Statistics, Canberra, Table 11, available at www.abs.gov.au/AUSSTATS/abs@.nsf/DetailsPage/5204.02006-07?OpenDocument.

BEA (Bureau of Economic Analysis) (2007), *New Release: GDP by Metropolitan Area for 2006 and Reveised 2004-2005*, US. Department of Commerce, Washington, DC, available at: www.bea.gov/newsreleases/regional/gdp_metro_newsrelease.htm

Dhakal, S. (2008), Urban Energy Use and Cities' Carbon Emissions in China, *Energy Policy*, Elsevier, London, forthcoming.

UNPD (United Nations Population Division) (2007a), *World Population Prospects: The 2006 Revision*, United Nations, New York.

— (2007b), *World Urbanization Prospects: The 2007 Revision*, United Nations, New York.

US Census Bureau (2000), *Metropolitan Areas*, US Census Bureau, Washington, DC, available at: www.census.gov/history/www/how_we_map/010899.html.

USGCRP (US Global Change Research Program) (2001), *Climate Change Impacts on the United States, The Potential Consequences of Climate Variability and Change, Final Synthesis Team Reports & Newsletter*, US Global Change Research Program, Washington DC.

Part B: Oil and gas production prospects

Chapter 9: Turning oil resources into reserves

ACR (Alberta Chamber of Resources) (2004), *Oil Sands Technology Roadmap – Unlocking the Potential*, Alberta Chamber of Resources, Edmonton, January 2004, available at www.acr-alberta.com/OSTR_report.pdf.

ARI (Advanced Resources International) (2006), *Ten Basin-Oriented CO_2-EOR Assessments Examine Strategies for Increasing Domestic Oil Production, Alaska, California, Onshore Gulf Coast, Mid-Continent, Illinois and Michigan, Permian Basin, Rocky Mountains, East and Central Texas, Offshore Louisiana, and Williston Basin*, US Department of Energy, available at www.fe.doe.gov/programs/oilgas/eor/Ten_Basin-Oriented_CO2-EOR_Assessments.html.

Boutte, D. (2007), Through the Continuous Life Cycle of Reservoir, Geophysics Makes its Mark, *The Leading Edge*, November 2007, pp. 1376-79, available at www.westerngeco.com/media/resources/articles.

BP (British Petroleum) (2008), *BP Statistical Review of World Energy*, British Petroleum, London, available at www.bp.com/productlanding.do?categoryId=6929&contentId=7044622.

Caruso, G. (2007), Annual Energy Outlook 2008, USDOE presentation on *Energy Markets Forecast*, 11 December 2007, available at www.eia.doe.gov/neic/speeches/caruso121207.pdf.

Couvillion, J.K. (2008), *Ultra Deepwater Developments in Drilling and Production*, OCS Committee Policy Meeting, 6 March 2008, available at www.mms.gov/mmab/PDF/WebPageOCSPCMeetingHerndonVAMarch2008/Couvillion%20 Ultra%20Deepwater%20Advances%20in%20Drilling%20and%20Development%20030608.pdf

Douglas-Westwood (2007), *Global Offshore Prospects*, 11 January 2007, available at www.dw-1.com/assets/documents/JW%20SUT1-07.pdf.

Etherington, J.R. and J.E. Ritter (2007), *The 2007 SPE/AAPG/WPC/SPEE Reserves and Resources Classification, Definitions and Guidelines: Defining the Standard!*, paper number SPE 10739, presented at the Society of Petroleum Engineers' Hydrocarbon Economics and Evaluation Symposium, 1-3 April 2007, Dallas, TX.

Green, D.W. and G.P. Whilhite (1998), *Enhanced Oil Recovery*, Society of Petroleum Engineers Textbook, Vol. 6, Richardson, TX.

Harper, F. (2005), *The Future of Global Hydrocarbon Exploration*, paper presented at APPEX meeting, March 2005, available at http://energy.ihs.com/NR/rdonlyres/0ED41670-ADE5-4F5B-868D-91BFC49030E9/0/harper.pdf.

IEA (International Energy Agency) (2005), *Resources to Reserves, Oil and Gas Technologies for the Energy Markets of the Future*, OECD/IEA, Paris.

— (2007), *World Energy Outlook 2007: China and India Insights*, OECD/IEA, Paris.

— (2008), *CO_2 Capture and Storage: A Key Carbon Abatement Option*, OECD/IEA, Paris.

Johnsen, H.G. and Økland O. (2008), *Frontier Arctic Technology Trends and Challenges*, paper presented at the IEA Resources to Reserves Workshop, 7-8 April 2008, Cambridge, UK.

Karlsen, J.D. (2008), *Deepwater Technology: Preliminary Findings*, paper presented at the IEA Advisory Group on Oil and Gas Technology, April 2008, Cambridge, UK.

Khatib, Z. (2006), *Clean Fossil Fuel Systems: Deployment and Dissemination*, The World Energy Council, paper presented at the Cleaner Fossil Fuels for Sustainable Development Workshop, 13 June 2006, available at www.usea.org/CFFS/CFFSNeptun/Zara_Khatib_CFFC_Workshop_final.pdf.

Klett, T.R. (2004), *Justification for Proposing a Study of Large Petroleum Fields*, paper presented at the UNECE Ad Hoc Group of Experts on Supply of Fossil Fuels, 11-14 November 2004, Geneva, available at www.unece.org/ie/se/pdfs/adclass/Klett_LargeFields.pdf.

Klett, T.R., D.L. Gautier, and T.S. Ahibrandt (2007), *An Evaluation of the World Petroleum Assessment 2000: Supporting Data*, USGS Open File Report 2007-1021, US Geological Survey available at http://pubs.usgs.gov/of/2007/1021.

Kuuskraa, V.A. (2006), *Undeveloped Domestic Oil Resources: The Foundation for Increasing Oil Production and a Viable Domestic Oil Industry*, prepared for the US

Department of Energy, available at www.fossil.energy.gov/programs/oilgas/publications/eor_co2/Undeveloped_oil_Document.pdf.

NPC (National Petroleum Council) (2007), *Global Oil and Gas Study - Impact of Technology on Conventional Wells*, 18 July 2007, NPC, available at www.npc.org.

O&GJ (Oil & Gas Journal) (2007), *Worldwide Look at Reserves and Production*, OGJ, Vol. 105, Issue 48, 24 December 2007, PennWell Corporation, Oklahoma City, OK.

— (2008), *2008 Worldwide EOR Survey*, OGJ, Vol. 106, Issue 15, -21 April 2008, pp. 4759, PennWell Corporation, Oklahoma City, OK.

O&G UK (Oil & Gas United Kingdom) (2008), *2008 Economic Report*, report available at http://www.oilandgasuk.co.uk/issues/economic/econ08/summary/index.cfm.

OPEC (Organization of the Petroleum Exporting Countries) (2008), *World Oil Outlook 2008*, OPEC Secretariat, Vienna.

Saleri, N., S. Salamy, H. Mubarak, R. Sadler, A. Dossary and A. Muraikhi (2003), *A Maximum Reservoir Contact (MRC) Well and its Implications for Developing Tight Facies Reservoirs*, paper SPE 81487, Society of Petroleum Engineers, Middle East Oil Show, 9-12 June 2003, Bahrain.

Sandrea, I. and R. Sandrea (2007), Global Oil Offshore 1: Exploration Trends Show Continued Promise in World's Offshore Basins, *Oil & Gas Journal*, Vol. 105, Issue 9, 5 March 2007, PennWell Corporation, Oklahoma City, OK.

Schulte, W. (2005), *Challenges and Strategy for Increased Oil Recovery*, Paper IPTC 10146, presented at the International Petroleum Technology Conference, 21-23 November 2005, Doha, Qatar.

SPE (Society of Petroleum Engineers) (2007), *The Petroleum Resources Management System*, available at www.spe.org/spe-site/spe/spe/industry/reserves/Petroleum_Resources_Management_System_2007.pdf.

Taber, J.J, Martin, F.D. and R. Seright (1997), EOR Screening Criteria Revised Part 1: Introduction to Screening Criteria and Enhanced Recovery Field Projects, *SPE Reservoir Engineering*, Vol. 12, No. 3, pp. 189-98.

Thomas, S. (2008), Enhanced Oil Recovery - An Overview, *Oil & Gas Science & Technology - Rev. IFP*, Vol. 63, No. 1, pp. 9-19.

Tzimas, V., Georgakaki, A., Garcia Cortes, G. and Peteves, S. (2005), EOR Using CO_2 in the European Energy System, *European DG JRC*, December 2005, available at http://ie.jrc.ec.europa.eu/publications/scientific_publications/2005/EUR21895EN.pdf.

USGS (United States Geological Survey) (2000), *World Petroleum Assessment 2000*, USGS, Washington, DC.

– (2008), *Circum-Arctic Resource Appraisal: Estimates of Undiscovered Oil and Gas North of the Arctic Circle*, USGS Fact Sheet 2008-3049, July 2008.

WEC (World Energy Council) (2007), *2007 Survey of Energy Resources*, WEC, London, available at www.worldenergy.org/documents/ser2007_final_online_version_1.pdf.

Chapter 10: Field-by-field analysis of oil production

Sanford Bernstein (2007), *Saudi and Ghawar from Space! Using Proprietary Satellite Data to Test the Conspiracy Theory*, 5 December 2007, Sanford Bernstein, London.

CERA (Cambridge Energy Research Associates) (2007), *Finding the Critical Numbers: What Are the Real Decline Rates for Global Oil Production?* private report, IHS/CERA, Cambridge.

Goldman Sachs (2007), *A Declining Future for the Integrated Oils*, 10 July 2007, Goldman Sachs Global Investment Research, London.

IEA (International Energy Agency) (2001), *World Energy Outlook Insights: Assessing Today's Supplies to Fuel Tomorrow's Growth*, OECD/IEA, Paris.

– (2003), *World Energy Investment Outlook: 2003 Insights*, OECD/IEA, Paris.
– (2005), *World Energy Outlook 2005: Middle East and North Africa Insights*, OECD/ IEA, Paris.

– (2008), *Medium-Term Oil Market Report*, OECD/IEA, Paris.

Chapter 11: Prospects for oil production

Eni (2006), *World Oil and Gas Review*, Eni, Rome.

IEA (International Energy Agency) (2005), *World Energy Outlook 2005: Middle East and North Africa Insights*, OECD/IEA, Paris.

– (2006), *Coal-to-liquids Workshop Summary*, OECD/IEA, November 2006, Paris.

– (2008), *Medium-Term Oil Market Report*, OECD/IEA, Paris.

Rahim, I. (2008), Special Report: GTL, CTL Finding Roles in Global Energy Supply, *Oil & Gas Journal*, Vol.106, Issue 12, 24 March 2008, PennWell Corporation, Oklahoma City, OK.

USGS (United States Geological Survey) (2000), *World Petroleum Assessment 2000*, USGS, Washington, DC.

Chapter 12: Natural gas resources and production prospects

Bourdarot, G. (2007), *Global Opportunities and Potential for CO_2-EOR*, paper presented at the IEA Advisory Meeting on Oil & Gas Technologies, Paris, September 2007.

BP (British Petroleum) (2008), *BP Statistical Review of World Energy*, British Petroleum, London, available at www.bp.com/productlanding.do?categoryId=6929&contentId=7044622.

Cedigaz (2008), *Natural Gas in the World*, Institut français du pétrole, Rueil-Malmaison.

Creedy, D. and H. Tilly (2003), Coalbed methane extraction and utilization, *Proceedings of the I MECH E Part A Journal of Power and Energy*, Vol. 217, No. 1, 1 February 2003, pp. 19-25.

DOE/EIA (Department of Energy/Energy Information Agency) (2007), *Coalbed Methane Proved Reserves and Production Series*, DOE/EIA, Washington, DC.

Frantz, J. and V. Jochen (2006), *Shale Gas*, White Paper, available at http://www.slb.com/media/services/solutions/reservoir/shale_gas.pdf.

Gale, J. (2004), Using Coal Seams for CO_2 Sequestration, *Geologica Belgica*, Vol. 7, No. 3-4, pp. 99-103.

Geoscience (2008), *Australian Atlas of Mineral Resources, Mines and Processing Centres*, Geoscience Australia, available at www.australianminesatlas.gov.au.

IEA (International Energy Agency) (2008), CO_2 *Capture and Storage: A Key Carbon Abatement Option*, OECD/IEA, Paris.

Laherrere, J. (2006), *Oil and Gas: What Future?* paper presented at Groningen Annual Energy Convention, 21 November 2006.

Mastalerz, M., H. Gluskoter, and J. Rupp (2004), Carbon Dioxide and Methane Sorption in High Volatile Bituminous Coals from Indiana, USA, *International Journal of Coal Geology*, Vol. 60, No. 1, pp. 43-55.

NPC (National Petroleum Council) (2007), *Topic Paper #29: Unconventional Gas*, Working Document of the NPC Global Oil & Gas Study, 18 July 2007.

O&GJ (Oil & Gas Journal), (2007), *Worldwide Look at Reserves and Production*, O&GJ, Vol. 105, Issue 48, 24 December 2007, PennWell Corporation, Oklahoma City, OK.

Reeves, S. (2003), *Enhanced Coal-bed Methane Recovery*, Society of Petroleum Engineers Distinguished Lecture Series, Richardson, TX.

Rogner, H. (1997), An Assessment of World Hydrocarbon Resources, *Annual Reviews of Energy and Environment*, Vol. 22, pp. 217-62.

RPS (RPS Energy) (2008), Development of Gas Hydrates, paper presented at the New Zealand Petroleum Conference, March 2008, Auckland, available at www.crownminerals.govt.nz/cms/pdf-library/petroleum-conferences-1/2008-conference-proceedings/presentations/s-hancock.

USGS (United States Geological Survey) (2000), *World Petroleum Assessment 2000*, USGS, Washington, DC.

— (2008), *Circum-Arctic Resource Appraisal: Estimates of Undiscovered Oil and Gas North of the Arctic Circle*, USGS Fact Sheet 2008-3049, July 2008.

Chapter 13: Upstream investment prospects

DOE/EIA (Department of Energy, Energy Information Administration), *Performance Profiles of Major Energy Producers 2006*, December 2007, DOE, Washington, DC.

IEA (International Energy Agency) (2001), *World Energy Outlook 2001: Assessing Today's Supplies to Fuel Tomorrow's Growth*, OECD/IEA, Paris.

— (2007), *World Energy Outlook 2007: China and India Insights*, OECD/IEA, Paris.

— (2008), *Medium-Term Oil Market Report*, OECD/IEA, Paris.

Lehman Brothers (2007), *The Original E&P Spending Survey*, December 2007, Lehman Brothers, Inc, New York.

NPC (National Petroleum Council) (2007a), *Facing the Hard Truths about Energy*, NPC/Department of Energy, Washington, DC.

— (2007b), *Working Document of the NPC Global Oil and Gas Study: Topic Paper 23: Human Resources*, NPC/Department of Energy, Washington, DC.

PFC (Petroleum Finance Corporation) (2008), *OPEC States: $100 Oil Wanted by All, Needed by Some*, 7 March 2008, PFC, New York.

Rostand, A. (2005), *Surviving the Skills Shortage: Results of a Global Survey Quantifying the Supply and Demand of Petrotechnical Expertise*, Schlumberger Business Consulting, Reuil-Malmaison.

— (2006) *Surviving the Skills Shortage 2006, Update of the Annual Oil and Gas Human Resources Survey*, Schlumberger Business Consulting, Reuil-Malmaison.

Spears and Associates (2007), *Drilling and Production Outlook*, December 2007, Spears and Associates, Inc., Tulsa, OK.

Chapter 14: The structure of the upstream industry

Eller, S., P. Hartley and K. Medlock (2007), *Empirical Evidence on the Operational Efficiency of National Oil Companies*, James A. Baker III Institute for Public Policy of Rice University, Houston, TX.

Fryklund, R. (2008), *The New Era: Producer Nations Take the Upper Hand*, IHS, Houston, TX.

Jaffe, A. and R. Soligo (2007), *The International Oil Companies*, James A. Baker III Institute for Public Policy of Rice University, Houston, TX.

John S. Herold, Inc. and Harrision Lovegrove and Company (2007), *2006 Global Upstream M&A Review*, John S. Herold, Inc., Norwalk, CT.

— (2008), *2007 Global Upstream M&A Review*, J.S. Herold, Inc, Norwalk, CT.

IEA (International Energy Agency) (2006), *World Energy Outlook 2006*, OECD/IEA, Paris.

— (2007), *World Energy Outlook 2007: China and India Insights*, OECD/IEA, Paris.

— (2008), *Gas Market Review*, OECD/IEA, Paris,

Lehman Brothers (2007), *The Original E&P Spending Survey*, December 2007, Lehman Brothers, Inc, New York.

Marcel, V. (2006), *Oil Titans*, Royal Institute of International Affairs, London.

O&GJ (Oil & Gas Journal), (2007), *Worldwide Look at Reserves and Production*, O&GJ, Vol. 105, Issue 48, 24 December 2007, PennWell Corporation, Oklahoma City, OK.

Osmundsen, P., F. Asche, B. Misund and K. Mohn (2005), *Valuation of International Oil Companies: The RoACE Era*, Center for Economic Studies, IFO Institute for Economic Research, Munich.

Chapter 15: Prospects in oil- and gas-exporting sub-Saharan African countries

Goldemberg, J., Thomas B., Johansson, A., Reddy, K.N. and Williams, R.H. (2004), "A global clean cooking fuel initiative" *Energy for Sustainable Development*, Vol. 8, No. 3, September.

Humphreys, M., J. Sachs and J. Stiglitz (eds.) (2007), *Escaping the Resource Curse*, Columbia University Press, New York.

IEA (International Energy Agency) (2006a), *Angola: Towards an Energy Strategy*, OECD/IEA, Paris.

— (2006b), *World Energy Outlook 2006*, OECD/IEA, Paris.

— (2007), *World Energy Outlook 2007: China and India Insights*, OECD/IEA, Paris.

— (2008), *Gas Market Review*, OECD/IEA, Paris.

Kabutha, J., M. Sengendo, J. Winiecki and E. Morris (2007), *Using Microfinance to Expand Access to Energy Services: The Emerging Experiences in East Africa of Faulu Kenya and Kenya Union of Savings and Credit Cooperatives (KUSCCO)*, USAID and Citi Foundation, November, the SEEP Network, Washington, DC.

Karekezi, S. and W. Kithyoma, (2008), *Renewable Energy Potential: Markets and Strategies*, African Energy Policy Research Network/ Foundation for Woodstove Dissemination (AFREPREN/FWD), available at www.afrepren.org.

Lange, G.-M. and M. Wright (2002), Sustainable Development in Mineral Economies: The Example of Botswana, *CEEPA Discussion Paper Series*, The Centre for Environmental Economics and Policy in Africa, March, Pretoria.

Moner-Girona, M., Ghanadan, R., Jacobson, A. and Kammen, D.M. (2006), "Decreasing PV costs in Africa: Opportunities for Rural Electrification using Solar PV in Sub-Saharan Africa", *Refocus*, Vol. 7, Issue 1, January-February.

NEPAD (New Partnership for Africa's Development) (2008), *Sectoral Energy Paper*, available at
http://www.businessinfo.cz/files/2005/071106_energy_Africa.doc.

O&GJ (Oil & Gas Journal) (2007), *Worldwide Look at Reserves and Production*, O&GJ, Vol. 105, Issue 48, December 24.

OECD (Organisation for Economic Co-operation and Development) (2008), *African Economic Outlook 2008*, OECD, Paris.

UNEP (United Nations Environment Programme) (2008), *Global Trends in Sustainable Energy Investment*, UNEP, Nairobi.

UNPD (United Nations Population Division) (2007), *World Population Prospects: The 2006 Revision*, United Nations, New York.

USGS (United States Geological Survey) (2000), *World Petroleum Assessment 2000*, USGS, Washington, DC.

World Bank (2007), *Top-20 Gas Flaring Countries*, Global Gas Flaring Reduction Partnership, World Bank, available at
http://go.worldbank.org/AHFOUQJATO.

WHO (World Health Organization) (2007), *Fuel for Life*, WHO, Geneva.

Part C: The role of energy in climate policy

Chapter 16: Implications of the Reference Scenario for the global climate

Airbus (2007), *Global Market Forecast 2007-2026*, Toulouse, available at www.airbus.com.

Bull, S.R., D.E. Bilello, J. Ekmann, M.J. Sale and D.K. Schmalzer (2007), Effects of Climate Change on Energy Production and Use in the United States, Chapter 3 in *Synthesis and Assessment Product 4.5*, report by the US Climate Change Science Program and the Subcommittee on Global Change Research, Washington DC.

EPA (Environmental Protection Agency) (2007), *Federal Implementation Plans for the Clean Air Interstate: Rule and Response to Section 126 Petition from North Carolina*, fact sheet of the EPA, available at www.epa.gov/cair/fs_fip_20060316.html.

Green Car Congress (2008), available at www.greencarcongress.com.

Hansen, J. E. (2005), *Is There Still Time to Avoid 'Dangerous Anthropogenic Interference' with Global Climate?*, available at: www.columbia.edu/~jeh1/2005/Keeling_20051206.pdf.

Horton, P., B. Schaefli, M. Abdelkader, B. Hingray and A. Musy (2005), *Prediction of Climate Change Impacts on Alpine Discharge Regimes under A2 and B2 SRES Emission Scenarios for Two Future Time Periods*, Bundesamt für Energy BFE, Bern, available at www.ewg-bfe.ch.

Houser T., R. Bradley, B. Childs, J. Werksman and R. Heilmayr (2008), *Leveling the Carbon Playing Field: International Competition and US Climate Policy Design*, Peterson Institute and World Resources Institute, Washington, DC.

IEA (International Energy Agency) (2007), *World Energy Outlook 2007: China and India Insights*, OECD/IEA, Paris.

— (2008), *Energy Technology Perspectives 2008*, OECD/IEA, Paris.

IPCC (Intergovernmental Panel on Climate Change) (2007), "Technical Summary" in: *Climate Change 2007: Mitigation*, contribution of Working Group III to the *Fourth Assessment Report of the IPCC* [Metz, B., Davidson, O.R., Bosch, P.R., Dave, R. and Meyer, L.A. (Eds.)], Cambridge University Press, Cambridge and New York.

Kundzewicz, Z. W., L.J. Mata, N.W. Arnell, P. Döll, P. Kabat, B. Jiménez, K.A. Miller, T. Oki, Z. Sen and I.A. Shiklomanov (2007), "Freshwater resources and their management", Chapter 3 in *Climate Change 2007: Impacts, Adaptation and Vulnerability*, contribution of Working Group II to the *Fourth Assessment Report of the IPCC*, (M.L. Parry, O.F. Canziani, J.P. Palutikof, P.J. van der Linden and C.E. Hanson [eds.]), Cambridge University Press, Cambridge and New York.

Lobell, D.B., M.B. Burke, C. Tebaldi, M.D. Mastrandrea, W.P. Falcon and R.L. Naylor (2008), Prioritizing Climate Change Adaptation Needs for Food Security in 2030, *Science*, Vol. 319 (5863), pp. 607-10.

Nakicenovic, N. (2007), *World Energy Outlook 2007: CO_2 Emissions Pathways Compared to Long-term CO_2 Stabilisation Scenarios in the Literature and IPCC AR4*, OECD/IEA, Paris, available at http://www.worldenergyoutlook.org/docs/weo2007/CO2_Scenarios.pdf.

OECD (Organisation for Economic Co-operation and Development) (2008), *Environmental Outlook 2008*, OECD, Paris.

Rosenzweig C., D. Karoly, M. Vicarelli, P. Neofotis, Q. Wu, G. Casassa, A. Menzel, T.L. Root, N. Estrella, B. Seguin, P. Tryjanowski, C. Liu, S. Rawlins and A. Imeson (2008), Attributing Physical and Biological Impacts to Anthropogenic Climate Change, *Nature*, Vol. 453, 15 May 2008, Nature Publishing Group, London.

UNCTAD (United Nations Conference on Trade and Development) (2008), International Trade Centre UNCTAD/WTO (ITC), databases available at www.trademap.org.

Weber, C.L., G.P. Peters, D. Guan and K. Hubacek (2008), The Contribution of Chinese Exports to Climate Change, *Energy Policy*, Vol. 36, pp. 3572-77, Elsevier, London.

Chapter 17: The post-2012 climate policy framework

Baron, R., J. Reinaud, M. Genasci and C. Philibert (2007), *Sectoral Approaches to Greenhouse Gas Mitigation: Exploring Issues for Heavy Industry*, OECD/IEA, Paris.

BMST (Brazilian Ministry of Science and Technology) (2000), *Technical Note on the Time-dependent Relationship Between Emissions of Greenhouse Gases and Climate Change*, Brazilian Ministry of Science and Technology, Brasilia.

Bodansky, D. (2004), *International Climate Efforts Beyond 2012: A Survey of Approaches*, Pew Center on Global Climate Change, Arlington, VA.

CICERO (Center for International Climate and Environmental Research) (2007), *CDM Baseline Approaches and Carbon Leakage*, CICERO, Oslo.

den Elzen, M.G.J., M. Höhne, P. Lucas, S. Moltmann and T. Kuramochi (2007), *The Triptych Approach Revisited: A Staged Sectoral Approach for Climate Mitigation*, Report no. 500114008, Netherlands Environmental Agency, available at www.mnp.nl/en.

den Elzen, M.G.J. and D.P. van Vuuren (2007), *Peaking Profiles for Achieving Long-term Temperature Targets with More Likelihood at Lower Costs*, National Academy of Sciences of the USA, Washington, DC, available at www.pnas.org/cgi/content/full/0701598104/DC1.

Ellis, J., R. Baron and B. Buchner (2007), *SD-PAMs: What, Where, When and How?* Information Paper COM/ENV/EPOC/IEA/SLT(2007)5, OECD/IEA, Paris.

Hansen, J., M. Sato, P. Kharecha, D. Beerling, V. Masson-Delmotte, M. Pagani, M. Raymo, D.L. Royer and J.V. Zachos (2008), *Target Atmospheric CO_2: Where Should Humanity Aim?* NASA/Goddard Institute for Space Studies, New York, www.giss.nasa.gov.

Höhne, N., C. Galleguillos, K. Blok, J. Harnisch and G. Phylipsen (2003), *Evolution of Commitments under the UNFCCC: Involving Newly Industrialized Economies and Developing Countries*, Report for the German Federal Environment Agency, Ecofys, Cologne.

Hourcade, J.C., D. Demailly, K. Neuhoff and M. Sato (2007) *Differentiation and Dynamics of EU ETS Industrial Competitiveness Impacts*, Climate Strategies, Cambridge, available at www.climatestrategies.org/reportfiles/1_climatestrategies_competitiveness_final_report_140108.pdf.

IEA (International Energy Agency) (2008a), *Energy Technology Perspectives*, OECD/IEA, Paris.

— (2008b), *Worldwide Trends in Energy Use and Efficiency* - Key Insights from IEA Indicator Analysis, OECD/IEA, Paris.

IMF (International Monetary Fund) (2008), World Economic Outlook: Housing and the Business Cycle, April, IMF, Washington, DC.

IPCC (Intergovernmental Panel on Climate Change) (2007), *Climate Change 2007: Synthesis Report, Contribution of Working Groups I, II and III to the Fourth Assessment Report of the Intergovernmental Panel on Climate Change*, eds. Pachauri, R.K and Reisinger, A., IPCC, Geneva, available at www.ipcc.ch/pdf/assessment-report/ar4/syr/ar4_syr.pdf.

Lempert, R., S. Popper and S. Resetar (2002), *Capital Cycles and the Timing of Climate Change Policy*, Pew Center on Global Climate Change, Arlington, VA.

Nakicenovic, N. (2007), *World Energy Outlook 2007: CO_2 Emissions Pathways Compared to Long-Term CO_2 Stabilization Scenarios in the Literature and IPCC AR4*, OECD/IEA, Paris, available at www.worldenergyoutlook.org/docs/weo2007/CO2_Scenarios.pdf.

Philibert, C. (2000), How Emissions Trading Could Benefit Developing Countries, *Energy Policy* Vol. 28, pp. 947-56, Elsevier, London.

Reinaud, J. (2008), *Competitiveness and Carbon Leakage*, OECD/IEA information paper, IEA, Paris, forthcoming.

Reinaud, J. and C. Philibert (2007), *Emissions Trading: Trends and Prospects*, OECD/IEA information paper, IEA, Paris.

UNFCCC (United Nations Framework Convention on Climate Change) (2007), *Revised Draft Decision -/CP.13*, Ad Hoc Working Group on Long-term Cooperative Action under the Convention, UNFCCC, Bonn.

Chapter 18: Climate policy scenarios

IEA (International Energy Agency) (2007), *World Energy Outlook 2007: China and India Insights*, OECD/IEA, Paris.

— (2008a), *Energy Technology Perspectives*, OECD/IEA, Paris.

— (2008b), *Worldwide Trends in Energy Use and Efficiency*, OECD/IEA, Paris.

IMF (International Monetary Fund) (2008), *World Economic Outlook: Housing and the Business Cycle*, April, IMF, Washington, DC.

IPCC (Intergovernmental Panel on Climate Change) (2007), *Climate Change 2007: Mitigation*, Contribution of Working Group III to the Fourth Assessment Report of the Intergovernmental Panel on Climate Change, ed. by B. Metz.

OECD (Organisation for Economic Co-operation and Development) (2008), *OECD Environmental Outlook to 2030*, OECD, Paris.

WRI (World Resources Institute) (2007), *Slicing the Pie: Sector-based Approaches to International Climate Agreement: Issues and Options*, WRI, Washington, DC.

Chapter 19: Implications for energy investment

Bouttes, J. P., J.M. Trochet and F. Dassa (2007), *Assessment of EU CO_2 Regulations*, Gouvernance européene et géopolitque de l'énergie, Tome 1, L'Institut français des relations internationales, France.

Castro, P. and M. Michaelowa (2008), *Empirical Analysis of Performance of CDM Projects*, Climate Strategies, Zurich.

Ecofys (2006), *Initial Assessment of National Allocation Plans for Phase II of the EU Emission Trading Scheme*, Utrecht, Netherlands.

European Commission (2008), Proposal for a Directive of the European Parliament and of the Council amending Directive 2003/87/EC so as to improve and extend the greenhouse gas emission allowance trading system of the Community, COM(2008) 16 final, 2008/0013 (COD).

Hepburn, C., M. Grubb, K. Neuhoff, F. Matthes and M. Tse (2006), Auctioning of EU ETS Phase II Allowances: How and Why? *Climate Policy*, Vol. 6, pp. 137-60.

IEA (International Energy Agency) (2008), *Energy Technology Perspectives*, OECD/IEA, Paris.

King, J. (2008), *The King Review of Low-Carbon Cars Part II: Recommendations for Action*, HM Treasury, London.

Park, W.G. and D.C. Lippoldt (2008), *Technology Transfer and the Economic Implications of the Strengthening of Intellectual Property Rights in Developing Countries*, OECD Trade Policy Working Papers 62, OECD, Paris.

Parry, I. (1997), *Revenue Recycling and the Costs of Reducing Carbon Emissions: Resources for the Future*. Climate Issues Brief No. 2, June 1997.

UK Commission on Intellectual Property Rights (2002), *Integrating Intellectual Property Rights and Development Policy*, UK Commission on Intellectual Property Rights, London.

UNEP (United Nations Environment Programme) (2008), *Global Trends in Sustainable Energy Investment - Analysis of Trends and Issues in the Financing of Renewable Energy and Energy Efficiency*, UNEP, Nairobi.

World Bank (2008), *State and Trends of the Carbon Market 2008*, World Bank, Washington, DC.

The Online Bookshop

International Energy Agency